Applied Factor Analysis

Applied
Factor Analysis

R. J. RUMMEL

EVANSTON: NORTHWESTERN UNIVERSITY PRESS 1970

*R. J. Rummel is Professor of Political Science
at the University of Hawaii and Director of the
Dimensionality of Nations Project.*

DEDICATED TO A SCIENCE OF CONFLICT

Acknowledgments

My orientation toward factor analysis, acquaintance with the methodology, sensitivity to the problems involved, and experience with application grew out of my work on the Dimensionality of Nations (DON) Project.[1] In a very real sense, therefore, this book is a product of research supported by the National Science Foundation,[2] and it is to the National Science Foundation that I would like to express my gratitude and debt for continued support.

My first exposure to factor analysis was in a course taught by Professor Jack Sawyer. I learned much from this course and from later interaction with Professor Sawyer during the early stages of the DON Project. He gave freely of his time in discussing the many questions that I had collected in attempts to grapple with the method, and he helped to lead me through the literature on factor analysis, almost all of which is contained in journals that are not normally familiar to the student of political science.

Many of the considerations raised in this book owe their inclusion to the influence of Professor Harold Guetzkow. His pointed questions and precise critiques on my factor analysis methodology, applications, and conclusions

1. See Rummel (1966c).
2. Grants GS-536 and GS-1230.

often forced me to justify and ground my points in the methodological literature. Much of whatever rigor this book has results from the intellectual honesty and responsibility Professor Guetzkow evinced both as my teacher and colleague.

Many of my colleagues have read and made very helpful comments on the first draft of this book. To all of them I wish to express my appreciation and thanks. In particular, I would like to thank Professor Brian Berry, Professor Bruce Russett, and Dr. Joseph Firestone, who critically evaluated the entire first draft, also Professors Harold Guetzkow, Michael Haas, and Raymond Tanter, and Mrs. Bette Bochelman and Miss Sumi Ono, all of whom read critically portions of the first draft.

Special thanks go to Mr. Fred Howard, who did a first-class job of editing a very complex manuscript for Northwestern University Press, to Mrs. Louise Levine, who strugged successfully with the task of typing a very rough first draft, and to Miss Marion You, who retyped most of the completely revised version from my all but illegible handwritten notes. Miss Bonnie Miyake, Miss Sara Katahara, and Mrs. Jeanette Matsuda of the Political Science Department, University of Hawaii, typed portions of the final manuscript; to them and to the Political Science Department of the University for providing their assistance, I wish to extend my thanks.

I am indebted to my research assistant, Herbert Hannah, for carefully checking the bibliography and the numerous quotations and page references.

It is with good reason that acknowledgments usually end with mention of one's wife. To my wife, Grace, I owe my deepest debt of gratitude.

Summary Table of Contents

Analytic Table of Contents

Part Two · Structure, Matrices, and Design of Factor Analysis

Part Three · Preparing the Data

Table of Notation

Matrix or Symbol	Order	Cell	Reference*	Concept
A	$n \times m$	x_{ij}	3.2.1	Raw data matrix of n cases and m variables
A'			4.2	The transpose of matrix A
$a^{1/2}$			3.1	The square root of a
C	$m \times m$	c_{jk}	4.3	Covariance matrix for m variables
E_l	$l \times 1$		(Def.) 4–23	The lth eigenvector of a matrix
E	$m \times m$		4.5	An eigenvector matrix
F	$m \times p$	a_{jl}	5.2	Factor loading matrix for m variables and p factors
H^2	$m \times m$	h_j^2	5.1	Diagonal matrix of communalities for m variables
h_j^2			5.1	Communality of variable j
I	square		4.2	Identity matrix
i,g			3.1; 3.2.1	ith or gth case; ith or gth row of a data matrix
j,k			3.1; 3.2.1	jth or kth variable; jth or kth column of a data matrix

* References are to the chapter and section in which the notation is first defined. References preceded by (Def.) are to Definitions rather than to Notations.

Matrix or Symbol	Order	Cell	Reference*	Concept
l			5.2; 5.3	lth factor; lth column of a factor loading, factor score, or eigen-vector matrix
m			3.2.1	Number of variables
n			3.2.1	Number of cases
p			5.2; 5.3	Number of common factors; dimensionality of the data
R	$m \times m$	r_{jk}	4.3	Correlation matrix for m variables
R^{-1}			4.2	The inverse of matrix R
r_{jk}			3.1	Product moment correlation between variables j and k
r_{jk}^2			(Def.) 3–7	Coefficient of determination between variables j and k
r_j			3.1	Multiple correlation coefficient of variable j on $n-1$ other variables
$S_{n \times p}$	$n \times p$	s_{il}	5.2	Factor score matrix for n cases and p factors
S_l	$l \times 1$	s_{nl}	5.2; 5.3	Common factor or factor dimension
s_{il}			5.2	Factor score for case i on factor l
SMC_j			3.1	Squared multiple correlation coefficient of variable j on $n-1$ other variables
U^2	$m \times m$	u_j	5.1	Diagonal matrix of uniquenesses for m variables
u_j^2			5.1	Uniqueness of variable j
X_j	$j \times 1$	x_{ij}	3.2.1; 3.1	jth variable; jth data vector
x_{ij}			3.2.1; 3.1	Data for case i on variable or vector j; the ith element of vector j
$\bar{X}_j$			3.1	Mean of variable j
Z	$n \times m$	z_{ij}	3.1	Standardized data matrix for n cases and m variables
z_{ij}			3.1	Standardized data for case i on variable j
α_{jl}			5.2	Factor loading for jth variable on the lth factor
λ_l			(Def.) 4–23	lth eigenvalue of a matrix
λ	$p \times p$	λ_l	4.5	Diagonal matrix of eigenvalues
$\sum$			3.1	Summation sign (operator)
σ_X^2			3.1	Variance of variable X
σ_X			3.1	Standard deviation of variable X

* References are to the chapter and section in which the notation is first defined. References preceded by (Def.) are to Definitions rather than to Notations.

Part One · Orientation

1. Introduction

1.1 A Calculus of Social Science

Factor analysis enables the social scientist to study behavioral phenomena of great complexity and diversity and to mold his findings into scientific theories. It offers both a technique of analysis and a theoretical structure. It allows for both inductive and deductive manipulation of qualitative as well as quantitative data.

But many techniques available to the social scientist share such attributes. What distinguishes factor analysis from these techniques? There are several distinguishing characteristics:

1. Factor analysis can analyze such a large number of phenomena with the assistance of an electronic computer that 100-variable analyses become routine.

2. It disentangles complex interrelationships among the phenomena into functional unities or separate or independent patterns of behavior and identifies the independent influences or causes at work.

3. It handles social phenomena *in the situation*. There is no need to

abstract phenomena to a laboratory setting or to select only certain variables and assume that others are constant. The interrelationships between behavior and environment can be analyzed as they exist in real life.

4. Factor analysis is a flexible instrument applicable to a wide range of research designs (hypothesis-testing, concept-mapping, case studies) and to a variety of data (time series, voting results, sample survey responses).

5. It has been widely studied by mathematicians, statisticians, and methodologists and has its roots in social science (psychology), mathematics (principal axes, diagonalizing a matrix, eigenvalues, eigenvectors), and natural science. Although an actual tabulation of the literature has not been made, it appears that far more methodology books have been written on the subject of factor analysis than on any other social science method or technique.

6. It has had wide application. Factor analysis is not a new method. Hundreds, perhaps thousands, of cases of its application are scattered through the social science literature. These applications have been and can be studied to gain an understanding of the capabilities of the method and to gain insight and confidence in its use.

7. Its mathematical structure is related to such commonly used techniques as multiple regression, product moment correlation, canonical analysis, partial correlation, and analysis of variance. It is thus theoretically capable of integrating many diverse findings.

8. It yields a set of equations that can be used to describe and predict behavior. Moreover, these equations are not structurally *ad hoc* but are developed as theorems in another field of mathematics—linear algebra. The factor analysis model can thus be used as a mathematical theory of behavior, drawing on a familiar field of mathematics to make deductions and behavioral predictions.

9. Factor analysis has a geometrical representation that allows for the visual portrayal of behavioral relationships. It allows for building physical models of social reality that can be studied in abstraction from the equations underlying them, much as the chemist builds physical (often colorful) representations of molecular systems. These physical models or geometric representations make it feasible to discuss and perceive relations and theory in a way not possible with equations alone.

These characteristics of factor analysis suggest that it is a *calculus of social science*. Factor analysis can be—and is being—so generally applied and the factor model is so amenable to structuring our social knowledge and theories that I hazard a prediction that courses in factor analysis will eventually be required for undergraduate social scientists. Eventually, perhaps, university social science departments will no more think of letting a student go on to upper-division social science courses without a knowledge of factor analysis than would a physics department allow a physics major to get by without a grounding in calculus.

Already the role that factor analysis plays in research is great. Much of the knowledge on personality, for example, is already factor analytic, and factor analysis has added considerably to our understanding of juvenile delinquency, crime, urbanism, primitive societies, national characteristics, conflicts, attitudes, and voting behavior, to name only a few topics. Already a communications gulf is being created between those who apply or understand factor analysis and those who do not. Given the present far-ranging use of factor analysis and its potential application to many additional social science concerns, it is understandable that most social scientists will want to become informed about the method. But being informed need not imply a profound mathematical understanding of the model. Being informed means having a comprehension of the purpose and significance of factor analysis and a sufficient familiarity with it to read and interpret factor results. The social scientist, if he is to be able to understand a growing source of knowledge and theory in his domain, must be able to grasp the meaning of "the factors delineated are . . ." and to appreciate such important comments as "these are oblique simple structure factors . . ." or "the communality of the variable is . . ."

For many social scientists, factor analysis will involve a new and complex terminology. This is not an artificial terminology created in lieu of a better and more understandable language, however. The nomenclature is generally related to the underlying mathematics of the model, and such terms as principal axes, rotation, transformation, oblique, orthogonal, components, and dimensions have precise meanings. Becoming acquainted with this terminology will amply repay the effort. The vocabulary of the social scientist will be enriched with a set of concepts of use in describing social phenomena and a mastery of the terminology will enable him to read, understand, and utilize the applied factor analytic literature. Most important, factor analysis will have been added to the repertoire of the scientist as a tool and model. Knowledge is, after all, *method applied to our perceptions and constructs of reality,* and the method of factor analysis enhances the ability of the social scientist to create new knowledge and theoretical integration.

1.2 Purposes and Organization of the Book

Within the social sciences, the writing of factor analysis texts has been the monopoly of psychologists. The applied terminology and the methodological issues discussed have been geared to psychological research. Issues of overriding concern to those analyzing social, political, economic, or cultural data have not been treated. Problems of measurement, data transformation, alternative correlation coefficients, missing data, systematic error, and distances have been generally ignored. *Applied Factor Analysis* is an attempt to deal with such data and research design problems. Specifically, it is organized to serve as a manual for researchers who want to:

- understand, comprehend, or get a "feel" for factor analysis;
- become acquainted with the terminology of factor analysis;
- study the distinctions between various factor models;
- acquaint themselves with the newer, postcomputer factor models;
- evaluate publications employing factor analysis;
- collect, organize, and prepare data for factor analysis;
- evaluate the applicability of factor analysis or various factor models to their data or research questions;
- carry through a factor analysis;
- prepare factor results for publication;
- check the adequacy of their factor analysis research design;
- survey the methodological literature relevant to particular research design questions, or
- find applications of the method to various social science problems.

The organization of this book reflects these objectives. It is divided into five parts. Part One, consisting of this and the following chapter, is nontechnical and attempts to give a methodological and philosophical context to factor analysis. It is designed to impart to the reader an appreciation of the method—a conceptual understanding of what is involved—and to answer the question "Why factor?"

Part Two (Chapters 3–7) focuses on the structure, matrices, and research design of factor analysis. Chapters 3 and 4 give the preliminary descriptive statistics and vector and matrix algebra basic to understanding the mathematical structure of the factor models. Chapter 5 presents the factor models themselves. These three chapters are technical; while many readers may wish to skip them, a sound appreciation of factor analysis requires that the reader come to grips with the statistics and algebra involved. These chapters lay out the analytic framework for a later consideration of factor analysis design and results and will be constantly referred to.

If necessary, however, the reader may by-pass Chapters 3 and 4. In Chapter 5, the consideration of each factor model is begun with a nonmathematical summary of the technical characteristics of the model, and at least these portions of Chapter 5 should be read in any case. Subsequent chapters present as many of the aspects of factor analysis in nonmathematical language as possible. For purposes of precision or explication, recourse to the statistics and algebra of Chapters 3 and 4 will often be made. Where possible, however, the mathematical discussion will be verbally summarized.

Chapter 6, presenting the various matrices resulting from a factor analysis, consolidates in a single chapter the diverse products of a factor analysis. Its purpose is to enable the nontechnical reader to understand and interpret factor results. Chapter 7 is an overview of research design. It treats factor analysis as a stepwise *process*, in which each step involves a nest of research design alternatives, the selection among which may well alter the factor results. The process is graphically presented in a flow diagram, and each step is briefly described. Chapters 6 and 7 are summary in nature. They have been designed as a reference source for those who wish a largely nontechnical overview of factor analysis results or wish to check on research design alternatives.

The six chapters of Part Three are concerned with the preparation of data for a factor analysis. These and the remaining chapters are organized according to the factor analysis process. That is, questions that come early in the design are found in the earlier chapters. The chapters are titled according to the design decisions of concern. Chapter 8 focuses on the various kinds of research questions that might be asked and attempts to delineate the particular characteristics of the question subjected to factor analysis. The nature of a data cube is discussed, together with the alternative data slices that may be factored. As a heuristic suggesting alternative data questions, this may well be one of the more important chapters in the book.

The operationalization of the research question is discussed in Chapter 9. Criteria for selecting cases and variables and measuring them are considered, and several prominent questions about the relationship between data and factor analysis (e.g., the relationship between R- and Q-factor analysis) are introduced and evaluated. This chapter is one of the longest in the book, and well it should be. Data operationalization is the link between research question and results, and inattention to details at this stage of the process can vitiate an otherwise impeccable design. Chapter 10 discusses several data problems in particular, especially the effect of error on the results and the influence of missing data—that bane of workers in the applied sciences.

Once the data are collected for a factor analysis, they may be transformed to better satisfy the requirements of the research question, the factor model, the factor technique selected, or the available computer programs. This transformation stage of the design is discussed in Chapters 11–13. The first of these chapters deals specifically with transforming data distributions and the factor analysis criteria for doing so. Chapter 12 moves from distributional transformations to transformations applied to the data matrix itself. One of these transformations, the correlation coefficient, is already familiar to most readers. Chapter 13 considers the communality problem in common factor analysis and the communality approximations that may be made prior to a factor analysis. It completes the data preparation stage of the research design.

Part Four is concerned with deriving factors from the data, and consists of six chapters. The various techniques of computing factors are considered in Chapter 14, with special emphasis on the principal axes technique. Chapter 15 points out the importance of the number of factors extracted and lists several criteria for making a "best" number-of-factors decision. Chapter 16 considers the question of factor rotation in general and orthogonal rotation in particular. Oblique rotation is the subject of Chapter 17. Higher-order factor analysis and factor scores are discussed in Chapters 18 and 19.

The fifth and last part of the book considers factor analysis results in detail. Chapter 20 focuses on techniques by which results of different factor analyses may be compared. Chapter 21 discusses the interpretation of the factors emerging from an analysis and the alternative models of presenting the results. Computing distances between cases on their factor scores (profiles) and grouping cases is discussed in Chapter 22. In addition, dimensional analysis, a very important extension of the capability of the factor analysis design, is delineated. Chapter 23, the last substantive chapter of this book, discusses publication and presents a checklist of aspects or results that should be included if replication or publication and evaluation of findings is desired.

Chapter 24, the final chapter, is an overview of factor analysis applications outside the field of psychology. It may prove helpful to those seeking such analyses in their own domain and may be suggestive to those in search of a design. This chapter and Chapter 21 on the interpretation of factors may be especially helpful to the reader not particularly interested in application but wishing to understand the substantive significance of such an analysis.

1.3 Strategy

The levels of difficulty of the chapters are graded. In most chapters, I have tried to verbalize and distinguish the essential points for ready reference, usually either in a table or in a listing. Moreover, wherever possible, points or aspects of the discussion are illustrated by figures or graphs and by examples, either artificial or from actual research work. These examples are mainly from research on nations, but are easily generalizable to other social units as well. Hopefully, these examples not only display the methodology but will also enable others to see the potential application of the method to international relations, comparative government, and, especially, conflict.

Throughout, I have tried to make clear the geometric representation of the factor analysis model and results. The approach is explicitly based on vector analysis, and geometric figures are freely used to illustrate this. If I succeed in making the reader aware of the vector characteristics of the factor model and the geometric picture involved, I will consider this book a success in communication. The factor model implies a geometric picture of social reality. It provides for the making of physical models and the visualization of this reality. It makes possible a theoretical structure that draws on the rich field of vector analysis for sustenance. Unless this vector—or geometric—feeling for the model is communicated, the reader may finish this book believing in the fallacy that factor analysis is merely a data reducing technique.

Parts of many of the chapters utilize matrix algebra, which is a helpful symbolic system for structuring the factor model. Matrix algebra, also known as linear algebra, is often presented as part of the geometry of vector spaces. To those familiar with the algebra, it is an elegant and concise way of expressing complex equations. To the social scientist, a knowledge of linear algebra is as important as a knowledge of statistics and is far easier to acquire. Accordingly, a chapter on matrix manipulation has been included, and a section of Chapter 24 lists several matrix algebra texts that will be helpful in this respect.

Social scientists may bring to this book differing conceptual schemes, as well as various connotations attached to such terms as dependent, relationship, explain, pattern, data, and so on. To communicate the sense of a concept or discussion, therefore, I will use different, somewhat synonymous terms (often in parentheses), whenever a rewording or a verbal "turning around" may be helpful for understanding a difficult concept.

Rather than assume that important distinctions and terms are automatically recalled from previous chapters, I will often reiterate such distinctions and terms. The sophisticated reader, I hope, will forgive me this redundancy, which is aimed at increasing the understanding of the non-factor analyst. Terms and ideas are frequently cross-referenced, both as memory-refreshers and as guides to the reader who merely wishes to consult salient material discussed elsewhere. It is hoped that the organization of the book into numbered sections and subsections will facilitate this cross-referencing.

I have attempted to be consistent in the notation employed throughout this volume and to use mnemonic symbols wherever possible. Where a notation has already become well established in the literature, such as R for the correlation matrix, the standard notation has been employed. For easy reference, a summary table of notation follows the table of contents.

One rule is consistently followed throughout the book: All (nonvector) matrices have their order subscripted. This rule may raise some eyebrows. Surely, writing $R_{m \times m} = F_{m \times p} F'_{p \times m}$ is more cumbersome and less aesthetically pleasing than $R = FF'$. Most of the users of this book, however, will probably not feel at home with matrix algebra. It should be helpful for such readers to be able to lean on the subscripted matrix order to distinguish nonvector matrices from scalars and vectors and to follow through various matrix manipulations. Moreover, I have found that, where the matrix order has not been subscripted in the literature, the matrix order is sometimes ambiguous. Yet knowing this order is often crucial to evaluating the matrix manipulations and methodological arguments employed.

A book is only as useful as its index is complete. Accordingly, the subject index has been constructed with the possible questions of the researcher in mind and with a view toward as complete a cross-referencing as possible. In a work of this type a glossary is customary. However, the important definitions are clearly set off in the text itself, and reference to these definitions through the subject index serves the purpose of a glossary.

This book is by no means sufficient for a full understanding or a confident application of factor analysis. It is meant to complement existing texts[1] not to compete with them. In recognition of this fact, there is little here on actual computational procedures. These procedures are to be found in most other texts and so are omitted here, although I might add that the advent of the computer and available factor analysis programs now usually make the knowledge of computational procedures unnecessary. Wherever required, however, the text containing the appropriate procedures is referenced.

1. An annotated list of such texts will be found in Section 24.1.

One learns a method by application and through the strategic comments of other researchers or methodologists. Accordingly, the reader may wish to follow up various points or to inform himself of other perspectives. Wherever possible, therefore, the methodological literature or applications are footnoted. These references are not meant to exhaust the salient literature, but they refer to major sources and will lead the reader to other discussions.

1.4 A Personal Caveat

Were I to have the background in applied factor analysis of L. L. Thurstone and R. B. Cattell, the technical competence of Harry Harman and Paul Horst, the mathematical skills of T. W. Anderson and Louis Guttman, and the philosophical insight of C. G. Hempel and Ernest Nagel, this book would be what I had hoped it to be. But I share few of the skills of these scientists, methodologists, mathematicians, and philosophers. My only claim to authority is wide reading in the factor analysis literature, a limited mathematical knowledge, a philosophical viewpoint, and several hundred actual analyses.

Why, then, do I presume to write a book aimed at readers who possess, perhaps, much more research maturity than I? There are two reasons: One is that no book has hitherto been written concerned wholly with the application of factor analysis to social variables as distinct from psychological tests. Many researchers, I feel, have been deterred from using factor analysis on social data because of the factor-test methodology and terminology specific to psychology. If it serves no other purpose, I hope this book will encourage others to utilize factor analysis in the social sciences and to improve on the imperfections of this first attempt. A second, personal reason for writing this book stems from the frustrations of my first factor analysis applications. Many data operationalization or research design questions (e.g., the best correlation coefficient) were not explicitly answered in existing texts; only after careful reading and searching of professional journals could an answer or discussion sometimes be found. The need for an applied factor analysis text to pull all these questions together and particularly to accent the questions relevant to social data was evident. Having gathered a considerable list of factor analysis problems from my own work and possible solutions suggested in the literature, I welcome this opportunity to make this material available to others.

2. Philosophy of Factor Analysis

If we first obtain a perspective on the role of factor analysis in science, it will help us later in understanding the descriptions of the factor analysis model, procedures, and design problems. Accordingly, this chapter will focus on the conceptual and philosophical aspects of factor analytic procedures and interpretations. Many of the methodological and technical concepts and considerations touched on here will be dealt with more precisely in subsequent chapters.

To unlock the door to understanding factor analysis, three key concepts are helpful: *patterned variation, vector,* and *dimension*. These concepts together enable us to comprehend the method as a tool for uncovering the order, patterns, or regularity in data or as a mathematical mold for casting scientific theory. The factors discovered by a factor analysis can themselves be treated as formal concepts expressing mathematical relationships, as theoretical concepts or constructs bridging diverse phenomena, or as empirical concepts categorizing concomitant relationships. The factors may be defined by an inductive application of the analysis or through deduction from a formal theory. They can be used to describe actual data regularities or to estimate universal patterns from a sample. The factors may also be employed to uncover causal order, explain uniformities, or classify correlations.

Application of factor analysis has a number of research aims. Interdependencies between variables can be delineated. Masses of data can be reduced to a parsimonious subset. Data can be scaled or transformed. Hypotheses and theories can be tested. An empirical domain can be explored and mapped. Causal analysis can be done. And an empirical typology can be defined.

2.1 Factor Analysis

Factor analysis is a general scientific method for analyzing data.[1] There is no restriction on the content of the data; they may be observational data on earthquakes, on movements of gas molecules, on group behavior, on attitudinal data derived from questionnaires or opinion polls; or they may be theoretical data on the probabilities of a Markov chain matrix, on the utilities of a game theory matrix, or on the hypothetical values of a transaction matrix.[2] Indeed, *any* matrix[3] can be factor analyzed.

Although it is possible to factor almost any matrix, not all matrices will yield scientifically useful factors. The value of a factor analysis is dependent on the meaningfulness of the variability in the data. If the data have no variation, that is, if all values are the same, then no more than one factor can be derived from the data. If the data have only random or chance variations (as in a random number table), then factor analysis will delineate only patterns of chance covariation.

What is meaningful variation, of course, varies with the research goal. But however such variation is defined, a common component will be a

1. For histories of factor analysis, see D. Wolfe (1940), Royce (1958), Harman (1967, pp. 3–6), and Burt (1966).

2. For example, factor analysis has been applied to cross-national data (Cattell, 1949a; Berry, 1960), world regional patterns (Russett, 1966), value orientations of culture groups (Kluckhohn and Strodtbeck, 1961), economic series (Rhodes, 1937), gang delinquency (Short *et al.*, 1963), urban crime (Schuessler, 1962), classification of groups (Borgatta and Cottrell, 1955), classification of primitive tribes (Schuessler and Driver, 1956), effectiveness of complex organizations (Godfrey *et al.*, 1958), dimensions of community systems (Jonassen and Peres, 1960), social change data (Gibb, 1956), political attitudes (Eysenck, 1954), issues of a profession (Somit and Tanenhaus, 1963), Senate roll call votes (Harris, 1948), UN roll call votes (Alker, 1964), and judicial voting behavior (Schubert, 1962). A bibliography of such applications to social data is given in Chapter 24.

3. For our purposes here, a matrix may be thought of as a table of numbers. The next two chapters will more explicitly define the concept of matrix.

notion of patterned relationships, of underlying order, or of causal uniformities. Gross national product per capita, for example, varies from nation to nation concomitantly with a number of societal characteristics. Variation in voting behavior is related to variations in social and economic characteristics. Variation in individual attributes exhibits an order that allows for the classification of personality types. Regardless of what variation is of concern, whether gross national product per capita, voting behavior, or individual attributes, the focus is on related variation. The interest is in those phenomena that vary uniformly with each other, such as education, income, and occupation, and are thus linked into a pattern. *The concept of patterned variation is the first of the three keys to understanding factor analysis.*

The meaning of variation may be made clear by reference to Table 2–1. Six characteristics of nations define the columns of the table. The rows refer to hypothetical nations (A, B, C, etc.). By considering the table as a matrix, variability in the data can be looked at from two major perspectives.[4] One perspective focuses on variation down the

Table 2–1. Characteristics of Hypothetical Nations

Nation	GNP per Capita (U.S. dollars)	Telephones per Capita	Vehicles per Capita	Population (millions)	National Income (millions of dollars)	Area (millions of km²)
A	60	.004	.003	57.6	3,500	1.30
B	78	.004	.001	1.7	140	.04
C	85	.010	.008	2.3	198	.12
D	114	.083	.026	23.5	2,731	.97
E	321	.122	.907	.8	303	.71
F	502	.679	.835	1.7	914	.63
G	1,361	1.421	.984	19.4	2,722	1.16

columns. That is, the concern is with variation in values on a single characteristic as one moves down the column *from nation to nation.* Another perspective focuses on variation along the rows. Then the concern is with variation in values for a single nation *from characteristic to characteristic.* Which is of more interest, column or row variation,[5]

4. Other perspectives, such as those due to "normative" and "ipsative" scaling or to centering a matrix, are technical in nature and are considered in Section 12.1.1.

5. When matrix columns refer to characteristics and rows to cases or individuals, factor-analyzing variation down columns is called R-factor analysis. The analysis of variation along the rows is called Q-factor analysis (see Section 8.3). One factor analysis technique—direct factor analysis—analyzes both kinds of variation simultaneously (see Section 14.3.5).

depends on the nature of the research. Although for simplicity only the variation down columns will be discussed, with some qualifications not significant here,[6] variability in nations across characteristics might serve equally well as an example.

Each of the columns of Table 2–1 can be considered a *vector* whose elements are the values for each nation. Therefore, the first column of data for nations (GNP per capita) would be one vector, the second column of data (telephones per capita) would be a second vector, and so on. Each of the six vectors is statistically *dependent* on the other five vectors. By dependence is meant that the values of nations on one vector (in one column) of data can be approximated (predicted, explained) from their values on the other vectors (in the other columns).[7] Some vectors form subsets of statistically *interdependent* vectors, in which one vector of the set can be approximated from the remaining members of the set without including other vectors from the matrix.

> *Example 2–1.* The first three vectors of Table 2–1 are statistically interdependent (correlated) among themselves but are little dependent on the last three vectors. These remaining vectors, therefore, are of small use in accounting for the variations in any one of the first three.

All the column vectors of a matrix form a *vector space*. The position of a column vector in this space is determined by its values for each row (for each nation in Table 2–1). Each row is therefore a coordinate axis for this space, on which each vector can be plotted. Vectors that are statistically interdependent will *cluster* together in this space. And each of these clusters will define a distinct *pattern* of regularity in the data.[8] *The concepts of vector and vector space comprise the second key to understanding factor analysis.*

A matrix may be composed of columns in which there is patterned variation. Each column may be conceived of as a vector, and subsets of vectors may be interdependent; all these vectors define a vector space. The clusters of vectors in the space describe the patterns of variation in the matrix. *What factor analysis does, then, is to determine the minimum number of independent coordinate axes necessary to plot (reproduce) the variation in vectors in the space.* Each such coordinate axis is called

6. For an analysis of the variation of nations across columns to be meaningful, the columns would first have to be standardized (see Sections 12.1.1.2 and 12.1.2).

7. Only *statistical* dependence (correlation) is of concern here. *Linear* dependence, in which the elements of one vector are equal to a linear combination of the elements of the other vectors, is discussed in Section 3.2.5.

8. The geometric concepts presented here are discussed more fully in Chapters 3 and 4.

a *dimension*. As many dimensions will be needed to reflect the variation in vectors as there are unrelated clusters of interdependent vectors. These dimensions then delineate the order, the uniformities, the regularities, the patterns in the data. *The concept of dimension is therefore the third and most crucial key to understanding and creatively using factor analysis.*

In different words, factor analysis uncovers the independent "sources" of data variation. Because interdependencies may exist between the data, factor analysts are asking whether the same amount of variation in the data can be represented equally well by dimensions smaller in number than the columns necessary to tabulate the data.

> *Example 2–2.* The variation of nations on the *six* column vectors in Table 2–1 can be almost as well described in terms of *two* hypothetical dimensions. Table 2–2 illustrates what these two dimensions might be. Nations vary down an "economic development" dimension almost to the same extent as they vary down the first three columns of Table 2–1. Similarly, "size" reflects national variation down the population, national income, and area columns.[9]

Table 2–2. Factor Scores for Two Hypothetical Dimensions

Nations	Economic Development	Size
A	−2.4	2.6
B	−2.1	−1.1
C	−1.6	−.4
D	−.4	1.8
E	.8	−2.0
F	1.3	−1.1
G	3.1	1.4

Dimensions disclosed by a factor analysis can be interpreted as measures of the amount of ordered or patterned variation in data. The *degree* to which such regularity or interdependency exists can be gauged by the number and strength of the dimensions.[10] To discover

9. Although hypothetical for the example, "economic development" and "size" actually have been delineated for 82 nations on 236 cross-national characteristics (see Example 9–7).

10. One of the best methods for understanding a technique is to apply it to physical data with well-known patterns of relationship or to contrived data with built-in structure. Reports of a number of such experiments have been published and are listed in Section 24.1.2.

order, pattern, and regularity in phenomena is the *raison d'être* of science. In this sense, factor analysis is a scientific tool par excellence.[11]

Factor analysis, as a general technique, has been criticized on three grounds. The first is that the data must have an underlying multinormal frequency distribution or at least must be measured on an interval scale. Both of these objections are based on misconceptions. Again, factor analysis can be applied to the data of any matrix. A multinormal, or near multinormal, distribution is required only when tests of statistical significance are applied to the factor results. As to measurement, factor analysis can be meaningfully applied even to nominally scaled data of a yes-no, or presence-absence type, the lowest and least demanding rung on the measurement ladder (Section 9.1.3).

A second criticism is that factor analysis assumes additivity and linearity in the data. Two objections can be raised against this criticism. One is that the dimensions themselves may involve complex functions of a nonadditive (e.g., log function) or nonlinear (e.g., second-degree polynomial) variety.[12] The "economic development" dimension of Table 2–2, for example, may involve an xy^2 type function, and "size"

11. Although they stress only the inductive or empirical use of factor analysis, the clear nontechnical discussion by Cattell (1952a, Chapters 1 and 20) and Thurstone (1947, pp. 51–62) will help the student understand the scientific nature of the method. For those with a mathematical background, the brief and highly sophisticated overview of factor analysis by Higman (1964, Chapter 11) is rewarding.

12. "The definition of a real vector space enables us to consider as vector spaces sets of elements that are not n-tuples of real numbers. For example, let the elements of V [a vector space] be polynomials $p(x)$ with real coefficients and such that $p(0) = 0$. For vector addition we take ordinary addition of polynomials, and for scalar multiplication, the multiplication of a polynomial by a real number. All the laws for a vector space over R [the real number field] are easily verified" (Paige and Swift, 1961, pp. 51–52). For a treatment of vector spaces involving multiplicative components, see Paige and Swift (1961, Chapter 8).

This point is so important that further documentation might be offered. "One of the most common misconceptions concerning the nature and significance of factor analysis is the belief that the linearity of the [factor model] . . . will restrict the accuracy and applicability of this method. This is not true, however. . . . In fact, it only means that the relationships between functions are analyzed in terms of linear vector fields. But the functions themselves can be of whatever nonlinear type, their expansions in terms of a given set of 'reference functions' [dimensions] . . . being linear only, i.e., they are series with some constant co-efficients of expansion." (Ahmavaara and Markkanen, 1958, pp. 62–63.) For a mathematical proof of this, see McDonald (1967). For very interesting empirical demonstrations of this characteristic, see Ahmavaara's and Markkanen's discussion (1958, pp. 63–66) of Thurstone's (1947, pp. 140–46) famous box example, or McDonald (1965, 1967). For a critical evaluation of the box and other demonstration problems, see Overall (1964).

may involve $x(y^2 + z)^2$, where x, y, and z are some unknown societal characteristics. Many complex functions can be reduced to linear vector spaces.[13]

A second objection to the above criticism is that equations are only conceptual schemes for ordering the world of our sensations. The degree to which these equations reflect "reality" is gauged by the economy with which they order and relate these sensations. Selection between linear or nonlinear models of this "reality" can be made on the basis of convenience and efficiency. The distinction between models need not be based on which is closer to "reality" but on which is able to predict observations with the least bother. This point is illustrated by the Ptolemaic and Copernican models describing the movements of heavenly bodies. Both models were conceptual systems predicting the motion of the stars and the planets. In this sense, both are true. However, the Copernican system eventually prevailed because of its greater mathematical simplicity.[14]

A final important criticism of factor analysis is that it is arbitrary—that different investigators can arrive at different answers using the same data and technique. With regard to the currently most often employed factor model (component factor analysis), this is not so. A complete factor analysis of a data matrix is mathematically unique. Different investigators using the same research design and factor technique on the same data must, within computation error, arrive at the same results. The idea of arbitrariness here has arisen, in part, from the problems associated with rotating[15] factors once a factor analysis has been completed. Rotation involves adjusting the factor results to a best fit with the separate patterns of interrelationship in the data. This adjustment sometimes involves an intuitive or manual determination of these patterns. The rotations will then vary to a certain degree with the intuition of the investigator, although, judging by the comparable precomputer rotations of different investigators, not with the arbitrariness sometimes alleged. Mathematical solutions of the rotation problem and the availability of high-speed computers have largely done away with this possible source of arbitrariness. As a scientific method, modern factor analysis can have a logical structure that is determinant. Only

---

13. For example, the complex nonlinear function $y = axz^2/w$ can be described linearly as $\log y = \log a + \log x + 2 \log z - \log w$.

14. See E. A. Burtt (1932, Chapter 2). At first, the Copernican model fitted astronomical data less well than did the Ptolemaic model. Nonetheless, the simpler perspective of the former influenced its increasing popularity among mathematicians of that period.

15. See Chapter 16.

research design decisions and the substantive content given this structure can be arbitrary.

2.2 Factors as Concepts

Three categories of concepts may be distinguished that are pertinent to the conceptual nature of factors.[16] One is that of *formal* (analytic) concepts that denote a class of logical or mathematical relationships among symbols (e.g., tautology, normality, function, regression line, linearity, correlation).

A second category is that of *theoretical* concepts, or *constructs*. The construct functions as an analytic device for generating other concepts of a theoretic or empirical nature, or for deriving theorems or hypotheses that can be tested. The construct may or may not be substantively interpreted, but what is important is a construct's validity within the structure of a theory and not its factual content.

The third category is that of *empirical* concepts. These define an existential class of things, events, or processes. Family, legislature, and planet are examples of such concepts. The important aspect of an empirical concept is its truth value—the degree to which the phenomena defined by the concept have operational meaning.

Where do factors as dimensions defining clusters of interdependent vectors fit into this typology of concepts? The answer is: into any one of the three categories depending on the purpose of the investigation. Factors can be formal concepts, theoretical concepts, or empirical concepts.

Factors as formal concepts. When considered as dimensions of a vector space, factors are coordinates defining the boundaries of the space and within it the location and magnitude of all vectors. Factors may therefore be viewed as symbolic *terms*, as formal concepts within a mathematical function, linking vectors and parameters to mathematical rules for their combination. As formal concepts, the factors can be utilized in the mathematical elaboration of a theory involving linear vector spaces or in the investigation of the analytic properties of factor analysis within the context of higher algebra.

Factors as constructs. As constructs, factors measure the inner working of the "black box" through which observed inputs are transformed to observed outputs. Imagine a box with a set of buttons at one end and a set of colored lights at the other. Let the input observations be the order and timing of the buttons pressed; let the output be the colors

16. The classification adopted here owes much to the stimulating work of Carl G. Hempel (1952).

and patterns of flashing lights. We can observe input and output, but not the intervening mechanism by which pressed buttons are associated, with flashing lights. This may be some highly complex function (e.g., $y = axwe^{-z}$) or some simple function ($y = a + bx$), but, whatever it is, the mechanism is hidden within the box.[17] This intervening mechanism of the box in our example, as the reader may have realized by now, is similar to the familiar intervening variable of the psychological stimulus-response model.[18]

If the input and output observations for the box are factor-analyzed together, the resulting dimensions will define a model of the box's inner mechanism. This model may not describe the real inner mechanism; its only function is to relate the two types of observation. In this sense, the vitamins A, B, C, and D of the dietician are models relating certain physiological inputs to specific physiological states. These vitamins—constructs—are analogous to dimensions that might emerge from a factor analysis of physiological and nutritional data.

> *Example 2-3.* If a matrix containing the voting charac-
> teristics and political, social, and economic characteristics
> of legislators is factor-analyzed,[19] it might be found that
> liberal voting and urban constituencies involve the same
> dimension. This dimension may then be considered a
> construct defining a sociopsychological mechanism relating
> urban constituency characteristics to liberal voting.

> *Example 2-4.* Consider the "economic development"
> dimension of Table 2-2. This dimension may comprise a
> complex socioeconomic and political mechanism linking
> a society's wealth, communication, and transportation.

The idea that factors are constructs involves the belief that they define the causal nexus underlying the observed patterns. Although the mechanism through which these causes operate may be unknown, the factors will delineate the phenomena that are involved.

17. For the "black box" concept, see Davis (1965, Chapter 7). A similar analogy is employed by Ahmavaara (1957, pp. 14–18) to distinguish between a *mechanistic* scientific theory that describes the box's inner mechanism and an *abstractive* theory that connects inputs and outputs in a predictive fashion. See also Royce (1963).

18. Royce (1963) views factors as variables that mediate between S (stimulus) inputs and R (response) outputs in psychological data. Factors can be considered as intervening variables or hypothetical constructs, depending on whether they are of the first, second, third, or higher order. For higher-order factors, see Chapter 18.

19. Grumm (1963) has done an analysis along these lines.

Factors as empirical concepts. Factors can be considered a *typology,* classifying or categorizing phenomena according to their interrelationships.

> *Example 2–5.* An empirical typology of tribes based on similarity in characteristics can be developed by factor-analyzing a matrix of characteristics for tribal groups. If the tribes rather than the characteristics are treated as vectors, the analysis will yield dimensions grouping tribes with similar profiles on the characteristics.[20]
>
> *Example 2–6.* Consider again the "economic development" and "size" dimensions of Table 2–2. Rather than viewing these dimensions as constructs, they may be interpreted as empirically defining or classifying two major types of characteristics contained in Table 2–1, those related to economic development and those related to size.

Besides employing factors as a typology, they may also be deemed characteristics or variables in their own right. A characteristic like gross national product per capita, for example, is itself an empirical concept embodying many characteristics, such as income from agriculture, manufactured products, and public administration expenditures. In turn, each of these may involve a range of related phenomena, and so on. Considering, then, that any characteristic entails an assumed dimension of interrelated subcharacteristics, the dimension delineated through a factor analysis may itself be thought of as an empirical characteristic. Thus, as GNP per capita is a characteristic of nations, economic development may also be considered a characteristic when derived from a factor analysis of cross-national data. Economic development may then be used to describe and systematically compare nations, as can be done with GNP per capita.

2.3 Factor Analysis and Scientific Method

Much of what will be considered in this section is implicit in the above discussion. However, the relationship of factor analysis to induction and deduction, to description and inference, and to causation and classification is important to an understanding and evaluation of the method and should be made explicit.

20. Schuessler and Driver (1956) report an empirical study along these lines.

2.3.1 INDUCTION AND DEDUCTION

The use of "and" rather than "versus" in the headings for this and the following subsection emphasizes that these different ways of interpreting or using factor analysis are not mutually exclusive. Instead, they may be different sides of the same coin, and which side we see will depend on the research question or on our orientation.

Factor analysis is most familiar to researchers as an exploratory device for uncovering basic concepts. The method is a screen through which data can be sifted to bare their underlying structure. Basic concepts thus discovered may corroborate those already of use in a field or may be so strange as to defy immediate labeling. Actually, factor analysis may be undertaken to net these strange unknown patterns of phenomena in the hope of making a catch of unsuspected influences at work in a domain. Factor analysis is a tool usable for reasoning from data to generalizations about underlying influences causing the discovered patterns. If a political scientist factors the attributes and votes of legislators and delineates a dimension connecting urban constituencies with liberal votes, for example, he can employ this finding as an ingredient in a theory linking urbanism and liberalism. Induction requires relating data. For doing this, factor analysis is a useful and efficient tool.[21]

Deduction involves two ways of using factor analysis.[22] One approach is to employ the factor analysis model (the mathematical structure of the method) as part of a theory. The model becomes an explicit and logical network for channeling theoretical deductions about phenomena. This approach is described more fully in Section 2.4, below.

A second deductive approach involves hypothesizing that certain patterns exist. The data then are factored to see if these patterns emerge.[23] Factor analysis has not often been employed to test hypotheses, but the restraint is due to research tradition and not to methodological difficulties.

21. Hanson (1958) gives a fascinating discussion of inductively relating data to "retroductively" arrive at a change in perspective or theory.

22. The distinction between induction and deduction is not a logical one. Induction, no matter how gross the data or atheoretical the investigator, involves deduction. The distinction here is of research orientation: Some investigators are mainly concerned with what they can learn from data while others approach data only to test their a priori notions. See Nagel (1961, Chapters 2 and 3).

23. With "factor analysis we can experiment with hypotheses that extend to statements about the *number* of factors at work in a situation, the *nature of the factors*, their degree of *interaction*, and the *magnitude* of their influence." (Cattell, 1952a, pp. 20–21; see also pp. 13–14). As an applied example, see van Arosdol *et al.* (1958), who employ factor analysis to test a hypothesis about dimensions of urban areas.

Example 2–7. The belief that ideology, power, and trade are central dimensions of international relations can be tested through factor analysis. Data can be collected on variables indexing international relations in all their diversity, including specific variables on ideology, power, and trade. A factor analysis would then test whether these dimensions exist.

2.3.2 DESCRIPTION AND INFERENCE

Interest can focus solely on a matrix of data. The research concern is describing the nature of these data, their interrelationships, and their patterns.[24] Statistical problems, such as the nature of the distribution, size of the sample, and randomness of selection, are not considered and need not be considered in the research design. As a case in point, all roll call votes in the Tenth Session of the United Nations General Assembly can be analyzed to describe either the voting dimensions of nations or the voting blocs into which nations were grouped for that session.[25]

Description may be an intermediate goal, however. The ultimate goal may be to generalize about dimensions of, for example, legislative voting, foreign conflict, political systems, personality, or role behavior.[26] Generalization from a number of descriptive studies is a form of inference. However, it is not statistical inference.

Although often considered a statistical technique, factor analysis is seldom employed for statistical inference. Factor analyses usually satisfy the requirement for statistical inference that a representative sample be analyzed, but additional data requirements, such as a multivariate normal distribution, are rarely met. The canonical factor model (Section 5.5), formulated so as to allow statistical inference, is seldom used; tests of significance for factor loadings are virtually unknown in application.

Description and generalization from a number of descriptive studies have been the tradition. This need not be the case, however. Currently available methods of factor analysis make it possible to apply tests of

---

24. Cf. Henrysson (1957, p. 86).

25. Alker (1964), Alker and Russett (1965), Rummel (1965b), and Russett (1966) report such factor analyses of UN sessions.

26. Henrysson (1957) describes extensively and in detail the applications of factor analysis in psychology. Thurstone (1947, Chapter 6) examines factors as explanatory concepts through a demonstration problem on the dimensions of cylinders. His illustration of this problem is helpful in understanding applied factor analysis.

significance of dimensions and loadings. The desirability of these tests for a specific project should be weighed *before* data collection and analysis are begun. For many applications, however, factor analysis will not require such tests. Factor analysis is a mathematical tool[27] like the calculus and not necessarily a technique of statistical inference like the chi-square, the analysis of variance, and sequential analysis.[28]

An understanding of the mathematical nature of the method contributes to its creative use.

> *Example 2–8.* Consider an international trade (transaction) matrix for all nations in 1960. The columns and rows of the matrix both refer to nations, and the intersection of a column and row contains the value of trade between the column nation and the row nation. Let the research question be: "How do nations group in terms of their trade with each other?" Now, as a statistical technique, factor analysis is usually applied to correlation coefficients. Since the trade data are not correlation coefficients, factor analysis may not seem to be an appropriate means of answering the question. But once it is realized that factor analysis is a tool for determining the dimensions of any symmetric matrix, then it may be applied directly to the trade data, and the analysis will yield a classification of nations based on their patterns of trade.[29]

2.3.3 CAUSATION, EXPLANATION, AND CLASSIFICATION

The relation of cause to effect has always had a fascination for scientists and philosophers. Books and scholarly papers have been devoted to the meaning and usage of the terms.[30] Nor has the relationship

27. Horst (1965, p. 7) argues for a mathematical rather than a statistical interpretation of factor analysis.

28. The correlation (product moment) coefficient and regression analysis are also mathematical tools for which many applications will not require available statistical tests. Their mathematical nature may be best understood through their geometric interpretation. The correlation coefficient between two arrays of data considered as vectors can represent the cosine of the angle between the vectors in space (Section 3.2.4). The regression equation measures one vector's (the dependent variable's) containment in a vector space spanned by a given set of dimensions (the independent variables). See Section 5.4.

29. A social choice matrix is a form of transaction matrix. For factor analyses of the former, see Wright and Evitts (1963) and MacRae (1960).

30. Some of the more excellent treatments are those of Frank (1955, Chapter 1), Kaufmann (1958, Chapter 6), the essays by Russell, Feigl, and Nagel in Part V of Feigl and Brodbeck (1953), and Nagel (1961).

between causation and factors been neglected. Much controversy in the literature centers on whether a factor is a cause of the pattern it defines.[31]

Before we attempt to answer this, the meaning of "cause" will be briefly discussed. Up to the middle of the nineteenth century physical science viewed causes as inanimate forces coupling phenomena according to discoverable natural law. A metaphysical necessity was attributed to cause-effect relationships: An effect *had to* follow from a given cause. This belief was consistent with pre-midnineteenth-century philosophy. A scientific conceptual scheme (such as Newton's system) was considered to be descriptive of *reality*. The scientist was merely a geographer of nature, drawing, on the basis of his observations, the configurations of the laws that shape all phenomena. Causal power was therefore an attribute of things as real as their color, size, or shape.[32]

Although it was attacked by philosophers like David Hume, a belief in causal necessity underlay all scientific work until developments in science itself displayed the inadequacy of this conception. Investigations into quantum physics in the latter half of the nineteenth century revealed that absolute predictability based on the necessity of causal laws was theoretically and practically unlikely. The consequent reanalysis of the foundation of necessary and absolute laws resulted in their virtual elimination from science.

Modern science now conceives of cause as, in Hume's words, "an object, followed by another, and where all the objects similar to the first are followed by objects similar to the second" (Hume, 1902, p. 76, italics omitted). The term "cause" is then simply an expression of uniform relationships, that is, of a generally observed concurrence and concomitance of phenomena. Even though this interpretation denies such popular connotations of the term as "to bring about," "to produce an effect," or "to influence," it removes the fuzziness from the concept and gives it a denotation consonant with scientific method and philosophy.

If we define "cause" as uniformity in relationships, then, does factor analysis uncover factors that are causes of the relationships they

31. "It would seem that in general the variables highly loaded in a factor are likely to be the causes of those which are less loaded, or, at least that the most highly loaded measure—the factor itself—is causal to the variables that are loaded in it" (Cattell, 1952a, p. 362). Cattell and Sullivan (1962) conducted a demonstration experiment by factoring data on cups of coffee to test whether the factors delineated would correspond to known patterns of causal influences.

32. An analogous situation exists today when social scientists consider linearity or nonadditivity a real characteristic of phenomena.

delineate? The answer must be "yes."[33] Each of the variables analyzed is mathematically related to the factors. Through this relationship the factors describe the regularities in the data and it is these regularities that define a causal *nexus*.[34] As the pattern of alignment of steel filings near a magnet can be *described* by the concept of magnetism, for example, so the concept of magnetism can be said to *cause* the alignment. Likewise, an economic development factor uncovered by factor analysis can also be called a cause. Similarly, a possible authoritarianism factor in attitudes causes fascist attitudes, a possible dimension of turmoil in the conflict behavior within nations causes riots, and a possible dimension of urbanism causes liberal voting.

The term "explanation" adds nothing new to the term "cause." Although laden in the social sciences with a surplus meaning associated with *verstehen*, a feeling of understanding or making sense,[35] to "explain" phenomena is nothing more than to predict or logically and mathematically relate phenomena. To explain an event implies the ability to predict it.[36] To explain that the Roman Empire fell because of disunity and moral decay is to say that the presence of these two elements in an empire such as the Roman Empire implies that (a prediction) the empire will break up or be conquered.

Prediction—and therefore explanation—is based on the identification of causal relations, that is, regularity. Thus, if a factor can be called a cause it certainly can also be called an explanation.

Perhaps because of the controversy in the social sciences associated with the idea of cause, or the desire to avoid saddling factors with meaning other than that of regularity in phenomena, factors are often treated as descriptive or classificatory.[37] A factor is then a class of

33. The experiment of Cattell and Sullivan (1962) discussed in note 31 is empirical evidence for this view. Of course, Cattell (1962b; 1952a, p. 362) has been a strong advocate of a causal interpretation of factors. A contrary view is argued by Hogben (1957, p. 275): "Because its raw data emerge from the domain of *concomitant* variation, factor analysis, like multivariate analysis, is legitimately at best descriptive. Of itself, it can at best lead to a more satisfactory taxonomy, but then only if we are clear about what and why we want to classify. It cannot disclose a causal nexus; and we must judge its usefulness as a means for unmasking unsuspected regularities of nature, of personality, or of society by its fruits alone." Burt (1941, pp. 65–71) also argues against a causal interpretation and views factors as classifications. See also Burt (1941, pp. 218–21).

34. Blalock (1961, pp. 167–68) displays the factor analysis causal model.

35. Abel (1953) presents a clear and explicit analysis of the operation of *verstehen* in the social sciences.

36. Hempel (1965, Chapter 10) lays out the logic and qualifications inherent in this view. See also Hanson (1959).

37. See Horst (1965, p. 23).

phenomena sharing one attribute: concomitant occurrence in time or space. Thus, "house," "horse," "social group," "legislature," "nation" are such classes. Factors may be conceived likewise. "Economic development" or "size" factors can be descriptive categories, subsuming telephones per capita, GNP per capita, and vehicles per capita in the former factor and population, area, and national income in the latter.

2.4 Factor Analysis and Theory

The aim of science is theory. Facts or data are meaningless in themselves. They must be illuminated by a conceptual scheme or theory. By their shadows, facts will then be known. Discrete facts would overwhelm man's capacity to manipulate, process, or understand them if he were not able to perceive their relations. If these relations are found to consistently recur they become scientific laws. Such laws may themselves be related and thus reducible to a theory covering the domain in which they are applicable.

A scientific theory consists of two components.[38] One is a system of abstract statements linked through chains of reasoning. These statements may obey logical rules but they have little or no operational-empirical content. They form an *analytic* system.[39] Symbols within these statements may be x, y, a, b, α, β, line, atom, dimension, force, power (mechanical or social), group, or ideology; the symbols may be connected grammatically (e.g., the ideology is a requisite for groups), logically (e.g., $A \supset B$), or mathematically (e.g., $2x + 3y = 0$). Whatever

38. The logical nature and scientific aspects of theory are discussed in Nagel (1961, Chapter 6). That theory construction comprises the two components to be discussed has been argued by Einstein. See the essays on Einstein's philosophy by Frank, Lenzen, and Northrop in Schilpp (1949).

39. An analytic system is made up of axioms, symbols, theorems, and rules by which theorems are derived from the axioms, and the symbols are related to each other. The system is completely independent of empirical content and need not have any empirical content at all. Algebra and geometry are familiar examples of such systems. Aristotelian logic is another such system, where the meaning and validity of conclusions such as A implies B, B implies C, therefore A implies C can be judged totally within the system without reference to empirical data. An *analytic* statement is then a statement within an analytic system. *Synthetic* or *empirical* statements, however, are statements making empirical assertions. For empirical statements the referents are phenomena; for analytic statements the referent is an analytic system. The analytic statement $y = (x + 1)(x - 1) = x^2 - 1$ has validity only in reference to the rules of algebra, for example, whereas the empirical statement that "Japan is more European than Asian" depends for its truth or falsity on observations.

symbols or reasoning are used, this analytic component of theories may be the creation of a scientist's imagination, the distillation of a scholar's experience with the subject matter, or the slow and tedious erection of a theoretical structure on a foundation of numerous experiments, investigations, and findings.

A second component of theory is empirical: the operationalizations fastening selected symbols in the analytic system to the facts. While the analytic system derives its validity from logical or mathematical rules, the empirical component must relate to data in a testable fashion. When the analytic system is valid and the empirical component is true, a theory is then a scientific theory explaining phenomena.

These two components of theory have not been well understood in the social sciences. In political science, for example, debate on the power theory of international relations has raged for over a decade. In essence, the theory states that nations basically are motivated to maintain or increase their political power. International politics is then theoretically explained largely on the basis of this motivation. The debate has focused on the meaning and reality of power as objective national capability and subjective motivation. But these aspects need not be the theoretical issue. Power and motivation can be treated as symbols functioning within an analytic system whose purpose is to derive predictions about nation behavior. Only the predictions then need be given empirical content and only their "reality" need be tested.

Such a misunderstanding of theory within the social sciences may have militated against a more theoretical use of factor analysis. Since it involves interconnected mathematical statements drawing on the field of linear algebra, the factor model potentially comprises an analytic system for a theory. Factors can be treated as symbols within analytic statements from which deductions can be made, empirically interpreted, operationalized, and tested.[40]

The factor model entails a mathematical formalism departing from the formalism of classical physics, which involves functions relating phenomena and their change in time by derivatives. Rather, the formalism of the factor model approaches that of quantum theory,[41] in which

40. An exciting use of factor analysis in this fashion has been reported by Cattell (1962a). He describes a theoretical model of role behavior that weaves together the personality, structure, and syntal dimensions of a group. Working also with the factor model as an analytic system, I have tried to develop a general theory of social behavior (Rummel, 1965a, 1965b).

41. Ahmavaara and Markkanen (1958, pp. 48–63) discuss the relationship of classical physics and quantum theory to factor analysis. See also Burt (1941, pp. 84–92, 100, 264; and 1938).

observations as linear relationships between unknown functions are the focus of concern. For example, quantum theory describes micro events *formally*, much in the fashion of a factor model of international relations.

Incorporating as it does an analytic potentiality for theory building and a set of empirical techniques for operationalizing symbols within the analytic system and testing deductions from them, factor analysis has great theoretical and heuristic possibilities. It opens new areas of development for the social sciences. Indeed, factor analysis and the complementary regression analysis model may augur a revolution in the social sciences as profound and far-reaching as that initiated by the calculus in the physical sciences.

2.5 Why Factor?

This section is devoted to a discussion of factor analysis applications. At the risk of redundancy, it will attempt to relate factor analysis explicitly to various research design possibilities.[42]

Patterns of interrelationship. If the investigator has a matrix of intricately related variables, say UN votes, personality characteristics, or answers to a questionnaire, factor analysis will bare the separate patterns of interrelationships involved. Moreover, the relationship of each variable to the separate patterns and the scores of each case (nation, group, or individual) on these patterns can be determined.

Parsimony or data reduction. Through factor analysis the variation in a mass of data can be described. Data on 50 variables for 300 individuals, for example, can be unwieldy to describe or manipulate. The management, analysis, and understanding of such data can be facilitated by factoring the matrix into its basic dimensions. These dimensions, which may be few in number, are a concise embodiment of the data variation in the original matrix and thus can be used in place of the 50 variables. It is easier to discuss and compare nations, for example, on economic development, size, and political system dimensions (if such exist) than on the hundreds of characteristics that each of these dimensions involve.

Structure. The basic structure of a domain may be the focus of concern. As a case in point, the interest may be in the primary independent lines or dimensions of variation in group characteristics and behavior.

---

42. Horst (1965, Section 1.5) discusses some applications of factor analysis. Burt (1941, Chapter 2) presents a comprehensive discussion with many examples of the uses of factors.

If a wide range of data were collected on a large sample of groups, factor analysis could usefully delineate this structure.

Classification or description. Factor analysis can be a tool for developing an empirical typology. It can be used to group interdependent variables into descriptive categories, such as size, liberal voting, and authoritarianism. It can be used to group cases into types on the basis of similar profile values.[43] Or it can be used on transaction or social choice type matrices to determine how individuals, social groups, or nations cluster in their transactions with, or choices of, each other.

Scaling. A scientist often desires to develop a scale on which individuals, groups, or nations can be rated. The scale may refer to such phenomena as political participation, voting behavior, segregation, or conflict. Such a scale involves the problem of weighting the various characteristics to be combined into a scale. Factor analysis offers a solution by dividing the characteristics into independent sources of variation termed factors or dimensions. Each factor defines a group of interrelated characteristics—a functional unity that can be used as a scale.[44] As part of the factor analysis results, weights are assigned to each characteristic for combining them into each factor (scale). These weights are derived from the variation that a characteristic has in common with a given factor. When characteristics are combined in terms of these weights, factor scores result. These are the desired scales.

Hypothesis-testing. Hypotheses about dimensions of attitude (e.g., liberalism versus conservatism), personality, group, social behavior, voting, and so forth, abound. Since the meaning usually associated with "dimension" is that of a cluster or group of highly intercorrelated characteristics or behaviors, factor analysis can test for their empirical existence. Which characteristics or behavior should by theory or hypothesis correlate with what dimensions can be postulated in advance, and the factor analysis can be done to see if the dimensions are there. Factor techniques are available that allow for statistical tests of significance.

Hypotheses about multivariate relations of various kinds can also be tested (see, for example, Sections 16.2.5 and 16.4.2.3). A hypothesis that economic development and instability are related, *holding other things constant*, can be examined by factoring data on economic and instability measures along with data on background variables that may

43. For example, see Borgatta and Cottrell's classificatory work on groups (1955) and Schuessler and Driver's work on tribes (1956). Selvin and Hagstrom (1963) show, through an example, how to use factor analysis to develop a classification of groups.

44. See Burt (1953), Krause (1966), and Kerlinger (1964, pp. 453–54).

affect (hide, depress) their relationship. The first factors can be computed (rotated) to maximally involve the background variables. A subsequent factor uncorrelated with the first factors can then be computed to maximally involve the economic and instability measures. This factor defines the relationship between the two measures, holding the other variables constant.

Data transformation. Factor analysis can transform data to a form required to meet the assumptions of other techniques.[45] For example, regression analysis assumes that if tests of significance are to be applied to the regression coefficients, the predictor or regressor variables are statistically independent.[46] If the predictor variables to be used are correlated, thus violating the assumption, factor analysis can be employed to reduce them to a smaller set of uncorrelated variables.[47] This smaller set can then be employed in the regression analysis with the knowledge that the variation in the original data has not been lost.[48] Likewise, if there is an embarrassment of dependent variables, their number may be reduced through factor analysis.

Exploratory uses. In a relatively new domain of interest in which the complex interrelations of phenomena have undergone little systematic investigation, factor analysis is useful for exploring the unknown. It can reduce complex linkages to a relatively simple linear expression, and it can uncover unsuspected relationships which may at first seem startling but later appear to be common sense. For the scientist who is unable to manipulate variables experimentally and therefore must deal with the multifold complexity of phenomena in their actual social setting, factor analysis is a substitute for the laboratory. It enables the social scientist to untangle interrelationships, to separate different sources of variation, and to control undesirable influences on the variables of concern.[49]

45. "Factor analytic investigation has its function predominantly . . . in *basic* research to provide the measurement foundations for later special problems in pure and applied research" (Cattell, 1952a, p. 17).

46. See Ezekiel and Fox (1959, pp. 283–84), and Johnston (1963, Section 8.1).

47. See Thurstone (1947, pp. 60–61).

48. For practical applications of this two-step design, see Buckatzsch (1947) and Berry (1960). For a discussion of the design, see Horst (1965, pp. 21–23, 469–70). Factor analysis can also be employed to increase the degrees of freedom in the data. See Horst (1965, Section 23.5), Burket (1964), and Royce (1963, p. 526).

49. On this and related points, see the particularly excellent Chapters 19 and 20 in Cattell (1952a). Cattell (1966a) has recently made a strong plea for interpreting factor analysis as a method that makes possible the experimental or laboratory analysis of data in its social or psychological setting. Cf. Kaiser (1964).

Mapping. Factor analysis enables a scientist to map a phenomeno-logical terrain. By mapping is meant systematically delineating major empirical concepts and sources of variation. These concepts may operate as categories for describing a substantive domain or may serve as input to further research. Some social domains, such as international relations, family life, or public administration have still to be mapped. For domains such as personality, attitudes, and cognitive meaning, however, considerable mapping has already been done (Cattell, 1965d; Eysenck 1953; Osgood *et al*, 1957).

Theory. As a model, factor analysis has roots in the field of linear algebra. The mathematical structure of the model can be employed to build a rigorous theoretical framework, and linear algebra can be drawn on to make deductions within the theory. Being consonant with the mathematics of such a theory, factor analysis can be applied to operationalize aspects of the theory or test empirical predictions derived from it.

Part Two · Structure, Matrices, and Design of Factor Analysis

3. Preliminary Descriptive and Vector Concepts

An understanding of factor analysis adequate for use in applications requires familiarity with a large number of algebraic and geometric concepts. Among researchers many of these concepts, such as mean, correlation, and standard score, are common knowledge. Some of these concepts, perhaps those dealing with regression and probably those related to vectors, may be unfamiliar. Since later chapters on the factor model and various aspects of factor analysis research design will often employ these concepts, the student should familiarize himself with them.

3.1 Descriptive Statistics

This section will define the various descriptive statistics of value in factor analysis. Most of these are no doubt familiar but are given here for convenience in reference.[1]

1. For the derivation of these concepts, see such excellent introductory statistical texts as Blalock (1960), Snedecor (1956), and Ezekiel and Fox (1959).

Notation 3–1. X_j = a variable, which is an array of data on a number of cases.

x_{ij} = the value for case i on variable X_j.

n = the number of cases.

$\sum_{i=1}^{n} x_{ij}$ = the sum of the value for the n cases on variable X_j, beginning with case x_{ij}, where $i = 1$. That is,

$$\sum_{i=1}^{n} x_{ij} = x_{1j} + x_{2j} + \cdots + x_{nj}.$$

$(x_{ij})^{1/2} = \sqrt{x_{ij}}$ = square root of any value x_{ij}.

Definition 3–1. The MEAN, or average, of a variable is the sum of its n values divided by n. For any variable X_j, the

$$\text{mean} = \frac{\sum_{i=1}^{n} x_{ij}}{n}.$$

Notation 3–2. $\bar{X}_j$ = mean.

Definition 3–2. The VARIANCE of a variable is the mean of the sum of the squared deviations of its values from $\bar{X}_j$. The deviation of each value x_{ij} is $x_{ij} - \bar{X}_j$. Therefore, the

$$\text{variance} = \frac{\sum_{i=1}^{n} (x_{ij} - \bar{X}_j)^2}{n}.$$

Definition 3–3. The STANDARD DEVIATION of a variable is the positive square root of the variance.[2] Therefore, the

$$\text{standard deviation} = \left(\frac{\sum_{i=1}^{n} (x_{ij} - \bar{X}_j)^2}{n} \right)^{1/2}.$$

Notation 3–3. σ_j^2 = variance of variable X_j.

σ_j = standard deviation[3] of variable X_j.

2. For statistical analysis of samples and for tests of significance, $n - 1$ rather than n is used for calculating the variance and standard deviation.

3. The standard notation for the variance and standard deviation of a sample is s^2 and s, respectively, and of the universe (or population) σ^2 and σ, respectively. The sample mean has the standard notation of $\bar{X}$, while the universe is μ. I have not adopted this notation for two reasons. First, I am not developing a sampling theory of factor analysis and do not require a clear distinction at the outset

The variance and standard deviation are measures of the scatter of cases on a variable. They describe the variation of cases around the mean. Because it has desirable mathematical qualities, the standard deviation is often employed in statistical derivations and analysis. We will have cause to refer to the variance and standard deviation often.

> *Definition 3–4.* The STANDARD SCORE of a case on a variable is the deviation of the case from the average divided by the standard deviation. For any case x_{ij}, the
>
> $$\text{standard score} = \frac{x_{ij} - \bar{X}_j}{\sigma_j}.$$
>
> A STANDARDIZED VARIABLE has had all its cases transformed to standard scores.
>
> *Notation 3–4.* z_{ij} = standard score for case x_{ij}.
> Z_j = standardized variable X_j.

The standardized variable has two properties of interest. It has a mean of zero,

$$\bar{Z}_j = 0,$$

and a standard deviation of unity,

$$\sigma_{Z_j} = \sigma_{Z_j}^2 = 1.0.$$

Moreover, if the frequency distribution of unstandardized values on the variable is a *normal* distribution—a bell-shaped curve (Section 11.2)—the standardized values will be distributed with known concentration: Close to 68 per cent of the values will fall between a standard score of $+1.00$ and -1.00, some 95.5 per cent will be between $+2.00$ and -2.00, and 99.7 per cent will be between $+3.00$ and -3.00. Thus, the standard score enables the extremeness of a case to be gauged and the *probability* of this extremeness to be judged by consulting a statistical table of areas under a normal curve.[4]

The importance of standardizing several variables, however, mainly lies in the variables being transformed to common, standardized units. Cases can then be compared as to their relative values on the variables,

---

between sample and universe means and variances. I require only a notation to describe a given set of data, which may be from a sample *or* universe. Second, $\bar{X}$ and σ^2 will not be confused with later notation. If I use s^2, for example (which might be expected since I employ $\bar{X}$ for the mean), s as the standard deviation might be confused with s and S used as notations later for the factor scores.

4. Almost all elementary statistical texts have such a table.

regardless of the original units in which these values were expressed.

Three statistics describing two-variable relationships should be defined. These are the covariance, correlation, and coefficient of determination.

Definition 3–5. The COVARIANCE of two variables is the ratio of the sum of the products of their deviation from the mean to the number of cases. For two variables X_j and X_k, their

$$\text{covariance} = \frac{\sum_{i=1}^{n} (x_{ij} - \bar{X}_j)(x_{ik} - \bar{X}_k)}{n}.$$

Notation 3–5. c_{jk} = covariance between variables X_j and X_k.

Definition 3–6. The product moment CORRELATION between two variables is the ratio of their covariance to the square root of the product of their variances. For two variables X_j and X_k, their

$$\text{correlation} = \frac{c_{jk}}{(\sigma_j^2 \sigma_k^2)^{1/2}} = \frac{c_{jk}}{\sigma_j \sigma_k}$$

$$= \frac{\sum_{i=1}^{n} (x_{ij} - \bar{X}_j)(x_{ik} - \bar{X}_k)}{\left\{ \left[\sum_{i=1}^{n} (x_{ij} - \bar{X}_j)^2 \right] \left[\sum_{i=1}^{n} (x_{ik} - \bar{X}_k)^2 \right] \right\}^{1/2}}.$$

Notation 3–6. r_{jk} = product moment correlation between variables X_j and X_k.

Definition 3–7. The COEFFICIENT OF DETERMINATION between two variables is the square of their correlation. For two variables X_j and X_k, the

$$\text{coefficient of determination} = r_{jk}^2.$$

The r^2 coefficient measures the proportion of variation in common for two variables; $r^2 \times 100$ measures the percentage of their variation in common.

If the variables are standardized, r^2, and consequently r, have simpler definitions than those just given. For two standardized variables Z_j and Z_k,

$$r_{jk}^2 = \frac{\left(\sum_{i=1}^{n} z_{ij} z_{ik} \right)^2}{n^2} \quad \text{and} \quad r_{jk} = \frac{\sum_{i=1}^{n} z_{ij} z_{ik}}{n}. \tag{3-1}$$

The correlation coefficient varies between $+1.00$ and -1.00. An $r = 0$ means that two variables have no relationship to each other: The variation in values of one variable are unrelated to the variation in the values of the other. An $r = 1.00$ means that the two variables have a perfect positive relationship; $r = -1.00$ means perfect negative relationship. In-between values of r, say .43 or .57, measure degrees of statistical relationship. The statistical significance of this relationship can be judged by consulting tables of significance[5] for r. For descriptive purposes, r^2 will give the actual proportion of variation in common at any level of correlation.

Three additional statistics that will be of much use in discussing factor analysis are the regression equation, regression coefficients, and multiple correlation. Before defining these, however, the idea of least squares and regression line should be introduced.

> *Definition 3–8.* The LEAST SQUARES fit of a variable X_j to another variable X_k is the straight line fitted to the plot of X_j (vertical coordinate axis) on X_k (horizontal coordinate axis) for which the sum of the squared vertical deviations of the values x_{ij} from the line are a minimum. This line is called the LINEAR REGRESSION LINE.

The variable X_j referred to in Definition 3–8 is called the *dependent* variable and X_k is the *independent* variable. The concepts of least squares and regression line now enable us to define intercept and regression coefficient.

> *Definition 3–9.* The INTERCEPT of the linear regression line for the least squares fit of X_j on X_k is the value of X_j at which the line crosses the X_j (horizontal coordinate) axis. The REGRESSION COEFFICIENT is the slope of this line.

> *Notation 3–7.* α_r = intercept.
> β = regression coefficient.

> *Definition 3–10.* The LINEAR REGRESSION EQUATION for the least squares fit of a variable X_j to another variable X_k is the equation of the linear regression line of X_j on X_k. This equation gives the best linear ESTIMATE of the values of X_j from the values of X_k. That is, the
>
> $$\text{estimate} = \alpha_r + \beta X_j.$$
>
> *Notation 3–8.* $\hat{X}_j$ = best linear estimate of X_j from the linear regression equation (read $\hat{X}$ as X upper hat).

5. See, for example, Snedecor (1956, p. 174).

From the notation and definitions established, then, the linear regression of a dependent variable X_j on an independent variable X_k is given by the equation

$$\hat{X}_j = \alpha_r + \beta_k X_k. \tag{3-2}$$

Example 3-1. A plot of two hypothetical variables is displayed in Fig. 3-1. The plot of eight cases as points is shown and the deviations of these points from the regression line are indicated by the dotted lines. The regression line is so located between these points that the sum of their squared vertical deviations is a minimum. The slope of this line is β_k. If the line is horizontal, $\beta_k = 0$, and X_k contributes nothing towards the estimate of X_j. In this case the best estimate of X_j is $\bar{X}_j$, i.e., $\hat{X}_j = \bar{X}_j = \alpha_r$.

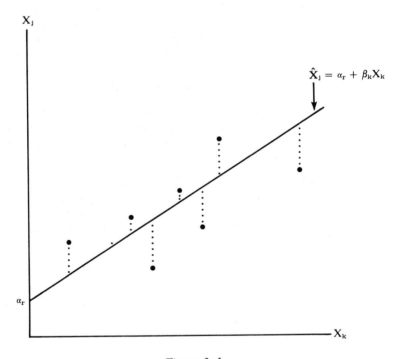

Figure 3-1

The estimate is good or bad as the values of $\hat{X}_j$ depart from those of X_j. A measure of this departure are the deviations $X_j - \hat{X}_j$. These are often called the linear regression residuals, or merely *residuals*.

A descriptive statistic for gauging the degree to which $\hat{X}_j$ approximates X_j is the coefficient of determination (Definition 3–7) between $\hat{X}_j$ and X_j. This will indicate the proportion of variation in X_j estimated by $\hat{X}_j$. If the coefficient is 1.00, then $\hat{X}_j = X_j$, i.e., the estimate is perfect.

The concept of linear regression for two variables now has a simple extension to *linear multiple regression*—the linear regression of one variable on a number of independent variables.[6]

> *Definition 3–11.* For a dependent variable X_j and m independent variables $X_1, X_2, \ldots, X_k, \ldots, X_m$, the LINEAR MULTIPLE REGRESSION of X_j on the independent variables is given by the equation
>
> $$\hat{X}_j = \alpha_r + \beta_1 X_1 + \beta_2 X_2 + \cdots + \beta_k X_k + \cdots + \beta_m X_m,$$
>
> where the regression coefficient for any of the variables, say β_k for X_k, is the *linear regression coefficient* for the *least squares* fit of X_j to X_k, *holding the other independent variables constant.*

The regression coefficients in multiple regression measure the independent linear contribution of each of the independent variables to the estimate of the dependent variable. A regression coefficient of zero then means that the particular variable contributes nothing to the estimate when the other variables are held constant.

If the data are standardized (Definition 3–4), then the intercept of the multiple regression equation equals zero and the regression coefficients vary between $+1.0$ and -1.0.

A descriptive statistic that will be of much use to us later is the multiple correlation coefficient.

> *Definition 3–12.* The MULTIPLE CORRELATION of a dependent variable X_j with m independent variables $X_1, X_2, \ldots, X_k, \ldots, X_m$ is the correlation (Definition 3–6) of X_j with $\hat{X}_j$, where $\hat{X}_j$ is the linear multiple regression estimate of X_j on the m independent variables.
>
> *Notation 3–9.* $r_j = $ the multiple correlation of variable X_j. With a single subscript, r will always refer to multiple correlation.[7] When two subscripts are given, e.g., r_{jk}, the correlation will be r between two variables X_j and X_k.

6. For some general social science applications of multiple regression, see Coleman (1964). Ezekiel and Fox (1959) present the method in detail. More technical discussions and derivations are given by Johnston (1963) and Williams (1959).

7. Usually, capital R is employed to denote multiple correlation. This notation will have to be reserved, however, for its traditional use in factor analysis—to denote the correlation matrix.

The multiple correlation indicates the variation in a variable that can be estimated from a number of independent variables. The proportion of this variance (Definition 3–2) that can be estimated is precisely measured by r_j^2. A specific notation for r_j^2 has developed in factor analysis.

> *Notation 3–10.* $\text{SMC}_j = r_j^2 =$ squared multiple correlation of variable X_j.

Multiple regression specifies the relationship of one dependent variable to a set of independent variables. The regression coefficient measures the linear contributions of a particular independent variable to the variation of the dependent variable, holding the other independent variables constant.

If we wish a specific measure of the correlation between any two variables, holding some other variables constant, we can use the *partial correlation coefficient.*

> *Definition 3–13.* The PARTIAL CORRELATION between two variables is the *product moment correlation* between them, holding the variance of some specified other variables constant.

> *Notation 3–11.* $r_{12.3} =$ partial correlation between variables X_1 and X_2, holding X_3 constant.
>
> $r_{12.m-1} =$ partial correlation between variables X_1 and X_2, holding $(m-1)$ other variables constant.

The partial correlation of two variables, holding one other constant, is

$$r_{12.3} = \frac{r_{12} - r_{13}r_{23}}{[(1 - r_{13}^2)(1 - r_{23}^2)]^{1/2}}, \tag{3-3}$$

where r_{12}, r_{13}, and r_{23} are the product moment correlations (Definition 3–6) between the subscripted variables.

For four variables the partial correlation is

$$r_{12.34} = \frac{r_{12.4} - r_{13.4}r_{23.4}}{[(1 - r_{13.4}^2)(1 - r_{23.4}^2)]^{1/2}} = \frac{r_{12.3} - r_{14.3}r_{24.3}}{[(1 - r_{14.3}^2)(1 - r_{24.3}^2)]^{1/2}}. \tag{3-4}$$

In the subsequent discussion of factor analysis, we will be most interested in the partial correlation between two variables, holding many variables constant. The formula for this is most conveniently handled in matrix notation and is presented in Section 4.3.

3.2 Vector Concepts

The geometry and algebra associated with vectors are helpful in discussing, understanding, and applying factor analysis. They are useful in giving visual meaning to data and factor results and are especially useful in employing the factor model theoretically and in developing the structure of such theory.

3.2.1 MATRIX, VECTOR, AND VECTOR SPACE

Definition 3–14. A MATRIX is any table of numbers. The number of rows by the number of columns in a matrix is the ORDER of the matrix.

Notation 3–12. A = a *data* matrix.

$j = j$th column of A.

$i = i$th row of A.

x_{ij} = an element (datum) of matrix A contained in row i and column j.

n = number of rows of A (cf. n in Notation 3–1).

m = number of columns of A.

$n \times m$ = order of A (n rows by m columns).

$A_{n \times m}$ = a data matrix, with its order defined by the subscripts $n \times m$.

Example 3–2. Table 3–1 presents in abbreviated form data on 10 political variables for 79 nations.[8] The rows of the table refer to nations, and the ith nation is denoted by i. The columns are the characteristics for these nations, and j refers to the jth characteristic. Any cell created by the intersection of one row, i, and a column, j, can be denoted x_{ij}. The whole table may be called a *matrix* and can be symbolized here by the letter A. The *order* of the matrix is 79×10. The notation $A_{79 \times 10}$ then refers concisely to the data of Table 3–1.

Definition 3–15. Algebraically, the column or row of a matrix is a VECTOR. If a row, it is called a ROW VECTOR; if a column, it it is called a COLUMN VECTOR. The numbers in the row or column are the VECTOR ELEMENTS of the row or column vector.

---

8. The data in the table have been purposely selected to display the applicability of factor analysis and associated statistical and geometric concepts to what are often considered to be immeasurable qualitative concepts.

Table 3–1. *Ten Political Characteristics*[a]

<table>
<tr><td></td><td colspan="10">Characteristic = j</td></tr>
<tr>
<th>Nation = i</th>
<th>System Style (1)</th>
<th>Constitutional Status (2)</th>
<th>Representative Character (3)</th>
<th>Electoral System (4)</th>
<th>Freedom of Group Opposition (5)</th>
<th>Non-Communist Regime (6)</th>
<th>Political Leadership (7)</th>
<th>Horizontal Power Distribution (8)</th>
<th>Monarchical Type (9)</th>
<th>Military Participation (10)</th>
</tr>
<tr><td>1. Afghanistan</td><td>0</td><td>1</td><td>1</td><td>1</td><td>1</td><td>1</td><td>0</td><td>0</td><td>1</td><td>1</td></tr>
<tr><td>2. Albania</td><td>2</td><td>0</td><td>1</td><td>0</td><td>0</td><td>0</td><td>0</td><td>0</td><td>0</td><td>1</td></tr>
<tr><td>3. Argentina</td><td>0</td><td>1</td><td>2</td><td>2</td><td>3</td><td>1</td><td>2</td><td>1</td><td>0</td><td>2</td></tr>
<tr><td>4. Australia</td><td>0</td><td>2</td><td>3</td><td>2</td><td>3</td><td>1</td><td>2</td><td>2</td><td>0</td><td>0</td></tr>
<tr><td>...
 i</td><td>...
 x_{i1}</td><td>...
 x_{i2}</td><td>...
 x_{i3}</td><td>...
 x_{i4}</td><td>...
 x_{i5}</td><td>...
 x_{i6}</td><td>...
 x_{i7}</td><td>...
 x_{i8}</td><td>...
 x_{i9}</td><td>...
 x_{i10}</td></tr>
<tr><td>76. Uruguay</td><td>0</td><td>2</td><td>3</td><td>2</td><td>3</td><td>1</td><td>2</td><td>2</td><td>0</td><td>0</td></tr>
<tr><td>77. Venezuela</td><td>0</td><td>1</td><td>3</td><td>2</td><td>2</td><td>1</td><td>2</td><td>1</td><td>0</td><td>1</td></tr>
<tr><td>78. Yemen</td><td>0</td><td>0</td><td>0</td><td>0</td><td>1</td><td>1</td><td>0</td><td>0</td><td>1</td><td>1</td></tr>
<tr><td>79. Yugoslavia</td><td>2</td><td>0</td><td>1</td><td>0</td><td>1</td><td>0</td><td>0</td><td>0</td><td>0</td><td>1</td></tr>
</table>

$$= A_{79 \times 10} = A_{n \times m}.$$

[a] Data for the full data matrix were derived from Banks and Textor (1963, Appendix A). The scaling of the data for each variable is as follows:

(1) System style: 0 = nonmobilization, 1 = limited mobilization, 2 = mobilizational.
(2) Constitutional status: 0 = totalitarian, 1 = authoritarian, 2 = constitutional.
(3) Representative character: 0 = nonpolyarchic, 1 = pseudopolyarchic, 2 = limited polyarchic, 3 = polyarchic.
(4) Electoral system: 0 = noncompetitive, 1 = partially competitive, 2 = competitive.
(5) Freedom of group opposition: 0 = autonomous group not tolerated, 1 = autonomous group tolerated informally, 2 = autonomous group can organize in politics but cannot oppose government, 3 = autonomous group can oppose government.
(6) Non-Communist regime: 0 = no, 1 = yes.
(7) Political leadership: 0 = elitist, 1 = moderate elitist, 2 = nonelitist.
(8) Horizontal power distribution: 0 = negligible, 1 = limited, 2 = significant.
(9) Monarchical type: 0 = nonmonarchical, 1 = monarchical or monarchical-parliamentary.
(10) Military participation: 0 = neutral, 1 = supportive, 2 = interventive.

Notation 3–13. X_j = a *j*th *data* column vector.

X_i' = an *i*th *data* row vector.

x_{ij} = the *i*th element (datum) of vector X_j or the *j*th element (datum) of vector X_i'.

n = the number of elements (data) in vector X_j.

m = the number of elements (data) in vector X_i'.

$$\begin{bmatrix} x_{1j} \\ x_{2j} \\ \vdots \\ x_{nj} \end{bmatrix} = X_j = \text{a column vector.}$$

$$[x_{i1}, x_{i2}, \ldots, x_{im}] = X_i' = \text{a row vector.}$$

Example 3–3. Each column, *j*, of *A* in Table 3–1 can be considered a vector with *n* elements, where each element x_{ij} is the value for a nation on the vector. Consider the column vector X_2 of *A*. It has the $n = 79$ elements:

$$X_2 = \begin{bmatrix} x_{1,2} \\ x_{2,2} \\ x_{3,2} \\ x_{4,2} \\ \vdots \\ x_{i,2} \\ \vdots \\ x_{76,2} \\ x_{77,2} \\ x_{78,2} \\ x_{79,2} \end{bmatrix} = \begin{bmatrix} 1 \\ 0 \\ 1 \\ 2 \\ \vdots \\ x_{i,2} \\ \vdots \\ 2 \\ 1 \\ 0 \\ 0 \end{bmatrix}.$$

In the section on descriptive statistics, a variable was defined by *X*. Here we are defining a data vector also as *X*. Since data on a variable form an array of column or row values for cases, the variable can also be treated as a vector. Thus, system style [column (1) in Table 3–1] can be considered both a vector and a variable.

All variables may be treated as vectors, but not all vectors can be treated as variables. The attribute of a variable is that some of its values vary. Otherwise it is a constant. A vector, however, may have all elements the same. Indeed, its elements may all be zero.

Since the vector X is defined as a *data* vector, we will assume that its elements will always vary. Variable X and vector X will therefore be treated as equivalent, although, depending on the context, we may prefer one term to the other.

> *Definition 3–16.* Geometrically, a VECTOR is a line segment with length and direction in space. The coordinate axes for locating a vector in space are given by the vector's elements.

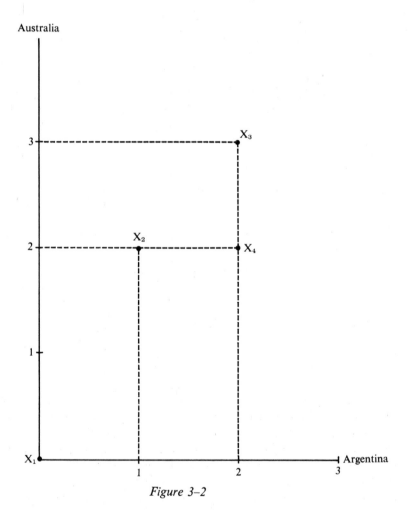

Figure 3–2

Example 3–4. Imagine for a moment that the $A_{n \times m}$ matrix of Table 3–1 has only two rows: Argentina and Australia. Each column vector, X_j, will then have only elements referring to these two nations, and these nations will be coordinate axes, geometrically locating the vectors. Figure 3–2 shows Australia and Argentina as axes of a space within which political characteristics X_1, X_2, X_3, and X_4 are plotted as points. Thus, the second characteristic is plotted according to its element of 1 for Argentina and an element of 2 for Australia. Dashed lines from each

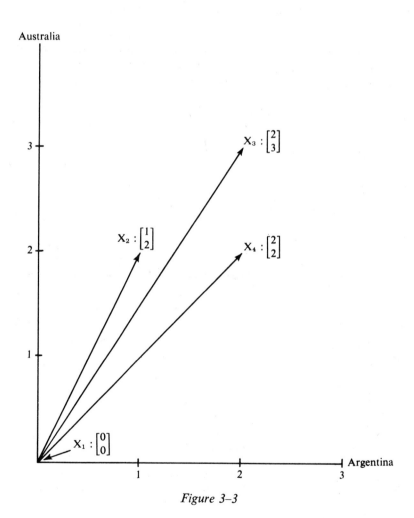

Figure 3–3

point in the figure show the plots. Now, as displayed in Fig. 3–3, a vector is represented by drawing a line from the origin to a point.[9] The *length* of the vector is the length of this line. The vector's *direction* is shown by placing an arrow point at the termination of the vector, and the direction is measured by the angle of the vector from the axis.

Definition 3–17. A VECTOR SPACE is defined by all the numbers in a matrix and includes all the (column or row) vectors of the matrix. If the space consists of the column vectors, the matrix rows are a coordinate system for this space.

The meaning, in the above definition, of "A vector space is defined by all the numbers ..." will be made clear in Definition 3–34 after several prerequisite concepts have been presented.

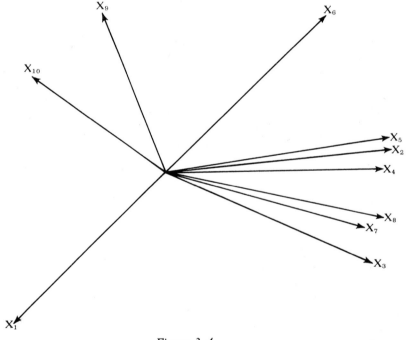

Figure 3–4

9. A vector may originate anywhere in a coordinate system, like the vector forces of physics for example. For our purposes, however, a vector will usually originate at the origin.

Example 3–5. It is not possible to plot all the vectors (characteristics) of Table 3–1 in a 79-row (nations) co-ordinate space. We can, however, display a two-dimensional configuration of vectors that approximates this space, as shown in Fig. 3–4. Were the matrix $A_{79 \times 10}$ to be reduced to just the vectors X_1, X_2, X_3, and X_4 on the coordinates Argentina and Australia, then Fig. 3–3 would precisely display this reduced space.

The introduction of the concept of vectors requires that nonvector values be defined.

Definition 3–18. A SCALAR is a number.

Scalars like 4.7, 2, 348, or 17 occur frequently in everyday life. Applied mathematics has traditionally dealt with scalar quantities. An equation like $y = 3 + 2x$, familiar from elementary algebra, states that a scalar number y equals three plus two times some other scalar number x.

Scalars are to be distinguished from vectors, which are an ordered set of numbers. The number 6 is a scalar; the set of numbers

$$\begin{bmatrix} 4 \\ 3 \\ 5 \end{bmatrix}$$

is a vector. The order of the numbers for a vector determines the vector's location in space and is therefore meaningful.

Notation 3–14. scalar = an unbracketed number.

Example 3–6. The numbers 5, 10, 2.4 are scalars. The bracketed set of ordered numbers [5], $\begin{bmatrix} 4 \\ 1 \end{bmatrix}$, [6, 2, 4] are vectors (Notation 3–13). The second set is a column vector and the third is a row vector. The vector [5] could be either a row or column vector, depending on the context.[10]

3.2.2 VECTOR ARITHMETIC

In order to employ vector concepts in discussing the factor model, several elementary rules of vector arithmetic need to be stated.

10. We will have to use brackets occasionally in expressions such as $[(x + y)^2 + 3]^{1/2}$. These brackets specify algebraic operations only and should not be confused with those denoting a vector like $[x, y, z]$.

Definition 3–19. VECTOR ADDITION is accomplished by adding the corresponding elements of the vectors. If X_j and X_k are vectors

$$\begin{bmatrix} x_{1j} \\ x_{2j} \\ \vdots \\ x_{nj} \end{bmatrix} \quad \text{and} \quad \begin{bmatrix} x_{1k} \\ x_{2k} \\ \vdots \\ x_{nk} \end{bmatrix},$$

then

$$X_j + X_k = \begin{bmatrix} x_{1j} + x_{1k} \\ x_{2j} + x_{2k} \\ \vdots \quad \vdots \\ x_{nj} + x_{nk} \end{bmatrix}.$$

Example 3–7.

$$\begin{bmatrix} 2 \\ 3 \end{bmatrix} + \begin{bmatrix} 4 \\ 6 \end{bmatrix} = \begin{bmatrix} 6 \\ 9 \end{bmatrix}, \quad \begin{bmatrix} 1 \\ 4 \\ 6 \end{bmatrix} + \begin{bmatrix} 2 \\ 4 \\ 1 \end{bmatrix} + \begin{bmatrix} 0 \\ 1 \\ 1 \end{bmatrix} = \begin{bmatrix} 3 \\ 9 \\ 8 \end{bmatrix},$$

and

$$[5, 4, 3] + [1, 1, 2] = [6, 5, 5].$$

The geometric interpretation of vector addition in a two-coordinate system is shown in Fig. 3–5. In reading the plot of the vectors, the first subscript of a vector element defines the coordinate axis and the second subscript defines the vector of concern. Thus, for $X_1 : \begin{bmatrix} x_{11} \\ x_{21} \end{bmatrix}$,

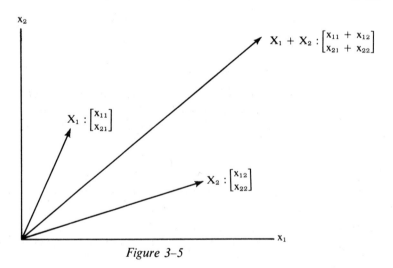

Figure 3–5

the value x_{11} is the projection of X_1 on the x_1 axis; the value x_{21} is the projection of X_1 on the x_2 axis.

In physics the vector resulting from the addition of several vectors has useful applications. If several physical forces are treated as vectors, then the addition of the force vectors yields a vector that is the resolution of these forces. The length and direction of this resolution vector describe the total force being applied and its direction of application.

Definition 3–20. VECTOR SUBTRACTION is accomplished by subtracting the corresponding elements of the vectors. If X_j and X_k are vectors

$$\begin{bmatrix} x_{1j} \\ x_{2j} \\ \vdots \\ x_{nj} \end{bmatrix} \quad \text{and} \quad \begin{bmatrix} x_{1k} \\ x_{2k} \\ \vdots \\ x_{nk} \end{bmatrix},$$

then

$$X_k - X_j = \begin{bmatrix} x_{1k} - x_{1j} \\ x_{2k} - x_{2j} \\ \vdots \quad \vdots \\ x_{nk} - x_{nj} \end{bmatrix}.$$

Example 3–8. $[1, 2, 3] - [4, 0, 1] = [-3, 2, 2]$, and

$$\begin{bmatrix} 4 \\ 5 \\ 5 \end{bmatrix} - \begin{bmatrix} 6 \\ 2 \\ 0 \end{bmatrix} = \begin{bmatrix} -2 \\ 3 \\ 5 \end{bmatrix}.$$

The geometric interpretation of subtraction is shown in Fig. 3–6 for two coordinates. The resulting vector, $X_2 - X_1$, is the *distance vector* between X_1 and X_2. This distance vector will be important in later discussions of factor analysis and, accordingly, should be defined explicitly.

Definition 3–21. The DISTANCE VECTOR between any two vectors X_j and X_k is

$$X_k - X_j.$$

A way of multiplying vectors that is very useful in factor analysis is called the *dot,* or *inner,* product. The term inner product will be adopted here.

Definition 3–22. The INNER PRODUCT of two vectors is the sum of the product of their corresponding elements. If X_j and X_k are two vectors, their inner product is

$$x_{1j}x_{1k} + x_{2j}x_{2k} + \cdots + x_{nj}x_{nk},$$

and is a *scalar.*

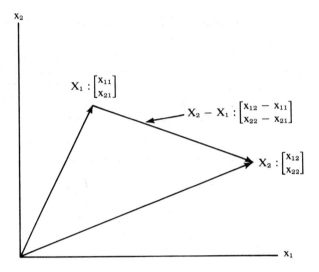

Figure 3–6

Notation 3–15. (X_j, X_k) = the inner product of vectors X_j and X_k.

Example 3–9. If

$$X_j = \begin{bmatrix} 5 \\ 1 \\ 4 \end{bmatrix} \quad \text{and} \quad X_k = \begin{bmatrix} 4 \\ 1 \\ 1 \end{bmatrix},$$

then

$$(X_j, X_k) = (5 \times 4) + (1 \times 1) + (4 \times 1) = 25.$$

For $X'_j = [2, 2, 4, 7]$ and $X'_k = [0, 1, 0, 2]$,

$$(X'_j, X'_k) = (2 \times 0) + (2 \times 1) + (4 \times 0) + (7 \times 2) = 16.$$

If one of the vectors is a row vector and the other a column vector, (X_j, X_k) is still the same. For example,

$$X_j = \begin{bmatrix} 5 \\ 2 \\ 2 \end{bmatrix}, \quad X'_k = [4, 1, 1],$$

and

$$(X_j, X'_k) = (5 \times 4) + (2 \times 1) + (2 \times 1) = 24.$$

Vectors may be multiplied by scalars, as well as multiplied by themselves.

Definition 3–23. The SCALAR PRODUCT of a vector is a scalar times each of the elements of the vector. If

$$X_j = \begin{bmatrix} x_{1j} \\ x_{2j} \\ \vdots \\ x_{nj} \end{bmatrix}$$

is a vector and α is some scalar, then the

$$\text{scalar product} = \begin{bmatrix} \alpha x_{1j} \\ \alpha x_{2j} \\ \vdots \\ \alpha x_{nj} \end{bmatrix}.$$

Notation 3–16. $\alpha X_j = $ the scalar product of scalar α times vector X_j.

Example 3–10. Let a scalar $\alpha = 3$, and a vector X_j be

$$\begin{bmatrix} 2 \\ 2 \\ 4 \\ 1 \end{bmatrix}.$$

Then,

$$\alpha X = 3 \begin{bmatrix} 2 \\ 2 \\ 4 \\ 1 \end{bmatrix} = \begin{bmatrix} 3 \times 2 \\ 3 \times 2 \\ 3 \times 4 \\ 3 \times 1 \end{bmatrix} = \begin{bmatrix} 6 \\ 6 \\ 12 \\ 3 \end{bmatrix}.$$

Similarly, for a row vector $X_j' = [2, 1, 1, 4]$,

$$3X_j = 3[2, 1, 1, 4] = [3 \times 2, 3 \times 1, 3 \times 1, 3 \times 4]$$

$$= [6, 3, 3, 12].$$

As shown in Fig. 3–7, the multiplication of a vector by a positive scalar lengthens or shortens the vector in space, depending on whether the scalar is greater or less than one. If the scalar equals plus or minus one, the length of a vector is not altered.

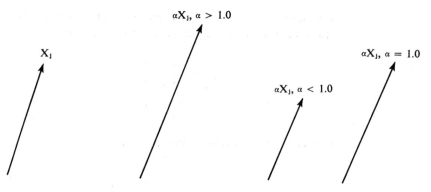

Figure 3–7

Multiplication by a negative scalar completely reverses the direction of a vector. If the scalar is zero, multiplication then transforms the vector into a point at the origin of the vector space.

3.2.3 VECTOR FUNCTIONS

With the definitions and notation now established, we can precisely define five important concepts: vector length, normal vector, distance, angle between vectors, and orthogonality.

Definition 3–24. The LENGTH of a vector is the square root of the inner product of a vector (a vector multiplied by itself). If X_j is a vector, its

$$\text{length} = (X_j, X_j)^{1/2}.$$

Notation 3–17.

$$|X_j| = \text{length of vector } X = (X_j, X_j)^{1/2}.$$

Example 3–11. For $X'_j = [2, 4, 1, 2]$,

$$|X'_j| = [(2 \times 2) + (4 \times 4) + (1 \times 1) + (2 \times 2)]^{1/2}$$

$$= (25)^{1/2} = 5.$$

Figure 3–8 shows the length of a vector $X'_j = [x_{1j}, x_{2j}] = [4, 3]$.

Definition 3–25. A NORMAL VECTOR has a *length* of unity. That is, for any normal vector X_j,

$$|X_j| = 1.$$

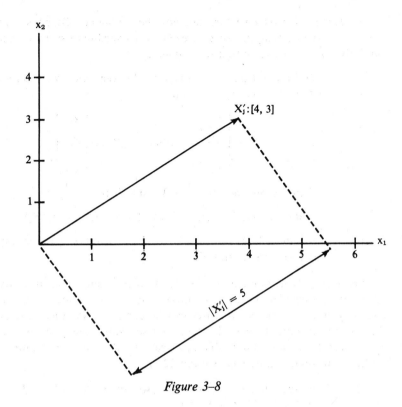

Figure 3–8

If a vector is not normal, it can be made so by dividing each of its elements by its length. For any vector X_j,

$$X_j^* = \frac{1}{|X_j|} X_j, \qquad (3-5)$$

where $\frac{1}{|X_j|}$ = a scalar, and X_j^* = normal form of X_j.

> *Example 3–12.* Consider the nonnormal vector $X_j' = [0, 4, 3]$, where $|X_j| = 5$. X_j can be be transformed to a normal vector X_j^* by
>
> $$X_j^{*\prime} = \frac{1}{5} [0, 4, 3] = \left[\frac{0}{5}, \frac{4}{5}, \frac{3}{5}\right],$$
>
> and
>
> $$|X_j^*| = \left[\left(\frac{0}{5} \times \frac{0}{5}\right) + \left(\frac{4}{5} \times \frac{4}{5}\right) + \left(\frac{3}{5} \times \frac{3}{5}\right)\right]^{1/2} = 1.$$

The *distance* between vectors can now be evaluated. To do so we must first assume that the vectors exist in a coordinate system with similarly scaled axes at mutual right angles.

> *Definition 3–26.* The DISTANCE between any two vectors X_j and X_k is $|X_k - X_j|$. If

$$X_j = \begin{bmatrix} x_{1j} \\ x_{2j} \\ \vdots \\ x_{nj} \end{bmatrix}, \quad \text{and} \quad X_k = \begin{bmatrix} x_{1k} \\ x_{2k} \\ \vdots \\ x_{nk} \end{bmatrix},$$

> then the distance between X_j and X_k is

$$[(x_{1k} - x_{1j})^2 + (x_{2k} - x_{2j})^2 + \cdots + (x_{nk} - x_{nj})^2]^{1/2}.$$

> *Notation 3–18.* $d_{jk} = |X_k - X_j| = $ distance between any two vectors X_j and X_k.

This notion of distance is a powerful tool for comparing data. By interpreting variables or cases as vectors and transforming values to common units,[11] variables or cases can be compared on the basis of their relative distance from each other.[12] These distances may themselves be subject to various kinds of statistical analysis, as, for example, multidimensional scaling (see Section 22.3).

> *Example 3–13.* Consider the two vectors $X_j' = [4, 1, 1, 2]$, and $X_k' = [2, 2, 0, 1]$. Then

$$d_{jk} = [(2 - 4)^2 + (2 - 1)^2 + (0 - 1)^2 + (1 - 2)^2]^{1/2}$$
$$= (4 + 1 + 1 + 1)^{1/2} = 7^{1/2} = 2.64.$$

This distance is shown in Fig. 3–9.

> *Definition 3–27.* The cosine of the ANGLE between two vectors is the ratio of their inner product to the product of their lengths. For two vectors X_j and X_k, whose angle is θ_{jk},

$$\cos \theta_{jk} = \frac{(X_j, X_k)}{|X_j| \, |X_k|}.$$

11. This may be done through standardization (Definition 3–4) or normalization as in Eq. (3–5).

12. Although we will have no use for the relationship between the inner product and the distance between vectors, the reader might be interested in this relationship given by Torgerson (1958, p. 255) for two vectors, X_j and X_k:

$$(X_j, X_k) = \tfrac{1}{2}(|X_j|^2 + |X_k|^2 - d_{jk}^2).$$

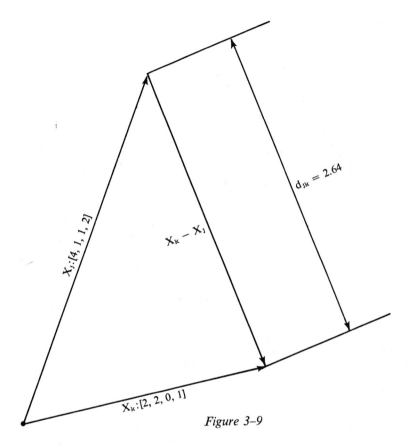

Figure 3–9

The angle between two vectors measures their relationship. Since the cosine of an angle varies from -1.00 for $180°$ through 0 for $90°$ to 1.00 for $0°$, if the cosine equals $+1.00$ or -1.00, one vector is exactly proportional to the other. That is, $X_k = \alpha X_j$. If α is positive, X_k is longer or shorter than X_j by a factor of α. If α is negative, X_k has a direction opposite that of X_j, and $\cos \theta_{jk} = -1.00$.

> *Example 3–14.* Figure 3–10 displays some of the values $\cos \theta_{12}$ can take for two vectors X_1 and X_2.

The cosine of the angle between two vectors and the correlation (Definition 3–6) between their elements both vary between $+1.00$ and -1.00. One might therefore suspect a functional relationship between $\cos \theta_{jk}$ and r_{jk}, and indeed there is such a relationship. It will be discussed in the next section.

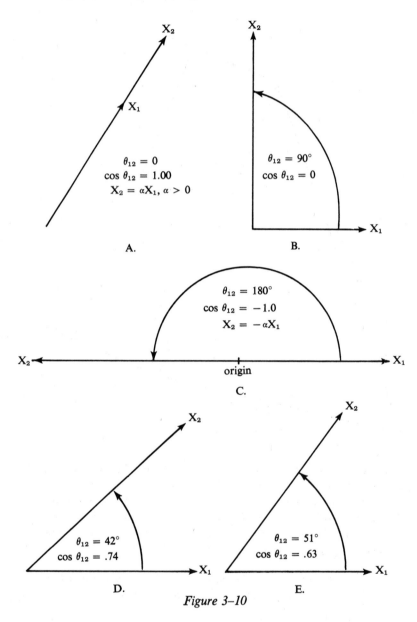

$\theta_{12} = 0$
$\cos \theta_{12} = 1.00$
$X_2 = \alpha X_1, \alpha > 0$

A.

$\theta_{12} = 90°$
$\cos \theta_{12} = 0$

B.

$\theta_{12} = 180°$
$\cos \theta_{12} = -1.0$
$X_2 = -\alpha X_1$

origin

C.

$\theta_{12} = 42°$
$\cos \theta_{12} = .74$

D.

$\theta_{12} = 51°$
$\cos \theta_{12} = .63$

E.

Figure 3–10

A vector function that plays a large role in factor analysis is that of orthogonality.

    Definition 3–28. Two vectors X_j and X_k are ORTHOGONAL to each other if $(X_j, X_k) = 0$. A *set* of vectors is orthogonal if each vector in the set is orthogonal to every other vector in the set. If two vectors X_j and X_k are orthogonal,

$$\cos \theta_{jk} = \frac{(X_j, X_k)}{|X_j| \, |X_k|} = \frac{0}{|X_j| \, |X_k|} = 0.$$

Since $\theta = 90°$ for $\cos \theta = 0$, orthogonal vectors in any plane containing them *must be at right angles to each other*. Vectors X_1 and X_2 in Fig. 3–10B are therefore orthogonal; those in Figs. 3–10A, C, D, and E are not.

3.2.4 VECTOR FUNCTIONS AND DESCRIPTIVE STATISTICS

Most social scientists are trained in descriptive statistics; standard deviation and the correlation coefficient are tools of the trade. Such descriptive statistics are not independent, however, of vector algebra. They can be directly related to vector functions, enabling us to transform results from one algebraic system to another.[13] *In particular, the ability to geometrically portray descriptive statistics as vectors, vector lengths, and vector angles allows us to visualize results and construct physical models of our findings.*

Before continuing, a previous point should again be noted. A variable of n cases can also be conceptualized as a vector of n elements. Thus a grade point average variable with data on 20 students can also be a vector of 20 grade point averages.

The standard deviation of the data for a variable X_j has a simple relationship to the length of the vector. Let the mean of the data be subtracted from each value. The resulting mean-deviation score for any case i is $(x_{ij} - \bar{X}_j)$. The standard deviation of these mean-deviation scores is proportional to the length of the vector, and the proportionality constant is the positive square root of the number of cases. From Definition 3–24,

$$|X_j| = (X_j, X_j)^{1/2} = \left[\sum_{i=1}^{n} (x_{ij} - \bar{X}_j)^2 \right]^{1/2},$$

and from Definitions 3–2 and 3–3,

$$\sigma_j = \frac{\left[\sum_{i=1}^{n} (x_{ij} - \bar{X}_j)^2 \right]^{1/2}}{n^{1/2}}.$$

13. Two helpful sources on the relationship of descriptive statistics to vectors and geometric concepts are Jackson (1924) and Harman (1967, Chapter 4).

Therefore,

$$n^{1/2}\sigma_j = \left[\sum_{i=1}^{n}(x_{ij} - \bar{X}_j)^2\right]^{1/2} = |X_j|. \tag{3-6}$$

We can thus move from the standard deviation for mean-deviation data $(x_{ij} - \bar{X}_j)$ to the length of the vector by multiplying σ_j by $n^{1/2}$. If our data are in standard scores (Definition 3–4), since $\sigma_{Z_j} = 1.0$, then

$$n^{1/2} = |Z_j|. \tag{3-7}$$

A vector of standardized scores has length equal to the square root of the number of cases.

A particular length often of interest is that of the *distance vector* (Definition 3–21). This length can be directly related to the *correlation* (Definition 3–6) between two standardized variables, say Z_j and Z_k. Jackson (1924, p. 276) has done this, and from him we can take the equation

$$r_{jk} = 1 - \frac{1}{2n}d_{jk}^2.$$

By algebraic manipulation we can express d_{jk} as a function of r_{jk}:

$$d_{jk}^2 = 2n(1 - r_{jk}). \tag{3-8}$$

The squared distance between two standardized variables is thus twice the sample size times one minus their correlation.

The *covariance* and *correlation* are also related to the inner product of vectors. Let two vectors, X_j and X_k, be vectors of mean-deviation scores $(x_{ij} - \bar{X}_j)$ and $(x_{ik} - \bar{X}_k)$, respectively. Then, from Definition 3–22,

$$(X_j, X_k) = \sum_{i=1}^{n}(x_{ij} - \bar{X}_j)(x_{ik} - \bar{X}_k),$$

and, from Definition 3–5, the covariance is

$$c_{jk} = \frac{\sum_{i=1}^{n}(x_{ij} - \bar{X}_j)(x_{ik} - \bar{X}_k)}{n}.$$

Therefore,

$$c_{jk} = \frac{(X_j, X_k)}{n}. \tag{3-9}$$

The covariance of mean-deviation scores for two variables is equal to the vector inner product of these scores divided by the sample size.

If the data are in standard scores, however, the vector inner product divided by the sample size equals the correlation. For two standardized variables Z_j and Z_k, the inner product is

$$(Z_j, Z_k) = \sum_{i=1}^{n} z_{ij}z_{ik},$$

and, from Eq. (3-1),

$$(Z_j, Z_k) = \sum_{i=1}^{n} z_{ij}z_{ik} = nr_{jk}.$$

Therefore,

$$r_{jk} = \frac{(Z_j, Z_k)}{n}. \tag{3-10}$$

Of great usefulness is the relationship between the correlation and the cosine of the angle between two vectors.[14] For mean-deviation data or standardized data, the correlation between two variables is equal to the cosine of the angle between their vectors. Consider the mean-deviation data first. For any vectors X_j and X_k of mean-deviation scores and from Definition 3-27 and Eqs. (3-9) and (3-6),

$$\cos \theta_{jk} = \frac{(X_j, X_k)}{|X_j| \, |X_k|} = \frac{nc_{jk}}{(n^{1/2}\sigma_j)(n^{1/2}\sigma_k)} = \frac{c_{jk}}{\sigma_j\sigma_k}.$$

By Definition 3-6, the expression on the right is equal to the correlation. Therefore, for mean-deviation data,

$$r_{jk} = \cos \theta_{jk}. \tag{3-11}$$

Equation (3-11) follows by Definition 3-24. Consider now the standardized variables Z_j and Z_k. From Eq. (3-7),

$$\cos \theta_{jk} = \frac{(Z_j, Z_k)}{|Z_j| \, |Z_k|} = \frac{nr_{jk}}{n^{1/2}n^{1/2}} = r_{jk}.$$

A specific relationship needs to be stated. By Definition 3-28, the angle between orthogonal vectors is 90° and has a cosine of zero. According to Eq. (3-11), therefore, vectors of mean-deviation or standardized data are orthogonal if their correlation is zero. That is,

$$r_{jk} = 0 = \text{orthogonality} = 90° \text{ angle between } X_j \text{ and } X_k. \tag{3-12}$$

14. Burt (1941, p. 88, n. 1) gives a short history of the idea of expressing correlations as angles.

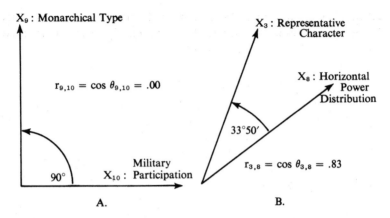

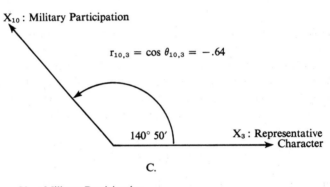

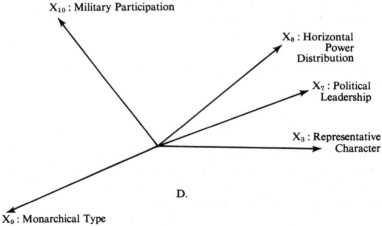

Figure 3–11

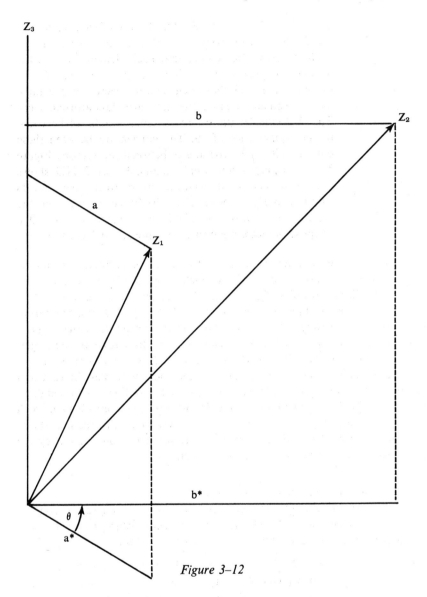

Figure 3–12

When there is no correlation between two variables, they can be visualized as at a right angle in space.

Equation (3–11) allows us to picture any relationship and to define it in terms of the commonly employed correlation coefficient. An example may be helpful.

Example 3–15. Figures 3–11A-D show selected vectors of standardized data from Table 3–1 on the 79-nation coordinate axes. (Remember that each element of a vector defines the projection of that vector on a separate coordinate axis and that each column vector of the table has 79 elements.) Since the data are standardized, from Eq. (3–7) the lengths of the vectors should all be equal to the square root of 79. The correlation between these data are shown by the angles between the vectors. Figure 3–11A displays orthogonal vectors. Figure 3–11D shows the two-dimensional relationship between five vectors simultaneously.[15] Note that the three vectors on the right form a *cluster* of highly interrelated vectors. One purpose of factor analysis is to delineate such clusters.

The geometric interpretation of two-variable correlations can be extended to partial correlations (Definition 3–13). Consider three standardized variables Z_1, Z_2, and Z_3, interpreted as vectors in Fig. 3–12. Following Jackson's presentation (1924, pp. 277–78), the partial correlation between Z_1 and Z_2, holding Z_3 constant, is the angle θ between lines a^* and b^*. As already stated, the cosine of the angles between Z_1 and Z_2, Z_1 and Z_3, and Z_2 and Z_3 in n-coordinate space is the product moment correlation between these variables. Lines a and b can be drawn from Z_3 to Z_1 and Z_2 so that both lines are perpendicular to Z_3. The projections a^* and b^* of these lines onto a plane at a right angle to Z_3 can be determined (any vector on this plane is therefore uncorrelated with Z_3), and the partial correlation is given by the cosine of the angle between these projections.

3.2.5 DEPENDENCE AND INDEPENDENCE

The cosine of the angle between vectors measures the degree of relationship between them. A specific type of relationship is called linear dependence and may refer to any number of vectors.

Definition 3–29. A vector X_j is LINEARLY DEPENDENT on a set of vectors $X_1, X_2, \ldots, X_k, \ldots, X_m$ $(j \neq k)$, if X_j is a linear combination of the m vectors. That is,

$$X_j = \alpha_1 X_1 + \alpha_2 X_2, \ldots, \alpha_k X_k, \ldots, \alpha_m X_m.$$

15. The actual relationship between these vectors is not quite two-dimensional. Consequently, the angle between two vectors is not the sum of their angles from a vector apparently lying between them, nor can all the correlations between these variables be simultaneously pictured here; the correlations are given in Table 4–1.

A vector is LINEARLY INDEPENDENT if it is not linearly dependent.

Example 3–16.   Let

$$X_1 = \begin{bmatrix} 0 \\ -2 \\ -2 \\ 16 \end{bmatrix}, \quad X_2 = \begin{bmatrix} 2 \\ 1 \\ 1 \\ 4 \end{bmatrix}, \quad X_3 = \begin{bmatrix} 1 \\ 0 \\ 0 \\ 6 \end{bmatrix}.$$

Then, since scalars α_2 and α_3 exist such that $X_1 = \alpha_2 X_2 + \alpha_3 X_3$, X_1 is linearly dependent on X_2 and X_3. The linear dependence is

$$\begin{bmatrix} 0 \\ -2 \\ -2 \\ 16 \end{bmatrix} = -2 \begin{bmatrix} 2 \\ 1 \\ 1 \\ 4 \end{bmatrix} + 4 \begin{bmatrix} 1 \\ 0 \\ 0 \\ 6 \end{bmatrix} = \begin{bmatrix} -4 \\ -2 \\ -2 \\ -8 \end{bmatrix} + \begin{bmatrix} 4 \\ 0 \\ 0 \\ 24 \end{bmatrix} = \begin{bmatrix} 0 \\ -2 \\ -2 \\ 16 \end{bmatrix}.$$

The linear dependence of a vector on a set of vectors can be determined by solving a set of simultaneous equations for the scalars α. A vector is dependent if a nonzero solution for one or more of the scalars can be found.

Example 3–17.   The vector

$$X_1 = \begin{bmatrix} x_{11} \\ x_{21} \\ x_{31} \end{bmatrix}$$

is linearly dependent on the vectors

$$X_2 = \begin{bmatrix} x_{12} \\ x_{22} \\ x_{32} \end{bmatrix}, \quad X_3 = \begin{bmatrix} x_{13} \\ x_{23} \\ x_{33} \end{bmatrix}, \quad \text{and} \quad X_4 = \begin{bmatrix} x_{14} \\ x_{24} \\ x_{34} \end{bmatrix}$$

if, for the simultaneous equations

$$x_{11} = \alpha_2 x_{12} + \alpha_3 x_{13} + \alpha_4 x_{14},$$
$$x_{21} = \alpha_2 x_{22} + \alpha_3 x_{23} + \alpha_4 x_{24},$$
$$x_{31} = \alpha_2 x_{32} + \alpha_3 x_{33} + \alpha_4 x_{34},$$

a nonzero solution for any of the scalars α_2, α_3, and α_4 can be found.

> *Definition 3–30.* A SET of vectors $X_1, X_2, \ldots, X_m$ is LINEARLY DEPENDENT if at least one *nonzero* scalar α exists such that $\alpha_1 X_1 + \alpha_2 X_2 + \cdots + \alpha_m X_m = 0$. If the equation is true if and only if all the scalars are zero, then the set of vectors is LINEARLY INDEPENDENT.

How does linear independence differ from statistical independence? As often applied, the notion of statistical independence means that the correlation between variables is zero or does not significantly deviate from zero. In terms of vectors, statistical independence implies that the vectors are orthogonal.

Using r as a measure of statistical dependence and independence, we can say the following for two vectors X_j and X_k of mean-deviation or standardized scores:

$$-1.00 < r_{jk} < 1.00 \quad \text{implies that } X_j, X_k \text{ are linearly independent.}$$

$$r_{jk} = \pm 1.00 \quad \text{implies that } X_j, X_k \text{ are linearly dependent.}$$

Since two linearly independent vectors can still have a high correlation, say .95, the fact that there is a distinction between linear and statistical independence should be kept in mind. For comparison with Definitions 3–29 and 3–30, let us make this distinction more specific in terms of the scalar multiples α and multiple regression (Definition 3–11).

> *Definition 3–31.* The vector X_j is STATISTICALLY DEPENDENT on a set of vectors $X_1, X_2, \ldots, X_k, \ldots, X_m$ $(j \neq k)$, if, for the linear regression equation
>
> $$\hat{X}_j = \beta_1 X_1 + \beta_2 X_2, \ldots, \beta_k X_k, \ldots, \beta_m X_m,$$
>
> at least one of the scalars β is not equal to zero. Otherwise it is STATISTICALLY INDEPENDENT.

Considering a variable as a vector, then, a vector is statistically dependent on a set of vectors when at least one vector in the set makes some contribution to its estimate. It is statistically independent when all the regression coefficients are zero, which is equivalent to the multiple correlation $r_j = 0$. A vector is linearly dependent if it is estimated exactly from the set of vectors, that is, $X_j = \hat{X}_j$ and $r_j = 1.00$.

3.2.6 BASIS AND DIMENSION

The concepts of basis and dimension bring us close to the heart of factor analysis. The idea is that a vector space might be reducible to two kinds of vectors: a set of independent vectors and a set of vectors that are linear combinations of (linearly dependent on) the independent vectors. This set of independent vectors is called a *basis* and is analogous to the factors that will be discussed in Chapter 5. The *dimensionality* of the space is the number of vectors in the basis; each of these independent vectors is called a *dimension* of the space.

Before defining basis and dimension more precisely, the concept of *span* will have to be introduced.

> *Definition 3–32.* Let a vector space be defined by m vectors. Let $X_1, X_2, \ldots, X_k$ of these vectors be linearly dependent on a *set* of linearly independent vectors X_{k+1}, $X_{k+2}, \ldots, X_m$. The set of linearly independent vectors then SPANS the vector space.

A vector space can therefore be divided into two sets of vectors: a set of independent vectors that *spans* the vector space and a set of the remaining vectors dependent on the independent set. That is, all the remaining vectors are linear combinations of those that are in the set spanning the space.

Any set of vectors that defines a vector space can be said to span the space. If these vectors are not linearly independent, however, the set will contain a smaller number of vectors that are linearly independent and that also span the space.

> *Definition 3–33.* A set of linearly independent vectors is a BASIS for a vector space if the set spans the vector space. All vectors of the space that are not in the basis are then linearly dependent on the vectors in the basis.

> *Example 3–18.* Let a vector space of column vectors be defined by the following matrix:

$$
\begin{array}{cccccccc}
X_1 & X_2 & X_3 & X_4 & X_5 & X_6 & X_7 & X_8 \\
\end{array}
$$

$$
\begin{bmatrix}
0 & 0 & 3 & 0 & 2 & -3 & 1 & 2 \\
0 & 0 & 0 & 0 & 0 & 2 & 0 & -1 \\
0 & 0 & 3 & 0 & 2 & 1 & 1 & 0 \\
3 & 1 & 2 & 0 & 0 & 0 & 0 & 0 \\
2 & 0 & -1 & 1 & 0 & 0 & 0 & 0
\end{bmatrix}
$$

> A set of linearly independent vectors that spans this space is X_2, X_4, X_7, and X_8. No one of these vectors can be derived from the other three. They are a basis of the space.

The remaining vectors are linear combinations of the members of the set:

$$X_1 = 3X_2 + 2X_4 + 0X_7 + 0X_8,$$

$$X_3 = 2X_2 - X_4 + 3X_7 + 0X_8,$$

$$X_5 = 0X_2 + 0X_4 + 2X_7 + 0X_8,$$

$$X_6 = 0X_2 + 0X_4 + X_7 - 2X_8.$$

It was previously noted in Definition 3–17 that a vector space is defined by the numbers of a matrix and that the space includes the vectors in the matrix. The meaning of this statement will now be made more explicit.

> *Definition 3–34.* A vector space containing vectors X_j and X_k also contains vectors $\alpha_j X_j + \alpha_k X_k$, where α_j and α_k are any scalars.

Thus, if two vectors are in a space, all linear combinations and scalar multiples of the vectors are in the space.[16]

A basis of a vector space is not unique. Other sets of linear independent vectors can also be found that are bases of the space.[17] What is unique is the *number of vectors* in a basis. Every basis of a vector space will have the same number of linearly independent vectors.

> *Definition 3–35.* The DIMENSIONALITY of a vector space is the number of vectors in a basis.

> *Definition 3–36.* A DIMENSION of a vector space is one of the vectors in a basis of the space.

To briefly summarize, a collection of vectors can define a vector space. These vectors may be divided into a set of linearly independent vectors that spans the vector space—a basis—and a set of vectors that are linear combinations of the vectors in the basis. The number of vectors in the basis is the dimensionality of the space, and each of these vectors is a dimension.

16. Here, and throughout this book, we are dealing with vector spaces of *real* numbers.

17. Since there are many bases of a vector space, factor analysts are faced with the problem of selecting a best basis. This involves the problem of rotation (see Chapter 16).

The geometric interpretation of these ideas is helpful. A one-dimensional space is a line. It has one vector in the basis, and all other vectors in this space are extensions or contractions of this line. All vectors are equal to αX_k, where X_k is the dimension.

A two-dimensional space is a plane. All vectors in this space are embedded in the plane and are equal to $\alpha_j X_j + \alpha_k X_k$, where X_j and X_k are a basis. Our everyday space is three-dimensional: All objects (vectors) within this space can be located in terms of (or are a linear combination of) our right-left, forward-backward, and up-down dimensions. Mathematically, but not physically, we can move on to spaces of dimensionality greater than three.

> *Example 3-19.* From Table 3-1, the following data matrix is formed.

$$
\begin{array}{c}
\\
\text{Albania} \\
\text{Argentina} \\
\text{Australia}
\end{array}
\begin{array}{cccc}
X_1 & X_2 & X_3 & X_4 \\
\left[\begin{array}{cccc}
2 & 0 & 1 & 0 \\
0 & 1 & 2 & 2 \\
0 & 2 & 3 & 2
\end{array}\right]
\end{array}.
$$

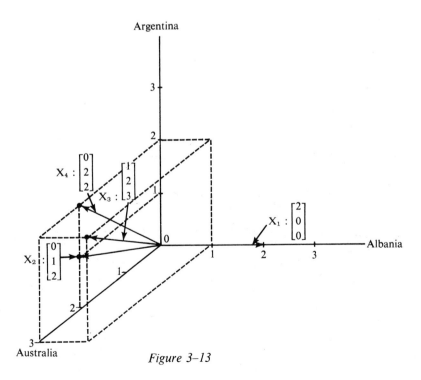

Figure 3-13

The vectors refer to system style (X_1), constitutional status (X_2), representative character (X_3), and electoral system (X_4). The four vectors can be plotted on the three nations that comprise the coordinate axes of the space as shown in Fig. 3–13.

What is evident from the figure is that the plot of the vectors is necessarily three-dimensional. Three dimensions are required to display the vectors. Since there are four vectors, this means that three of the vectors are linearly independent and a basis of this space and that a fourth is a linear combination of these vectors. In this case X_1, X_3, and X_4 are a basis, and $X_2 = -\frac{1}{2}X_1 + X_3 - \frac{1}{2}X_4$. That is,

$$
\begin{bmatrix} 0 \\ 1 \\ 2 \end{bmatrix} = -\frac{1}{2} \begin{bmatrix} 2 \\ 0 \\ 0 \end{bmatrix} + \begin{bmatrix} 1 \\ 2 \\ 3 \end{bmatrix} - \frac{1}{2} \begin{bmatrix} 0 \\ 2 \\ 2 \end{bmatrix}.
$$

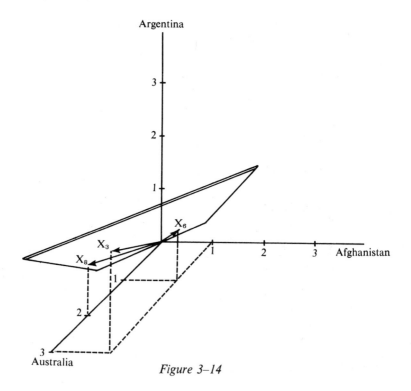

Figure 3–14

Example 3–20. Consider another data matrix formed from Table 3–1,

$$
\begin{array}{ccc}
& X_3 & X_6 & X_8 \\
\text{Afghanistan} & \begin{bmatrix} 1 \\ 2 \\ 3 \end{bmatrix} & \begin{matrix} 1 \\ 1 \\ 1 \end{matrix} & \begin{matrix} 0 \\ 1 \\ 2 \end{matrix} \end{bmatrix},
\end{array}
$$

	X_3	X_6	X_8
Afghanistan	1	1	0
Argentina	2	1	1
Australia	3	1	2

in which the vectors refer to representative character (X_3), non-Communist regime (X_6), and horizontal power distribution (X_8). The plot of these three vectors for the three-nation coordinate axes is shown in Fig. 3–14. As can be seen in the figure, a plane can be placed through the origin such that all three vectors are on the plane. The vector space of these vectors is therefore two-dimensional. Although the space was originally represented by three axes, it can be reduced to two dimensions, which will also represent variations in the data: One of these vectors is linearly dependent on the other two. For this data, $X_3 = X_6 + X_8$.

4. Preliminary Matrix Algebra

Since factor analysis is applied to matrices of data, a brief survey of matrix algebra—a special algebra for manipulating matrices—will greatly simplify the description and derivation of the factor model and its matrices. Only the principal features of matrix algebra and its concepts will be touched on here. Those interested in a more complete treatment of the subject are referred to any of the several excellent texts listed in Section 24.1.3.

Although the presentation will be couched in the language of matrix algebra—and will refer to adding matrices, multiplying matrices, etc.— we will still be dealing with vector spaces. In manipulating matrices we are often transforming one vector space to another; the theorems that apply to the manipulation of matrices apply equally to the transformation of vector spaces (Paige and Swift, 1961, p. 162).

4.1 Matrix Arithmetic

A *matrix* has been defined as a table of numbers, and the order $(n \times m)$ of a matrix has been defined as the number of its rows and columns

(Definition 3–14). The order of a matrix is crucial: It defines the permissible algebraic operations on a matrix. To clearly define a matrix and its order, a capital letter will usually be used to represent the matrix, and its order will be subscripted. Hence, $A_{n \times m}$ is a data matrix of n rows and m columns (Notation 3–12), $B_{r \times q}$ is a matrix of r rows and q columns, and $C_{p \times w}$ is a matrix of p rows and w columns.

Any vector is also a matrix (Definition 3–15). A data row vector X_j' is a matrix $X_{1 \times m}$; a data column vector X_j is a matrix $X_{n \times 1}$. Whenever matrix algebra is being applied to a vector, the order of the vector will be given, e.g., $Y_{p \times 1}$. Row vectors, i.e., matrices of order $1 \times a$, where a is any number ≥ 2, will be denoted by a prime. Hence, $Y_{p \times 1}$ is a column vector while $Y_{1 \times p}'$ is a row vector. Later, the prime will be given specific meaning as the *transpose* of a matrix.

> *Definition 4–1.* . EQUALITY OF MATRICES implies that the matrices have the same elements in the same order.

> *Example 4–1.* If $A_{3 \times 3}$ is
>
> $$\begin{bmatrix} 0 & 2 & 1 \\ 4 & 2 & 4 \\ 1 & 3 & 1 \end{bmatrix}, \text{ and } B_{3 \times 3} \text{ is } \begin{bmatrix} 0 & 2 & 1 \\ 4 & 2 & 4 \\ 1 & 3 & 1 \end{bmatrix},$$
>
> then $A_{3 \times 3} = B_{3 \times 3}$. However, if $B_{3 \times 4}$ is
>
> $$\begin{bmatrix} 0 & 2 & 1 & 0 \\ 4 & 2 & 4 & 0 \\ 1 & 3 & 1 & 1 \end{bmatrix}, \text{ then } A_{3 \times 3} \neq B_{3 \times 4}.$$

> *Definition 4–2.* ADDITION AND SUBTRACTION OF MATRICES involves adding or subtracting the corresponding elements for matrices *with the same order*. For any matrix $B_{p \times q}$ and matrix $C_{p \times q}$,
>
> $$B_{p \times q} + C_{p \times q} =$$
>
> $$\begin{bmatrix} b_{11} + c_{11} & b_{12} + c_{12} & \cdots & b_{1q} + c_{1q} \\ b_{21} + c_{21} & b_{22} + c_{22} & \cdots & b_{2q} + c_{2q} \\ \vdots & \vdots & & \vdots \\ b_{p1} + c_{p1} & b_{p2} + c_{p2} & \cdots & b_{pq} + c_{pq} \end{bmatrix},$$
>
> $$B_{p \times q} - C_{p \times q} =$$
>
> $$\begin{bmatrix} b_{11} - c_{11} & b_{12} - c_{12} & \cdots & b_{1q} - c_{1q} \\ b_{21} - c_{21} & b_{22} - c_{22} & \cdots & b_{2q} - c_{2q} \\ \vdots & \vdots & & \vdots \\ b_{p1} - c_{p1} & b_{p2} - c_{p2} & \cdots & b_{pq} - c_{pq} \end{bmatrix}.$$

Example 4–2.

$$\begin{bmatrix} 2 & 4 & 1 & 3 \\ 2 & 7 & 2 & 0 \\ 3 & 1 & 1 & 0 \end{bmatrix} + \begin{bmatrix} 1 & 4 & 1 & 4 \\ 1 & 2 & 1 & 0 \\ 0 & 3 & 1 & 0 \end{bmatrix}$$

$$= \begin{bmatrix} 2+1 & 4+4 & 1+1 & 3+4 \\ 2+1 & 7+2 & 2+1 & 0+0 \\ 3+0 & 1+3 & 1+1 & 0+0 \end{bmatrix} = \begin{bmatrix} 3 & 8 & 2 & 7 \\ 3 & 9 & 3 & 0 \\ 3 & 4 & 2 & 0 \end{bmatrix}.$$

However,

$$\begin{bmatrix} 2 & 3 \\ 4 & 2 \\ 1 & 1 \end{bmatrix} + \begin{bmatrix} 1 & 3 & 1 \\ 1 & 2 & 4 \\ 1 & 0 & 0 \end{bmatrix}$$

is undefined, since the matrices are of unequal order (3×2 and 3×3).

The addition and subtraction of matrices is comparable to the addition and subtraction of their corresponding column or row vectors. Thus, if one $p \times 2$ matrix consists of vectors X_1 and X_2 with p elements each, and another $p \times 2$ matrix consists of vectors Y_1 and Y_2 with p elements each, then the matrices sum to a matrix with two vectors $(X_1 + Y_1)$ and $(X_2 + Y_2)$.

Definition 4–3. SCALAR MULTIPLICATION OF A MATRIX consists of the scalar multiplication of each of the matrix elements. For any matrix B of any order $p \times q$ and for any scalar α,

$$\alpha B_{p \times q} = \begin{bmatrix} \alpha b_{11} & \alpha b_{12} & \cdots & \alpha b_{1q} \\ \alpha b_{21} & \alpha b_{22} & \cdots & \alpha b_{2q} \\ \vdots & \vdots & & \vdots \\ \alpha b_{p1} & \alpha b_{p2} & \cdots & \alpha b_{pq} \end{bmatrix}.$$

Example 4–3. Let

$$B_{3 \times 3} = \begin{bmatrix} 2 & 0 & 0 \\ 2 & 1 & 1 \\ 3 & 4 & 1 \end{bmatrix} \qquad \text{and} \qquad \alpha = 6.$$

Then

$$\alpha B_{3\times3} = 6\begin{bmatrix} 2 & 0 & 0 \\ 2 & 1 & 1 \\ 3 & 4 & 1 \end{bmatrix} = \begin{bmatrix} 6\times2 & 6\times0 & 6\times0 \\ 6\times2 & 6\times1 & 6\times1 \\ 6\times3 & 6\times4 & 6\times1 \end{bmatrix}$$

$$= \begin{bmatrix} 12 & 0 & 0 \\ 12 & 6 & 6 \\ 18 & 24 & 6 \end{bmatrix}.$$

If the matrix is a vector, i.e., of order $1\times q$ or $q\times1$, then Definition 4–3 for the scalar multiplication of a matrix is the same as Definition 3–23 for the scalar multiplication of a vector. The scalar multiplication of any matrix is the scalar multiplication of all the vectors of the matrix.

The next definition concerns matrix multiplication. Although perhaps the most difficult operation on matrices for students to learn, the procedure should be well understood before continuing. It might be helpful at this point to review the definition of inner products (Definition 3–22).

Definition 4–4. MULTIPLICATION OF TWO MATRICES is accomplished by computing the inner product of the ith row vector of the left matrix and the jth column vector of the right matrix. For any two matrices $B_{p\times q}$ and $C_{q\times r}$, and row vectors B_i' of $B_{p\times q}$ and column vectors C_j of $C_{q\times r}$,

$$B_{p\times q}C_{q\times r} = \begin{bmatrix} (B_1', C_1) & (B_1', C_2) & \cdots & (B_1', C_r) \\ (B_2', C_1) & (B_2', C_2) & \cdots & (B_2', C_r) \\ \vdots & \vdots & & \vdots \\ (B_p', C_1) & (B_p', C_2) & \cdots & (B_p', C_r) \end{bmatrix}.$$

The typical element, say d_{ij}, of the matrix resulting from the multiplication, $B_{p\times q}C_{q\times r}$, is

$$d_{ij} = \sum_{k=1}^{q} b_{ik}c_{kj} = (B_i', C_j) = b_{i1}c_{1j} + b_{i2}c_{2j} + \cdots + b_{iq}c_{qj}.$$

The *inner order* of the matrices determines whether multiplication is possible. The number of columns of the left matrix must equal the number of rows of the right matrix. That is, in

$$B_{p\times q}C_{q\times r},$$

the inner order must be equal ($q = q$) for multiplication to be defined.

The number of rows of the left matrix and the number of columns of the right matrix are the order of the product matrix:

$$B_{p \times q} C_{q \times r} = D_{p \times r}.$$

We have used the notation (X_j', X_k) for inner product. To help clarify the meaning of matrix multiplication, an additional notation will be introduced.

Notation 4–1.

$$[x_{j1}, x_{j2}, \ldots, x_{jn}] \begin{bmatrix} x_{1k} \\ x_{2k} \\ \vdots \\ x_{nk} \end{bmatrix} = (X_j', X_k)$$

$$= x_{j1}x_{1k} + x_{j2}x_{2k} + \cdots + x_{jn}x_{nk}.$$

With a notation allowing inner products (X_j', X_k) to be expressed by juxtaposing row and column vectors, matrix multiplication can be clearly illustrated.

Example 4–4.

$$\begin{bmatrix} 2 & 1 \\ 4 & 2 \end{bmatrix}_{2 \times 2} \begin{bmatrix} 3 & 1 & 4 \\ 2 & 0 & 1 \end{bmatrix}_{2 \times 3}$$

$$= \begin{bmatrix} [2, 1]\begin{bmatrix} 3 \\ 2 \end{bmatrix} & [2, 1]\begin{bmatrix} 1 \\ 0 \end{bmatrix} & [2, 1]\begin{bmatrix} 4 \\ 1 \end{bmatrix} \\ [4, 2]\begin{bmatrix} 3 \\ 2 \end{bmatrix} & [4, 2]\begin{bmatrix} 1 \\ 0 \end{bmatrix} & [4, 2]\begin{bmatrix} 4 \\ 1 \end{bmatrix} \end{bmatrix}_{2 \times 3}$$

$$= \begin{bmatrix} 8 & 2 & 9 \\ 16 & 4 & 18 \end{bmatrix}_{2 \times 3}.$$

$$\begin{bmatrix} 1 & 0 \\ 1 & 3 \\ 4 & 2 \end{bmatrix}_{3 \times 2} \begin{bmatrix} 2 \\ 1 \end{bmatrix}_{2 \times 1} = \begin{bmatrix} [1, 0]\begin{bmatrix} 2 \\ 1 \end{bmatrix} \\ [1, 3]\begin{bmatrix} 2 \\ 1 \end{bmatrix} \\ [4, 2]\begin{bmatrix} 2 \\ 1 \end{bmatrix} \end{bmatrix}_{3 \times 1} = \begin{bmatrix} 2 \\ 5 \\ 10 \end{bmatrix}_{3 \times 1}.$$

The following equalities govern the algebraic manipulation of matrices (α is a scalar):

1. $B_{p \times q} + C_{p \times q} = C_{p \times q} + B_{p \times q}$.
2. $(B_{p \times q} + C_{p \times q}) + D_{p \times q} = B_{p \times q} + (C_{p \times q} + D_{p \times q})$.
3. $\alpha(B_{p \times q} + C_{p \times q}) = \alpha B_{p \times q} + \alpha C_{p \times q}$.
4. $(B_{p \times q} C_{q \times r}) D_{r \times s} = B_{p \times q} (C_{q \times r} D_{r \times s})$.
5. $(B_{p \times q} + C_{p \times q}) D_{q \times r} = B_{p \times q} D_{q \times r} + C_{p \times q} D_{q \times r}$.
6. $B_{p \times p} C_{p \times p} \neq C_{p \times p} B_{p \times p}$.
7. $\alpha(B_{p \times q} C_{q \times r}) = (\alpha B_{p \times q}) C_{q \times r} = B_{p \times q} (\alpha C_{q \times r}) = (B_{p \times q} C_{q \times r}) \alpha$.

Note equality 6, above. In arithmetic the *commutative* law of multiplication states that $ab = ba$. In matrix multiplication, however, the commutative law does not hold. Therefore, the left or right position of a matrix *is* important and must be kept in mind in manipulating matrices.

Example 4–5. Let $B_{2 \times 2} = \begin{bmatrix} 1 & 4 \\ 0 & 1 \end{bmatrix}$ and $C_{2 \times 2} = \begin{bmatrix} 2 & 1 \\ 0 & 3 \end{bmatrix}$.

Then $B_{2 \times 2} C_{2 \times 2} = \begin{bmatrix} 2 & 13 \\ 0 & 3 \end{bmatrix}$, while $C_{2 \times 2} B_{2 \times 2} = \begin{bmatrix} 2 & 9 \\ 0 & 3 \end{bmatrix}$.

With regard to the multiplication of matrices, therefore, two useful terms should be made clear. The *left-multiplication* of a matrix $B_{p \times q}$ by a matrix $A_{n \times p}$ is the product $A_{n \times p} B_{p \times q}$. The *right-multiplication* of a matrix $B_{p \times q}$ by a matrix $A_{q \times r}$ is the product $B_{p \times q} A_{q \times r}$. It follows that the left- and right-multiplication of a matrix $B_{p \times p}$ by a matrix $A_{p \times p}$ is the product $A_{p \times p} B_{p \times p} A_{p \times p}$.

One type of matrix often of concern in factor analysis has the same number of rows and columns (we will later define this as a square matrix) i.e., its order is $p \times p$. The permissible operations on this matrix and some of its characteristics are often defined by the *determinant* of the matrix, which is a scalar value assigned to the matrix.

Notation 4–2.

$$
\begin{vmatrix}
x_{11} & x_{12} & \cdots & x_{1p} \\
x_{21} & x_{22} & \cdots & x_{2p} \\
\vdots & \vdots & & \vdots \\
x_{p1} & x_{p2} & \cdots & x_{pp}
\end{vmatrix} = \Delta
$$

$$
= \text{determinant of matrix} \begin{bmatrix}
x_{11} & x_{12} & \cdots & x_{1p} \\
x_{21} & x_{22} & \cdots & x_{2p} \\
\vdots & \vdots & & \vdots \\
x_{p1} & x_{p2} & \cdots & x_{pp}
\end{bmatrix}.
$$

Note that the elements of a matrix are enclosed in brackets and the determinant in vertical bars. Note also that the scalar value of the determinant is denoted by Δ (read delta).

$$\Delta B_{p \times p} = \text{determinant of matrix } B_{p \times p}.$$

Students of elementary algebra are familiar with determinants of 2×2 and 3×3 matrices. A 2×2 matrix is evaluated as follows:

$$\begin{vmatrix} x_{11} & x_{12} \\ x_{21} & x_{22} \end{vmatrix} = x_{11}x_{22} - x_{12}x_{21}. \tag{4-1}$$

A 3×3 matrix is evaluated as:

$$\begin{vmatrix} x_{11} & x_{12} & x_{13} \\ x_{21} & x_{22} & x_{23} \\ x_{31} & x_{32} & x_{33} \end{vmatrix} = \begin{aligned} &x_{11}x_{22}x_{33} - x_{11}x_{32}x_{23} + x_{21}x_{32}x_{13} \\ &- x_{21}x_{12}x_{33} + x_{31}x_{12}x_{23} - x_{31}x_{22}x_{13}. \end{aligned} \tag{4-2}$$

The evaluation of Δ for matrices of order greater than 3×3 becomes increasingly tedious. There is a method, however, of breaking down the Δ of large-order matrices into the evaluation of determinants of order 2×2 or 3×3. This method involves the concepts of *minor* and *cofactor*. For later use the *principal diagonal* of a $p \times p$ matrix will also be defined.

Definition 4–5. The MINOR of a $p \times p$ matrix is the determinant of the reduced matrix formed by removing the ith row and jth column.

Notation 4–3. Δ_{ij} is the minor of a matrix $B_{p \times p}$ with row i and column j removed.

Definition 4–6. The COFACTOR of a $p \times p$ matrix is the minor of the matrix with sign given by $(-1)^{i+j}$, where the exponent $i + j$ is the number of the row i plus the number of the column j removed to form the minor.

Definition 4–7. The PRINCIPAL DIAGONAL of a $p \times p$ matrix is the diagonal running from the upper left of the matrix to the lower right. For any $p \times p$ matrix

$$\begin{bmatrix} b_{11} & b_{12} & \cdots & b_{1p} \\ b_{21} & b_{22} & \cdots & b_{2p} \\ \vdots & \vdots & & \vdots \\ b_{p1} & b_{p2} & \cdots & b_{pp} \end{bmatrix},$$

the principal diagonal elements are $b_{11}, b_{22}, \ldots, b_{pp}$.

Notation 4–4. $C_{ij} = (-1)^{i+j}\Delta_{ij} = $ cofactor of an $n \times n$ matrix.

Example 4–6. Let a $p \times p$ matrix be

$$\begin{bmatrix} 4 & 2 & 3 & 4 \\ 0 & 3 & 2 & 0 \\ 1 & 2 & 1 & 1 \\ 1 & 1 & 0 & 2 \end{bmatrix}.$$

Then

$$\Delta_{2,3} = \begin{vmatrix} 4 & 2 & 4 \\ 1 & 2 & 1 \\ 1 & 1 & 2 \end{vmatrix}$$

$$= (4)(2)(2) - (4)(1)(1) + (1)(1)(4)$$

$$- (1)(2)(2) + (1)(2)(1) - (1)(2)(4)$$

$$= 16 - 4 + 4 - 4 + 2 - 8 = 6.$$

And $C_{ij} = (-1)^{2+3}\Delta_{2,3} = (-1)^5 6 = -6.$

Determinants of any order $p \times p$ can now be successively reduced to order 2×2 or 3×3 by *expanding the determinant by means of minors* according to the equation

$$\Delta = x_{i1}C_{i1} + x_{i2}C_{i2} + \cdots + x_{ip}C_{ip}, \tag{4–3}$$

where i may have any row value $1, 2, \ldots, p$.

Example 4–7.

$$\begin{vmatrix} 2 & 0 & 2 \\ 3 & 4 & 2 \\ 1 & 3 & 1 \end{vmatrix} = -3\begin{vmatrix} 0 & 2 \\ 3 & 1 \end{vmatrix} + 4\begin{vmatrix} 2 & 2 \\ 1 & 1 \end{vmatrix} - 2\begin{vmatrix} 2 & 0 \\ 1 & 3 \end{vmatrix}$$

$$= -3(-6) + 4(0) - 2(6) = 6.$$

The determinant is expanded by minors of the second row.

It is not always necessary to expand a determinant by minors. The value of a determinant can often be evaluated from the following properties.

$$\Delta B_{p \times p} = 0 \text{—if } B_{p \times p} \text{ contains a row or column of zeros.}$$
$$= -\Delta C_{p \times p} \text{—if the only difference between } B_{p \times p} \text{ and } C_{p \times p} \text{ is the interchange of rows and columns.}$$

$= \alpha\Delta C_{p \times p}$—if the only difference between $B_{p \times p}$ and $C_{p \times p}$ is some row or column of $C_{p \times p}$ that is α times a row or column of $B_{p \times p}$.

$= 0$—if two rows or columns are identical, or if one row or column is a multiple of another row or column.

$= \Delta C_{p \times p}$—if the only difference between $B_{p \times p}$ and $C_{p \times p}$ is some row or column of $C_{p \times p}$ that is the sum of a multiple of another row or column of $B_{p \times p}$.

A matrix may have its rows or columns interchanged, multiplied, and added according to the properties of determinants until only zeros exist below the principal diagonal (Definition 4–7). Then

$$\Delta B_{p \times p} = x_{11}x_{22}x_{33}, \ldots, x_{pp}, \tag{4-4}$$

where $x_{ij} = 0$ for $i > j$.

In Definition 3–29 the linear dependence of vectors was defined. *Determinants now yield an explicit procedure for evaluating linear dependence of vectors.* The $X_1, X_2, \ldots, X_m$ vectors of a $B_{m \times m}$ matrix are linearly dependent if and only if the determinant of $B_{m \times m}$ equals zero, as stated in the following theorem (Paige and Swift, 1961, p. 128).

Theorem 4–1. *The* m *row or* m *column vectors of a* $B_{m \times m}$ *matrix are linearly dependent if and only if* $\Delta B_{m \times m} = 0$.

4.2 Types of Matrices

Permissible algebraic operations on matrices often depend on the type of matrices involved. Moreover, discussion of factor analysis models and research design often employs concepts referring to different types of matrices. These matrices and their properties will be defined here.

Definition 4–8. A SQUARE MATRIX has the same number of rows and columns. Any matrix B is square if its order is $p \times p$.

Example 4–8.

$$\begin{bmatrix} 2 & 4 & 1 \\ 3 & 2 & 3 \\ 0 & 1 & 0 \end{bmatrix} \text{ is square.}$$

$$\begin{bmatrix} 2 & 1 \\ 3 & 2 \\ 1 & 0 \end{bmatrix} \text{ is not square.}$$

Definition 4–9. A matrix is SYMMETRICAL if it is square and if the element in the ith row and jth column is equal to the element in the jth row and ith column. That is, for any element b_{ij},

$$b_{ij} = b_{ji}.$$

Example 4–9.

$$\begin{bmatrix} 1 & 3 & 4 \\ 3 & 2 & 1 \\ 4 & 1 & 4 \end{bmatrix}$$

is symmetrical, since $b_{21}(3) = b_{12}(3)$, $b_{31}(4) = b_{13}(4)$, and $b_{32}(1) = b_{23}(1)$.

Example 4–10. A *correlation* matrix for m variables gives the correlations between all possible pairs of variables, such as $r_{11}, r_{12}, r_{13}, \ldots, r_{21}, r_{22}, \ldots, r_{mm}$. A correlation matrix for variables X_1, X_2, X_3, and X_4 is

$$\begin{bmatrix} r_{11} & r_{12} & r_{13} & r_{14} \\ r_{12} & r_{22} & r_{23} & r_{24} \\ r_{13} & r_{32} & r_{33} & r_{34} \\ r_{14} & r_{42} & r_{43} & r_{44} \end{bmatrix}.$$

The matrix is obviously square and since $r_{ij} = r_{ji}$, it is symmetrical. Because of this symmetrical property, only the values below the principal diagonal of a correlation matrix are usually displayed. Table 4–1 shows such a correlation matrix for the 10 political variables of Table 3–1.

Definition 4–10. A DIAGONAL MATRIX is a square matrix with zero elements except for the principal diagonal. For any square matrix $B_{p \times p}$, the matrix is diagonal if $b_{ij} = 0$, when $i \neq j$, and if at least one $b_{ij} \neq 0$, when $i = j$.

Example 4–11.

$$\begin{bmatrix} 4 & 0 & 0 & 0 \\ 0 & 1 & 0 & 0 \\ 0 & 0 & 2 & 0 \\ 0 & 0 & 0 & 3 \end{bmatrix}$$ is a diagonal matrix.

Diagonal matrices play a large role in the factor model. The following four rules may facilitate understanding their algebraic manipulation.

Table 4–1. Correlations between Ten Political Characteristics[a]

Characteristic	(1)	(2)	(3)	(4)	(5)	(6)	(7)	(8)	(9)	(10)
(1) System style	1.00									
(2) Constitutional status	-.67	1.00								
(3) Representative character	-.39	.78	1.00							
(4) Electoral system	-.61	.87	.81	1.00						
(5) Freedom of group opposition	-.72	.92	.74	.88	1.00					
(6) Non-Communist regime	-.87	.71	.34	.60	.75	1.00				
(7) Political leadership	-.38	.73	.76	.77	.75	.47	1.00			
(8) Horizontal power distribution	-.51	.85	.83	.84	.86	.49	.80	1.00		
(9) Monarchical type	-.14	-.13	-.44	-.22	-.23	.15	-.29	-.37	1.00	
(10) Military participation	.12	-.49	-.64	-.47	-.36	-.06	-.55	-.53	.00	1.00

[a] Correlations are product moment. $N = 79$.

1. *Left-multiplication* of a matrix by a diagonal matrix multiplies the elements in each ith row of the matrix by the ith diagonal element of the diagonal matrix. For a $B_{3 \times 3}$ matrix and a diagonal matrix $D_{3 \times 3}$,

$$D_{3 \times 3} B_{3 \times 3} = \begin{bmatrix} d_{11} & 0 & 0 \\ 0 & d_{22} & 0 \\ 0 & 0 & d_{33} \end{bmatrix} \begin{bmatrix} b_{11} & b_{12} & b_{13} \\ b_{21} & b_{22} & b_{23} \\ b_{31} & b_{32} & b_{33} \end{bmatrix}$$

$$= \begin{bmatrix} d_{11}b_{11} & d_{11}b_{12} & d_{11}b_{13} \\ d_{22}b_{21} & d_{22}b_{22} & d_{22}b_{23} \\ d_{33}b_{31} & d_{33}b_{32} & d_{33}b_{33} \end{bmatrix}.$$

2. *Right-multiplication* of a matrix by a diagonal matrix multiplies the elements in each jth column of the matrix by the jth diagonal element of the diagonal matrix. For a $B_{3 \times 3}$ matrix and a diagonal matrix $D_{3 \times 3}$,

$$B_{3 \times 3} D_{3 \times 3} = \begin{bmatrix} b_{11} & b_{12} & b_{13} \\ b_{21} & b_{22} & b_{23} \\ b_{31} & b_{32} & b_{33} \end{bmatrix} \begin{bmatrix} d_{11} & 0 & 0 \\ 0 & d_{22} & 0 \\ 0 & 0 & d_{33} \end{bmatrix}$$

$$= \begin{bmatrix} b_{11}d_{11} & b_{12}d_{22} & b_{13}d_{33} \\ b_{21}d_{11} & b_{22}d_{22} & b_{23}d_{33} \\ b_{31}d_{11} & b_{32}d_{22} & b_{33}d_{33} \end{bmatrix}.$$

3. *Left- and right-multiplication* of a matrix by diagonal matrices multiplies each element b_{ij} of the matrix by the ith element of the diagonal matrix on the left and the jth diagonal element of the diagonal matrix on the right. For a $B_{3 \times 3}$ matrix and diagonal matrices $D_{3 \times 3}$ and $C_{3 \times 3}$,

$$D_{3 \times 3} B_{3 \times 3} C_{3 \times 3} = \begin{bmatrix} d_{11}b_{11}c_{11} & d_{11}b_{12}c_{22} & d_{11}b_{13}c_{33} \\ d_{22}b_{21}c_{11} & d_{22}b_{22}c_{22} & d_{22}b_{23}c_{33} \\ d_{33}b_{31}c_{11} & d_{33}b_{32}c_{22} & d_{33}b_{33}c_{33} \end{bmatrix}.$$

4. The product of two diagonal matrices is the product of their corresponding diagonal elements. For diagonal matrices $D_{3 \times 3}$ and $C_{3 \times 3}$,

$$D_{3 \times 3} C_{3 \times 3} = \begin{bmatrix} d_{11} & 0 & 0 \\ 0 & d_{22} & 0 \\ 0 & 0 & d_{33} \end{bmatrix} \begin{bmatrix} c_{11} & 0 & 0 \\ 0 & c_{22} & 0 \\ 0 & 0 & c_{33} \end{bmatrix}$$

$$= \begin{bmatrix} d_{11}c_{11} & 0 & 0 \\ 0 & d_{22}c_{22} & 0 \\ 0 & 0 & d_{33}c_{33} \end{bmatrix}.$$

Definition 4–11. An IDENTITY MATRIX is a diagonal matrix with unities in the principal diagonal. For any diagonal element b_{ij} $(i = j)$ of a diagonal matrix, b_{ij} is equal to unity.

Notation 4–5.

$$I = \begin{bmatrix} 1 & 0 & \cdots & 0 \\ 0 & 1 & \cdots & 0 \\ \vdots & \vdots & & \vdots \\ 0 & 0 & \cdots & 1 \end{bmatrix} = \text{identity matrix.}$$

Example 4–12.

$$\begin{bmatrix} 1 & 0 & 0 \\ 0 & 1 & 0 \\ 0 & 0 & 1 \end{bmatrix} \text{ is an } I_{3 \times 3} \text{ identity matrix.}$$

The identity matrix plays the same role in matrix algebra as unity in scalar algebra. For any matrix $B_{p \times q}$,

$$B_{p \times q} I_{q \times q} = B_{p \times q} \quad \text{and} \quad I_{p \times p} B_{p \times q} = B_{p \times q}.$$

If $B_{p \times p}$ is square,

$$B_{p \times p} I_{p \times p} = I_{p \times p} B_{p \times p} = B_{p \times p}.$$

It should be noted that the determinant of $I_{p \times p}$ equals unity:

$$\Delta I_{p \times p} = 1. \tag{4–5}$$

Definition 4–12. A TRANSPOSED MATRIX has its rows and columns interchanged such that the ith row becomes the jth column $(i = j)$, and the jth column becomes the ith row $(j = i)$. The *order* of the transposed matrix is the reverse of the order of the original matrix.

Notation 4–6. $B'_{q \times p}$ = transpose (indicated by the prime) of matrix $B_{p \times q}$.

Example 4–13.

$$\text{If } B_{2 \times 3} = \begin{bmatrix} 2 & 4 \\ 1 & 0 \\ 3 & 5 \end{bmatrix}, \quad B'_{3 \times 2} = \begin{bmatrix} 2 & 1 & 3 \\ 4 & 0 & 5 \end{bmatrix}.$$

$$\text{If } B_{3 \times 3} = \begin{bmatrix} 0 & 1 & 3 \\ 2 & 1 & 5 \\ 3 & 4 & 9 \end{bmatrix}, \quad B'_{3 \times 3} = \begin{bmatrix} 0 & 2 & 3 \\ 1 & 1 & 4 \\ 3 & 5 & 9 \end{bmatrix}.$$

The prime has already been employed in Notation 3–13 to denote row vectors. We can now generalize that notation to any vector. For any *column* vector Y_j, the transpose of Y_j is a *row* vector and is written Y_j'. For any *row* vector Y_i', the transpose of Y_i' is a column vector Y_i and is written $(Y_i')'$. Transposing a matrix is then equivalent to transposing each of the column or row vectors of the matrix.

The transpose of a matrix or combination of matrices obeys the following algebraic equalities.

$$(B_{p \times q} + C_{p \times q})' = B_{q \times p}' + C_{q \times p}'.$$

$$(B_{p \times q} - C_{p \times q})' = B_{q \times p}' - C_{q \times p}'.$$

$$(B_{q \times p}')' = B_{p \times q}.$$

$$(B_{p \times q} C_{q \times p})' = C_{p \times q}' B_{q \times p}'.$$

$$B_{q \times p}' B_{p \times q} = \text{a } q \times q \text{ symmetric matrix.}$$

$$B_{p \times q} B_{q \times p}' = \text{a } p \times p \text{ symmetric matrix.}$$

$$B_{p \times q} B_{q \times p}' \neq B_{q \times p}' B_{p \times q}.$$

$$(B_{p \times q} C_{q \times r} D_{r \times s})' = D_{s \times r}' C_{r \times q}' B_{q \times p}'.$$

$$B_{p \times p} = B_{p \times p}', \text{ if } B_{p \times p} \text{ is a symmetric matrix.}$$

$$\Delta B_{p \times p} = \Delta B_{p \times p}'.$$

> *Definition 4–13.* The INVERSE OF A MATRIX is another matrix such that the matrix *product* of the two is an identity matrix. If $B_{p \times p}$ and $C_{p \times p}$ are square matrices and $B_{p \times p} C_{p \times p} = I_{p \times p}$, then $C_{p \times p}$ is the *inverse* of $B_{p \times p}$, and $B_{p \times p}$ is the inverse of $C_{p \times p}$.

> *Notation 4–7.* $B_{p \times p}^{-1} = $ inverse of matrix $B_{p \times p}$. This is equivalent to scalar notation, where $\alpha(\alpha^{-1}) = \alpha(1/\alpha) = 1$.

The inverse of a square matrix is *unique*. For any square matrix there is only one inverse. But not all matrices have an inverse. From Hohn (1958, p. 93), we can state the following theorem.

> Theorem 4–2. *A square matrix* $B_{p \times p}$ *has an inverse if and only if* $\Delta B_{p \times p} \neq 0$.

We can combine Theorems 4–1 and 4–2 to state that an inverse of a $p \times p$ matrix exists if and only if the p number of row or column vectors of the matrix are linearly independent.

For any square matrix $B_{p \times p}$ where $\Delta B_{p \times p} \neq 0$, the following algebraic equalities apply.

$$B_{p \times p} B_{p \times p}^{-1} = B_{p \times p}^{-1} B_{p \times p} = I_{p \times p}. \tag{4-6a}$$

$$B_{p \times p}^{-1} = \begin{bmatrix} \dfrac{1}{b_{11}} & 0 & \cdots & 0 \\ 0 & \dfrac{1}{b_{22}} & \cdots & 0 \\ \vdots & \vdots & & \vdots \\ 0 & 0 & \cdots & \dfrac{1}{b_{pp}} \end{bmatrix}, \tag{4-6b}$$

when $B_{p \times p}$ is a diagonal matrix with no diagonal elements equal to zero.

$$(B_{p \times p} C_{p \times p})^{-1} = C_{p \times p}^{-1} B_{p \times p}^{-1}. \tag{4-6c}$$

$$(B_{p \times p} C_{p \times p} D_{p \times p})^{-1} = D_{p \times p}^{-1} C_{p \times p}^{-1} B_{p \times p}^{-1}, \tag{4-6d}$$

where

$$\Delta D_{p \times p} \neq 0 \text{ and } \Delta C_{p \times p} \neq 0.$$

$$(B_{p \times p}^{-1})' = (B_{p \times p}')^{-1}. \tag{4-6e}$$

$$(\Delta B_{p \times p}^{-1})(\Delta B_{p \times p}) = \Delta I_{p \times p} = 1. \tag{4-6f}$$

Definition 4–14. A matrix is NONSINGULAR if it has an inverse. That is, for any matrix $B_{p \times p}$, it is nonsingular if $\Delta B_{p \times p} \neq 0$. If $\Delta B_{p \times p} = 0$, the matrix is SINGULAR.

Definition 4–15. A symmetric matrix is POSITIVE DEFINITE if all the principal diagonal minors are greater than zero. The matrix is POSITIVE SEMIDEFINITE if all the principal diagonal minors are greater than or equal to zero. For any $B_{p \times p}$ symmetric matrix, $B_{p \times p}$ is positive definite if (from Notation 4–3) all $\Delta_{ii} B_{p \times p} > 0$, $(i = 1, 2, \ldots, p)$; the matrix is positive semidefinite if all $\Delta_{ii} B_{p \times p} \geq 0$, $(i = 1, 2, \ldots, p)$.

The last two definitions allow the properties of a Gramian matrix to be specified. This matrix plays a large role in factor analysis derivations and applications. We will see later that a Gramian matrix is a crucial concept with regard to analyses involving missing data (Section 10.3.1.1).

Definition 4–16. A GRAMIAN MATRIX is a positive semidefinite symmetric matrix.

The above definition gives the formal properties of a Gramian matrix. A Gramian matrix results from the left- or right-multiplication of a matrix by its transpose (Horst, 1965, p. 83). Thus,

$$B_{p \times q} B'_{q \times p} = \text{Gramian matrix.}$$
$$B'_{q \times p} B_{p \times q} = \text{Gramian matrix.}$$

(4–7)

We will see later [Eq. (4–12)] that a correlation matrix is Gramian.

Two types of matrices often occurring in discussions of factor analysis are *orthogonal* and *orthonormal* matrices.

> *Definition 4–17.* An ORTHOGONAL MATRIX is any matrix that, when *left*-multiplied by its transpose, equals a diagonal matrix. For any matrix $B_{p \times q}$, when $B'_{q \times p} B_{p \times q} = D_{q \times q}$ (diagonal matrix), $B_{p \times q}$ is orthogonal.

> *Definition 4–18.* An ORTHONORMAL MATRIX is any matrix that when *left*-multiplied by its transpose equals an *identity* matrix. For any matrix $Q_{p \times q}$, when $Q'_{q \times p} Q_{p \times q} = I_{q \times q}$, $Q_{p \times q}$ is orthonormal. An orthonormal matrix is a special case of an orthogonal matrix.[1]

The definitions of orthogonal and orthonormal matrices are extensions of those of normal and orthogonal vectors, respectively (Definitions 3–25 and 3–28). From the definition of matrix multiplication (Definition 4–4), the product $B'_{q \times p} B_{p \times q}$ has as elements the inner products of each column vector with every other column vector in the matrix $B_{p \times q}$. The principal diagonal of $B_{p \times q}$ contains the inner products of vectors with themselves. If vectors are orthogonal, then $(X_j, X_k) = 0$ when $j \neq k$, and $(X_j, X_k) \neq 0$ when $j = k$. Thus $B'_{q \times p} B_{p \times q}$ is diagonal. If the vectors are also normal vectors, then $(X_j, X_k) = 1$ when $j = k$, and $B'_{q \times p} B_{p \times q} = I_{q \times q}$.

The salient algebraic equalities governing an *orthogonal* matrix B are:

$$B'_{q \times p} B_{p \times q} = D_{q \times q}, \qquad D \text{ is a diagonal matrix.} \tag{4–8a}$$

$$B_{p \times q} B'_{q \times p} \neq D_{p \times p}, \qquad D \text{ is a diagonal matrix and } D \neq I. \tag{4–8b}$$

$$B^{-1}_{q \times q} = D^{-1}_{q \times q} B'_{q \times p}, \qquad \begin{array}{l} D \text{ is the same diagonal matrix as} \\ \text{in Eq. (4–8a) and } p = q \text{ (from} \\ \text{Horst, 1963, p. 409).} \end{array} \tag{4–8c}$$

1. Our definitions of orthogonal and orthonormal differ from customary mathematical definitions. What is defined here as an orthonormal matrix is usually called an orthogonal matrix, and what we have defined as an orthogonal matrix is generally not distingished in the mathematical literature (an exception is Horst, 1963). The distinction between orthogonal and orthonormal matrices as here defined, however, is necessary in discussing factor analysis.

The salient equalities for an *orthonormal* matrix Q are:

$$Q'_{q \times p} Q_{p \times q} = I_{q \times q}. \tag{4-9a}$$

If $p > q$,

$$Q_{p \times q} Q'_{q \times p} \neq I_{p \times p}. \tag{4-9b}$$

If $p = q$,

$$Q_{p \times q} Q'_{q \times p} = I_{p \times p} = Q'_{q \times p} Q_{p \times q}. \tag{4-9c}$$

If w is any exponent,

$$(Q_{p \times q} Q'_{q \times p})^w = Q_{p \times q} Q'_{q \times p}. \tag{4-9d}$$

If $p = q$,

$$Q^{-1}_{q \times p} = Q'_{q \times p}. \tag{4-9e}$$

$$\Delta Q_{p \times q} = \pm 1. \tag{4-9f}$$

If $Q_{p \times p}$ and $W_{p \times p}$ are both orthonormal (Davis, 1965, p. 317), then

$$(Q_{p \times p} W_{p \times p})'(Q_{p \times p} W_{p \times p}) = I_{p \times p} = (W_{p \times p} Q_{p \times p})' W_{p \times p} Q_{p \times p}. \tag{4-9g}$$

In the previous chapter (Section 3.2.6) the concepts of basis and dimensions were considered. For any orthogonal matrix the column vectors of the matrix form a basis of the vector space defined by the matrix. The number of columns is the dimensionality, and each column vector is a dimension of this space.

4.3 Special Matrix Functions

The matrix algebra and terminology developed above enable us to cast some of the descriptive statistics given in Section 3.1.1 in matrix form. Since matrix algebra will be employed almost exclusively in subsequent chapters, the major equations are given here.

Let the data matrix $A_{n \times m}$ consist of *mean-deviation* data. This is data transformed by subtracting the mean for each variable from the values for each case. That is, for each of the variables X_j, a datum $x_{ij} = x^*_{ij} - \bar{X}^*_j$, where x^*_{ij} is the original (raw) datum and $\bar{X}^*_j$ is the original jth variable mean.

Now, all the *covariances* c_{jk} between all possible pairs of m variables X_j and X_k ($j, k = 1, 2, \ldots, m$) can be arrayed in a *covariance matrix*.

Notation 4–8.

$$C_{m \times m} = \begin{bmatrix} c_{11} & c_{12} & \cdots & c_{1m} \\ c_{21} & c_{22} & \cdots & c_{2m} \\ \vdots & \vdots & & \vdots \\ c_{m1} & c_{m2} & \cdots & c_{mm} \end{bmatrix} = \text{covariance matrix.}$$

The matrix $C_{m \times m}$ is symmetrical: $c_{jk} = c_{kj}$. $C_{m \times m}$ can be computed by *left*-multiplying the mean-deviation data matrix by itself and by the scalar reciprocal of the number of cases. That is,

$$C_{m \times m} = \frac{1}{n} A'_{m \times n} A_{n \times m}. \tag{4-10}$$

The *correlation matrix* (see Example 4–10) can be computed directly from the covariance matrix by left-multiplying and right-multiplying $C_{m \times m}$ by a diagonal matrix, consisting of the reciprocal square roots of the variances for the variables. First let us consider the notation for a matrix of variances and a correlation matrix.

Notation 4–9.

$$V_{m \times m} = \begin{bmatrix} \sigma_1^2 & 0 & \cdots & 0 \\ 0 & \sigma_2^2 & \cdots & 0 \\ \vdots & \vdots & & \vdots \\ 0 & 0 & \cdots & \sigma_m^2 \end{bmatrix} \begin{array}{l} = \text{diagonal matrix of} \\ \textit{variances } \sigma_j^2 \text{ for each} \\ \text{variable } X_j \, (j = 1, 2, \\ \ldots, m). \end{array}$$

$$R_{m \times m} = \begin{bmatrix} r_{11} & r_{12} & \cdots & r_{1m} \\ r_{21} & r_{22} & \cdots & r_{2m} \\ \vdots & \vdots & & \vdots \\ r_{m1} & r_{m2} & \cdots & r_{mm} \end{bmatrix} \begin{array}{l} = \text{correlation matrix} \\ \text{for } m \text{ variables.} \end{array}$$

Then,

$$R_{m \times m} = V_{m \times m}^{-1/2} C_{m \times m} V_{m \times m}^{-1/2}. \tag{4-11}$$

If the data are in standard scores (Definition 3–4), the correlation matrix equals the *left*-multiplication of the standardized matrix by the transpose of itself times the reciprocal of the number of cases. Considering $Z_{n \times m}$ as the standardized data matrix (Notation 3–4),

$$R_{m \times m} = \frac{1}{n} Z'_{m \times n} Z_{n \times m}. \tag{4-12}$$

The multiple regression equation (Definition 3–11) and derivation of the regression coefficients can be elegantly shown by matrix algebra. Let us first establish the notation.

Notation 4–10. $\hat{Z}_{n \times 1}$ = a column vector of regression estimates of the dependent variable $Z_{n \times 1}$, a column vector of n cases.

$Z^*_{n \times m}$ = the data matrix of m standardized independent variables.

$B_{m \times 1}$ = column vector of m regression coefficients, one for each of the m independent variables.

The regression equation is then

$$\hat{Z}_{n \times 1} = Z^*_{n \times m} B_{m \times 1}. \tag{4–13}$$

That is, for independent variables $Z_1, Z_2, \ldots, Z_m$,

$$
\begin{array}{cccccc}
\hat{Z} & Z_1 & Z_2 & \ldots & Z_m & B
\end{array}
$$

$$
\begin{bmatrix} \hat{z}_1 \\ \hat{z}_2 \\ \vdots \\ \hat{z}_n \end{bmatrix} =
\begin{bmatrix} z_{11} & z_{12} & \cdots & z_{1m} \\ z_{21} & z_{22} & \cdots & z_{2m} \\ \vdots & \vdots & & \vdots \\ z_{n1} & z_{n2} & \cdots & z_{nm} \end{bmatrix}
\begin{bmatrix} b_1 \\ b_2 \\ \vdots \\ b_m \end{bmatrix}.
$$

The *least squares* calculation of $B_{m \times 1}$ (Johnston, 1963, p. 109) is

$$B_{m \times 1} = (Z^{*\prime}_{m \times n} Z^*_{n \times m})^{-1} Z^{*\prime}_{m \times n} Z_{n \times 1}, \tag{4–14}$$

where $Z^{*\prime}_{m \times n} Z^*_{n \times m}$ is nonsingular.

The nonsingularity requirement (Definition 4–14) assures that an inverse exists. For empirical data, a sufficient condition for nonsingularity is usually that $n > m$.

The regression of a nonstandardized variable X_j on m others can be given a geometric interpretation. The m independent variables are the basis of an m-dimensional space. The regression analysis then determines to what degree the dependent variable fits into this space. If X_j is standardized, the regression estimate $\hat{Z}_j$ is the projection of Z_j onto the m-dimensional space spanned by the independent variables. The *multiple correlation coefficient* r_j is then the length of this projection.

Equation (4–14) is the conventional matrix formula for the regression coefficients. Perhaps less known is another formula that is useful in developing one of the factor analysis models.

Notation 4–11. $D^2_{m \times m}$ = a diagonal matrix with diagonal elements equal to the reciprocal principal diagonal elements of $R^{-1}_{m \times m}$. That is, $D^2_{m \times m}$ = (diagonal $R^{-1}_{m \times m}$)$^{-1}$.

We assume $R_{m \times m}$ is nonsingular. If $R_{m \times m}$ is derived from empirical data, each variable X_j will usually contain some random error and specific variance uncorrelated with the other variables. $R_{m \times m}$ will then be nonsingular. This assumption for $R_{m \times m}$ is equivalent to that for $Z_{m \times n}^{*\prime} Z_{n \times m}^*$ in Eq. (4–14).

From Kaiser (1963, p. 158, Eq. 5), the matrix of regression coefficients $B_{m \times m}$, giving, by column,[2] the regression coefficients of each variable regressed on the $(m - 1)$ other standardized variables is

$$B_{m \times m} = I_{m \times m} - R_{m \times m}^{-1} D_{m \times m}^2. \qquad (4\text{–}15)$$

The elements of the matrix $D_{m \times m}^2$ are of interest in themselves. They are the variances of the *residuals* for each variable regressed on the $m - 1$ others. Thus, the jth diagonal element of $D_{m \times m}$ is the variance of $Z_j - \hat{Z}_j$.

The matrix of residuals can also be given as a function of $D_{m \times m}$ and the inverse of a nonsingular $R_{m \times m}$. From Harris (1962, p. 253, Eq. 8), the residuals $(Z_{n \times m} - \hat{Z}_{n \times m})$ for each variable regressed on the $m - 1$ others are

$$Z_{n \times m} - \hat{Z}_{n \times m} = Z_{n \times m} R_{m \times m}^{-1} D_{m \times m}^2. \qquad (4\text{–}16)$$

The asterisk defining $Z_{n \times m}$ as a matrix of independent variables is now dropped, since we are dealing with a data matrix in which each variable becomes successively a dependent variable.

The squared multiple correlations can also be obtained from $D_{m \times m}^2$, once we establish a notation.

> *Notation 4–12.* $r_{m \times m}^2$ = diagonal matrix of SMC values. The jth diagonal element is the squared multiple correlation of variable j with the remaining $m - 1$ variables.

Then, from Harris (1964b, p. 198),

$$r_{m \times m}^2 = I_{m \times m} - D_{m \times m}^2. \qquad (4\text{–}17)$$

We have previously defined the partial correlation between two variables, holding one or two other variables constant [Eqs. (3–3) and (3–4)]. The matrix relationships presented now enable us to understand the general definition given by Guttman (1953, p. 289, Theorem 3).

> *Definition 4–19.* For m variables, the PARTIAL CORRELATION between two of them, X_j and X_k, holding the remaining

2. Kaiser gives the regression coefficients for each variable by row, in $B_{m \times m}$. Therefore, in Kaiser, the inverse of $R_{m \times m}$ is multiplied on the left by $D_{m \times m}^2$ rather than on the right as in Eq. (4–15).

$(m - 2)$ variables constant, is the *negative* of the *correlation* between the *residuals*, $(X_j - \hat{X}_j)$ and $(X_k - \hat{X}_k)$, resulting from the regression of X_j and X_k on the $(m - 2)$ variables.

Notation 4–13. $P_{m \times m}$ = matrix of partial correlation coefficients, where element p_{jk} is the partial correlation between X_j and X_k, holding the $(m - 2)$ other variables constant.

The relationship between $P_{m \times m}$ and nonsingular $R_{m \times m}$ can be stated explicitly (Guttman and Cohen, 1943) as

$$P_{m \times m} = - D_{m \times m}^{-1} R_{m \times m}^{-1} D_{m \times m}^{-1}. \qquad (4\text{--}18)$$

4.4 Matrix Trace and Rank

The trace and especially the rank of a matrix are fundamental concepts in factor analysis.

Definition 4–20. The TRACE of a square matrix is the sum of its principal diagonal elements. For any square matrix $B_{p \times p}$ with principal diagonal elements $b_{11}, b_{22}, \ldots, b_{pp}$,

$$\text{trace} = b_{11} + b_{22} + \cdots + b_{pp}.$$

Notation 4–14. $\text{tr} B_{p \times p}$ = trace of matrix $B_{p \times p}$.

Example 4–14. Consider

$$B_{p \times p} = \begin{bmatrix} 2 & 3 & 2 \\ 0 & 1 & 1 \\ 4 & 2 & 4 \end{bmatrix}.$$

Then

$$\text{tr} B_{p \times p} = 2 + 1 + 4 = 7.$$

The following algebraic equalities apply to the trace of any square matrices B and C:

$$\text{tr} B_{p \times p}' = \text{tr} B_{p \times p}. \qquad (4\text{--}19a)$$

$$\text{tr} B_{p \times p} C_{p \times p} = \text{tr} C_{p \times p} B_{p \times p}. \qquad (4\text{--}19b)$$

$$\text{tr}(B_{p \times p} + C_{p \times p}) = \text{tr} B_{p \times p} + \text{tr} C_{p \times p}. \qquad (4\text{--}19c)$$

$$\text{tr} B_{p \times p} B_{p \times p}' = \text{tr} B_{p \times p}' B_{p \times p}. \qquad (4\text{--}19d)$$

The *rank* of a matrix may be defined in several different ways. The definition employed has been selected as the one most consonant with the vector space approach of this book.

> *Definition 4–21.* The RANK of a matrix is the maximum number of linearly independent column vectors in the matrix.

> *Notation 4–15.* $r(B_{p \times q}) = $ rank of matrix $B_{p \times q}$.

Linear independence of vectors has been defined and discussed in Section 3.2.5.

Some additional definitions of matrix rank equivalent to Definition 4–21 are:

1. The *maximum number* of linearly independent row vectors.
2. The *dimensionality* of the vector space defined by the matrix.
3. The *order* of the largest matrix with nonzero *determinant* formed by deleting rows and columns from the original matrix.

> *Example 4–15.* Consider a $B_{p \times q}$ matrix where $p > q$. Then the largest square matrix that may be formed from $B_{p \times q}$ is $B^*_{q \times q}$. If $\Delta B^*_{q \times q} \neq 0$, then $r(B_{p \times q}) = r(B^*_{q \times q}) = q$. If $\Delta B^*_{q \times q} = 0$, then $r(B_{p \times q}) < q$. In this case, consider *all* the determinants formed by removing a row and column, i.e., $\Delta B^*_{(q-1) \times (q-1)}$. If one of these determinants is not zero, then $r(B_{p \times q}) = (q - 1)$. If all of these determinants are zero, then $r(B_{p \times q}) < (q - 1)$. Next, repeat the procedure by eliminating two rows and columns, and consider all determinants $\Delta B^*_{(q-2) \times (q-2)}$. By successively reducing the order of the determinants a nonzero determinant will eventually be found.

Several equalities and inequalities governing the rank of a matrix are given below.

$$r(B_{p \times q}) \leq p \text{ or } q \quad \text{(whichever is smaller).} \quad (4\text{–}20\text{a})$$

Equation (4–20a) states that the rank of a matrix is less than or equal to the smaller side of the matrix. If $\Delta B_{p \times p} \neq 0$,

$$r(B_{p \times p}) = p. \quad (4\text{–}20\text{b})$$

That is, a nonsingular matrix has a rank equal to its order.

$$r(B'_{q \times p} B_{p \times q}) = r(B_{p \times q} B'_{q \times p}) = r(B_{p \times q}). \quad (4\text{–}20\text{c})$$

If $q < s$ and $B_{q \times q}$, $D_{s \times s}$ are nonsingular (Johnston, 1963, pp. 92–93), then

$$r(B_{q \times q}C_{q \times s}) = r(C_{q \times s}D_{s \times s}) = r(C_{q \times s}). \qquad (4\text{–}20d)$$

$$r(B_{p \times q}C_{q \times r}) \leq r(B_{p \times q}) \text{ or } r(C_{q \times r}) \qquad \text{(whichever is smaller).} \qquad (4\text{–}20e)$$

$$r(B_{p \times q} + C_{p \times q}) \leq r(B_{p \times q}) + r(C_{p \times q}) \qquad \text{for } p = q. \qquad (4\text{–}20f)$$

Additional equalities for the rank of a matrix are given in Horst (1963, Chapter 15).

Another definition that is useful in understanding factor analysis is rank defined in terms of the factors of a product, where the concept of factors is used in an algebraic sense. If we have a scalar number 6, then 6 can be factored into 2×3. The numbers 2 and 3 are the factors of 6. Similarly, matrices can be factored into two matrices.[3] If we have a matrix $B_{p \times q}$, factors $C_{p \times q}$ and square $D_{q \times q}$ can always be found (Horst, 1963, p. 333)[4] such that

$$B_{p \times q} = C_{p \times q}D_{q \times q}. \qquad (4\text{–}21)$$

Some matrices can be factored into other matrices with common order less than that of the product. That is,

$$B_{p \times q} = C_{p \times s}D_{s \times q}, \qquad (4\text{–}22)$$

where $s < p, q$.

Now, the rank of $B_{p \times q}$ is then the smallest possible common order s of any of the factors of $B_{p \times q}$:

$$r(B_{p \times q}) = r(C_{p \times s}D_{s \times q}) = \text{minimum } s < p, q. \qquad (4\text{–}23)$$

If a symmetric matrix $B_{p \times p}$ is the product of another matrix times its transpose, then $B_{p \times p}$ can be factored into any one of an infinite number of matrices, each times its transpose (Horst, 1965, p. 78). This point will be useful to us later and is stated as a theorem:

> **Theorem 4–3.** *If a symmetric matrix* $B_{p \times p}$ *equals* $C'_{p \times q}C_{q \times p}$ *or* $C_{p \times q}C'_{q \times p}$, *then an infinite number of matrices* $D_{p \times q}$ *or* $D_{q \times p}$ *can be found such that* $B_{p \times p} = D'_{p \times q}D_{q \times p}$ *or* $B_{p \times p} = D_{p \times q}D'_{q \times p}$.

In the chapters to follow we will have special use for a concept denoting a matrix that has a rank equal to the number of its rows (or

---

3. In the next chapter it will be shown that factor analysis does indeed divide a matrix into factors in the algebraic sense. See Eq. (5–5), for example.

4. The determination of the matrix factors of a matrix has been extensively discussed by Horst (1963, Chapters 15–17; 1965, Chapter 3).

columns, whichever is smaller). Horst (1963, Chapter 15) calls such a matrix basic, and we will adopt his terminology.

> *Definition 4–22.* A BASIC MATRIX is one with rank equal to its smallest order. If $B_{p \times q}$ is any matrix and $q \leq p$, then $B_{p \times q}$ is basic if $r(B_{p \times q}) = q$.

Assume that we have a data matrix $A_{n \times m}$ where the number of cases n exceeds the number of variables m. Then, if the matrix is basic, all the column vectors (variables) of the matrix are linearly independent and form a basis of the vector space defined by the matrix. Moreover, the dimensionality of the space equals m.

Some particular types of basic matrices might be mentioned. A square basic matrix, $B_{p \times p}$, has rank equal to p and is consequently *nonsingular*. All orthogonal matrices are basic. All diagonal matrices are basic if all their diagonal elements are nonzero. An identity matrix is thus basic.

4.5 Eigenvalues and Eigenvectors

The concepts of *eigenvalues* and *eigenvectors* will be encountered often in subsequent chapters. Basic derivations of factor models are dependent on these concepts, and eigenvalues are used frequently in scientific applications.

Consider any square matrix $B_{p \times p}$. One problem in mathematics is to find a $p \times 1$ order vector E_j and a scalar λ_j such that

$$B_{p \times p} E_j = \lambda_j E_j, \tag{4-24}$$

where $E_j \neq 0$. The condition $E_j \neq 0$ means that at least one element of E_j is nonzero.

Geometrically, the matrix $B_{p \times p}$ is a transformation of the vector E_j to another vector space wherein E_j has the same direction (except possibly for complete reversal), but its length has been lengthened or shortened proportional to the scalar λ_j.

From Eq. (4–24), $B_{p \times p} E_j - \lambda_j E_j = 0$, and

$$(B_{p \times p} - \lambda_j I_{p \times p}) E_j = 0, \tag{4-25}$$

where 0 refers to a matrix (vector) of zeros.

If $(B_{p \times p} - \lambda_j I_{p \times p})$ is a nonsingular matrix (Definition 4–14), then the equation can be solved for E_j by multiplying both sides by the inverse of $(B_{p \times p} - \lambda_j I_{p \times p})$. However, E_j will then equal zero in violation of the condition for Eq. (4–24). Consequently, an $E_j \neq 0$ solution to Eq.

(4–25) will exist if and only if $(B_{p \times p} - \lambda_j I_{p \times p})$ is singular, that is, if and only if the determinant of the matrix $(B_{p \times p} - \lambda_j I_{p \times p}) = 0$. The equation

$$\Delta(B_{p \times p} - \lambda_j I_{p \times p}) = |B_{p \times p} - \lambda_j I_{p \times p}| = 0 \qquad (4\text{–}26)$$

is called the *characteristic equation*. Its properties have been extensively investigated by mathematicians,[5] and it has many scientific and engineering applications.

> *Definition 4–23.* The vector E_j and scalar λ_j in the equation $B_{p \times p} E_j = \lambda E_j$ are the EIGENVECTOR and EIGENVALUE of the matrix $B_{p \times p}$.

Eigenvalues and eigenvectors are also known as *latent* roots and vectors, or *characteristic* roots and vectors. That the eigenvalue is a root of a characteristic equation can be seen in the simple case of a 2×2 matrix such as

$$\begin{bmatrix} b_{11} & b_{12} \\ b_{21} & b_{22} \end{bmatrix}.$$

Example 4–16. The problem is to solve for

$$\begin{bmatrix} b_{11} & b_{12} \\ b_{21} & b_{22} \end{bmatrix} \begin{bmatrix} e_1 \\ e_2 \end{bmatrix} = \lambda \begin{bmatrix} e_1 \\ e_2 \end{bmatrix} \text{ by solving for } \lambda \text{ in}$$

$$\Delta\left(\begin{bmatrix} b_{11} & b_{12} \\ b_{21} & b_{22} \end{bmatrix} - \begin{bmatrix} \lambda & 0 \\ 0 & \lambda \end{bmatrix}\right) = \Delta\begin{bmatrix} b_{11} - \lambda & b_{12} \\ b_{21} & b_{22} - \lambda \end{bmatrix} = 0.$$

This second-order determinant has the solution

$$(b_{11} - \lambda)(b_{22} - \lambda) - b_{12}b_{21} = 0,$$

$$b_{11}b_{22} - \lambda b_{22} - \lambda b_{11} + \lambda^2 - b_{12}b_{21} = 0,$$

$$\lambda^2 - \lambda(b_{22} + b_{11}) + (b_{11}b_{22} - b_{12}b_{21}) = 0.$$

This is a quadratic equation with two roots λ_1 and λ_2 given by

$$\tfrac{1}{2}\{(b_{22} + b_{11}) \pm [(b_{22} + b_{11})^2 - 4(b_{11}b_{22} - b_{12}b_{21})]^{1/2}\}.$$

With the roots λ_1 and λ_2 evaluated, the elements e_1 and e_2 of the eigenvector can be solved from

$$\begin{bmatrix} b_{11} & b_{12} \\ b_{21} & b_{22} \end{bmatrix} \begin{bmatrix} e_1 \\ e_2 \end{bmatrix} = \lambda \begin{bmatrix} e_1 \\ e_2 \end{bmatrix},$$

5. Hohn (1958, Chapter 8) presents an especially good elementary treatment of characteristic equations.

which reduces to

$$b_{11}e_1 + b_{12}e_2 = \lambda e_1$$
$$b_{21}e_1 + b_{22}e_2 = \lambda e_2$$

and further reduces to

$$(b_{11} - \lambda)e_1 + b_{12}e_2 = 0,$$
$$b_{21}e_1 + (b_{22} - \lambda)e_2 = 0.$$

These last equations can then be solved simultaneously for e_1 and e_2. There will be an eigenvector solution for each eigenvalue. In the 2×2 case, then, the complete solution will be

$$\begin{bmatrix} b_{11} & b_{12} \\ b_{21} & b_{22} \end{bmatrix} \begin{bmatrix} e_{11} & e_{12} \\ e_{21} & e_{22} \end{bmatrix} = \begin{bmatrix} \lambda_1 & 0 \\ 0 & \lambda_2 \end{bmatrix} \begin{bmatrix} e_{11} & e_{12} \\ e_{21} & e_{22} \end{bmatrix}.$$

Notation 4–16. $E_{p \times p}$ = matrix of p column eigenvectors for a $p \times p$ matrix.

$\lambda_{p \times p}$ = diagonal matrix of eigenvalues ordered such that the jth eigenvalue is the associated eigenvalue for the jth column eigenvector of $E_{p \times p}$.

Every $p \times p$ matrix will have as many eigenvalues and eigenvectors as its order. Not all of the eigenvalues may be distinct or nonzero, however. We can express all these eigenvalue solutions to the characteristic equation in matrix form:

$$B_{p \times p}E_{p \times p} = \lambda_{p \times p}E_{p \times p},$$
$$B_{p \times p}E_{p \times p} - \lambda_{p \times p}E_{p \times p} = 0, \qquad (4\text{–}27)$$
$$(B_{p \times p} - \lambda_{p \times p}I_{p \times p})E_{p \times p} = 0.$$

When a square matrix $B_{p \times p}$ is also symmetric, its eigenvalues are all real and the associated eigenvectors are orthogonal. The eigenvectors form an orthogonal basis of the vector space defined by $B_{p \times p}$.

If there are k-number of eigenvalues λ_j of symmetric $B_{p \times p}$ that are identical, there will be k corresponding orthogonal eigenvectors for λ_j. For one or more eigenvalues equal to zero, a theorem of some importance (Hadley, 1961, p. 274, Problem 7–7) should be stated:

> *Theorem 4–4. If* k-*number of eigenvalues of a matrix* $B_{p \times p}$ *are zero, then the rank of the matrix is* $r(B_{p \times p}) = p - k$.

There are several equalities involving eigenvalues that will be useful in subsequent chapters and are accordingly given here. Let $E_{p \times p}$ and $\lambda_{p \times p}$ be the eigenvector and eigenvalue matrices of symmetric $B_{p \times p}$.

Then, if $B_{p \times p}$ is an orthonormal matrix,

$$\lambda_j = \pm 1. \tag{4-28}$$

If $B_{p \times p}$ is any symmetric matrix,

$$B_{p \times p}^k E_{p \times p} = \lambda_{p \times p}^k E_{p \times p} \qquad \text{for any exponent } k. \tag{4-29}$$

$$B_{p \times p}' E_{p \times p} = \lambda_{p \times p} E_{p \times p}. \tag{4-30}$$

$$\text{tr} B_{p \times p} = \sum_{j=1}^{p} \lambda_j. \tag{4-31}$$

$$\Delta B_{p \times p} = \lambda_1 \lambda_2 \lambda_3 \cdots \lambda_p. \tag{4-32}$$

$$B_{p \times p}^{-1} E_{p \times p} = \lambda_{p \times p}^{-1} E_{p \times p}. \tag{4-33}$$

$$(k B_{p \times p}) E_{p \times p} = (k \lambda_{p \times p}) E_{p \times p} \qquad \text{for any scalar } k. \tag{4-34}$$

We have seen that any symmetric matrix will have matrices of eigenvalues and eigenvectors. The eigenvectors are not unique, however. For any symmetric matrix and its eigenvalues there may be an infinite number of associated eigenvector matrices. There is at least one such matrix (Hadley, 1961, pp. 241, 247) of associated eigenvectors that is orthonormal. By Definition 4–18 and Eq. (4–9), if $E_{p \times p}$ is orthonormal,

$$E_{p \times p}' E_{p \times p} = I_{p \times p} \qquad \text{and} \qquad E_{p \times p}' = E_{p \times p}^{-1}.$$

Moreover, from Hadley (1961, p. 270) we can state that, if the columns of $E_{p \times p}$ are orthonormal, *the rows are also orthonormal* and that, for any separate orthonormal[6] matrices $E_{p \times p}$ and $E_{p \times p}^*$, the product $E_{p \times p} E_{p \times p}^*$ is also orthonormal:

$$(E_{p \times p} E_{p \times p}^*)' E_{p \times p} E_{p \times p}^* = I_{p \times p}. \tag{4-35a}$$

$$(E_{p \times p} E_{p \times p}^*)^{-1} = (E_{p \times p} E_{p \times p}^*)'. \tag{4-35b}$$

The previous discussion of eigenvalues and eigenvectors enables us to define the similarity relationship between matrices. Consider any

6. The reader who wishes to check these points should note that Hadley uses the term orthogonal matrix to refer to what we have defined as an orthonormal matrix.

nonsingular matrix $P_{p \times p}$ and square matrices $B_{p \times p}$ and $C_{p \times p}$ such that

$$C_{p \times p} = P_{p \times p}^{-1} B_{p \times p} P_{p \times p}. \tag{4-36}$$

Then, by matrix manipulation,

$$
\begin{aligned}
P_{p \times p}^{-1} B_{p \times p} P_{p \times p} &= C_{p \times p}, \\
B_{p \times p} P_{p \times p} &= P_{p \times p} C_{p \times p}, \\
B_{p \times p} &= P_{p \times p} C_{p \times p} P_{p \times p}^{-1}.
\end{aligned} \tag{4-37}
$$

If a matrix $P_{p \times p}$ exists for matrices $C_{p \times p}$ and $B_{p \times p}$ such that Eq. (4-37) holds, then $C_{p \times p}$ *and* $B_{p \times p}$ have identical eigenvalues.

> *Definition 4-24.* If $B_{p \times p} = P_{p \times p} C_{p \times p} P_{p \times p}^{-1}$ for any non-singular matrix $P_{p \times p}$, then $B_{p \times p}$ is SIMILAR to $C_{p \times p}$ and $B_{p \times p}$ is obtained from $C_{p \times p}$ by a SIMILARITY TRANS-FORMATION.

If we define $P_{p \times p}$ as equal to the orthonormal eigenvectors of $B_{p \times p}$ and define $B_{p \times p}$ as symmetric, we get an important result: *The similarity transformation* of $B_{p \times p}$ yields the diagonal matrix of eigenvalues of $B_{p \times p}$. Rewriting Eq. (4-36),

$$\lambda_{p \times p} = E_{p \times p}^{-1} B_{p \times p} E_{p \times p}. \tag{4-38}$$

We can also rewrite Eq. (4-37) to explicitly state a central equality in factor analysis: A symmetric matrix can be *factored* into its eigenvalue matrix, left-multiplied by its orthonormal eigenvector matrix and right-multiplied by its transposed orthonormal eigenvector matrix:

$$
\begin{aligned}
E_{p \times p}^{-1} B_{p \times p} E_{p \times p} &= \lambda_{p \times p}, \\
B_{p \times p} = E_{p \times p} \lambda_{p \times p} E_{p \times p}^{-1} &= E_{p \times p} \lambda_{p \times p} E_{p \times p}'.
\end{aligned} \tag{4-39}
$$

> *Definition 4-25.* The PRINCIPAL AXES of a symmetric matrix are the orthonormal eigenvectors of the matrix for which the similarity transformation is its eigenvalue matrix. If $\lambda_{p \times p} = E_{p \times p}^{-1} B_{p \times p} E_{p \times p}$ for symmetric $B_{p \times p}$ and orthonormal $E_{p \times p}$, then $E_{p \times p}$ is the matrix of the principal axes of $B_{p \times p}$.

The principal axes technique of factor analysis to be considered in Chapter 14 is based on this definition, as is the derivation of several factor models in the next chapter.

So far the discussion of eigenvalues and eigenvectors has often required that $B_{p \times p}$ be symmetric. What if $B_{p \times p}$ is square but not symmetric? From Hadley (1961, Section 7-6) we can state the following:

1. Not all eigenvalues are necessarily real.
2. The eigenvectors corresponding to different eigenvalues are linearly independent but not necessarily orthogonal.
3. The eigenvectors may not span the vector space even if all the eigenvalues are real.
4. If all the eigenvalues are distinct (no one eigenvalue equals another) or $B_{p \times p}$ has p linear independent eigenvectors, then Eq. (4–39) will hold.

5. Factor Analysis Models

The mathematical model underlying factor analysis is now undergoing considerable refinement. *Common factor analysis*, the traditional model and still the most often applied, has been revised to give a precise meaning to the concept of "common" and to move from hypothetical to measurable factors. This revised model is called *image factor analysis*.

Another refinement of the traditional common factor analysis model is *canonical factor analysis*. Applied to a sample of cases, this variant enables those common factors in the population of cases to be determined in such a way that they have maximum canonical correlation with the sample data. It is a statistical model that permits tests of significance to be applied.

A third alteration of the common factor analysis model, *alpha factor analysis*, changes the direction of inference. It considers a selection of variables to be a sample from a universe of content and delineates the common factors for the sample having maximum generalizability to this universe.

These newer models have extended and refined our factor analytic capability in significant ways. We can now operationalize the concept of commonness among variables. We can now apply significance tests in relation to a known statistical model. We can now measure factors with maximum generalizability. Utilizing a property of some of these new models, we can determine factors that are invariant within a proportionality constant of the units in the data.[1]

As a preliminary to considering these models in detail, the first section of this chapter will break down a variable's variance into its various components. These variance components play a basic role in common factor analysis and in the newer factor analysis models.

5.1 Variance Components of a Variable

The total data variation in a matrix can be divided into several component parts.

> *Definition 5–1.* The COMMUNALITY of a variable X_j in a matrix of m variables is that variance of X_j common to the other $(m - 1)$ variables.

> *Notation 5–1.* h_j^2 = the communality of standardized variable Z_j.
>
> $H_{m \times m}^2$ = a diagonal matrix of communalities for the m variables, where the jth diagonal element h_j^2 is the communality for variable Z_j with regard to the $(m - 1)$ other variables.

> *Definition 5–2.* The UNIQUENESS of a variable X_j in a matrix of m variables is that variance component of X_j not common to the other $(m - 1)$ variables.

> *Notation 5–2.* u_j^2 = uniqueness of standardized variable Z_j.
>
> $U_{m \times m}^2$ = a diagonal matrix of uniquenesses for m variables, where the jth element u_j^2 is the uniqueness for variable Z_j with regard to the $(m - 1)$ other variables.

1. A new type of factor analysis, sometimes called nonmetric factor analysis, determines invariant factors of the scale of data measurement (ordinal, interval, or ratio scale). This type of analysis, which we may also call dimensional analysis, is basically different from the factor analysis model and will be discussed in Section 22.3.

The total variance of a standardized variable is unity. A basic equality is therefore

$$h_j^2 = 1 - u_j^2,$$

or, for m variables,

$$H_{m \times m}^2 = I_{m \times m} - U_{m \times m}^2. \tag{5-1}$$

Three additional components of variance need to be distinguished: *specific, reliable,* and *random error.*

> *Definition 5–3.* The SPECIFICITY of a variable X_j is that portion of its uniqueness that is reliable.

> *Definition 5–4.* The RELIABILITY of a variable X_j is its common plus its specific variance.

Reliability means reproducibility. It is that portion of the data variability that remains constant through replication. That portion of variance that cannot be reproduced when the data are collected anew is random error (Section 9.1.3.4).

> *Definition 5–5.* The RANDOM ERROR of a variable X_j is that portion of its uniqueness that is unreliable.

The variance components of a variable are shown in Figure 5–1. The total variance of X_j is the length of the line. The line itself is divided into 10 units. The common variance can then be seen to involve about 55 per cent of the variance for X_j, with unique variance comprising the remainder. About 80 per cent of the variance is reliable, and 20 per cent is random error. Specific variance accounts for 25 per cent. *The common and specific variances are relative to a particular set*

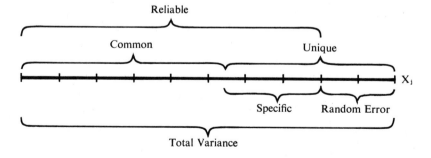

Figure 5–1

of variables containing X_j. Were this set altered by removing or adding variables, then the common and unique variances of X_j would shift. Consider, for example, a variable X_j little correlated with the other variables. If another variable with which X_j is highly correlated is added to the set, the communality of X_j would increase considerably. The reliable and random error components should remain unchanged, however. They are particular to a variable's measurement and content.

5.2 Common Factor Analysis

The *common factor analysis* model was originally developed by Spearman (1927) for two factors and extended to multiple factors by Thurstone (1935). The Spearman-Thurstone approach has dominated applied factor analysis to the present time. It assumes that data on a variable consists of common and unique parts. The common parts of all the variables then define a common vector space. In addition, it is assumed that the unique parts of the variables are uncorrelated with each other or with their common parts.

The object of common factor analysis is to define the dimensions of this common vector space. These dimensions are called *common factors*. A basic assumption in this type of factor analysis is that the number of dimensions needed to span the common vector space is much less than the number required as a basis for the vector space of the data (common plus unique parts). Indeed, it is assumed (Guttman, 1956, see also 1954) that the number of common factors will be small as the number of variables, m, increases to infinity. Mathematically, the assumption can be stated as

$$\lim_{m \to \infty} \frac{p}{m} = 0,$$

for p common factors.

The common factor analysis model is a partial correlation approach (Definition 3–13) to the data. In effect, the search for common factors is the search for hypothetical variables that will cause the partial correlation between all possible pairs of m variables to tend to zero, when the hypothetical variables are held constant. Since, by Eq. (4–18), the partial correlations between m variables is a function of the inverse of their correlation matrix, $R_{m \times m}$, the assumption is that $R^{-1}_{m \times m}$ will tend to a diagonal matrix as the number of variables becomes infinite. If $R^{-1}_{m \times m}$ is diagonal, the r^{-1}_{jk} $(j \neq k)$ values will be zero and the partials $r_{jk.(m-2)}$ will be zero.

A test (Guttman, 1953) for whether the common factor analysis model is applicable, therefore, is to compute $R^{-1}_{m \times m}$ and to check the off-diagonal elements. If they are near zero, the common factor analysis model is applicable. If these elements are not near zero, the selection of variables may not be comprehensive, or the common factor analysis model may not be applicable as $m \to \infty$.

A basic indeterminacy is entailed by the common factor model. The length of a standardized data vector in common factor space is the square root of its communality. Until the common factors of this space are defined, the common parts of the variables, and thus their communalities, cannot be precisely determined. But the delineation of the common factors involves a foreknowledge of the communalities. This dilemma has yet to be satisfactorily solved within the confines of the model. The problem of communality will be discussed in Chapter 13.

Another indeterminacy has to do with the common factors of the common vector space. The number of these common factors—the dimensionality of the common space—is determinate for a given communality estimate. The factors themselves, however, are indeterminate. Actually, for a given data matrix, there will be an infinite number of different sets of common factors. Which set is selected depends on criteria external to the model. Chapter 14 will discuss different factoring techniques, which are in essence different criteria for selecting the "best" set of common factors, and Chapters 16 and 17 will consider criteria for altering one set of common factors to another more "desirable" set defining the same space.

Now for the common factor model itself. Before displaying the model, the notation should be under control. The m column vectors of a data matrix are $X_1, X_2, \ldots, X_m$. The model expresses these data vectors as a linear combination of unknown linearly independent vectors (called common factors) and a unique factor. Scalars weight each common factor according to its contribution to the data vector. (At this point, the reader may find it useful to review Section 3.2.5.)

> *Notation 5–3.* $\quad S_l =$ a common factor.
> $\alpha_{ji} =$ a scalar weighting the contribution of S_l to the common variance of X_j.
> $p =$ number of common factors.
> $S_{ju} =$ a unique factor contributing to the unique variance of X_j.
> $\alpha_{ju} =$ a scalar weight for S_{ju}.

The common factor model is then

$$X_1 = \alpha_{11}S_1 + \alpha_{12}S_2 + \cdots + \alpha_{1p}S_p + \alpha_{1u}S_{1u},$$

$$X_2 = \alpha_{21}S_1 + \alpha_{22}S_2 + \cdots + \alpha_{2p}S_p + \alpha_{2u}S_{2u},$$

$$\vdots \qquad \vdots \qquad \vdots \qquad \vdots \qquad \vdots \qquad (5\text{–}2)$$

$$X_m = \alpha_{m1}S_1 + \alpha_{m2}S_2 + \cdots + \alpha_{mp}S_p + \alpha_{mu}S_{mu}.$$

The data for the vectors on the left of Eq. (5–2) are known. Geometrically they define a vector space. The goal of common factor analysis is to determine the common factor dimensions spanning (reproducing, generating, predicting) the space of the common parts of the data vectors.

Algebraically, a traditional approach to expressing relationships is to establish the mathematical function $f(X, V, W)$ connecting one dependent variable Y, and a set of independent variables, X, V, and W. Such a function[2] might be $Y = 2X + 3V - 2W$ or $Y = 4VW/X$. The variables on both the right and left sides of the equation are known, and data are available. It is then only a question of determining the best function describing the relationships.

Let us say, however, that we have a number of dependent variables, X_1, X_2, X_3, and so on, but that we know neither the independent variables to enter on the right side of an equation for each dependent variable nor the functions involved. This might be the situation with United Nations voting, for example. We may know the votes of nations on one roll call (X_1), a second roll call (X_2), a third (X_3), and so on, but we may not know what nation characteristics are related to what roll calls in what way. Moreover, we may not be able to measure the characteristics well (characteristics such as nationalism, ideology, and democracy) that we feel might be closely related to United Nations voting. In other words, we have data that we wish to explain mathematically, but the variables that would give us this explanation are unknown or unmeasurable. We are thus in a dilemma similar to that faced by the nuclear physicist a few decades ago in describing quantum phenomena, and, like him, we resort to an untraditional mathematical approach. We assume that our dependent variables are related to a number of functions operating linearly, as in Eq. (5–2).

2. "Function" in this book will always mean that mathematical relationship between variables in which any values of the independent variables (called the *domain* of the function) are equated with one value on the dependent variables (called the range of the function). If y is the dependent variable and x an independent variable, for example, y as a function of x is usually written as $y = f(x)$, where $f(x)$ can equal any equation for which the equality holds. If $y = 2 + 3x^2$, then $y = f(x) = 2 + 3x^2$.

It is crucial to comprehending factor analysis (whether the common factor analysis model or the other models we will discuss) to understand that *S stands for a function of variables and not a variable*. For example, the functions might be $S_1 = f(W) = (W^2 - 1)/(2)^{1/2}$, and $S_2 = f(W) = [W(W^2 - 3)]/(6)^{1/2}$. The *unknown* variables entering into each function, S_l, of Eq. (5–2) are related in *unknown* ways although the functions *themselves* are linear. To be more specific, consider the equality for X_1 in Eq. (5–2). By letting $S_l = f_i(W_1, W_2, \ldots, W_t)$, where $W_1, W_2, \ldots, W_t$ are t number of unknown variables related to S_l by the function, we can rewrite the equality for X_1 as

$$X_1 = \alpha_{11}f_1(W_1, W_2, \ldots, W_t) + \alpha_{12}f_2(W_1, W_2, \ldots, W_t) + \cdots$$
$$+ \alpha_{1p}f_p(W_1, W_2, \ldots, W_t) + \alpha_{1u}f_u(W_1, W_2, \ldots, W_t).$$

To take our United Nations voting example again, two functions related to voting behavior, $S_1 = f_1(W_1, W_2, \ldots, W_t)$ and $S_2 = f_2(W_1, W_2, \ldots, W_t)$, may be ideology and nationalism. But each of these two functions may by itself be the result of a complex interaction between the unknown socioeconomic and political variables—the W's.

Within this algebraic perspective, what does common factor analysis do? By application to the known data on the X variables, *common factor analysis defines the hypothetical unknown S functions related to the common variance components of the variables*. The loadings emerging from a factor analysis are the α constants. The factors are the S functions. The size of each loading for each factor measures how much that specific function is related to X. For any of the X variables of Eq. (5–2), we may write

common factors   unique factor

$$X_j = \overset{\downarrow}{\underset{\uparrow}{\alpha_{j1}}}\overset{\downarrow}{\underset{}{S_1}} + \overset{\downarrow}{\underset{\uparrow}{\alpha_{j2}}}\overset{\downarrow}{\underset{}{S_2}} + \cdots + \overset{\downarrow}{\underset{\uparrow}{\alpha_{jp}}}\overset{\downarrow}{\underset{}{S_p}} + \overset{\downarrow}{\underset{\uparrow}{\alpha_{ju}}}\overset{\downarrow}{\underset{}{S_{ju}}}.$$

loadings

Definition 5–6. A COMMON FACTOR is algebraically a *function* linearly contributing to the common variance of a variable. It can be represented geometrically as a dimension of the common vector space of the data.

Definition 5–7. A UNIQUE FACTOR is algebraically a function linearly contributing to the unique variance of a variable. It can be represented geometrically as a dimension contributing to the unique space of a vector.

> *Definition 5–8.* A LOADING is a weight for each factor dimension measuring the variance contribution the factor makes to the data vector. For any vector X_j, scalar α_{jl} and factor S_l, α_{jl} is a loading.

Besides determining the loadings, α, common factor analysis will also generate data (scores) for each case (individual, group, or nation) on each of the S functions uncovered. These derived values for each case are called *factor scores*. They, plus the data on X_j and Eq. (5–2), yield a mathematical relationship between data as useful and important as the classical equations like $X = 2V + 3W$.

> *Definition 5–9.* The FACTOR SCORES for n cases on a factor are the elements of the factor vector S.

> *Notation 5–4.* $s_{il} =$ factor score on factor S_l for case i.

To make sure these terms are understood, the factor model for the elements of vector X_j can be displayed for n cases,

factor scores

$$
\begin{bmatrix} x_{1j} \\ x_{2j} \\ \vdots \\ x_{nj} \end{bmatrix} = \alpha_{j1} \begin{bmatrix} s_{11} \\ s_{21} \\ \vdots \\ s_{n1} \end{bmatrix} + \alpha_{j2} \begin{bmatrix} s_{12} \\ s_{22} \\ \vdots \\ s_{n2} \end{bmatrix} + \cdots + \alpha_{jp} \begin{bmatrix} s_{1p} \\ s_{2p} \\ \vdots \\ s_{np} \end{bmatrix} + \alpha_{ju} \begin{bmatrix} s_{1u} \\ s_{2u} \\ \vdots \\ s_{nu} \end{bmatrix}
$$

data for X_j factor loadings

Let us extend our notation to the factor matrices.

> *Notation 5–5.* $F_{m \times p} =$ matrix of loadings α_{jl} for each variable (row) on each common factor (column).
>
> $S_{n \times p} =$ matrix of factor scores for each case (row) on each common factor (column).
>
> $U_{m \times m} =$ diagonal matrix of loadings α_{ju} for each variable (row) on its unique factor S_{ju} (column).
>
> $S^*_{n \times m} =$ matrix of factor scores of each case (row) on the unique factors (column).

For convenience in developing the factor model, assume that the data are standardized for m variables and n cases. The factor model is then, in matrix notation,

$$Z_{n \times m} = S_{n \times p}F'_{p \times m} + S^*_{n \times m}U_{m \times m}. \tag{5-3}$$

The object of common factor analysis is to determine the elements for the matrices $S_{n \times p}$ and $F'_{p \times m}$ in Eq. (5–3).

Consonant with our discussion in the previous section of a variable's variance components, let each standardized variable Z_j be divided into a common (Z^*_j) and a unique (U^*_j) part. The data matrix can be similarly divided:

$$Z_{n \times m} = Z^*_{n \times m} + U^*_{n \times m}, \tag{5-4}$$

where $Z^*_{n \times m}$ = matrix of common parts of $Z_{n \times m}$, and $U^*_{n \times m}$ = matrix of unique parts of $Z_{n \times m}$. Then

$$
\begin{aligned}
Z'_{m \times n}Z_{n \times m} &= (Z^*_{n \times m} + U^*_{n \times m})'(Z^*_{n \times m} + U^*_{n \times m}) \\
&= (Z^{*'}_{m \times n} + U^{*'}_{m \times n})(Z^*_{n \times m} + U^*_{n \times m}) \\
&= Z^{*'}_{m \times n}Z^*_{n \times m} + Z^{*'}_{m \times n}U^*_{n \times m} + U^{*'}_{m \times n}Z^*_{n \times m} + U^{*'}_{m \times n}U^*_{n \times m}.
\end{aligned} \tag{5-5}
$$

The common factor analysis model assumes that the unique parts of a variable are uncorrelated with its common parts or with the unique or common parts of the other variables. Recalling from Eq. (4–12) that the correlation matrix $R_{m \times m} = (1/n)Z'_{m \times n}Z_{n \times m}$, we can state this assumption as

$$\frac{1}{n} Z^{*'}_{m \times n}U^*_{n \times m} = \frac{1}{n} U^{*'}_{m \times n}Z^*_{n \times m} = 0, \tag{5-6}$$

where 0 is a matrix of zeros. Moreover,

$$\frac{1}{n} U^{*'}_{m \times n}U^*_{n \times m} = U^2_{m \times m}, \tag{5-7}$$

where $U^2_{m \times m}$ is the diagonal matrix of *unique variances* of each variable (Notation 5–2). Making use of Eq. (4–12) again, we can multiply Eq. (5–5) through by $1/n$ and employ Eqs. (5–6) and (5–7) to derive

$$R_{m \times m} = \frac{1}{n} Z^{*'}_{m \times n}Z^*_{n \times m} + U^2_{m \times m}. \tag{5-8}$$

Now, the common factor model expressed in Eq. (5–3) has common parts of the data equal to

$$Z^*_{n \times m} = S_{n \times p}F'_{p \times m}. \tag{5-9}$$

Therefore, by substituting Eq. (5–9) into Eq. (5–8), we have

$$R_{m \times m} = \frac{1}{n} (S_{n \times p} F'_{p \times m})'(S_{n \times p} F'_{p \times m}) + U^2_{m \times m}$$

$$= \frac{1}{n} F_{m \times p} S'_{p \times n} S_{n \times p} F'_{p \times m} + U^2_{m \times m}. \tag{5–10}$$

Assume that the factor scores $S_{p \times n}$ are standardized by column and that the columns of factor scores are orthogonal (Definition 3–28). Then $S'_{p \times n} S_{n \times p} = n I_{p \times p}$ and Eq. (5–10) can be simplified to

$$R_{m \times m} = \frac{1}{n} F_{m \times p} n I_{p \times p} F'_{p \times m} + U^2_{m \times m} = F_{m \times p} F'_{p \times m} + U^2_{m \times m}, \tag{5–11}$$

and

$$R_{m \times m} - U^2_{m \times m} = F_{m \times p} F'_{p \times m}. \tag{5–12}$$

Equation (5–12) is a fundamental derivation in the common factor analysis model. It indicates that the common factor loadings $F_{m \times p}$ in the factor model [Eq. (5–3)] can be determined by factoring the variable's correlation matrix with the uniqueness of each variable subtracted from the principal diagonal value of 1.00 (the correlation of a variable with itself).

Since the data are standardized, from Eq. (5–1), $U^2_{m \times m} = I_{m \times m} - H^2_{m \times m}$. The matrix $(R_{m \times m} - U^2_{m \times m})$ can therefore be alternatively given as $(R_{m \times m} - I_{m \times m} + H^2_{m \times m})$. This latter matrix is equivalent to subtracting out the unity in the principal diagonal for a variable and replacing it with the variable's h^2. The problem of what values for h^2 to insert in the diagonal of $R_{m \times m}$ is called the *problem of communality* and is discussed further in Chapter 13. Communalities (or the uniquenesses) must be determined or estimated to define the elements of the common factor matrix. For the remainder of this section let us assume that $U^2_{m \times m}$ is known.

The problem of finding $F_{m \times p}$ for $(R_{m \times m} - U^2_{m \times m})$ can be solved by determining the eigenvalues and eigenvectors of the matrix (Section 4.5). $(R_{m \times m} - U^2_{m \times m})$ is symmetric and, we will assume, Gramian.[3] Its eigenvalues are therefore real numbers and its eigenvectors span the common vector space.

The characteristic equation [see Eq. (4–27)] is

$$|(R_{m \times m} - U^2_{m \times m}) - \lambda I_{m \times m}| = 0. \tag{5–13}$$

---

3. When $U^2_{m \times m}$ is *estimated*, $(R_{m \times m} - U^2_{m \times m})$ may not be Gramian and some eigenvalues may be negative as a result. See Guttman (1954).

From Eq. (4–39) and Definition 4–25, the roots of the equation will yield the principal axes and eigenvalues[4]:

$$R_{m \times m} - U^2_{m \times m} = E_{m \times m}\lambda_{m \times m}E'_{m \times m} = (E_{m \times m}\lambda^{1/2}_{m \times m})(\lambda^{1/2}_{m \times m}E'_{m \times m}). \quad (5\text{–}14)$$

> *Definition 5–10.* The COMMON FACTOR LOADINGS of a correlation matrix with communalities in the diagonal are equal to the eigenvectors of the matrix scaled by the square roots of the eigenvalues. That is, $F_{m \times m} = E_{m \times m}\lambda^{1/2}_{m \times m}$.

Let the eigenvalues be ordered in the diagonal of $\lambda_{m \times m}$ from high to low. If there are k number of zero eigenvalues then the last k columns of $F_{m \times m}$ will be all zeros and the rank of $F_{m \times m}$ will be $m - k = p$. Only these p factors are of concern to us. We may now extend Eq. (5–13), using Definition 5–10 and ignoring the k number of factors with all zero loadings, as:

$$R_{m \times m} - U^2_{m \times m} = (E_{m \times m}\lambda^{1/2}_{m \times m})(\lambda^{1/2}_{m \times m}E'_{m \times m}) = F_{m \times p}F'_{p \times m}. \quad (5\text{–}15)$$

The *rank* of $(R_{m \times m} - U^2_{m \times m})$ will be p, the number of factors.

One of the goals of common factor analysis is to reduce the common variance among m variables to a small number, p, of linearly independent factors that reflect this variance. These p factors are a basis of the common vector space of $Z_{m \times n}$, and the ratio p/m should tend to zero as $m \to \infty$.

The equation $(R_{m \times m} - U^2_{m \times m}) = F_{m \times p}F'_{p \times m}$ has been called by Thurstone (1947) the fundamental theorem of factor analysis. Since the matrix $F_{m \times p}$ has as elements the weights α for each factor spanning the common space of the variables, it describes which variable is a linear combination of which common factors. This matrix thus delineates a basis of the common vector space and the linear dependence of each data vector on the basis dimensions. In other words, the matrix $F_{m \times p}$ contains the scalars α in the vector function $(X_j = \alpha_{j1}S_1 + \alpha_{j2}S_2 + \cdots + \alpha_{jp}S_p)$ for any vector X_j with common part in the p-dimensional common space with basis $S_1, S_2, \ldots, S_p$.

Apart from their geometric interpretation, the scalars α have a useful descriptive interpretation. For orthogonal factors, these weights are the correlations of the variables with the factor scores: The factor loading α_{jl} of variable X_j on orthogonal factor S_l is the product moment correlation of X_j with S_l. That is, for orthogonal $S_{n \times p}$,

$$\alpha_{jl} = r_{X_jS_l}. \quad (5\text{–}16)$$

---

4. These derivations underlie the commonly applied *principal axes* factor analysis technique. See Section 14.3.4.

Therefore, the squared loadings for the orthogonal factors measure the proportion of variance in the variables accounted for by the various common factors. That is, the sum of the squared factor loadings for a variable, X_j, gives its communality, h_j^2,

$$h_j^2 = \alpha_{j1}^2 + \alpha_{j2}^2 + \cdots + \alpha_{jp}^2. \tag{5–17}$$

Returning to the geometric interpretation, since the loadings are the elements of a data vector in common factor space, then the *length* (Definition 3–24) of the vector in common factor space is

$$(Z_j, Z_j)^{1/2} = (\alpha_{j1}^2 + \alpha_{j2}^2 + \cdots + \alpha_{jp}^2)^{1/2} = h_j. \tag{5–18}$$

Equations (5–17) and (5–18) show the circularity of the factor model. The h_j^2 value for a variable is required to solve for the loadings via $R_{m \times m} - U_{m \times m}^2$, *but the loadings must first be at hand to calculate* h_j^2.

5.3 Component Analysis

Whereas common factor analysis is concerned with the dimensions of the space of common parts of the variables, *component factor analysis*, or component analysis as it is now commonly called in the literature, is interested in the space defining their total variance. No assumption is made about the data having common and unique parts. The data are taken as given, and the dimensions of the space defining these data are determined.

Since there is no assumption about a variable's common parts, there is no problem about communality, and this source of indeterminacy in common factor analysis is avoided. The correlation matrix is factored with unities in the diagonal, and the number of factors, p, is almost always equal to the number of variables, m. Since $p = m$ is hardly a parsimonious reduction in the number of variables, component analysis is generally done using a technique (e.g., principal axes) that orders the factors found in terms of the amount of variance they define. The last factors accounting for trivial variance are then ignored in subsequent analysis.

It should be clear that component analysis simply defines the basis dimensions of the data. There is no assumption about common factors. Indeed, the factor dimensions emerging from a component analysis mix up common, specific, and random error variances.

Often the results of component analysis and common factor analysis are quite similar. This is usually the case when the uniquenesses $U_{m \times m}^2$ of the variables approach zero. That is, when $(R_{m \times m} - U_{m \times m}^2) \rightarrow R_{m \times m}$. Although the results may occasionally be similar, this should not obscure the basic difference in models. It is one thing to talk about common factors and quite another to talk about dimensions or factor-dimensions of the data.

Before considering the component analysis model, a change in notation is required.

$\qquad$ *Notation 5–6.* $\quad S_l$ = a factor-dimension of the data.
$\qquad\qquad\qquad\qquad p$ = the dimensionality of the data.

Either by context or qualification it will be made clear in the subsequent discussion whether S is a common factor within the common factor model or a *dimension* (Definition 3–36) of component analysis. Moreover, this change in notation will also hold for $F_{m \times p}$ and $S_{n \times p}$.

The *component analysis model* does not involve unique factors. The model is

$$
\begin{aligned}
X_1 &= \alpha_{11}S_1 + \alpha_{12}S_2 + \cdots + \alpha_{1p}S_p, \\
X_2 &= \alpha_{21}S_1 + \alpha_{22}S_2 + \cdots + \alpha_{2p}S_p, \\
&\ \ \vdots \qquad\ \ \vdots \qquad\ \ \vdots \qquad\qquad \vdots \\
x_m &= \alpha_{m1}S_1 + \alpha_{m2}S_2 + \cdots + \alpha_{mp}S_p,
\end{aligned}
\tag{5–19}
$$

or, in matrix form for standardized data,

$$
Z_{n \times m} = S_{n \times p}F'_{p \times m}.
\tag{5–20}
$$

By steps similar to Eqs. (5–9-15) we can arrive at the basic component analysis equality:

$$
R_{m \times m} = F_{m \times p}F'_{p \times m}.
\tag{5–21}
$$

Since $Z_{n \times m}$ will usually be an empirical data matrix with specific and random variance ingredients mixed in, we can expect that the rank of the correlation matrix equals m. Therefore (from the discussion in Sections 4.4 and 4.5), $p = m$. In practice we will thus find that $R_{m \times m} = F_{m \times m}F'_{m \times m}$, that is, the dimensionality equals the number of variables. Most researchers, however, will probably be interested only in those factors that account for all but a trivial amount of the variance in $R_{m \times m}$. The factoring of $R_{m \times m}$ will proceed until the residual variance in the correlations is small or attributable to random error. At this point the number of factors are considered a least squares fit to the space.

5.4 Image Factor Analysis

Like common factor analysis, *image factor analysis*, as developed by Guttman (1953), is concerned with the dimensions of the common vector space of the data. Unlike common factor analysis, however, image analysis has a basic definition for the common parts of the data that enables the common space to be precisely delineated.

The common parts of the data are defined as the regression estimates of each variable regressed on all the others. The unique parts are then the regression residuals—that portion of the variance unrelated to the other variables. What is factor analyzed is the covariance matrix of the regression estimates. These estimates form a delimitable vector space for which the image factors can be determined.

In effect, image analysis is taking the correlation matrix, $R_{m \times m}$, and inserting squared multiple correlations in the diagonal. The off-diagonal correlations are then "adjusted" to maintain the Gramian properties of the matrix. This is a reversal of the practice in common factor analysis, where the off-diagonal correlations are inviolate for the matrix $(R_{m \times m} - U_{m \times m})$, and $U_{m \times m}$ is estimated. In image analysis, $U_{m \times m}$ is given as $(I_{m \times m} - r^2_{m \times m})$, where $r^2_{m \times m}$ is the diagonal matrix of squared multiple correlations, and the off-diagonal elements of $(R_{m \times m} - I_{m \times m} + r^2_{m \times m})$ are altered.

Although common factor analysis and image analysis differ in a number of respects, they approach each other in the limit if the ratio of common factors to variables $\rightarrow 0$ as $m \rightarrow \infty$. In the limit, image and common factors are identical. Common factor analysis is thus a special case of image analysis.

The geometrical picture of image analysis follows from that of regression analysis. Each data vector is projected onto the vector space of the $m - 1$ other variables, as shown in Fig. 5–2.

> *Definition 5–11.* The IMAGE of a variable with regard to $m - 1$ other variables is its projection onto the vector space of the $m - 1$ variables; its ANTI-IMAGE is the projection onto a vector space orthogonal to that of the $m - 1$ other variables. For any variable X_j, its image is its regression estimate (Definition 3–10), and its anti-image is its residual.

The *image space* corresponding to the hypothetical common factor space in common factor analysis is the space of vector projections $\hat{X}_j$ for each variable. The length of each vector in image space is its multiple correlation with the other variables for standardized data: $h_j = r_j$.

A feature of the multiple correlation coefficient is that it cannot decrease as independent variables are added to the regression. Limits for the image model thus exist, whereas, for the common factor analysis

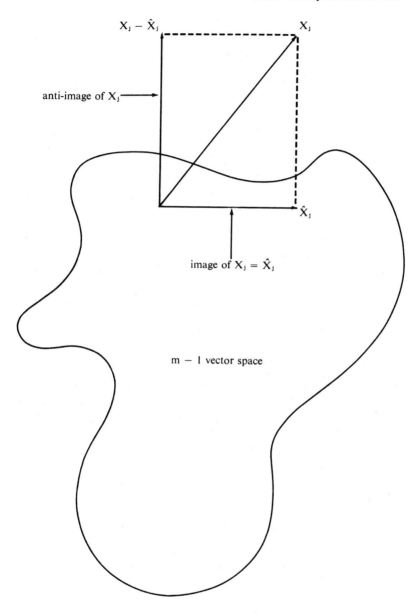

Figure 5–2

model, this may not be the case. In image analysis, large selections of variables may thus enable an approximation to the image factors existing in the domain (or what is often called the universe) of content.

> *Definition 5–12.* An IMAGE FACTOR is a dimension of image space, that is, of the regression estimates of the data.

We will refer to image factors as S, to the image factor matrix as $F_{m \times p}$, and to the image factor score matrix as $S_{n \times p}$. These will be distinguished from the factors of common factor analysis or component analysis when necessary. The dimensionality of image space is p.

There is not only an image space for the data, but also an anti-image space consisting of the anti-image projections of the data vectors.

> *Definition 5–13.* An ANTI-IMAGE FACTOR is a dimension of anti-image space, that is, of the regression residuals of the data.

We will refer to anti-image factors as S^u to distinguish them from the unique factors, S_u, of common factor analysis.

Before moving on to the image model we will need a notation for the regression residuals of standardized data.

> *Notation 5–7.* $e_j = Z_j - \hat{Z}_j$, a vector of residuals for the regression of Z_j on $m - 1$ other standardized variables.
>
> $e_{n \times m} = Z_{n \times m} - \hat{Z}_{n \times m}$, a matrix of residuals for each variable regressed on the $m - 1$ other variables; e_j is thus the jth column vector of $e_{n \times m}$.

With the above notation established, we can develop the image model for standardized data. Corresponding to Eq. (5–4) for common factor analysis, the data can be divided into two parts:

$$Z_{n \times m} = \hat{Z}_{n \times m} + e_{n \times m}. \tag{5–22}$$

Both parts are precisely defined by regression analysis.

For a variable Z_j, the model is then

$$Z_j = \alpha_{j1}S_j + \alpha_{j2}S_2 + \cdots + \alpha_{jp}S_p + \alpha_{jp+1}S_1^u$$

$$+ \alpha_{jp+2}S_2^u + \cdots + \alpha_{jp+q}S_q^u, \tag{5–23}$$

where q = dimensionality of image space.

In matrix form,

$$Z_{n \times m} = S_{n \times p}F'_{p \times m} + S^*_{n \times q}F^{*'}_{q \times m}, \qquad (5\text{-}24)$$

where $S_{n \times p}$ = image factor scores,

$F_{m \times p}$ = image factor loadings,

$S^*_{n \times q}$ = anti-image factor scores, and

$F^*_{m \times q}$ = anti-image factor loadings.

A question is whether the image or the anti-image factors of Eq. (5–24) should be considered more basic in some sense. Guttman (1953) believes the anti-image factors more important for determining the structure of the data, whereas Harris (1962) and Kaiser (1963) in their expositions of the model seem to consider the image factors more important. We will return to this question after we present some of the equations of image analysis.

The basic assumption of image analysis is that the residuals of the dependent variable and the $m - 1$ independent variables are uncorrelated. That is,

$$r_{e_j z_1} = r_{e_j z_2} = \cdots = r_{e_j z_k} = \cdots = r_{e_j z_{m-1}} = 0 \qquad (j \neq k). \quad (5\text{-}25)$$

This assumption is necessary and sufficient for image analysis.

For simplicity, in the following derivations we will drop the number of cases, n, from the equations. For example, we will allow $Z'_{m \times n}Z_{n \times m} = R_{m \times m}$, and $I_{p \times p} = S'_{p \times n}S_{n \times p}$ for standardized factor scores. This is tantamount to assuming that we are dealing with the population of cases rather than a sample. Assume also that $R_{m \times m}$ is nonsingular ($Z_{n \times m}$ is *basic*).

Now, the images

$$\hat{Z}_j = Z_{n \times (m-1)}B_{(m-1) \times 1}$$

from Eq. (4–13), where $B_{(m-1) \times 1}$ is the matrix of regression coefficients for a particular dependent variable Z_j. For each of the m variables regressed on the $m - 1$ other variables in turn, the matrix of regression coefficients is

$$B_{m \times m} = I_{m \times m} - R^{-1}_{m \times m}D^2_{m \times m}$$

from Eq. (4–15). The diagonal matrix $D^2_{m \times m}$ gives the *variances* of the residuals e_j for each estimate $\hat{Z}_j$.

The matrix of images of the variables is then

$$\hat{Z}_{n \times m} = Z_{n \times m}B_{m \times m} = Z_{n \times m}(I_{m \times m} - R^{-1}_{m \times m}D^2_{m \times m}). \quad (5\text{-}26)$$

As in the development for common factor analysis, we wish to determine a symmetrical matrix that will enable us to define the image or anti-image factors in the model of Eq. (5–24). These symmetrical matrices can be the *covariances* of the images and anti-images.

Notation 5–8. $G_{m \times m} = \hat{Z}'_{m \times n} \hat{Z}_{n \times m}$, the covariances of the images.

$\Omega_{m \times m} = e'_{m \times n} e_{n \times m}$, the covariances of the anti-images.

Using Eq. (5–26), the covariance matrix of images is then

$$
\begin{aligned}
G_{m \times m} &= \hat{Z}'_{m \times n} \hat{Z}_{n \times m} \\
&= (I_{m \times m} - R^{-1}_{m \times m} D^2_{m \times m})' Z'_{m \times n} Z_{n \times m} (I_{m \times m} - R^{-1}_{m \times m} D^2_{m \times m}) \\
&= (I_{m \times m} - D^2_{m \times m} R^{-1}_{m \times m}) R_{m \times m} (I_{m \times m} - R^{-1}_{m \times m} D^2_{m \times m}) \\
&= R_{m \times m} + D^2_{m \times m} R^{-1}_{m \times m} D^2_{m \times m} - 2 D^2_{m \times m},
\end{aligned} \tag{5-27}
$$

where the principal diagonal of $G_{m \times m}$ contains the *squared multiple correlation* for each variable with the $m - 1$ other variables, and $G_{m \times m}$ is Gramian.

Using Eq. (4–16), the anti-image covariance matrix is

$$
\begin{aligned}
\Omega_{m \times m} &= e'_{m \times n} e_{n \times m} = (Z_{m \times n} - \hat{Z}_{m \times n})'(Z_{m \times n} - \hat{Z}_{m \times n}) \\
&= (Z_{n \times m} R^{-1}_{m \times m} D^2_{m \times m})'(Z_{n \times m} R^{-1}_{m \times m} D^2_{m \times m}) \\
&= (D^2_{m \times m} R^{-1}_{m \times m}) R_{m \times m} (R^{-1}_{m \times m} D^2_{m \times m}) \\
&= D^2_{m \times m} R^{-1}_{m \times m} D^2_{m \times m}.
\end{aligned} \tag{5-28}
$$

From this equation and Notation 4–11, we know that the principal diagonal of Ω must equal $D^2_{m \times m}$, the variances of the residuals. The matrix $\Omega_{m \times m}$ is also Gramian.

One other relationship may be derived that relates image analysis to common factor analysis: The covariances of the images with the standardized data equals the correlation matrix with squared multiple correlations (SMC's) in the diagonal. That is,

$$
Z'_{m \times n} \hat{Z}_{n \times m} = Z'_{m \times n}[Z_{n \times m}(I_{m \times m} - R^{-1}_{m \times m} D^2_{m \times m})] = R_{m \times m} - D^2_{m \times m}, \tag{5-29}
$$

and from Eq. (4–17),

$$
R_{m \times m} - D^2_{m \times m} = R_{m \times m} - I_{m \times m} + r^2_{m \times m}. \tag{5-30}
$$

Thus, common factor analysis with communality estimates equal to the SMC values is tantamount to an incomplete image analysis. Assuming $\lim_{m \to \infty} (p/m) = 0$, the matrix $G_{m \times m} \to (R_{m \times m} - D^2_{m \times m})$ in the limit as $m \to \infty$. $R_{m \times m} - D^2_{m \times m}$ is a special case of $G_{m \times m}$: Common factor analysis is a special case of image factor analysis.

It can also be shown that an incomplete anti-image analysis is the diagonal matrix of residual variances:

$$Z'_{m \times n}e_{n \times m} = Z'_{m \times n}(Z_{n \times m}R^{-1}_{m \times m}D^2_{m \times m}) = D^2_{m \times m} = I - r^2_{m \times m}. \quad (5\text{--}31)$$

The specification of $G_{m \times m}$ and $\Omega_{m \times m}$ allow the correlation matrix to be divided into the image covariance matrix minus the anti-image covariance matrix plus two times the diagonal matrix of anti-image covariances. From Eqs. (5–27) and (5–28),

$$\begin{aligned} R_{m \times m} &= G_{m \times m} - D^2_{m \times m}R^{-1}_{m \times m}D^2_{m \times m} + 2D^2_{m \times m} \\ &= G_{m \times m} - \Omega_{m \times m} + 2D^2_{m \times m}. \end{aligned} \quad (5\text{--}32)$$

This is a basic theorem of image analysis. It shows the functional relationship between image covariances and a correlation matrix, but it is also of importance in general correlation theory. Ignoring the diagonal matrix $D^2_{m \times m}$ (which only contributes to making the principal diagonal of $R_{m \times m}$ consist of unities), we can say, from Eq. (5–32), that any correlation between two variables is due to the covariance of their parts in common with a number of other variables minus the covariance of their uncommon parts. In other words, a correlation itself is insufficient evidence to state that a direct link between two variables exists.

With a specification of the image covariance and anti-image matrices, the image and anti-image factors can be computed—as in the case of $(R_{m \times m} - U^2_{m \times m})$ for common and $R_{m \times m}$ for component factor analysis —through the characteristic equation of Section 4.5.

With a development similar to Eqs. (5–13-15) for the $(R_{m \times m} - U^2_{m \times m})$ of common factor analysis, we find that

$$G_{m \times m} = F_{m \times p}F'_{p \times m}, \quad (5\text{--}33)$$

and

$$\Omega_{m \times m} = F^*_{m \times q}F^{*\prime}_{q \times m}, \quad (5\text{--}34)$$

where the asterisk distinguishes between image and anti-image factor matrices.

Let us return to a question previously raised. Which should be analyzed, $G_{m \times m}$ or $\Omega_{m \times m}$? Guttman (1953, p. 295) feels that $\Omega_{m \times m}$ is more "basic to the structural analysis" of $R_{m \times m}$ than is $G_{m \times m}$. From the equation $\Omega_{m \times m} = D^2_{m \times m}R^{-1}_{m \times m}D^2_{m \times m}$, knowing $\Omega_{m \times m}$ enables us to know $R_{m \times m}$. $G_{m \times m}$, however, does not enable us to know $R_{m \times m}$. Moreover, $G_{m \times m}$ can be computed from $\Omega_{m \times m}$, but the reverse is not true.

If $R^{-1}_{m \times m}$ tends to a diagonal matrix, however, then $\Omega_{m \times m}$ also tends to a diagonal. In this case an image space is a good approximation to a common factor space, and we are left with $G_{m \times m}$ to analyze. Therefore, if the concern is to define a common factor space among the variables, then $G_{m \times m}$ will be the matrix to study. The validity of $G_{m \times m}$ as a measure of this space can be gauged by the degree to which $R_{m \times m}^{-1}$ approaches a diagonal matrix.

5.4.1 HARRIS IMAGE FACTORS

Chester Harris (1962) has introduced a variant of image analysis that has some useful properties. One is that it makes image analysis scale-free of the data. Within a proportionality constant, the same image factors will be found regardless of the scaling of the correlation matrix—whether correlation matrix or covariance matrix is used, or whether the data are standardized or not.

A second useful feature is that the Harris image eigenvectors can be shown to equal similar variants of other factor models and that the only mathematical differences in the variants is in the eigenvalues. This comparison will be made in Section 5.6, below.

The diagonal matrix of residual variances, $D_{m \times m}^2$, plays a large role in image analysis, and Harris also makes use of it as follows. Scale the image covariance matrix by left- and right-multiplication by $D_{m \times m}^{-1}$:

$$D_{m \times m}^{-1} G_{m \times m} D_{m \times m}^{-1}.$$

This operation divides each image covariance by the product of the standard deviation of the residuals for each variable. The less unique variance the two variables have, the more weight their image covariances are given.

The eigenvalues and eigenvectors of $D_{m \times m}^{-1} G_{m \times m} D_{m \times m}^{-1}$ are

$$D_{m \times m}^{-1} G_{m \times m} D_{m \times m}^{-1} = E_{m \times m} \lambda_{m \times m} E_{m \times m}'. \tag{5-35}$$

Then

$$
\begin{aligned}
G_{m \times m} &= (D_{m \times m} E_{m \times m} \lambda_{m \times m}^{1/2})(\lambda_{m \times m}^{1/2} E_{m \times m}' D_{m \times m}) \\
&= D_{m \times m} F_{m \times m} F_{m \times m}' D_{m \times m},
\end{aligned}
\tag{5-36}
$$

where $m - p$ factor columns of $F_{m \times m}$ with all zero loadings are retained. $F_{m \times m}$ is thus a factor loading matrix of $D_{m \times m}^{-1} G_{m \times m} D_{m \times m}^{-1}$. The scaling of $F_{m \times m}$ by $D_{m \times m}$ in Eq. (5–35) then constrains the loadings to vary between $+1.00$ and -1.00 as in regular image analysis.

As for the scaling of the data, Kaiser (1963, p. 162) points out that any diagonal nonsingular matrix used to scale $R_{m \times m}$, say $T_{m \times m}$, to a matrix $T_{m \times m} R_{m \times m} T_{m \times m}$ only scales the columns of the Harris image factor matrix $D_{m \times m} F_{m \times m}$ by $T_{m \times m}$. Thus, if $R_{m \times m}$ yields Harris image factors $D_{m \times m} F_{m \times m}$, then $T_{m \times m} R_{m \times m} T_{m \times m}$ yields $T_{m \times m} D_{m \times m} F_{m \times m}$. A change of scale in the data will only change the factor columns proportionally: *The factors derived from different scalings will be perfectly correlated.*

5.5 Canonical Factor Analysis

Canonical regression and correlation analysis (Anderson, 1958; Cooley and Lohnes, 1962) are not as well known as other multivariate techniques, such as analysis of variance, multiple regression and correlation, and factor analysis. Briefly, canonical regression and correlation is similar to regression analysis. In the latter, *one* variable is given a least squares fit to a *set* of other variables. The multiple correlation coefficient then describes how much of the variance in the one variable is accounted for by the set of variables. In canonical analysis, a *set* of variables is given a least squares fit to another *set* of variables. The *canonical correlation* measures how much the variance in the one set is accounted for by the variance in the other. Canonical analysis thus generalizes regression analysis to designs with more than one dependent variable.

The mathematical model associated with canonical analysis can be developed so as to enable us to perform statistical tests of significance. The model that we will consider here has been developed by C. R. Rao (1955). Implications of the model have been drawn out and refinements introduced by Chester Harris (1956, 1962, 1963, 1964b) and Henry Kaiser (1963, 1964).

The canonical factor analysis model is itself a refinement of the *maximum likelihood factor model* derived by D. N. Lawley (1940, 1943). Lawley employed the maximum likelihood statistical method to derive a set of common factor estimates for the correlation matrix. Although the number of such factors has to be assumed in the beginning, application of a chi-square test to this number for the resulting factors can test this assumption, thus enabling the significant common factor estimates for a sample of cases to be determined with regard to the population of cases (Section 15.2.1). We will focus on Rao's refinement of this technique, since it allows a direct comparison with other factor models and with the use of the squared multiple correlation as a communality estimate in common factor analysis.

The canonical factor analysis model postulates that the variables are combinations of common and unique factors, as does the common factor analysis model in Eqs. (5–2) and (5–3). In common factor analysis, the common factors are determined through the factoring of the correlation matrix with estimates of communality in the diagonal $(R_{m \times m} - U_{m \times m}^2)$. Canonical factor analysis, however, delineates the common factor estimates having the maximum canonical correlation with the variables. The communalities are then given uniquely for an assumed number of common factors, say p. As in the maximum likelihood model, the factor estimates can be subject to a statistical test as to whether p common factor estimates are significant for the sample of cases. Increasing or decreasing the number of cases in this sample may alter the outcome of the statistical test. Usually, the larger the sample, the larger the number of factors that will be significant.[5]

If a population of cases is involved or can be assumed, significance tests need not be applied. The best communality value will be the squared multiple correlation for each variable and the appropriate number of factors will be those with eigenvalues greater than or equal to unity (Harris, 1962).

Canonical factor analysis involves rescaling the correlation matrix of the variables by the unique parts of the data. Factor estimates are then determined for this rescaled correlation matrix. The higher the uniquenesses of two variables, the less weight their correlation will have in determining these estimates. Variables which have the largest part of their variance in common factor space will thus play the largest role in estimating the dimensions of this space. This is a basic departure from common factor analysis in which the off-diagonal correlations are unchanged and only the correlation of a variable with itself is altered.

A second basic difference is that the canonical common factor estimates and factor scores are invariant of scale. Differences in scale of the data will only proportionally alter the common factor estimates. The estimates will still be perfectly correlated. This is not true of common factor analysis (or component analysis) where, for example, the factoring of a correlation matrix will produce factors usually quite different from the covariance matrix for the same data.

Invariance of scale is an important property of a factor model. It relieves the researcher of making what are many times arbitrary decisions about the appropriate scaling to apply (as, for example,

---

5. Anderson and Rubin (1956) present a unified development of the factor analysis model from the viewpoint of the mathematical statistician. In particular, they give a statistical test of the fit of the factor analysis model to the data and of the number of factors. See also Bartlett (1950) and especially Jöreskog (1963, Chapter 1).

whether the correlation or covariance matrix should be analyzed). Canonical analysis, however, is not alone in this feature. The Harris variant of image analysis, discussed above in Section 5.4.1, and the alpha factor analysis model, to be discussed in Section 5.7, have this ability.

Before developing the details of canonical factor analysis, a review of the notation may be helpful. As in common factor analysis, the model begins with the assumption that the standardized variables consist of common parts $Z^*_{n \times m}$ and unique parts $U_{n \times m}$. The correlation matrix between the common parts is $(R_{m \times m} - U^2_{m \times m})$, where $U^2_{m \times m}$ is a diagonal matrix of unique variances for each variable. Moreover, from Eq. (5–16), we know that the correlation between the variables $Z_{n \times p}$ and orthogonal common factor scores $S_{n \times p}$ is $F_{m \times p}$, the common factor loading matrix.

With this notation in mind, form a combined matrix of observed data and unknown factor scores:

$$[Z_{n \times m}, S_{n \times m}]_{n \times 2m}.$$

In regular canonical analysis, the matrix $S_{n \times m}$ would be a second set of known variables whose canonical correlation with $Z_{n \times p}$ was desired. The canonical matrix is formed by left-multiplying the matrix by the transpose of itself,

$$\begin{bmatrix} Z'_{m \times n} \\ S'_{m \times n} \end{bmatrix}_{2m \times n} [Z_{n \times m}, S_{n \times m}]_{n \times 2m} = \begin{bmatrix} Z'_{m \times n}Z_{n \times m} & Z'_{m \times n}S_{n \times m} \\ S'_{m \times n}Z_{n \times m} & S'_{m \times n}S_{n \times m} \end{bmatrix}_{2m \times 2m} \quad (5\text{–}37)$$

Multiplying the matrix on the right of the equality by n, the number of cases, and keeping in mind that $(1/n)Z'_{m \times n}S_{n \times m}$ is the correlation between the variables and factors and equals $F_{m \times m}$, we get

$$\begin{bmatrix} R_{m \times m} & F_{m \times m} \\ F'_{m \times m} & I \end{bmatrix}_{2m \times 2m} \quad (5\text{–}38)$$

The second-order determinant of this matrix is

$$R_{m \times m} - F_{m \times m}F'_{m \times m}.$$

Assume that $R_{m \times m}$ is *positive definite* (Definition 4–15). Now, a solution (Anderson, 1958, p. 296, Eq. 52) to the canonical correlations between $Z_{n \times m}$ and $S_{n \times m}$, the hypothetical common factors, results by solving the determinant

$$|F_{m \times m}F'_{m \times m} - aR_{m \times m}| = 0 \quad (5\text{–}39)$$

for the scalar a. The roots $a_1, a_2, \ldots, a_p$ of Eq. (5–39) are the squared canonical correlations between $Z_{n \times m}$ and $S_{n \times m}$.

Since we wish to define the common factor estimates for $p < m$ common factors, and since, by Eq. (5–15), $F_{m \times m}F'_{m \times m} = R_{m \times m} - U^2_{m \times m}$, Eq. (5–39) can be written as

$$|R_{m \times m} - U^2_{m \times m} - aR_{m \times m}| = |R_{m \times m}(I_{m \times m} - a) - U^2_{m \times m}|$$

$$= \left| R_{m \times m} - \frac{1}{(1 - a)} U^2_{m \times m} \right| \tag{5–40}$$

$$= \left| U^{-1}_{m \times m}R_{m \times m}U^{-1}_{m \times m} - \frac{1}{(1 - a)} \right| = 0,$$

where $R_{m \times m}$ and $U^2_{m \times m}$ are positive semidefinite, and $a \neq 1$. The assumption of positive semidefiniteness for $U^2_{m \times m}$ implies that no communality equals unity (Harris, 1963, p. 142).

Let $\lambda = 1/(1 - a)$ for $a \neq 1$. Then Eq. (5–40) becomes

$$|U^{-1}_{m \times m}R_{m \times m}U^{-1}_{m \times m} - \lambda I_{m \times m}| = 0. \tag{5–41}$$

This is a characteristic equation yielding a set of eigenvalues $\lambda_{m \times m}$ and eigenvectors $E_{m \times m}$ for the matrix $U^{-1}_{m \times m}R_{m \times m}U^{-1}_{m \times m}$.

Since $\lambda = 1/(1 - a) = 1 + \lambda a$, the size of an eigenvalue λ_j is directly proportional to the size of the squared canonical correlation a_j. Harris (1963, p. 141) points out that canonical factor analysis assumes $Z_{n \times m}$ will only be approximated by the common factors $S_{n \times p}F'_{p \times m}$. Therefore, $a_i < 1.00$, and the restriction $a_i \neq 1.00$ will be satisfied.

Since, from Eq. (5–41),

$$U^{-1}_{m \times m}R_{m \times m}U^{-1}_{m \times m} = E_{m \times m}\lambda_{m \times m}E'_{m \times m},$$

and

$$R_{m \times m} = (U_{m \times m}E_{m \times m}\lambda^{1/2}_{m \times m})(\lambda^{1/2}_{m \times m}E'_{m \times m}U_{m \times m}),$$

the canonical factor loadings $F_{m \times m}$ are given by

$$F_{m \times m} = U_{m \times m}E_{m \times m}\lambda^{1/2}_{m \times m}. \tag{5–42}$$

The role of the uniquenesses of the variables can be seen in Equation (5–42). First, each correlation coefficient is divided by the product of the standard deviations of the uniquenesses of the two variables. Then, to bring the scale back to that of the variables, the eigenvector matrix in Eq. (5–42) is multiplied by the standard deviations, $U_{m \times m}$, of the uniquenesses.

Equation (5–42) gives the canonical factor estimates. Assuming a random sample and multivariate normal distributions, the hypothesized number of common factors can be tested against the estimates found, as discussed in Rao (1955) or Harman (1967, Chapter 10).

A question is what initial estimates of $U^2_{m \times m}$ to employ in canonical factor analysis.[6] One suggestion of Harris (1963) is to use the matrix of residual variances $D^2_{m \times m} = I_{m \times m} - r^2_{m \times m}$ as initial estimates and to hypothesize p common factors, where p is the number of eigenvalues greater than unity. From the function $\lambda_i = 1 - \lambda_i a_i$ we can see that this number of common factors will correspond to the squared canonical correlations greater than zero. The $D^2_{m \times m}$ values can then be converged to a stable set of estimates for p factors and the significance test applied.

Another possibility, also suggested by Harris (1963), is to let each uniqueness u^2_j be a function of the diagonal elements of $R^{-1}_{m \times m}$ and the inverse of the squared elements of $R^{-1}_{m \times m}$. Let the elements of $R^{*-1}_{m \times m}$ be the squares of the elements of $R^{-1}_{m \times m}$ and let $d_{1 \times m}$ be a row vector of diagonal elements of $R^{-1}_{m \times m}$. Then a $1 \times m$ order vector of diagonal estimates for $U^2_{m \times m}$ could be

$$d_{1 \times m} R^{*-1}_{m \times m},$$

where $R^{*-1}_{m \times m}$ is nonsingular. The hypothetical number of factors for these initial estimates could then be the number of eigenvalues greater than one. These estimates of $U^2_{m \times m}$ are those values for which the covariances between the unique factors maximally approach an identity matrix. That they will equal an identity matrix is assumed by the common factor analysis model.

5.6 Some Intermodel Relationships

In 1962, Harris published a significant clarification of the mathematical relationship between image, canonical, component, and common factor analysis. He showed that if the correlation matrix for component and canonical analysis is scaled by the reciprocal unique (residual) variances, $D^{-1}_{m \times m}$, the results differ only in their eigenvalues. The factor scores will be the same in each case; the factor loadings will differ only proportionally.

If the scaling matrix of reciprocal unique variances is employed for the various models, therefore, it is possible to see the relationship

6. Jöreskog (1963) has developed a statistical model very similar to canonical factor analysis. The diagonal matrix $U^2_{m \times m}$ of uniquenesses involved in the scaling $U^{-1}_{m \times m} R_{m \times m} U^{-1}_{m \times m}$ is made proportional to $D^2_{m \times m}$, the matrix of residual variances for standardized data.

between their results and the content significance of accepting one model over another. Following Harris (1962), this comparison will be sketched here.

First, let us review the symmetrical matrices that are factored for each model.

Component Analysis:

$$R_{m \times m} = \text{correlation matrix with unities in the principal diagonal.}$$

Common Factor Analysis:

$$R_{m \times m} - U^2_{m \times m} = \text{correlation matrix with communality estimates in the principal diagonal.}$$

Image Analysis:

$$G_{m \times m} = \text{image covariance matrix with squared multiple correlations in the principal diagonal.}$$

$$\Omega_{m \times m} = \text{anti-image covariance matrix with one minus the squared multiple correlations in the principal diagonal.}$$

Canonical Analysis:

$$U^{-1}_{m \times m} R_{m \times m} U^{-1}_{m \times m} = \text{matrix of correlations divided by the product of the standard deviations of the uniquenesses.}$$

Secondly, to develop the relationships between these models we will assume that $R_{m \times m}$ is nonsingular and Gramian, that $U^2_{m \times m} = D^2_{m \times m}$, and that $D^2_{m \times m}$ is nonsingular and Gramian (no uniquenesses equal zero). Employing $D^2_{m \times m}$ means that our communality estimates are the squared multiple correlations of the variables.

Now, canonical factor analysis involves determining the eigenvalues and eigenvectors of

$$D^{-1}_{m \times m} R_{m \times m} D^{-1}_{m \times m} = E^c_{m \times m} \lambda^c_{m \times m} E^{c'}_{m \times m};$$

$$R^*_{m \times m} = D_{m \times m} E^c_{m \times m} \lambda^c_{m \times m} E^{c'}_{m \times m} D_{m \times m}.$$

$$(5\text{--}43)$$

The common factor estimates are then $F^c_{m \times m} = D_{m \times m} E^c_{m \times m} \lambda^{1/2}_{m \times m}$. The superscript c, used with the eigenvector, eigenvalue, and factor matrices indicates that the matrices are specific to canonical factor analysis, and the asterisk in $R^*_{m \times m}$ avoids confusion with the eigenvalues and eigenvectors of $R_{m \times m}$ in component factor analysis. Equation (5–43) indicates that a left and right scaling of the correlation matrix of component analysis by $D^{-1}_{m \times m}$ (and computing the eigenvectors and eigenvalues of the resulting matrix) will yield the canonical factor analysis results.

Consider now the common factor analysis matrix $R_{m \times m} - D^2_{m \times m}$. Scaling both sides of the matrix by the standard deviation of the uniquenesses,

$$D^{-1}_{m \times m}(R_{m \times m} - D^2_{m \times m})D^{-1}_{m \times m} = D^{-1}_{m \times m}R_{m \times m}D^{-1}_{m \times m} - I_{m \times m}. \quad (5\text{--}44)$$

From Eq. (5–43), the eigenvectors and eigenvalues of $D^{-1}_{m \times m}R_{m \times m}D^{-1}_{m \times m}$ are $E^c_{m \times m}$ and $\lambda^c_{m \times m}$, and the eigenvectors of $I_{m \times m}$ in Eq. (5–44) will also be $E^c_{m \times m}$ (Harris, 1962, p. 254). The eigenvalues of $I_{m \times m}$ will be $I_{m \times m}$, however. Therefore, the eigenvalue-eigenvector solution of Eq. (5–44) is

$$\begin{aligned} D^{-1}_{m \times m}(R_{m \times m} - D^2_{m \times m})D^{-1}_{m \times m} &= E^c_{m \times m}(\lambda^c_{m \times m} - I_{m \times m})E^{c'}_{m \times m}; \\ (R_{m \times m} - D^2_{m \times m})^* &= D_{m \times m}E^c_{m \times m}(\lambda^{c'}_{m \times m} - I_{m \times m})E^{c'}_{m \times m}D_{m \times m}. \end{aligned} \quad (5\text{--}45)$$

According to Eq. (5–45) a scaling of the common factor analysis matrix, $R_{m \times m} - D^2_{m \times m}$, by the reciprocal standard deviations of the uniquenesses will produce the same eigenvectors as canonical factor analysis and scaled component analysis. The eigenvalues will only differ by a constant value of one.

If we let $F^0_{m \times m}$ be the factor matrix for $(R_{m \times m} - D^2_{m \times m})^*$ of Eq. (5–45), then the factors of $F^0_{m \times m}$ and $F^c_{m \times m}$ will be proportional to each other. Therefore, they will be perfectly correlated.

A representation of the image and anti-image matrix in terms of $D_{m \times m}E^c_{m \times m}$ can also be found. From Eqs. (5–27) and (5–43),

$$G_{m \times m} = R_{m \times m} + D^2_{m \times m}R^{-1}_{m \times m}D^2_{m \times m} - 2D^2_{m \times m};$$

$$\begin{aligned} D^{-1}_{m \times m}G_{m \times m}D^{-1}_{m \times m} &= D^{-1}_{m \times m}R_{m \times m}D^{-1}_{m \times m} + D_{m \times m}R^{-1}_{m \times m}D_{m \times m} - 2I_{m \times m} \\ &= E^c_{m \times m}\lambda^c_{m \times m}E^{c'}_{m \times m} + E^c_{m \times m}(\lambda^c_{m \times m})^{-1}E^{c'}_{m \times m} \\ &\quad + E^c_{m \times m}(-2I_{m \times m})E^{c'}_{m \times m} \\ &= E^c_{m \times m}[\lambda^c_{m \times m} + (\lambda^c_{m \times m})^{-1} - 2I_{m \times m}]E^{c'}_{m \times m}. \end{aligned} \quad (5\text{--}46)$$

Each eigenvalue of Eq. (5–46), say λ^g_i, is

$$\lambda^g_i = \lambda^c_i + \frac{1}{\lambda^c_i} - 2. \quad (5\text{--}47a)$$

Multiply the right side of Eq. (5–47a) by λ^c_i/λ^c_i to get

$$\lambda^g_i = \frac{[(\lambda^c_i)^2 + 1 - 2\lambda^c_i]}{\lambda^c_i} = \frac{(\lambda^c_i - 1)^2}{\lambda^c_i}. \quad (5\text{--}47b)$$

Therefore, Eq. (5–46) can be rewritten as

$$G^*_{m \times m} = D_{m \times m}E^c_{m \times m}[(\lambda^c_{m \times m} - I_{m \times m})^2(\lambda^c_{m \times m})^{-1}]E^{c'}_{m \times m}D_{m \times m}. \quad (5\text{--}48)$$

A similar analysis of the anti-image covariance matrix $\Omega_{m \times m}$ will derive the following:

$$\Omega^*_{m \times m} = D_{m \times m} E^c_{m \times m} (\lambda^c_{m \times m})^{-1} E^{c'}_{m \times m} D_{m \times m}. \qquad (5\text{–}49)$$

All these solutions differ only in eigenvalues that are functionally related to each other. The factor loadings of $R^*_{m \times m}$, $(R_{m \times m} - D^2_{m \times m})^*$, $G^*_{m \times m}$, and $\Omega^*_{m \times m}$ will differ only by a scalar multiple.

To have a concept for the results of scaling $R_{m \times m}$, $(R_{m \times m} - D^2_{m \times m})$, $G_{m \times m}$, and $\Omega_{m \times m}$ by $D^{-1}_{m \times m}$, the following definition will be useful.

> *Definition 5–14.* SCALED COMPONENT, COMMON, IMAGE, or ANTI-IMAGE ANALYSIS refers to the factoring of the matrices $R_{m \times m}$, $(R_{m \times m} - D^2_{m \times m})$, $G_{m \times m}$, or $\Omega_{m \times m}$, left- and right-multiplied by $D^{-1}_{m \times m}$, where $D^2_{m \times m}$ equals the residual variances of the standardized variables. That is, $D^2_{m \times m} = I - r^2_{m \times m}$.

As presented in Section 5.4.1, the Harris variant of image analysis is scaled image analysis, as we will now use the term.

The relationship between the eigenvalues of the scaled matrices are shown in Table 5–1. The scaled eigenvectors are the same for each

Table 5–1. Relationship between Scaled Models [a]

Factor Analysis Model	Matrix Factored	Scaled Eigenvectors	Typical Eigenvalue	Comments
Canonical Scaled component	$R^*_{m \times m}$	$D_{m \times m} E^c_{m \times m}$	λ^c_i	All $\lambda^c_i > 0$
Scaled common	$(R_{m \times m} - D^2_{m \times m})^*$	$D_{m \times m} E^c_{m \times m}$	$\lambda^c_i - 1$	One or more $(\lambda^c_i - 1)$ are negative
Scaled image	$G^*_{m \times m}$	$D_{m \times m} E^c_{m \times m}$	$(\lambda^c_i - 1)^2 / \lambda^c_i$	All $[(\lambda^c_i - 1)^2 / \lambda^c_i] \geq 0$
Scaled anti-image	$\Omega^*_{m \times m}$	$D_{m \times m} E^c_{m \times m}$	$1 / \lambda^c_i$	All $(1 / \lambda^c_i) > 0$

[a] Adapted from Harris (1962, Table 1, p. 254).

matrix factored. The eigenvalues differ as a function of those for canonical analysis and the resulting factors of each solution differ only proportionally.

Since $R_{m \times m}$ consists of empirical correlations, it can safely be assumed to be nonsingular. Therefore, all the eigenvalues of $R^*_{m \times m}$ will be greater than zero. For m variables there will be m factors. Since the canonical correlations are greater than zero for eigenvalues greater than one, only those factors with eigenvalues greater than one may be retained for interpretation or subsequent analysis. Moreover, since the eigenvalues of $(R_{m \times m} - D^2_{m \times m})^*$ are $\lambda^c_i - 1$, the number of eigenvalues of

$R^*_{m \times m} > 1$ equals Guttman's strongest lower bounds (Section 15.3.1) for the number of common factors.

At least one negative eigenvalue will exist for scaled common factor analysis. This implies that the matrix $(R_{m \times m} - D^2_{m \times m})^*$ with squared multiple correlations in the diagonal is non-Gramian and that one or more of the factors will be imaginary.

According to Eq. (5–29) factoring $(R_{m \times m} - D^2_{m \times m})^*$ is tantamount to an incomplete image analysis. This can also be seen from Table 5–1. The factors of $G^*_{m \times m}$ will all be real, since their eigenvalues are all nonnegative. At least one factor of $(R_{m \times m} - D^2_{m \times m})^*$, however, will be imaginary. An analysis of $G^*_{m \times m}$, therefore, will extract some real common factors with no real counterpart in scaled common factor analysis. Accordingly, an analysis of $(R_{m \times m} - D^2_{m \times m})^*$ only partially brings out the common factors that may exist.

The Spearman-Thurstone tradition of factor analysis involves the common factor analysis model and the factoring of a correlation matrix $(R_{m \times m} - U^2_{m \times m})$, with estimates of communalities in the principal diagonal. As described in this section, the relationships developed "strongly suggest that this practice be abandoned" (Harris, 1962, p. 258). The analysis of $(R_{m \times m} - U^2_{m \times m})$, with $U^2_{m \times m} = I_{m \times m} - r^2_{m \times m} = D^2_{m \times m}$, is a partial analysis of $G_{m \times m}$. Since $G_{m \times m}$ can itself be analyzed, and since the analysis of $(R_{m \times m} - D^2_{m \times m})$ will lead to at least one imaginary factor, the usual approach to common factor analysis is incomplete and unnecessary.

The correspondence between the eigenvalues and the equality of the eigenvectors of the scaled matrices and canonical factor analysis has been shown, and a proportionality between their factor loadings has been pointed out. What about the factor scores?

Harris (1962, pp. 256–57) proves that the factor scores, $S_{n \times m}$, of the scaled matrices $R^*_{m \times m}$, $G^*_{m \times m}$, and $\Omega^*_{m \times m}$ are the *same*. The factor scores of the one matrix are those of the other. Moreover, these factor scores are proportional to those of $(R_{m \times m} - D^2_{m \times m})^*$.

5.7 Alpha Factor Analysis

A distinction can be made between statistical inference and generalizability. In the context of common factor analysis, statistical inference refers to estimation of population common factors from common factors of a sample of cases. For this, canonical factor analysis is appropriate since it enables the investigator to test the statistical significance for a population of the number of canonical factors of a sample.

If our interest is not in inference to a population of cases, but rather in reliable generalization to a *universe of variables* from a sample of variables, then another technique is needed. Assuming that the data are for a population of cases, we desire a method that will enable us to make conclusions about the common factors existing for the universe of variables within the domain being analyzed.

Kaiser and Caffrey (1965) have developed such a method, which they call *alpha factor analysis*. The basic principle they employ is that the common factors of the sample of variables must be determined so that they have maximum correlation with those in the corresponding universe of variables. The square of these correlations may be called the generalizability of a common factor.

Notation 5–9. α^g = a coefficient of *generalizability*.

Many derivations of α^g have been published; for references the reader is referred to Kaiser and Caffrey (1965, p. 6). The determination of the best common factors for m variables in the sense of their generalizability involves maximizing α^g between these common factors and those for the relevant universe of content. Maximizing α^g leads (Kaiser and Caffrey, 1965, p. 6) to the characteristic equation,

$$|H_{m \times m}^{-1}(R_{m \times m} - U_{m \times m}^2)H_{m \times m}^{-1} - \lambda I_{m \times m}| = 0, \qquad (5\text{–}50)$$

where, in our notation, $H_{m \times m}^2$ is the diagonal matrix of communalities for the variables and $U_{m \times m}^2 = I_{m \times m} - H_{m \times m}^2$. The generalizability coefficient for each common factor is a linear function of the corresponding eigenvalue. For any factor F_l, associated eigenvalue λ_l, and m variables,

$$\alpha_l^g = \left(\frac{m}{m-1}\right)\left(\frac{\lambda_l - 1}{\lambda_l}\right). \qquad (5\text{–}51)$$

For large values of λ_l and even small samples of variables, α_l^g is close to unity—perfect generalizability. For example, for 10 variables and an eigenvalue of 5.0 (a common factor accounting for 50 per cent of the variance), $\alpha_l^g = .89$.

By solving Eq. (5–50) for its eigenvectors and eigenvalues, we get

$$H_{m \times m}^{-1}(R_{m \times m} - U_{m \times m}^2)H_{m \times m}^{-1} = E_{m \times m}\lambda_{m \times m}E_{m \times m}', \qquad (5\text{–}52)$$

and

$$R_{m \times m} - U_{m \times m}^2 = H_{m \times m}E_{m \times m}\lambda_{m \times m}E_{m \times m}'H_{m \times m}$$
$$= (H_{m \times m}E_{m \times m}\lambda_{m \times m}^{1/2})(\lambda_{m \times m}^{1/2}E_{m \times m}'H_{m \times m}). \qquad (5\text{–}53)$$

The alpha factor matrix is then

$$F_{m \times m} = H_{m \times m}E_{m \times m}\lambda_{m \times m}^{1/2}. \qquad (5\text{–}54)$$

The initial values for the communalities $H_{m \times m}^2$ are unknown. To solve for the common factors, trial values of $H_{m \times m}^2$ can be taken and the characteristic equation solved for successive values of $H^2_{m \times m}$ until the row values squared of $E_{m \times m} \lambda^{1/2}_{m \times m}$ sum to unity. Squared multiple correlations may be used as initial estimates of $H^2_{m \times m}$, but these may cause $R_{m \times m} - U^2_{m \times m}$ to be singular. Using trial values of $H^2_{m \times m} = I_{m \times m}$ (i.e., $h^2_j = 1.00$) will avoid this possibility. A computational outline and example is given in Kaiser and Caffrey (1965) and the details of a computer program in Hunka (1966).

At what point should an alpha factor be considered nongeneralizable? Kaiser and Caffrey (1965, p. 11) suggest that an alpha factor "is so tenuous as not to be worthy of consideration" when it has nonpositive generalizability. By Eq. (5–51), this occurs when the eigenvalue is less than or equal to unity. Therefore, extracting all alpha factors with eigenvalues greater than unity enables any common factors existing in the universe of content to be retained in the alpha solution. Incidentally, Kaiser and Caffrey point out that this number of alpha factors for alpha analysis will be the same as the number of components of component analysis with eigenvalues greater than one.

A virtue of canonical analysis and scaled image analysis is that the common factors delineated are scale-free, that is, they are proportional to the scale of the data. This important property is shared by alpha factor analysis. The alpha factors found are invariant of the units of measurement of the data.

A comparison between canonical scaling by U^{-1} and alpha scaling by H^{-1} is interesting. Using u_j and h_j as the standard deviations of the unique and common parts, respectively, the scaling of a correlation r_{jk} between two variables is then,

$$\frac{r_{jk}}{u_j u_k} : \text{canonical scaling of } R_{m \times m},$$

$$\frac{r_{jk}}{h_j h_k} : \text{alpha scaling of } (R_{m \times m} - U^2_{m \times m}).$$

Canonical factor analysis thus gives a correlation more weight in the results if the uniquenesses of the variables are lower. Since $u_j = 1 - h_j$, the higher the communality of two variables, the more weight their correlation is given. This is reversed in alpha factor analysis. The higher the communality of two variables, the lower the weight of their correlation in the results. If two variables have a high correlation in spite of their having low communalities, they are assured of a common alpha factor.

5.8 A Summary Table

Table 5–2 summarizes the discussion of the various factor models.

Table 5–2. Factor Analysis Models

Characteristic	Component	Common	Image	Scaled Image	Canonical	Alpha
1. Basic matrix	R	$R - U^2$	$G = R + D^2R^{-1}D^2 - 2D^2$ $\Omega = D^2R^{-1}D^2$	$D^{-1}GD^{-1}$	$U^{-1}RU^{-1}$	$H^{-1}(R - U^2)H^{-1}$
2. Statistical property	Descriptive	Descriptive	Descriptive	Descriptive	Inference from sample of cases to population	Generalize from sample of variables to universe
3. Operating principle	Correlations between variables	Correlations between common parts of variables	Covariance of estimates of each variable regressed on $m - 1$ other variables	Same as image model	Maximizing squared canonical correlation with hypothetical common factors for population of cases	Maximizing squared correlation with hypothetical common factors for universe of content
4. Data scale dependent?	Yes	Yes	Yes	No	No	No
5. Assume common and unique parts to the data?	No	Yes	Yes	Yes	Yes	Yes
6. Communality	None	Estimate	SMC	Unity	Initial estimate with convergence to best value	Initial estimate with convergence to best value
7. Number of factors p	$p = m$	$p < m$	$p \leq m$	$p \leq m$	$p = m$	$p = m$
8. Best number of factors	Arbitrary[a]	Arbitrary[a]	Arbitrary[a]	All $\lambda > 1.0$	Statistical test	All $\lambda > 1.0$

[a] The question of the best number of factors in these arbitrary cases is answered in terms of the several rules of thumb given in Section 15.4.

6. The Factor Matrices

This chapter will be devoted to a discussion of the various types of factor matrices and their attributes. The first section will present some of the characteristics of the correlation matrix. Subsequent sections will consider the unrotated matrix, the orthogonally rotated and oblique factor matrices, the factor correlation matrix, and the factor score matrix.

6.1 The Correlation Matrix

The correlation matrix is basic to all the factor analysis models presented in the last chapter. It is the bridge over which a worker in the applied sciences often moves from the data to a factor loading matrix delineating the factors in the data. In its own right, however, the correlation matrix contains much useful knowledge, and it is there that we may look for relationships between pairs of variables. Specifically, the correlation matrix has the following features.

1. The coefficients of correlation express the degree of relationship between the row and column variables of the matrix. The closer to

Table 6–1. Selected Sample Data[a]

	(1) GNP per Capita (dollars)	(2) Trade (millions of dollars)	(3) Power (rank)[b]	(4) Stability[c]	(5) Freedom of Group Opposition[d]	(6) Foreign Conflict[e]	(7) Agreement with U.S. in UN[f]	(8) Defense Budget (millions of dollars)	(9) Per cent of GNP for Defense	(10) Acceptance of International Law[g]
Brazil	91	2,729	7	0	2	0	69.1	148	2.8	0
Burma	51	407	4	0	1	0	−9.5	74	6.9	0
China	58	349	11[h]	0	0	1	−41.7[h]	3,054	8.7	0
Cuba	359	1,169	3	0	1	0	64.3	53	2.4	0
Egypt	134	923	5	1	1	1	−15.4	158	6.0	1
India	70	2,689	10	0	2	0	−28.6	410	1.9	1
Indonesia	129	1,601	8	0	1	0	−21.4	267	6.7	0
Israel	515	415	2	1	2	1	42.9	33	2.7	1
Jordan	70	83	1	0	1	1	8.3[i]	29	25.7	0
Netherlands	707	5,395	6	1	2	0	52.3	468	6.1	1
Poland	468	1,852	9	0	0	1	−41.7	220	1.5	0
U.S.S.R.	749	6,530	13	1	0	1	−41.7	34,000[j]	20.4[j]	0
U.K.	998	18,677	12	1	2	1	69.0	3,934	7.8	0
U.S.	2,334	26,836	14	1	2	1	100.0	40,641	12.2	1

[a] Data are for 1955, from the Dimensionality of Nations Project, University of Hawaii.
[b] Inverse ranking based on product of population × energy production.
[c] 0 = unstable, as indicated by extensive rioting, guerrilla warfare, coups, purges, or frequent general strikes, 1955–57: 1 = stable.
[d] 0 = political opposition not permitted; 1 = restricted opposition permitted but not campaigns for control of government; 2 = unrestricted.
[e] 0 = little, if any, foreign conflict; 1 = intensive foreign conflict as evidenced by frequent threats, severance of diplomatic relations, protests, or military action 1955–57; 0 = little, if any, foreign conflict.
[f] Per cent of votes in agreement minus per cent in opposition (not including abstentions). Voting data are for the Tenth Session.
[g] 0 = does not subscribe to statute of International Court of Justice; 1 = subscribes with or without reservation.
[h] Estimate.
[i] Estimated to be the same as Iran's vote.
[j] Geometric mean of several modes of computation.

zero the coefficient, the more tenuous the relationship; the closer to an absolute value of 1, the greater the relationship. A negative sign indicates that the variables are inversely related (Definition 3–6).

2. To interpret the coefficient, square it and multiply by 100. This will give the percentage of linear variation in common for the data on the two variables.

> *Example 6–1.* Consider the 1955 data given in Table 6–1 on a selected sample of nations. (The correlation matrix for the 10 characteristics is shown in Table 6–2.) From this table we can see that the correlation between gross national product per capita and foreign conflict is .36 and that $(.36)^2 \times 100 = 13$ per cent of the variation of the 14 nations on these two characteristics is in common. In other words, by knowing the nation values on one of the two variables you can produce (predict, generate, explain) 13 per cent of the linear variation in values on the other.

3. The correlation coefficient between two variables is the cosine of the angle between the variables [Eq. (3–11)] plotted as vectors on the cases (coordinate axes).

> *Example 6–2.* The correlation of .93 between gross national product per capita and trade in Table 6–2 can be interpreted as a cosine of .93 (corresponding to an angle of 21.5°) for the two vectors plotted on the 14-nation coordinate axis. (See also Example 3–15.)

4. The principal diagonal of a correlation matrix usually contains the correlation of a variable with itself, which is 1. However, when the correlation matrix is to be employed in a common factor analysis (Section 5.2), estimates of communality (Definition 5–1) will often be substituted for 1's in the principal diagonal. An estimate commonly employed is the *squared multiple correlation coefficient* (SMC) of a variable with all the other variables. The SMC $\times$ 100 measures the percentage of linear variation that can be produced (predicted, generated, explained) for one variable from the others (Definition 3–12).

> *Example 6–3.* Table 6–2 has SMC values in the principal diagonal. For foreign conflict, the SMC is .61. This means that 61 per cent of the linear variation in foreign conflict data in Table 6–1 can be predicted from (is dependent upon) the data on the remaining nine characteristics.

Table 6–2. Selected Sample Data—Correlation Matrix[a]

Characteristic	(1)	(2)	(3)	(4)	(5)	(6)	(7)	(8)	(9)	(10)
(1) GNP per capita	**.97**									
(2) Trade	(.93)	**.97**								
(3) Power	(.55)	(.66)	**.89**							
(4) Stability	(.62)	(.55)	.25	**.63**						
(5) Freedom of opposition	.31	.40	-.10	.32	**.91**					
(6) Foreign conflict	.36	.30	.25	.46	-.32	**.61**				
(7) U.S. agreement	(.58)	(.59)	-.07	.36	(.75)	.11	**.89**			
(8) Defense budget	(.79)	(.71)	(.66)	.49	-.07	-.38	-.18	**.90**		
(9) % GNP for defense	.17	.17	.06	.15	-.28	-.44	.11	.47	**.73**	
(10) International law acceptance	.34	.22	-.02	(.56)	(.57)	-.04	-.24	.14	-.24	**.82**

[a] These are product moment correlation coefficients. The data for these characteristics are given in Table 6–1. Elements in the principal diagonal are the squared multiple correlation coefficient of the variable with all the others.

6.2 Unrotated Factor Matrix

Two factor matrices are often displayed. The first, the unrotated factor matrix, is usually presented without comment; the second, the rotated factor matrix, is generally the object of interpretation. The rotated matrix will be briefly discussed in the next section and again, with more detail, in Chapters 16 and 17.

The unrotated matrix we have previously defined as $F_{m \times p}$ (Definition 5–6 and Notation 5–5) in the common factor model; later we generalized the notation to factor matrices arising from the other models.

Table 6–3 displays the format of an unrotated factor matrix. These are actual factor results for a common factor analysis of the data of Table 6–1. The columns of the matrix define the common factors; the rows refer to variables. The intersection of row and column gives the loading for the row variable on the column common factor. The h^2 column on the right of the table and the rows beneath the table for total and common variance and eigenvalues give additional information, which will be described below. The features of the matrix useful for interpretation are as follows.

1. The number of common factors (columns) are the largest statistically independent (uncorrelated) patterns of relationships between the variables.[1] As can be seen from the number of factors in Table 6–3, there are *four* statistically independent patterns of relationship common to the data. These may be thought of as evidencing four different kinds of influences (causes) on the data, as presenting four categories by which these data may be classified, or as illuminating four empirically different concepts for describing national characteristics.

2. The *loadings*, α, measure which variables are involved in what factor and to what degree (Definition 5–8). They are correlation coefficients between variables and factors. The square of the loading times 100 equals the per cent variation that a variable has in common with an unrotated common factor.

A way of looking at this percentage figure is as the per cent of variation on a variable that can be produced (predicted) by knowing the values of a case (such as a nation) on the factor or on the other variables involved in the factor. By comparing the factor loadings for all factors and variables, those particular variables involved in an independent factor can be defined, and those variables most closely related to a factor can be seen.

---

1. The number of factors extracted may vary, depending on which rule of thumb is employed (see Section 15.4).

Table 6-3. Selected Sample Data—Unrotated Factor Matrix $F_{m \times p}$ [a]

$\alpha_{11}^2 = .96^2 = .92$ = proportion of variable's variance accounted for by this factor

A loading α_{11}: correlation of the variables with this factor

Separate common factors—patterns of relationship—in the variables; 4-dimensional common factor space for the variables

The communality: proportion of variance of each variable involved in the factor space

$$h_1^2 = \sum_{i=1}^{p} \alpha_{1i}^2$$

Per cent of variance among all the variables that is accounted for by the factors:

$$\frac{\sum_{j=1}^{m} h_j^2}{m} \times 100 = \sum_{i=1}^{p} V_i^t$$

V_4^t = Per cent of variance among all the variables that is accounted for by the factor:

$$\frac{\sum_{j=1}^{m} \alpha_{j4}^2}{m} \times 100$$

V_4^c = variance among all the variables that is accounted for by this factor (as a per cent of that accounted for by all the factors):

$$\frac{\sum_{j=1}^{m} \alpha_{j4}^2}{\sum_{j=1}^{m} h_j^2} \times 100$$

Variables	Factors				h^2
	S_1	S_2	S_3	S_4	
(1) GNP per capita	.96	-.02	-.08	-.04	.93
(2) Trade	.94	.00	-.26	-.05	.95
(3) Power	.58	-.42	-.42	.43	.87
(4) Stability	.69	.07	.41	.08	.65
(5) Freedom of opposition	.39	.84	-.03	-.07	.86
(6) Foreign conflict	.38	-.49	.41	-.04	.55
(7) U.S. agreement	.56	.61	-.17	-.42	.89
(8) Defense budget	.79	-.44	-.04	.00	.82
(9) % GNP for defense	.22	-.57	.25	-.48	.67
(10) International law acceptance	.41	.50	.49	.40	.82
% Total variation (V^t)	40.9	22.5	9.1	7.6	80.1
% Common variation (V^c)	50.9	28.1	11.4	9.6	
Eigenvalues	4.09	2.25	.91	.76	

Sum of column of squared factor loadings =
algebraic roots of a characteristic equation =

$$\sum_{j=1}^{m} \alpha_{ji}^2$$

[a] Principal axes technique. Squared multiple correlation coefficients were inserted in the main diagonal of the correlation matrix as communality estimates, and only common factors with eigenvalues $\geq$ .50 were extracted.

$\frac{Eigenvalue}{\# \ of \ Factors} \times 100$

$\Sigma \ (loading^2)$

Example 6–4. Consider the unrotated factor loadings for the 10 characteristics in Table 6–3. Let a factor be limited to those variables with 16 per cent (loading of $\pm.40$ squared $\times$ 100) or more of their variation involved in a factor. Then from Table 6–3 we can lay out the results according to the common factor model given in Eq. (5–2):

(1) GNP per
   capita $= .96S_1$
(2) Trade $= .94S_1$
(8) Defense budget $= .79S_1 - .44S_2$ $+.42S_{u8}$
(4) Stability $= .69S_1$ $+.41S_3$ $+.59S_{u4}$
(3) Power $= .58S_1 - .42S_2 - .42S_3 + .43S_4$
(7) U.S. agreement $= .56S_1 + .61S_2$ $- .42S_4$
(10) International
   law accep-
   tance $= .41S_1 + .50S_2 + .49S_3 + .40S_4 + .42S_{u10}$
(5) Freedom of
   opposition $=$ $+.84S_2$
(9) % GNP for
   defense $=$ $-.57S_2$ $-.48S_4 + .57S_{u9}$
(6) Foreign
   conflict $=$ $-.49S_2 + .41S_3$ $+.67S_{u6}$

The coefficients in the equations are the loadings in Table 6–3. The coefficient for a *unique* factor S_{uj} is derived from the communality h_j^2 and equals $1 - h_j$. These unique factors are shown here to illustrate the complete common factor model, via an empirical factor matrix and communalities.

Example 6–5. Table 6–4 displays the common factor matrix for the 79-nation data on 10 political system characteristics, partly shown in Table 3–1. The correlation matrix is given in Table 4–1. Leaving out the unique factors and loadings that account for less than 16 per cent (loading squared $\times$ 100) of a variable's variance, the common factor equations for the political variables are

(2) Constitutional status $=$ $.95S_1$
(5) Freedom of group opposition $=$ $.95S_1$
(4) Electoral system $=$ $.93S_1$
(8) Horizontal power distribution $=$ $.92S_1$
(3) Representative character $=$ $.86S_1$
(7) Political leadership $=$ $.84S_1$
(6) Non-Communist regime $=$ $.70S_1 + .65S_2$
(1) System style $= -.69S_1 - .62S_2$
(10) Military participation $= -.54S_1 + .40S_2 + .69S_3$
(9) Monarchical type $=$ $+.66S_2 - .67S_3$

Table 6–4. Ten Political Characteristics—Unrotated Factor Matrix

Characteristic	Factors[a]			h^2
	S_1	S_2	S_3	
(1) System style	−.69	−.62	−.09	.86
(2) Constitutional status	.95	.10	−.05	.91
(3) Representative character	.86	−.38	−.03	.89
(4) Electoral system	.93	−.01	.01	.87
(5) Freedom of group opposition	.95	.13	.14	.94
(6) Non-Communist regime	.70	.65	.12	.93
(7) Political leadership	.84	−.24	−.07	.77
(8) Horizontal power distribution	.92	−.20	.05	.89
(9) Monarchical type	−.25	.66	−.67	.95
(10) Military participation	−.54	.40	.69	.93
% Total variance	62.8	16.7	9.7	89.2
% Common variance	70.4	18.7	10.9	100.0

[a] Principal axes technique. Unity was employed in the main diagonal of the correlation matrix as a communality estimate, and only factors with eigenvalues greater than or equal to unity were extracted.

3. The loadings are the projections of each variable on the factor-axes of the data. The loadings may therefore be employed to give a spatial representation of the findings. Each variable can be displayed as a vector in the factor space. The row of loadings for a variable are then the elements (Definition 3–15) of the variable-vector.

> *Example 6–6.* Figure 6–1 displays the plot for the 10 national characteristics of Table 6–4 on the first two unrotated factors. The smaller the acute angle (or the larger the obtuse angle) between two vectors, the more highly correlated the variables they represent (see Example 3–15). Hence we can see that the first factor has defined an intercorrelated pattern of relationships between variables (2), (3), (4), (5), (7), and (8).

4. For component or common factor analysis, the inner product (Definition 3–22) of the row vectors of loadings for two variables reproduces the correlation coefficient between them. This follows from Eq. (5–15) of common factor analysis,

$$R_{m \times m} - U_{m \times m} = F_{m \times p}F'_{p \times m},$$

and Eq. (5–21) of component analysis,

$$R_{m \times m} = F_{m \times p}F_{p \times m}.$$

Thus, for any two variables, with row vectors of loadings $X_j^{*\prime}$ and $X_k^{*\prime}$, using Notation 3–15 for inner product,

$$(X_j^{*\prime}, X_k^{*\prime}) = \alpha_{j1}\alpha_{k1} + \alpha_{j2}\alpha_{k2} + \cdots + \alpha_{jp}\alpha_{kp} = r_{jk}, \qquad (6\text{–}1)$$

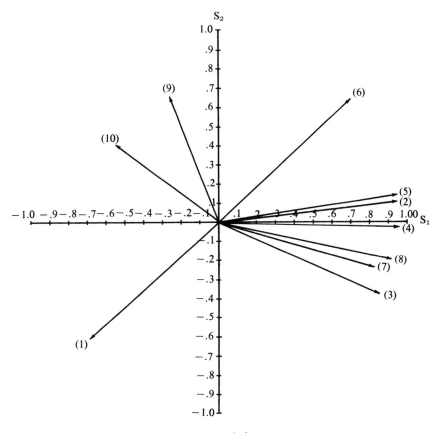

Figure 6–1

where $X_j^{*'}$ = row vector of p loadings for X_j from the $F_{m \times p}$ factor matrix, and $X_k^{*'}$ = row vector of p loadings for X_k from the $F_{m \times p}$ factor matrix.

In applied analysis, however, not all p factors are extracted. Factors that are "trivial" according to some criterion will not be displayed in a factor table, and the correlations between the variables will not be exactly reproducible. The difference between the reproduced correlation calculated from the factors extracted and the actual correlation is called the residual correlation.

> *Definition 6–1.* The REPRODUCED CORRELATION between two variables is the correlation computed according to Eq. (6–1) from their loadings on the factors extracted from the data. The RESIDUAL CORRELATION is the difference

between the reproduced and actual correlation between the variables.

Example 6–7. From the loadings on four factors of trade and foreign conflict in Table 6–3, the reproduced correlation for these two variables is

$$(.94 \times .38) + (.00 \times -.49) + (-.26 \times .41)$$
$$+ (-.05 \times -.04) = .25.$$

From Table 6–2 we can see that the actual correlation is .30. The residual correlation is then $.30 - .25 = .05$. This residual correlation can best be interpreted in terms of variance. Since the square of the correlation gives the proportion of variance in common between two variables, we can take the difference between the squared *reproduced* and squared *actual* correlation to get the residual variance unaccounted for by the four factors. For trade and foreign conflict, $30^2 - 25^2 = .09 - .06 = .03$. Therefore, only 3 per cent of the variance in common between trade and foreign conflict is residual—accounted for by the trivial factors not extracted from the data.

5. For the usually employed centroid or principal axes techniques (Section 14.3) of factor analysis, the first unrotated factor delineates the most general pattern of relationships in the data; the second factor delineates the next most general pattern that is orthogonal to (uncorrelated with) the first; the third delineates the third most general pattern orthogonal to the first and second; and so on. Thus, the amount of variation in the data described by each factor decreases successively with each factor. In this sense, the first factor is the strongest, the last factor the weakest. Note that unrotated factors are uncorrelated with each other.

6. The column headed h^2 displays the communality of each variable. This is the proportion of a variable's total variance that is accounted for by the factors and is the sum of the squared loadings for a variable [Eq. (5–17)]. The per cent of variance in a variable X_j accounted for by the factors is $h_j^2 \times 100$. Geometrically, the square root of the communalities equals the length of the variable-vectors in the factor space [Eq. (5–18)].

This communality may also be looked at as a measure of the common, or unique, variance of a variable (Section 5.1) in the common factor analysis model. By subtracting the communality from 1 the uniqueness of a variable is determined. This indicates to what degree a variable is unrelated to the others, that is, the degree to which the variance of a variable cannot be derived from (predicted from) the common factors.

> *Example 6–8.* In Table 6–3, foreign conflict has a communality of $.38^2 - .49^2 + .41^2 - .04^2 = .55$ for the common factors. Its uniqueness is $1 - .55 = .45$, and, as shown in Example 6–4, its loading on the uniqueness factor is $(.45)^{1/2} = .67$. The communality of .55 indicates that approximately[2] 55 per cent of the total variance in foreign conflict behavior (as measured) for the 14 nations can be predicted from a knowledge of nation values on the four factors. This leaves approximately 45 per cent of the variance in foreign conflict behavior as unique variance—variance unrelated to the other nine characteristics.

7. The sum of the column of h^2 values $\times$ 100 equals the per cent of total variation in the data that is patterned, that is, the total variance accounted for by the factors. This sum, therefore, measures the order, uniformity, or regularity in the data.

> *Example 6–9.* For the 10 national characteristics in Table 6–3, the four common factors can be seen to involve 80.1 per cent of the data's variance. In other words, we could reproduce 80.1 per cent of the total variance of the 14 nations on these 10 characteristics by knowing the nation scores on the four factors.

8. At the foot of the factor columns in Table 6–3, the per cent of total variance figures shows the per cent of total variance among the variables related to a particular common factor.

> *Notation 6–1.* $V_i^t =$ per cent of total variance for factor S_i.

This figure thus measures the amount of data variation in the original matrix that can be reproduced by a factor: It measures a factor's comprehensiveness and strength.

The sum of the V^t's for all factors equals the sum of the column of $h^2 \times 100$. A glance along the V^t row and up the h^2 column will show how the order in the data is divided by factor and variable.

2. The communality is approximate because of the indeterminacy of the common factor model (see Section 5.2).

The per cent of total variance figure for a factor is determined by summing the column of squared loadings for a factor, dividing by the number of variables, and multiplying by 100:

$$V_l^t = \frac{\sum_{j=1}^{m} \alpha_{jl}^2}{m} \times 100, \qquad (6\text{-}2)$$

and

$$\sum_{l=1}^{p} V_l^t = \sum_{j=1}^{m} h_j^2 \times 100. \qquad (6\text{-}3)$$

9. The per cent of common variance figures indicates how the regularity existing in the data—the common variance—is divided among the factors.

Notation 6–2. V_l^c = per cent of common variance for factor S_l.

The V^t figures discussed above measure how much of the data variance is involved in a factor; the V^c figures measure how much of the variance accounted for by *all* the factors is involved in *each* factor. These latter figures are arrived at in the same way as the per cent of total variance, except that the divisor is now the sum of the column of h^2 values (which measures the total common variance in the data):

$$V_l^c = \frac{\sum_{j=1}^{m} \alpha_{jl}^2}{\sum_{j=1}^{m} h_j^2} \times 100, \qquad (6\text{-}4)$$

and

$$\sum_{l=1}^{p} V_l^c = 100. \qquad (6\text{-}5)$$

10. The eigenvalues equal the sum of the column of squared loadings for each factor. They measure the amount of variation accounted for by a factor and are the roots of the characteristic equation (Definition 4–23) of the correlation matrix. Dividing the eigenvalues by either the number of variables or the sum of h^2 values and multiplying by 100 determines the per cent of total or common variance figures. Often only the eigenvalues will be displayed at the foot of factor tables.[3]

3. The eigenvalues are extracted only if the principal axes technique (Section 14.3.4) of factor analysis is employed.

Recalling that our notation (Definition 4–23) for eigenvalue is λ,

$$\lambda_l = \sum_{j=1}^{m} \alpha_{jl}^2 = \frac{m}{100} V^t. \tag{6–6}$$

Moreover,

$$\sum_{l=1}^{p} \lambda_l = \sum_{j=1}^{m} h_j^2. \tag{6–7}$$

6.3 Rotated Factor Matrix

It has been customary in applied factor analysis to alter the initial factor solution to a solution with more desirable properties. This transformation consists of rotating the factor-axes around the origin until they are aligned with the variable-vectors in some specified fashion. The rotated factors are linear transformations of the unrotated factors; the angles between the variable-vectors and their lengths (h) in the factor space remain invariant through rotation. We will consider rotation criteria and procedures in more detail in Chapters 16 and 17. Here our concern is only with the rotated factor matrices, and we will assume that the most generally applied rotation criterion of simple structure (Section 16.2.2) has been used.

Simple structure attempts to maximize the number of high loadings on each factor, while minimizing the number of factors with high loadings for each variable. This tends to make each factor uniquely define a distinct cluster of intercorrelated variables (if such clusters exist).

Turning to the characteristics of the rotated matrix, the format should not differ from the unrotated factor matrix except that the h^2 may not be given, and eigenvalues are not appropriate.

The following features characterize the rotated matrix.

1. If the rotated matrix is orthogonal, this is pointed out in the title to the matrix (e.g., orthogonally rotated factors) or by assigning the name *varimax* or *quartimax* to the matrix.[4] An orthogonally rotated matrix is displayed in Table 6–5 for the 10 national characteristics. The unrotated factor matrix from Table 6–3 is also given for comparison. Ignore the oblique factors for a moment. For an orthogonally rotated matrix the following aspects can be noted.

1*a*. Six of the 10 features of the unrotated matrix listed above are preserved by the orthogonally rotated matrix, viz., point (1) on the number of factors indicating the number of independent patterns,

4. These are techniques of orthogonal rotation discussed in Section 16.4.

Table 6–5. Selected Sample Data—Factor Matrices[a]

| | Unrotated Factors[b] | | | | | Orthogonally Rotated Factors[c] | | | | Primary Factors | | | | | | | |
| | | | | | | | | | | Oblique Pattern Factors[d] | | | | Oblique Structure Factors[d] | | | |
Variables	1	2	3	4	h²	1	2	3	4	1	2	3	4	1	2	3	4
(1) GNP per capita	(.96)	−.02	−.08	−.04	.93	(.73)	.47	.29	.30	(.64)	.46	.21	.19	(.78)	(.57)	.42	.46
(2) Trade	(.94)	.00	−.26	−.05	.95	(.79)	(.51)	.19	.16	(.73)	(.52)	.09	.04	(.81)	(.60)	.33	.34
(3) Power	(.58)	−.42	−.42	.43	.87	(.92)	−.17	−.03	−.01	(.98)	−.15	−.17	−.07	(.90)	−.08	.14	.08
(4) Stability	(.69)	.07	.41	.08	.65	.32	.25	.34	(.63)	.17	.16	.31	(.60)	.40	.35	.39	(.69)
(5) Freedom of opposition	.39	(.84)	−.03	−.07	.86	−.02	(.77)	−.34	.40	−.07	(.73)	−.34	.32	−.04	(.81)	−.34	.49
(6) Foreign conflict	.38	−.49	.41	−.04	.55	.25	−.19	(.64)	.23	.12	−.23	(.62)	.26	.35	−.14	(.67)	.25
(7) U.S. agreement	(.56)	(.61)	−.17	−.42	.89	.13	(.93)	−.03	.11	.05	(.94)	−.03	−.01	.12	(.94)	−.01	.27
(8) Defense budget	(.79)	−.44	−.04	.00	.82	(.75)	.10	.48	.12	(.67)	.09	.39	.06	(.82)	.17	(.61)	.24
(9) % GNP for defense	.22	(−.57)	.25	−.48	.67	.07	−.03	(.79)	−.17	−.05	.00	(.82)	−.18	.17	−.05	(.79)	−.15
(10) International law acceptance	.41	.50	.49	.40	.82	.03	.18	−.13	(.87)	−.06	.06	−.15	(.89)	.08	.30	−.13	(.89)
% Total variation	40.9	22.5	9.1	7.6	80.1	27.6	21.0	16.2	15.3								
% Common variation	50.9	28.1	11.4	9.6		34.7	26.5	20.4	19.4								
Sum of squares										2.41	2.01	1.52	1.39				

a Loadings greater than an absolute value of .50 are shown in parentheses.
b From Table 6-3.   c Varimax rotation.   d Biquartimin rotation at 12 major cycles and 712 iterations (see Chapter 17).

point (2) on interpreting loadings, point (3) on spatially representing the factors, point (4) on reproducing the correlations, point (8) on the per cent of total variance, and point (9) on the per cent of common variance.

1*b*. The values of h^2 given for the unrotated factors do not change with orthogonal rotation. Hence, they may be given with the unrotated or rotated factor matrix.

1*c*. In the unrotated matrix, factors are ordered by the amount of data variation they account for, with the first defining the greatest degree of relationship in the data. In the orthogonally rotated matrix, no significance is attached to factor order.

1*d*. Factors are orthogonal and hence factor scores are uncorrelated.

2. If the rotated matrix is oblique, the title or description of the matrix will indicate this. The title may also contain strange terms like *covarimin, quartimin,* or *biquartimin.* These refer to various criteria for the rotation and need not concern us until we reach Chapter 17.

Oblique simple structure rotation means that the best definition is sought of the uncorrelated *and* correlated factors necessary to delineate the clusters of interrelated variables. Orthogonal rotation only defines uncorrelated factors; oblique rotation has greater flexibility in searching out factors regardless of their correlation.

Oblique simple structure rotations take place in one of two coordinate systems—either a system of primary axes or a system of reference axes. The reference axes give a slightly better definition of the clusters of interrelated variables than do the primary ones. For each set of axes there are two possible matrices—factor structure and factor pattern matrices. Differences between oblique primary or reference factors are slight. There is an important difference, however, between the pattern and structure matrix.

2*a*. The *primary* factor pattern matrix and *reference* factor structure matrix delineate the oblique simple structure patterns or clusters of interrelationship among the variables. Their loadings define the separate clusters and degree of involvement of each variable. Unlike the orthogonally rotated or unrotated factors, however, their loadings cannot be interpreted as the correlation of a variable with a factor and the loadings squared do not precisely give the per cent of variation of a variable accounted for by a factor. Nevertheless, as in the orthogonal factor matrix, loadings are zero when a variable is not related to a factor, and they are close to 1 when a variable is almost perfectly related to a factor.[5] The less correlated the oblique factors, the more

5. The pattern matrix loadings are best understood as regression coefficients of the variables on the factors.

their loadings are like correlations of variables with factors. With this understanding in mind, the reader might—roughly—interpret the primary pattern matrix or reference structure matrix loadings as correlations. Squaring them and multiplying by 100 to get an idea of the *approximate* per cent of variations involved, will provide a conceptual anchor for understanding the configuration of loadings.

> *Example 6–10.* Table 6–5 displays the (primary) oblique pattern factor matrix for the 10 nation characteristics. These may be compared with orthogonally rotated factors, also shown. Note how more distinct the clusters are defined by oblique rotation (the pattern matrix) than by orthogonal rotation. There are fewer moderate loadings and more high and low loadings, thus giving a better definition of the pattern of relationships.

2*b*. The *primary* factor structure matrix and *reference* factor pattern matrix give the correlation of each variable with each factor. The loadings are strictly interpretable as correlations. They can be squared and multiplied by 100 to measure the per cent of variation of a variable accounted for by a factor. Table 6–5 shows the (primary) oblique structure factors matrix for the 10 nation characteristics. The basic difference between the primary structure and pattern matrices (or reference pattern and structure matrices) relevant for interpretation is this: The primary pattern loadings best show what variables are highly involved in what clusters. They distinctly display the patterns. The primary structure loadings, however, do not display the patterns as well but rather measure the correlation of variables with the factors.

By this time the many distinctions made may have created more confusion than understanding. Table 6–6 shows the important differ-

Table 6–6. Differences in Characteristics of Loadings of Factor Matrices

Characteristic of Loadings	Ortho- gonal[a]	Primary Axes[a]		Reference Axes[a]	
		Pat- tern	Struc- ture	Pat- tern	Struc- ture
Loadings distinguish clusters of interrelated variables	Yes	Yes	No	No	Yes
Loadings measure corre- lation between cluster and variable	Yes	No	Yes	Yes	No

[a] Rotation is to a simple structure solution.

ences for the several matrices considered. The difference between primary pattern and reference structure matrices is one of geometric perspective and magnitude of loadings. The latter matrix gives a slightly better definition of the oblique patterns and is preferred by psychologists. However, the former gives a simpler geometrical representation.

2c. The oblique factors will have a correlation between them as shown in a factor correlation matrix. This matrix is discussed in Section 6.4 below.

2d. Per cent of common variance and per cent of total variance figures are not given for the oblique factors. In order to have some measure of the strength of the separate oblique factors, the sum of a column of squared factor loadings may be computed. This has been done for the oblique factors for 10 nation characteristics in Table 6–5.

6.4 Factor Correlation Matrix

This is a correlation matrix between oblique factors found through oblique rotation. Some studies call this a matrix of factor cosines. The cosines, however, can be read as correlations between factors, and vice versa [Eq. (3–11)]. The characteristics of a correlation matrix discussed in Section 6.1 apply equally here.

What does a nonzero correlation between two factors mean? It means that the data patterns themselves have variance in common to the degree measured by the factor correlations squared. The idea that patterns of relationship as measured by the factors can themselves be intercorrelated is not strange, since we continuously deal with such notions in social theorizing. Weather patterns are correlated with transportation patterns, for example, and modernization patterns are correlated with cultural patterns. Factor analysis makes these links explicit through oblique rotation and the factor correlation matrix.

> *Example 6–11.* Table 6–7 presents the factor correlations for the oblique primary factors shown in Table 6–5. In Table 6–7, it can be seen that factor 2 (voting agreement with the U.S.)[6] and factor 3 (foreign conflict) are in fact orthogonal to (uncorrelated with) each other. However,

---

6. These labels are in terms of the variables loading highest on the factor. Approaches to naming factors are discussed in Chapter 21.

Table 6–7. Selected Sample Data Factor Correlations

Factors	(1)	(2)	(3)	(4)
(1) Power	1.00			
(2) Agreement with U.S. in UN	.09	1.00		
(3) Foreign conflict	.31	.00	1.00	
(4) Acceptance of international law	.20	.28	.04	1.00

the foreign conflict factor does have some positive relationship (.31) with the power factor. Sometimes the factor correlation matrix will be factor-analyzed as was the variable correlation matrix. This will uncover the patterns of relationships among the factors; the interpretation of these patterns does not differ from the interpretation of those found for the variable correlations. The reduction of factor interrelationships to their patterns is called *higher-order* factor analysis and is discussed in Chapter 18.

6.5 Factor Score Matrix

The factor matrix presents the loadings, α, by which the existence of a factor for the variables can be ascertained. The factor score matrix gives a score for each case, such as a nation, on these factors.

The factor scores are derived in the following way. Each variable is weighted proportionally to its involvement in a factor; the more involved a variable, the higher the weight. Variables not at all related to a factor (such as the defense budget as per cent of GNP and the orthogonally rotated S_1 in Table 6–5) would be weighted near zero. To determine the score for a case on a factor, then, the case's data on each variable is multiplied by the factor weight for that variable. The sum of these weight-times-data-products for all the variables yields the factor score. This weighted summation will give cases high (or low) scores if their values are high (or low) on the variables involved with a factor.

> *Example 6–12.* For an economic development factor involving GNP per capita, telephones per capita, and vehicles per capita, the factor scores derived from the weighted summation of data of nations on these variables would place the United States at the top, Japan somewhere in the middle, and Yemen near the bottom.

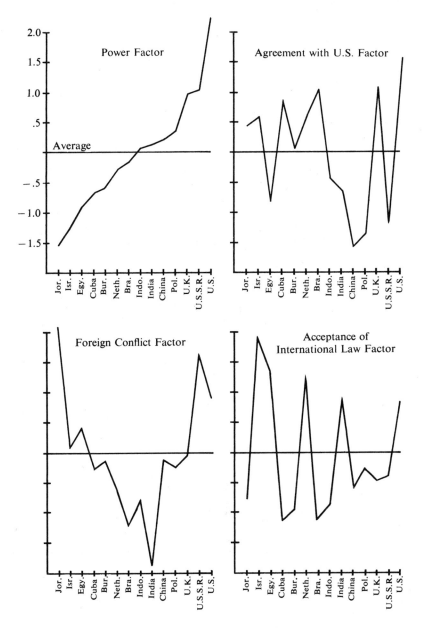

Figure 6–2

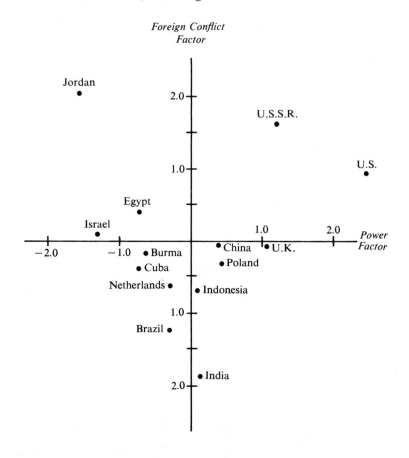

Figure 6–3

How are these factor scores to be interpreted? They are interpreted as data on any variable are interpreted. Gross national product, as a variable, for example, is a composite of such variables as hog production, steel production, and vehicle production. Similarly, population is a composite of population subgroups. In the same fashion, scores on a possible economic development factor are a composite. These composite variables made up of factor scores can be used in other analyses or as a means of comparing cases on the factors. But the factor scores have one feature that may not be shared by many other variables. They embody phenomena with a functional unity: The phenomena are highly interrelated in time or space.

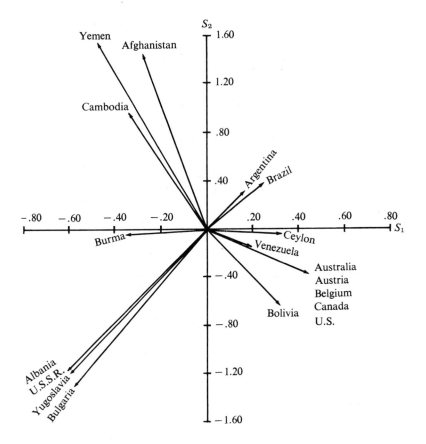

Figure 6–4

Example 6–13. Table 6–8 displays the factor scores for the 14 nations on the (orthogonally rotated) four patterns of Table 6–5. These scores are standardized (Definition 3–4). Figure 6–2 plots these factor scores for the four factors separately, and Fig. 6–3 plots scores on the power and foreign conflict factors against each other. The four plots of Fig. 6–2 show quite clearly how factor analysis has pulled out four different patterns of common variance in the data.

Example 6–14. Table 6–9 shows the unrotated factor scores for 79 nations on the 10 political characteristics of Table 6–4, and Fig. 6–4 gives a plot of selected factor scores on the first two factors. Note that factor scores may be given a vector interpretation in contrast to the point plot of scores in Fig. 6–3.

Table 6–8. *Selected Sample Factor Scores*[a]

	Orthogonally Rotated Factors			
	(1)	(2) *Agreement with U.S. in UN*	(3) *Foreign Conflict*	(4) *Acceptance of International Law*
	Power			
Brazil	−.389	1.053	−1.227	−1.070
Burma	−.584	.010	−.097	−.955
China	.325	−1.601	−.083	−.641
Cuba	−.662	.859	−.325	−1.183
Egypt	−.716	−.761	.448	1.331
India	.182	−.639	−1.807	.909
Indonesia	.027	−.480	−.712	−.757
Israel	−1.275	.518	.097	1.897
Jordan	−1.577	.426	2.018	−.719
Netherlands	−.315	.570	−.638	1.292
Poland	.410	−1.382	−.296	−.267
U.S.S.R.	1.129	−1.336	1.726	−.304
U.K.	1.081	1.178	−.024	−.404
U.S.	2.365	1.586	.919	.906

a Standardized regression estimates (Section 19.2.2).

Table 6–9. Factor Scores on the Unrotated Dimensions of Ten Political Characteristics

	S_1	S_2	S_3		S_1	S_2	S_3
Afghanistan	−.273	1.440	−1.800	Israel	.388	−.738	−.525
Albania	−.663	−1.174	−.290	Italy	.444	−.371	−.403
Argentina	.160	.302	1.415	Japan	.444	−.371	−.403
Australia	.444	−.371	−.403	Jordan	−.218	1.496	−1.668
Austria	.444	−.371	−.403	North Korea	−.663	−1.174	−.290
Belgium	.444	−.371	−.403	South Korea	−.081	.547	1.388
Bolivia	.320	−.632	−.589	Lebanon	.200	.098	.502
Brazil	.244	.382	1.505	Liberia	−.242	.333	.341
Bulgaria	−.601	−1.299	−.378	Libya	.034	1.094	−2.648
Burma	−.318	−.011	1.161	Mexico	.188	−.188	−.525
Cambodia	−.338	.956	−2.024	Nepal	−.325	1.607	−1.769
Canada	.444	−.371	−.403	Netherlands	.444	−.371	−.403
Ceylon	.314	−.140	−.379	New Zealand	.444	−.371	−.403
Chile	.330	−.078	−.284	Nicaragua	−.143	.672	1.476
China	−.663	−1.174	−.290	Norway	.444	−.371	−.403
Republic of				Outer			
China	−.091	.505	1.445	Mongolia	−.663	−1.174	−.290
Colombia	.190	.035	−.362	Pakistan	−.149	.653	1.324
Costa Rica	.444	−.371	−.403	Panama	.228	.320	1.410
Cuba	−.081	.547	1.388	Paraguay	−.211	.778	1.412
Czechoslovakia	−.663	−1.174	−.290	Peru	−.081	.547	1.388
Denmark	.444	−.371	−.403	Philippines	.382	−.246	−.315
Dominican				Poland	−.663	−1.174	−.290
Republic	.191	−.213	−.507	Portugal	−.373	.441	.433
Ecuador	.157	.382	.635	Rumania	−.663	−1.174	−.290
Egypt	−.317	−.137	.948	Saudi Arabia	−.396	1.615	−1.783
El Salvador	−.214	.681	1.462	Spain	−.416	.671	1.328
Ethiopia	−.273	1.440	−1.800	Sweden	.444	−.371	−.403
Finland	.444	−.371	−.403	Switzerland	.444	−.371	−.403
France	.401	−.141	.491	Syria	−.026	.603	1.520
East Germany	−.663	−1.174	−.290	Thailand	−.319	.889	1.312
West Germany	.444	−.371	−.403	Turkey	.358	.089	1.386
Greece	.444	−.371	−.403	Union of South			
Guatemala	−.143	.672	1.476	Africa	.278	.034	.508
Haiti	−.276	.605	1.178	U.S.S.R.	−.663	−1.174	−.290
Honduras	.114	.612	1.530	United			
Hungary	−.663	−1.174	−.290	Kingdom	.444	−.371	−.403
India	.444	−.371	−.403	United States	.444	−.371	−.403
Indonesia	−.101	−.069	.220	Uruguay	.444	−.371	−.403
Iran	−.208	1.538	−1.725	Venezuela	.200	−.151	.357
Iraq	−.081	.547	1.388	Yemen	−.475	1.556	−1.721
Ireland	.444	−.371	−.403	Yugoslavia	−.608	−1.118	−.158

7. The Factoring Design

The previous chapters have been concerned with the philosophy of factor analysis, basic mathematical concepts, the mathematics of the factor analysis models, and the factor matrices. Explicit in these chapters was a focus on the factor results and the underlying mathematical model. With this chapter and those to follow the definition of factor analysis will be broadened. The discussion will shift from understanding the model and results to understanding the factor analysis process. The focus will be the factor analysis research design.

A *research design* involves the prior organization of research procedures as a flow *from* the theory or research goals *to* the research findings. The particular steps in the design will vary with the methodology appropriate to the research question.[1]

1. For a *philosophy of science* approach to theoretical problems and research strategy, see Feigl and Brodbeck (1953), Hanson (1958), Kemeny (1958), and Nagel (1961). For *general research design* and technical details, see Wilson (1952), Fisher (1960), and Sidman (1960). For *research designs in the study of social relations*, see Chapin (1947), Festinger and Katz (1953), and Selltiz *et al.* (1959). For *general social research discussion and examples of application*, see Lerner and Lasswell (1951), and Lazarsfeld and Rosenberg (1955). On *computer problems and*

Figure 7–1 presents a flow diagram of a factor analysis research design. The arrows indicate the directions, alternatives, and sequence of computations; heavy arrows describe the sequence usually followed. Since the concern in this chapter is to sketch the main features of the factoring process, the design given in the figure is a simplified version of the most important aspects of factor analysis. Considerations which are relevant at various points, such as sample size, significance tests, number of factors, and computing facilities, are not given in the figure. Nor are the feedbacks from points further along in the sequence shown. These considerations and feedbacks will be (or have been) covered in detail in the chapters indicated at the left of the diagram.

This chapter will serve as a summary of the major considerations raised or to be raised in each of the chapters listed in the figure and as an overview of the relationship between the various research steps.

7.1 Step 1: Theory; Design Goals

The relationship between theory and factor analysis has been discussed in Section 2.4. Moreover, the possible goals that might be satisfied through factor analysis have also been discussed (Section 2.5). It is basic to any research design that theory or research goals be articulated as a first step. This helps clarify the nature of the problem and the kinds of questions that may be asked, and it provides guidance for selecting among the alternative procedures throughout the design.

7.2 Step 2: The Research Question

This is the most important step of the research design. The care and precision with which the research question is framed will determine the subsequent design. More specifically, the question should be precise and complete enough to select the factor model. The question should define the cases and variables of the data matrix. It should unambiguously point to the proper factor technique of step 9. Moreover, the question should help decide either for or against orthogonal or oblique rotation, factor scores, factor comparison, and distances.

---

usage, see Borko (1962). On the *technical details of applying the computer to multivariate designs*, see Cooley and Lohnes (1962). On *design steps in regression analysis*, see Ezekiel and Fox (1959, Chapter 26). For a fruitful discussion of the need for conceptually laying out a research design before factor analysis, see Guttman (1958b).

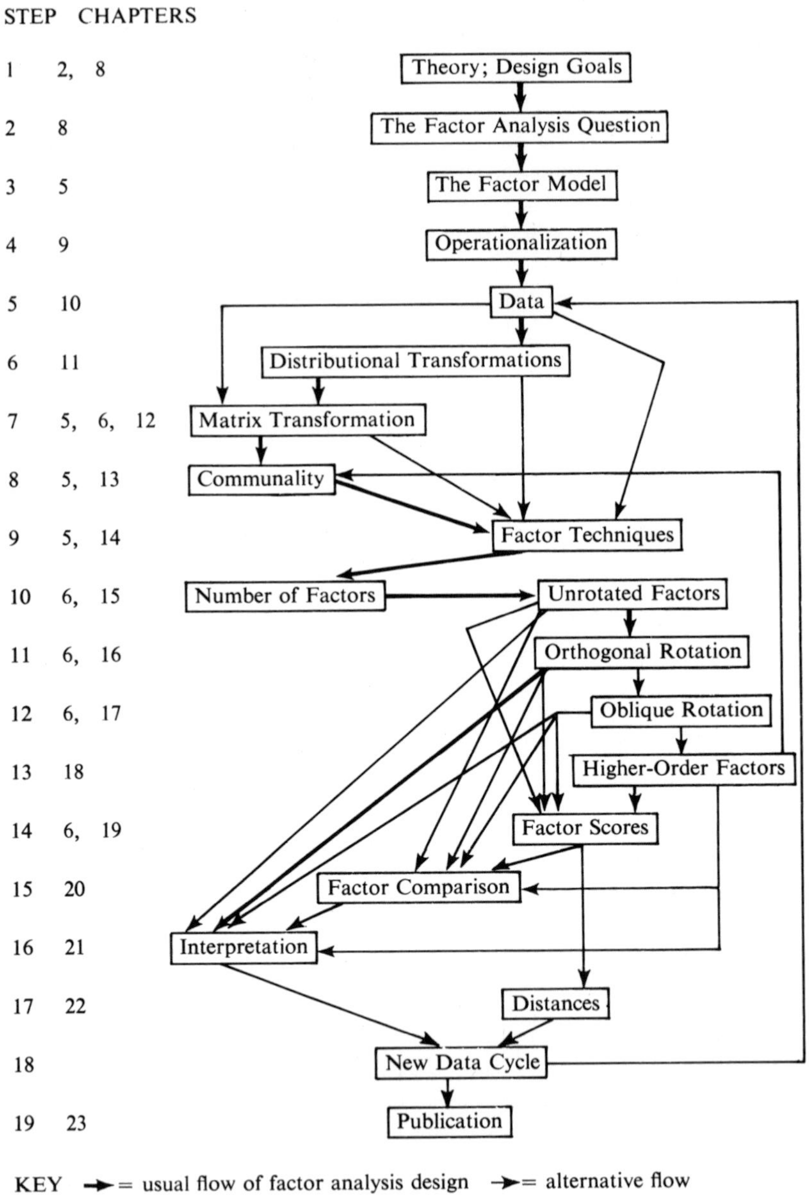

STEP   CHAPTERS

1	2, 8	Theory; Design Goals
2	8	The Factor Analysis Question
3	5	The Factor Model
4	9	Operationalization
5	10	Data
6	11	Distributional Transformations
7	5, 6, 12	Matrix Transformation
8	5, 13	Communality
9	5, 14	Factor Techniques
10	6, 15	Number of Factors / Unrotated Factors
11	6, 16	Orthogonal Rotation
12	6, 17	Oblique Rotation
13	18	Higher-Order Factors
14	6, 19	Factor Scores
15	20	Factor Comparison
16	21	Interpretation
17	22	Distances
18		New Data Cycle
19	23	Publication

KEY   ➤ = usual flow of factor analysis design   ➤ = alternative flow

Figure 7–1. Factor analysis research design flow diagram.

The question, in short, is the basis for the research and should guide the sequential flow leading to the proper answers. There is another aspect to an explicit question that should be emphasized. It serves as a guide for critically evaluating the published results of the design. Without knowing the precise question that guided the research, it is difficult to judge whether the proper alternatives at the various steps in the design have been selected. Should a particular study have used principal axes factor analysis or direct factor analysis? Should the study have used rotation? Should factor score regression estimates have been calculated? A well-articulated question helps to gauge such alternatives.

7.3 Step 3: The Factor Model

There is a choice to be made between two basically different factor analysis models: component analysis and common factor analysis. The *component analysis* model involves no assumption about unique or error variance in the data. *All* the data variance is analyzed, and the resulting factors are basis dimensions of the vector space of the data. If this model is selected, then no communality estimates need be made and step 8 of the design can be by-passed.

The *common factor analysis* model, however, assumes that the variance in a variable can be divided into common and unique components, where the latter variance can be further divided into specific and random error variance. The model, then, involves determining the factors defining the common variance among the variables—the dimensions of the common vector space of the data. A basic indeterminacy of this model results from an inability to determine the common variance of a variable until the common factors are delineated. Thus, an estimate of communality is required, and step 8 of the design must be considered.

Three variants of the common factor analysis model have recently been developed: image analysis, canonical factor analysis, and alpha factor analysis.

Image analysis defines the common factor space in terms of the regression estimates of each variable. The communality is then precisely given by the squared multiple correlation of each variable with all the others. No communality estimate is required. *Canonical factor analysis* delineates for a sample of cases the common factors that have the maximum canonical correlations with the unknown common factors existing for the population of cases. Beginning with initial trial values for the communalities, the factors and communalities are iterated to a best solution. A significance test for the number of factors is possible. *Alpha factor analysis* determines the common factors most generalizable to a universe of content (variables). Also beginning with trial values for communalities, the common factors and communalities are iterated until the latter converge to unities.

The characteristics of these models are given in Table 5–2. Once the factor model is decided upon relative to the research question, then the characteristics of each model will help to make decisions with regard to the communality step and the number of factors step of the design and will play a central role in the interpretation of the results.

7.4 Step 4: Operationalization

Operationalization involves defining the cases and variables of the data matrix and selecting explicit criteria for their inclusion. Are the variables going to be time units, for example, and the cases attributes of a single entity, as in the Cattell (1953) study of the interdependent economic, political, and social changes of Great Britain over 100 years? Are the cases going to be issues put to a roll call vote in a state legislature, and are the variables legislators, as in the Grumm study (1963) of the Kansas legislature? Or are the variables going to be tribal characteristics, as in the Schuessler and Driver study (1956) of clusters of tribal groups?

Once the variables and cases are defined, we must determine whether the data will consist of a sample or a population. If a population, the empirical characteristics of inclusion of each member and of exclusion of nonmembers must be specified. If a sample is to be employed, however, not only must the population of which the sample is a part be defined empirically, but the method of selecting the sample must also be specified.

Operationalization is also concerned with the measurement characteristics of the data. Should the data be dichotomized, ordinal, or interval-scaled? This problem involves some knowledge of the data that will be used and an analysis of the underlying distribution that the data approximate. This leads to another aspect of operationalization. The mode of data collection should be specified at this step. Will the data be from content analyses of public documents? From newspapers? Will the data be from statistical sources or field data? Or will the data consist of expert ratings?

Obviously, the four aspects of operationalization—specifying the data matrix, defining the sample, determining the data scaling, and the mode of data collection—are not independent or sequential. They interact in such a way that a decision at one point, say mode of data collection, will influence the operationalization at another point, say scaling. These operational considerations revolve around the data matrix. Another set of operational considerations concerns the research design itself.

This second set, which will be designated *design operationalizations* to distinguish them from data operationalizations, involves considering each subsequent step in the research design to decide whether a selection can be made of alternative steps, such as rotation, and alternative procedures within the steps, such as the factor technique to be applied. As the various possibilities along the design flow are considered, possible changes in the data operationalizations may be suggested.

This is the virtue of weighing the whole design at this point. Revisions in procedures and data operationalizations can be made *before time and resources have been committed to a particular set of operationalizations*. Moving ahead in an *ad hoc* manner without prior specification of the design may end in much backtracking and frustration. For example, after doing a canonical factor analysis, it may not be possible to apply significance tests because the data matrix does not satisfy the sampling and distribution requirements of the tests—something that should have been thought out beforehand. As another example, no consideration may have been given to factor comparison until that step has been reached. By then, unfortunately, one may find that he has included few variables or cases similar to those of other studies that have been done and that his ability to compare studies has been foreclosed.

Data and design operationalization is an *iterative process* requiring an understanding of the theory and goals of the research, an explicit research question, and a specification of the factor model. Once completed, the operationalization step leads directly into the data stage of the factor analysis design.

7.5 Step 5: Data

Four considerations are involved in the data step. The first is *data collection*. This includes the marshaling of data sources, tabulation of data, the computations involved in putting data in the form required by the operationalizations (for example, calculating the per capita part of GNP per capita), and so forth. This aspect in itself may involve a data collection flow design if much data are involved.

The second consideration is *coding*. This should not be confused with measurement or scaling. Coding is the tabulation of the data in a form amenable to IBM card punching and to the format requirements of available computer programs to be used at later stages of the design. Lack of anticipation of coding requirements at this stage may mean expensive recoding later or even the loss of various design alternatives. Recoding may require expensive re-collection of the data, if the mode of data collection involved content analysis, for example, or public opinion polls.[2]

A third consideration is *missing data*. In many designs, a portion of the data matrix may have to be left blank because of unavailable data, data too expensive in resources to collect, or because of the inapplicability of variable definitions to some of the cases. To clarify the last possibility, if a variable is minimum voting age and the cases refer to nations, then this variable would not be applicable to nations where no voting takes place. Data for these nations, therefore, would be treated as missing data.

Missing data lead to a number of mathematical problems that require care in selecting alternatives along the research design and care in the ultimate interpretation of the results. The existence of missing data at this stage necessitates a selection of one of four alternatives: (1) The data matrix may be left as is, using procedures at subsequent steps that compensate for missing data. (2) Only the missing data that can be estimated with a fair level of confidence may be filled in. (3) All missing values may be estimated. (4) Variables or cases (or both) containing missing data may be omitted.

The problem of missing data overlaps a fourth consideration—*data error*. The collected data may be incomplete, involve estimates, contain clerical errors or source bias, and be noncomparable in the sense of having definitions or meanings that shift from case to case. Data error may be classed as *random* or *systematic* error. These two types of error have different effects on the factor analysis and different implications for the kinds of error controls the researcher may use. It is at the data stage that the nature of the data error must be evaluated, for the errors that exist in the data may call for a revision of the research design; they may call for the introduction of error controls at various steps or for the completion of a secondary or parallel analysis.

Once data are collected and the data step completed, three alternative steps are possible. Transformation of data distributions at step 6 may be selected. Or, this step may be by-passed and the data matrix as is

2. This point may seem obvious, but the writer knows of a well-funded sample survey that coded data in a way that foreclosed computing several interesting factor analyses. Since the coding was carried out as respondents were interviewed, the survey could not be recoded.

may be transformed at step 7. The third alternative is to go directly from step 5 to step 9 and to select direct factor analysis as the factoring technique.

7.6 Step 6: Distributional Transformations

By-passing this step in the sequence need not be decided until the procedures of the previous step are completed. Moreover, the procedures at this step may be left undecided until the data matrix is filled and the characteristics of the data error evaluated.

The purpose of the transformations is to alter the data distributions so that they match the theory or goals of the analysis, the basic question, and the requirements and assumptions of the subsequent design steps. Although the data may already have the required distributions, the effect of improper distributions is so great on factor results as to prescribe the consideration of transformations as a possibility in every design.

A number of considerations weigh the choice of a distributional transformation. One consideration has to do with the concepts the data are meant to reflect (e.g., democracy, conflict, ideology, leadership). Do the data represent the range of possibilities for a concept, or only a tail of the latent distribution? Are the quantitative values on a concept additive or not? That is, is there a qualitative jump from one value, say zero, to another, say unity, that does not exist for the other values in the distribution?

Another consideration in weighing the transformation is the assessment of error in the data. Such error may indicate that the data should be, for example, dichotomized, grouped, or log-transformed, to compensate for the error. Other considerations determining the transformation depend on the assumptions of the data matrix transformation to be used, the factor analysis technique, the use of significance tests, and the need for uniformity with those other studies to which results will be compared. In general, the overriding concern of the distribution transformations will be to match the range of potential values of the concepts operationalized to the data, to reduce the effect of extreme data values on the analysis, and to linearize relationships between the variables.

The transformation procedures involve two phases. The first is the determination of the actual characteristics of the distributions for each variable. Descriptive statistics—the mean and standard deviation—are usually calculated and the frequency distribution is delineated. This gives a profile of the distribution that may then be used in transforming the data. The second phase—the computations of the transformations—may require a number of different transformations to be calculated until that transformation yielding a distribution with the desired properties is determined.

7.7 Step 7: Matrix Transformations

The previous step was concerned with the distribution of data on a variable. The distributional transformations could vary from variable to variable, although the criteria underlying the transformation will have the same purpose (such as to normalize distributions or remove extreme values). In the *matrix transformation* step, on the other hand, the criteria for transforming all the data is not only the same, but the transformations must all be the same. The vector space represented by the data matrix is itself being transformed. This transformation of the space may take a number of forms. Before outlining them, however, some remarks on the nature of the matrix transformation step should be made.

The considerations and alternatives involved in this step are optional. The step itself may be by-passed in the design, but the decision to do so must be made at the operationalization stage. Moreover, if matrix transformations are to be employed, the selection among alternative transformations should also have been decided at step 4. The reason is that the choice of alternatives, say the product moment correlation coefficient rather than ϕ, should have influenced the choice of variables and their measurement characteristics at step 4, decisions about error controls at step 5, and transformations at step 6.

The matrix transformation may take three forms: *covariance, correlation*, and *matrix scaling*. The covariance and correlation matrix transformations involve computing the covariance and correlation matrices, respectively, for the variables. The covariances measure the amount of variance around their means shared by the variables and may be a desirable transformation if the data are all measured in the same units.

If, however, the units in the data are not comparable, the correlation matrix transformation may be employed. In computing the correlations, one is not limited to the product moment coefficient. Depending on considerations discussed in Chapter 12, the correlation matrix may be calculated using the nonparametric Spearman or Kendall rank coefficients, the ϕ or tetrachoric measures of correlation for dichotomous data, or the interclass correlation coefficient.

The third kind of matrix transformation has to do with scaling all the data according to some common criteria. For example, take a symmetrical trade matrix for *n* nations. Each cell of the trade matrix may give the total trade (exports plus imports) between row and column nations. This trade data may be transformed to a "transaction" matrix in which each cell measures whether the trade between row and column nations is greater or less than expected values (on a null model), given the total trade figures for each nation.[3] These departures-from-expectations-values may serve as the data for direct factor analysis or may involve further scaling.

Symmetrical matrices, such as the above transaction matrix, may be scaled so that all values lie between 0 and $+1.00$ or between -1.00 and $+1.00$. The resulting matrix may be input directly into a principal axes factor analysis program (without going through the correlation subroutine first), as though the scaled matrix represented a correlation matrix. Many other techniques of scaling exist, among which are removing the mean of the matrix values or standardizing the whole matrix according to the same mean and standard deviation.

Besides scaling the data matrix or computing the covariance or correlation matrix, however, one of the scale-free matrix transformations may be employed, as dictated by a selection of the scaled image, canonical, or alpha factor analysis models discussed in Chapter 5. The factor results of these models are proportionally invariant of the units in the original data. Were one of these models selected, the present step would still entail a decision about the best correlation coefficient to use in arriving at the scale-free transformation.

The matrix scaling technique applied is dependent on the theory or goals of the analysis, factor model, scale of data, comparability of units and magnitudes of measurement, missing data, nature and degree of error, and the frequency distribution. In addition, the resources available, existing computer facilities, and computer program library will certainly play a role in the selection. The subsequent flow of the research design after step 7 is also important. The factor technique to be employed and the selection of the factor scores and distance options will be of great concern in transforming the matrix. It should not be forgotten, moreover, that the results may be compared with those of similar studies. Accordingly, the matrix transformation form and technique used in the other studies will influence the selection here.

One more comment on this step might be made. One is not limited to a single kind of matrix transformation for a particular research

3. On the transaction matrix, see Savage and Deutsch (1960), Alker (1962), and Goodman (1963). For applied examples, see Russett (1963; 1967b).

design. A number of matrix transformations may be carried out before the matrix has the desirable properties for the factor analysis step. For example, one may standardize the whole matrix by the same mean and standard deviation and then calculate the correlation matrix on the result. Or a transaction matrix may first be calculated and then transformed to a correlation matrix.

7.8 Step 8: Communality

The communality step involves deciding upon the communality values or their estimates to be inserted in the principal diagonal of the correlation matrix to be factored in *common* factor analysis. The communalities restrict the analysis to the common variance between the variables.

The principal diagonal of the correlation matrix gives the correlation of a variable with itself, which is unity of course. To factor the correlation matrix with unities in the principal diagonal implies the component factor analysis model, and will normally have two results. First, self-correlation of a variable usually includes variance unique to the variable and variance common to the other variables. As discussed in Section 5.1, unique variance includes specific and random error parts. Accordingly, the result of factoring the correlation matrix with unities in the diagonal is usually to delineate dimensions that account for the specific variance, random error, and common variance among the vectors. If, however, it can be assumed that the variables have only common variance, then only common variance will be defined by the dimensions.

Secondly, the *rank* of the correlation matrix will be the same as the smaller side of the $n \times m$ data matrix. If variables ordinarily number less than cases, then the number of factors required to fully account for all the variance in the data will equal the number of variables. The lack of parsimony inherent in this result is usually avoided by extracting for interpretation only those factors accounting for "significant" or "meaningful" portions of the total variance.

Instead of retaining unities in the diagonal of the correlation matrix, reliabilities or measures of reliable variance can be inserted in their place. Reliabilities exclude from the factor analysis the unique variation among the variables due to random error. The estimates for reliabilities to insert in the diagonal depend on the techniques used by the researcher to gauge the error in his data. For example, the correlations between data collected on the same variable by independent collectors may be used as an estimate of reliability.

Common variance is that which the variables share with each other. Inserting measures of this common variance—communalities—in place of unities in the diagonal of the correlation matrix limits the factor analysis to delineating common factors. Moreover, the rank of the correlation matrix will be reduced to the number of such common factors, which will usually be much less than the number of variables.

Communality estimation has been of concern to factor methodologists. A number of solutions have been proposed, among which are inserting in the diagonal of the correlation matrix the highest correlation of a variable with the others, the average correlation of a variable, the squared multiple correlation of a variable with the others, or the communality of a variable resulting from an initial factor analysis with unities in the diagonal. The squared multiple correlation of a variable with the others appears to be the best estimate of the variable's communality. This estimate is the lower bound on the communality and approaches the true communality as the number of variables increases (assuming that the ratio of the number of common factors to variables approaches zero as the number of variables approaches infinity).

If the component factor analysis model is selected at step 3, no communality estimation problem exists. Unities will be used in the diagonal of the correlation matrix. If the common factor analysis model is selected, however, the communalities estimates should be carefully considered. What estimate is preferred will depend, in part, on the operationalizations. If factor comparisons are to be done, for example, it may be desirable to elect the same estimate as the other studies to be compared. The estimate selected will also depend on the number of variables included in the analyses. As the number of variables in the data matrix increases, the effect of a particular communality estimate decreases.

The communality step of the design leads directly to considerations involved in selecting the factor analysis technique. Communality concerns thus mark the end of the data preparation stage of factor analysis.

7.9 Step 9: Factor Techniques

Until recent years, the most popular technique of factor analysis was the *centroid* solution. This technique involves successively fitting the factor dimensions to the center of the configuration of variable vectors representing the data. As a factor solution, however, it is only an approximation meant to save on the computational labor of the *principal axes* technique. With the advent of high-speed computing facilities, the principal axes technique has virtually supplanted the centroid in popularity. Together, the centroid and principal axes techniques are probably used for over 95 per cent of published findings.

Since the principal axes technique has now become the dominant factoring tool, a few descriptive comments might be made here. Chapter 14 will discuss the technique at greater length. The geometric concept underlying the principal axes approach is that the cases of the data matrix represent a swarm of points in the space with coordinate axes defined by the variables. The more ellipsoidal the swarm of points, the more interrelated are the variables. The principal axes of the ellipsoid of these points constitute the principal axes factor solution. This solution has four very important characteristics.

First, since each principal axis is parallel to the eigenvectors of the data matrix, the principal axes can be computed by solving the data matrix for its eigenvalues and eigenvectors. Secondly, the first principal axis is through that portion of the ellipsoid of maximum density (i.e., that accounts for the maximum covariance), with each successive axis defining lesser densities of the ellipsoid (i.e., lesser amounts of covariance). Third, the axes are mutually orthogonal. And, last, the number of axes defines the basis dimensions of the vector space of the data.

Other factor solutions besides principal axes are possible. The *diagonal*, or *algebraic*, technique can be applied to any correlation matrix and is relatively simple in computation. More demanding in computational labor and requiring a computer for any reasonable data matrix is the canonical factor solution, which allows for a chi-square significance test of the number of factors. Other solutions lying between these two in computational difficulty are possible. One is the *multiple-group* technique applied to groups of highly interdependent variables. The technique fits centroids to those groups and extracts several factors at once. Another technique is *direct factor analysis*. Because of computer program availability, its popularity has been largely confined so far to publications emanating from the University of Chicago. The technique can be applied to the raw data without the necessity of transforming the data matrix to one that is symmetrical. All these techniques are similar in that they delineate or approximate the basis dimensions of the data matrix. Although the bases defined by the various techniques may differ, they are linear transformations of each other.

The selection of a technique will depend on many considerations. The units and scales of measurement will affect the choice. The factor technique employed by other studies in the same substantive area will be influential, by reason of the greater confidence gained from wide use of a technique and the possible need to hold techniques constant for a factor comparison. Probably, however, computational labor and the availability of computer programs will be deciding factors.

The nature of the factor technique to be employed should be decided at the operationalization stage. This decision will interact with decisions regarding measurement and with the selection of a matrix transformation.

Once a factor technique is selected, the appropriate (in some sense) number of factors to retain in the application of the technique must be determined. This is the factor number problem, the next step of the design.

7.10 Step 10: Number of Factors

Instead of extracting all the factors existing in the data, factoring usually stops at the point where no additional significant or meaningful variance remains. How we define significant or meaningful variance is important, for the number of factors retained can influence the rotated factor results.

For some models, the number of factors is no problem. In canonical factor analysis, this number is determined by a significance test. In alpha factor analysis, this number depends on those factors with eigenvalues greater than unity. In common, component, and image factor analysis models, however, the best number of factors to use depends on the researcher's judgment.

Several rules of thumb can be employed, such as size of the residual correlations, distribution of loadings, distribution of eigenvalues, and interpretability. A generally useful procedure is to extract all factors with eigenvalues greater than zero and then to evaluate factors with eigenvalues near unity for a factor cutoff on the basis of interpretability, of a sharp drop in eigenvalues for subsequent factors, or on the basis of auxiliary criteria.

Once the best (in some sense) number of factors are decided upon, a factor solution has been achieved. We now have a set of linearly independent factors that account for the variance in the data independently. Some factor analysis designs will stop at this point, since such a parsimonious set of factors is all that is desired. In a few cases, the design may call for computing the factor scores at step 14 and factor comparisons at step 15. Usually, the unrotated factors will also be interpreted. Most designs, however, will move from the unrotated factors to the rotation steps of design before computing factor scores and comparisons or interpreting the results.

7.11 Step 11: Orthogonal Rotation

Although the unrotated factors may be unique to a given data matrix, an infinite number of rotated solutions exist. Of these solutions, however, an appropriate rotation according to three criteria may be found. First, the factors may be rotated according to the *substantive qualities* they should exhibit. One such substantive criteria is called *simple structure* and is employed in almost all factor rotations currently being published. Simple structure involves rotating the factors such that each better defines a separate cluster of highly interrelated variables and is as specific to this cluster as possible.

Other substantive criteria besides simple structure are possible, although seldom employed. For example, one may wish to rotate the first factor so that it wholly accounts for the variance in a particular variable. The remaining factors may then be rotated orthogonally to this factor to partial out the effect of the particular variable. This type of rotation is especially desirable when one has a measure of systematic error. By rotating factors orthogonal to this measure, such systematic error can be removed from (partialled out of) the analysis.

The factors may also be rotated so that all factors are mutually orthogonal. That is, the rotated factors will be uncorrelated. This may be desirable if the factors provide input to another analysis, such as multiple regression, or it may be theoretically desirable to delineate a substantive area, say international relations, in terms of an ortho-gonal structure. If, instead of requiring orthogonal factors, it is decided to allow the factors to become correlated—oblique—then we resort to the oblique rotation step of the factoring design. This step will be discussed subsequently.

Besides *substantive* and *orthogonality* criteria, a third criterion concerns the mode of rotation: Should the rotation be analytic or graphical? The graphical approach to rotation is visual, involving the plot of the variables in terms of their loadings on each pair of factors. The factor axis may then be visually rotated around the origin to better define the configuration of variables as substantive and ortho-gonal criteria dictate.

When the number of variables or factors is large, the labor and time consumed in graphical rotation is prohibitive. The growth in availa-bility of high-speed computers has made feasible the *analytic* mode of rotation. This consists of rotating the initial factors until they maximize or minimize a mathematical criterion.

For *orthogonal* rotation, the varimax criterion has by consensus become the best function for simple structure analytic rotation. It is employed by virtually all orthogonal rotations currently published. Orthogonal rotation may or may not be done prior to oblique rotation. Often, however, it is desirable to have an orthogonally rotated solution for comparing the oblique results. An informed choice can then be made between the two solutions for subsequent interpretation and possible factor score computations.

7.12 Step 12: Oblique Factors

If oblique rotation to simple structure is employed, the interrelated clusters of variables are better defined and the correlation between the clusters can be found. The orthogonal solution is a subcase of the oblique. If orthogonality empirically exists between the clusters of variables, then an oblique rotation will result in orthogonal dimensions.

Several oblique analytic rotation criteria exist, such as promax, binormamin, biquartimin, and maxplane, but there is litttle consensus as to which of the criteria best achieves simple structure. The adequacy of those criteria is usually gauged by reference to visually determined graphical solutions and the computer time required for a solution. On these grounds, the maxplane criteria appears the best, with promax a close second choice. Binormamin and biquartimin criteria also give solutions very close to the visual results, but require much more time on the computer.

However arrived at, the oblique solution will result in factor-pattern and structure matrices and a factor correlation matrix. The factor matrices allow us to go on to steps 14–16, involving the factor scores, comparison, and interpretation. The factor correlations, however, provide us with an option: We can now delineate higher-order factors. This is the next design step.

7.13 Step 13: Higher-Order Factors

The same question asked about variables can be asked about oblique factors: What are the patterns of relationship between the factors? And factor analysis can again be employed to answer the question.

The factor correlation matrix can be treated like any correlation matrix arrived at from step 7 of the design. The proper communality estimate, if any is to be used, must be selected; the proper factor technique must be selected and the number of factors determined; orthogonal or oblique rotation, or both, may be employed. Oblique rotation of these second-order factors of the factor correlation matrix will again generate a factor correlation matrix. And again, this correlation matrix can be looped back through the factor design to define factors at a third level.

These higher-order factors describe the most general patterns of relationship: the patterns among the factors in the data. For this reason, the higher-order factors may be the most theoretically interesting. As with the first-order unrotated and rotated factors from higher-order factors we can move on to the computation of factor scores and comparisons and to the interpretation of the results.

7.14 Step 14: Factor Scores

The alternatives faced by the researcher at this step involve the mode of computing factor scores. Exact factor scores may be calculated or regression estimates employed in their place. Instead of either, however, composite estimates or basic variables may be chosen. The first alternative is available for the component analysis model and gives scores as a unique linear combination of the data. For the common factor analysis model, an exact solution to the scores is not possible. In this case, a set of scores with a best fit to the data can be found through regression analysis.

Regression estimates for the common factor scores are determined by first computing the best regression coefficients for estimating the factor scores from the variables, and then by multiplying the standardized raw data by these weights to get the actual score estimates. The standard deviation of the estimates equals the multiple correlation of the factor scores with the data and is a measure of the uniqueness of the estimates. With the availability of computers, calculating regression estimates has become routine and popular.

Computing *composite estimates* involves only those variables with high loadings on the particular factor. A small number of variables will be selected and their data will be summed to yield factor scores. Variants of this approach entail weighting the data by the variable loadings on the dimensions and standardizing the data prior to summation.

The *basic variable* approach to factor scores requires no computation. The highest loading variable for a factor is selected as an indicator. The variable's data then constitute the factor scores. Although these scores will be less precise than the composite or regression estimates, their virtue lies in using (to represent a factor) a relatively well-known variable (say, GNP per capita) that may have a history of research behind it rather than using derived scores specific to the analysis.

The selection among the alternatives for computing factor scores can wait until this step in the design is reached, or factor scores may not be computed at all. In fact, factor scores are seldom reported in published studies. A consideration involved in computing scores is whether the sample of cases is meaningful only in the aggregate (e.g., a factor analysis of the attitudes of a *sample* of urban dwellers) or whether each case is of interest in its own right (e.g., a factor analysis of legislators, nations, cities, parties, industries, tribes, or interest groups). In the latter case, the factor scores of cases will be of great interest and, indeed, these scores may be the ultimate purpose of the research design.

Once determined, factor scores can become new data to be used in another research design, such as multiple regression or analysis of variance, or they can be merged with other variables at step 5 in another factor analysis. Factor scores may also provide input to the computation of *distances* between cases at step 17, or they may be involved in the factor comparisons to be done at the next step.

7.15 Step 15: Factor Comparison

The corpus of knowledge within any science is built through confirmation (or refutation) of its empirical propositions. Accordingly, a dominant interest of factor analysts is confirmation of their findings through comparison with the factor results of other studies.

The possibility of factor comparison should be weighed in any factor analysis design. As indicated in the descriptions of the previous steps, the possibility of factor comparisons can enter into the decisions made at a number of places in the analysis. It may be desirable to make the design as congruent as possible with those of other studies in order to minimize compounding the effect of methodological differences with the variance in empirical results.

The inclusion of a factor comparison step in the design, however, is optional. Comparisons with other studies may not be possible, either because no other such studies in the same area exist or because the research designs might vary too greatly from those of other studies. Although optional, the possibility of factor comparisons must be considered at the operationalization step so that variables can be selected and the design adjusted to facilitate comparison, if comparison is desired.

The mode of comparison can be either intuitive or systematic. *Intuitive* comparison, which is perhaps the most common approach, entails a visual comparison of factor loadings and a judgment of their similarity. The *systematic* mode of comparison involves a numerical measure of the similarity of factors. There are several systematic comparison techniques. For convenience, they may be divided into two types: matrix comparison and vector comparison.

Matrix comparison consists of comparing the factor matrix of one study with that of another. The factor loadings may depend on a number of characteristics of the data unique to a study. Although the factors of separate studies may have different loadings as a result of these specific study characteristics, the factors may be linearly related to each other, reflecting an underlying general similarity in data. The matrix comparison technique transforms the factor solution of one study to a least squares fit to the factors of another study, so that the incidental characteristics of the data or research designs will be minimized in the comparison. The comparison then consists of measuring the correlations between the transformed factor matrix and factors and comparing them to those of the other study.

The *vector comparison* approach does not alter the original factor solutions before comparing them. The factors as given are compared to each other in a one-to-one fashion. The correlation between the loadings can be computed using the product moment coefficient if pattern similarity is of interest. The interclass correlation coefficient may be employed if both pattern and magnitude similarity are of concern.

Vector comparison techniques not involving correlation coefficients are occasionally employed. The root mean square of the deviations between the loadings of two factors is proportional to the geometric distance between the factors in the space defined by the loadings of the factor matrices. Another measure, the coefficient of congruence can give the cosine of the angle between the two factors being compared in the space defined by their loadings.

Whether matrix or vector comparison approaches are applied, comparisons will inform the interpretation of the factor results at the next step of the design.

7.16 Step 16: Interpretation

Interpretation entails affixing labels to either or both the unrotated and rotated factors. The labels reflect the researcher's evaluation of the factors results and serve as easily understood concepts that ease communication and discussion or as tags useful in further manipulation, mnemonic recall, and research. Factors may be labeled in essentially three ways: symbolically, descriptively, or causally.

Symbolic labels are simply any symbols with no meaning of their own which are used to denote the factors. For example, three factors might be denoted D_1, D_2, and D_3, or F_1, F_2, and F_3, or A, B, and C. Symbolic tags have no connotations that may carry over to and be confused with the factors. Although symbolic tags are precise and help avoid conceptual confusion, they create problems in communication of research findings and factor comparisons. To call a factor D_1 in communicating findings requires a description of the dimension so labeled and constant reference to the description whenever D_1 is mentioned.

Descriptive labels are concepts from the substantive area of concern and reflect or embody the pattern of interrelationships defined by the factors. The descriptive label is meant to be typological—to categorize the conceptual characteristics of the findings. The third type of labeling —causal—goes beyond this.

In *causal* labeling an inference is made from the interrelationships between the variables to an underlying cause. In this sense, the causal tag is a capsule explanation of why a particular group of variables should form a factor. For example, a factor having high loadings for a number of conflict variables, such as coups and purges, may be symbolically labeled C_1, descriptively labeled *revolution*, or causally labeled *modernization* (if the researcher believes that the occurrence and intercorrelation among a number of revolutionary processes within a nation is due to the stresses and strains of a rapid shift from a traditional society to a modern social and industrial nation). As another example, a factor analysis of congressional roll call votes may define a highly correlated group of foreign policy issues. This factor may be descriptively named *foreign policy* or causally termed *isolationist* (inferring that an isolationist-internationalist attitude continuum underlies the high intercorrelation among foreign policy issues).

The approach to the interpretation of factor dimensions is largely a matter of personal taste and long-run research strategy. However, it is desirable to use concepts that are congenial with the interests and knowledge of the research community to facilitate communication and use of the results.

7.17 Step 17: Distances

The computation of factor scores at step 14 makes it possible to consider another step of the design: computing distances between cases in the space of the factor dimensions. These distances will measure how close together cases are in this space, that is, how congruent their factor scores are.

Computing distances involves decisions about how factors are to be weighed and the number of factors to employ. If distances between cases were computed on equally weighted factors, it would equate those factors accounting for considerable variance and those accounting for little. A solution would be to multiply the factor scores by the per cent of total or common variance accounted for by the factor. It might be argued, however, that this weighting is inappropriate since the particular strength of the factors would vary from analysis to analysis as a function of the characteristics involved.

In addition to weighting, a decision has to be made about the number of factors to include in computing distances. Do we want to include all factors, the largest factors, or one factor?

Whatever the weighting or number of factors involved, the distances computed can be arranged in a symmetric matrix with rows and columns defined by the cases. Two questions may be asked regarding this matrix. First, how do the cases group in terms of their distances? That is, what clusters of nations are close together in factor space? To provide an answer, cluster analysis or hierarchical decomposition might be applied to the distances.

A second question that might be asked of the distances is concerned with the interrelationship between the column vectors of the distance matrix. This is a traditional factor analysis question. Its purpose is to reduce the variation in the distance matrix to a minimum number of independent factor dimensions. How this will be done involves setting up a new factor analysis design, which is to say that the distance matrix becomes data for a new factor analysis.

7.18 Step 18: New Data Cycle

This step makes explicit the possibility that the factor results may be input to a new factor analysis run. The substantive findings of one design may be used as criteria in deciding on a new design and its data alternatives. Several successive factor analyses may be linked in this fashion, gradually converging on answers to a research question.

Moreover, the methodological procedures of a design may be systematically altered through successive runs on the same data to determine whether choices of correlation coefficient, communality estimate, or number of factors, to name a few possibilities, make a difference in the results.

A decision to go through a new cycle should be made in the formalization stage of the design—at step 4. The virtue of an early decision is that the design procedures throughout the analysis can be selected with a view to efficiently and comparably linking up the factor analyses that will follow each other.

7.19 Step 19: Publication

The research report is an effort to convey to the interested community the nature of the design and substantive findings. It makes the results available for use and for confirmation or refutation. Failure to consider these reasons for publishing can vitiate the value of a good research design and slow down the flow of findings into the mainstream of scientific knowledge.

Publication of factor analysis results is dominated by several considerations. The first is to make possible (to evoke) critical evaluation of the research so that its substantive conclusions can be given proper weight. The second is to enable others to independently confirm or refute the results, that is, to allow replication. A third consideration, which is often the primary purpose of the research, is to advance knowledge through publication of the findings. The fourth consideration, the heuristic value of the research design, may encourage, through publication, similar efforts in allied areas or suggest alternative designs. Lastly, but perhaps most importantly in the view of some researchers, the results may be of great interest in public and private policy-making.

Evaluation of these considerations depends on two related characteristics of the publishing endeavor. The *mode of publication* is extremely important. Whether book, monograph, research report, or journal, the vehicle of publication will influence what can be included. The nature of the publishing house or the particular journal to which the manuscript is sent should help the writer to decide what aspects of the design should be given particular emphasis.

Besides the mode of publication, the type of audience to which the manuscript is directed should be carefully considered before writing. Is the report directed to the researcher in the same area, who is technically competent to understand and interpret the subtleties of the research design? Or is it directed to the specialist in the same substantive area, who has only slight conceptual understanding of factor analysis? Or, as a third possibility, is it directed to the general scientific community, to most of whom factor analysis, or even quantitative analysis, may be unknown? Or is it directed to the final possible audience—the interested layman or policy-maker?

The decisions made about audience and mode of publication and the resulting weight given the several considerations discussed will influence a number of aspects of the report. The amount of technical information about the research design will depend on the tastes of the publisher and the requirements of the reader. The raw findings included (e.g., correlation and factor matrices) will be governed by space considerations as well as the desire for critical evaluation and replication. The basic results and their substantive interpretation will be included, undoubtedly, in any report. The degree to which they can stand on their own feet or be placed in the context of an extended discussion depends on the audience. The need, finally, to place the whole research design in a larger substantive and research context and to justify the approach in an introduction will vary with the mode of publication and the audience.

Evaluation of these elements will vary, but a rigorous research design alone is not sufficient to give new findings a place in the corpus of science. Others must be able to gauge these findings relative to the procedures that generated them, and the findings must be confirmed by other studies. The published report should make this possible.

Part Three · Preparing the Data

8. The Factor Analysis Question

Section 2.5 presents a number of theoretical objectives or goals of factor analysis. These might be to determine the interdependencies among a set of variables, to achieve a parsimonious description of the data, to determine the structure of a domain, to classify, to scale, to test hypotheses, to transform data, to explore or map a domain, or to build theory.

The choice and implementation of these goals is either implicitly or explicitly related to a theory or theories about the substantive domain of interest. At one extreme, the theory may be an explicitly structured set of mathematical propositions; at the other extreme, it may be an intuitive feel for the data. Regardless of the level of specification of the theory, some sort of theory forms the context for articulating the goals of the design. The relation between the theory and goals stage of a factor analysis research design and the subsequent two steps of the design (Fig. 7–1) is elaborated in Fig. 8–1.

The concern of this chapter will be step 2 of the design, the research question. Section 8.1 will discuss the importance of the research question. Section 8.2 will place the factor question in the context of research

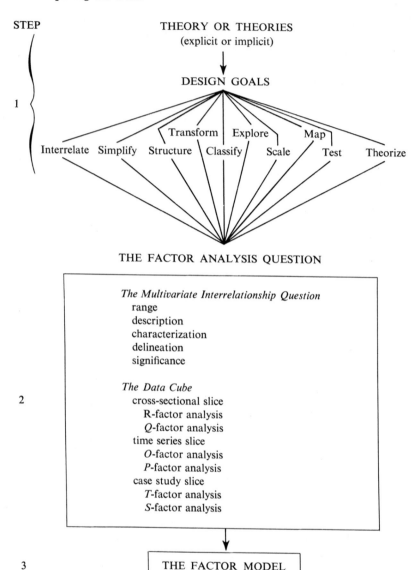

Figure 8–1

questions in general and help clarify the particular characteristics of the factor question. The concluding section will delineate the alternative *data* matrices that may be analyzed through factor analysis.

8.1 Importance of the Research Question

The goals of the research project should be given explicitly through the statement of the research question, which tells what the researcher wants to know in language that is as precise and unambiguous as possible. The desire, for instance, to map a domain—to determine its major empirical concepts—is not a sufficient guide for operationalization. What phenomena within the domain are of concern? What, exactly, does the researcher want to determine about them? Answers to such questions about the goals enable the researcher to formulate the design of the analysis.

The research question forms a bridge between the goals of the design and its operationalization. It is couched in the language of the analysis and thus serves as a guide for operationalizing a design that will achieve the desired goals. Although a design can be operationalized without an explicit question, there is the danger that the final result will be "off the point"—not entirely related to what is wanted. The time to clarify what may be a hazy goal is not at the end of the analysis (e.g., "Now let's see, how are these results related to what I wanted?"), but at the stage where resources have yet to be committed.

Besides relating results to research goals, a research question facilitates communication. When included with the published results, an explicit question guides the reader in evaluation of the design and findings. We are all familiar with book reviews or critiques of published papers that missed the point—that aimed their arrows at the wrong target. The frustration and misinformation that result from being criticized for not doing something originally excluded by one's goals can be avoided by wording an explicit research question at the outset and including it with the published results.

In addition to assuring pertinent evaluations, an explicit research question facilitates replication. It enables those interested in duplicating or extending the results to determine why certain decisions were made. For example, why were these data selected over others? Why this transformation instead of another? Why this community estimate, and why a particular rotation or lack of it?

In sum, the research question clarifies the goals, relates them to the design and the results through the operationalization stage, communicates the purposes of the analysis, and facilitates replication of the results. Research questions can have many forms and levels of abstraction. The purpose of the following section is to classify these forms and levels in a way that will bring out the salient characteristics of the factor analysis question.

8.2 Typology of Research Questions

8.2.1 LEVELS AND FORMS

The research question can be asked at several *levels* of abstractness, as shown in Fig. 8–2. Moving from left to right in the figure, levels of definition, range, description, characterization, delineation, and significance are indicated. Each level presupposes an answer to the question of the previous level. The question may also take a number of *forms*, connected as indicated by the arrows in Fig. 8–2 between the levels. The figure does not represent an exhaustive methodological or epistemological categorization of research. Rather, its purpose is to suggest the span and content of research questions in general and to present a context for our discussion of the factor analysis research question.

Let us consider this typology in detail. The *definition* level has only one form: the theory (or theories) and goal (or goals) of the analysis. These constitute the base of any design; they demarcate the methodological and substantive characteristics of the questions. Bounded by this definition, the remaining levels enable the design to be operationalized.

The next level indicates the *range* of the question with regard to the number of variables. Here, there are three forms: *univariate*, or one-variable questions (e.g., the presidency; race riots; poverty in American cities; history of France from 1848 to 1871), *bivariate*, or two-variable questions (e.g., voting patterns and income; legislative committee membership and seniority; juvenile delinquency and family cohesion), and *multivariate*, or many-variable questions (e.g., trade, national income, and conflict behavior of nations). The *range* of questions is of primary importance for their forms at subsequent levels. For example, a univariate question forecloses the use of correlation and associational techniques, and a bivariate question is not amenable to factor analysis.

The next level of the question is *description*. This refers to the question's substantive content mirrored by the data to be collected. These data embody the empirical focus. The examples in parentheses in the last paragraph give illustrations of data at the three ranges of the question.

Level of Research Question*

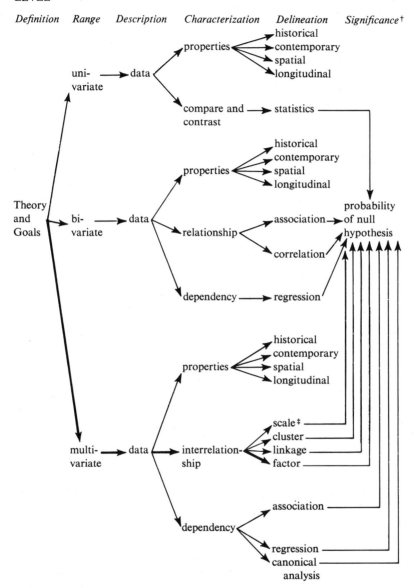

* Heavy arrows denote levels and forms of the factor analysis question.
† Includes the concept of the *generalizability* of a sample of variables to a universe
  of content (Section 5.7).
‡ Includes dimensional analysis as discussed in Section 22.3.

Figure 8–2. Typology of Questions.

Following the description level of a question is its *characterization.* This level is concerned with the structure of the data in terms of their properties, or their dependency or interdependency relationships.

The subsequent *delineation* level specifies more precisely the structural concern of the question. At this level, for example, the particular qualities, or the type of interdependency, sought after are clarified. As can be seen from Fig. 8–2, the form of the question at this level depends on the form at the characterization level, and this in turn is dependent on the range.

If the range of the question is univariate, two characterizations of the data may be possible:

1. Their properties may be assessed. That is, the peculiar nature of the data may be described to bring out the prominent features. At the delineation level, these features may be considered for a historical period or contemporaneously, and spatially at a point in time or longitudinally over time. For example, the data of concern may be the American presidency and the question may entail distinguishing its contemporary powers and limitations.

2. Although a focus on the properties of the data is possible for any of the three ranges of a question, a concern with *similarities and differences* in the data is specific to the univariate question. This characterization involves comparing different cases or samples of data on the same variable to see if they differ in a particular way. The *delineation* of this difference at the next level may be in terms of means, standard deviations, or whatever statistics are warranted by the question. Taking the example of the presidency again, the univariate question may concern the powers of the office vis-à-vis the powers of Congress in the 1930's as contrasted with today. The *delineation* of this question may be in terms of the average power (however defined) at each period.[1]

For the *bivariate range,* the characterization of the data may be in terms of *properties* or *relationship.* The relationship form of the question bears on the degree of connection between the data on two variables: their statistical association or correlation. For the dependency form of the question, however, the focus is on how data on one variable changes with that on the other. The interest is in the mathematical function connecting two variables. As a case in point, the data for a bivariate question may be on juvenile delinquency and family cohesion.

1. For statistical univariate comparisons, see Part I of Russett *et al.* (1964). Chapter 3 of Dixon and Massey (1957) and Chapter 2 of Johnson and Jackson (1959) discuss univariate data and techniques. Alker and Russett (1964) present several univariate measures for determining equality. Schubert and Press (1964) present an answer to a comparison question on univariate (apportionment) data.

Besides the properties of the data (e.g., the distribution of delinquency, the mean, and the largest values), the characterization may involve their correlation or their dependence in terms of the amount of delinquency per unit of family cohesion.

The question about the relationship between two variables may be *delineated* in terms of their *association* or *correlation*. The former is concerned with either the presence or degree of statistical relationship; the latter with both degree of relationship and the direction (positive or negative). Association may be assessed through such techniques[2] as the chi-square, contingency coefficient (*C*), the Kendall coefficient of concordance (*W*), or analysis of variance (Siegel, 1956). Correlation between two variables may be measured through the product moment, Spearman's or Kendall's rank correlation techniques, or the tetrachoric technique, among others, as discussed in Section 12.3. The question as to the dependence of one variable on another is delineated by its *regression*.[3] Multiple regression is often posed in opposition to factor analysis; Appendix 8.1 discusses regression analysis in more detail.

The delineation of data dependence differs between the bivariate and multivariate questions. In the multivariate case our concern may be with the dependence of one variable on a *set* of two or more variables. A delineation of this question is in terms of multiple *regression*.[4] Alternatively, our concern may be with the dependence of a set of two or more variables on a set of two or more other variables. For this case, a delineation is in terms of *canonical analysis*.[5]

Multiple regression and canonical analysis yield a mathematical function connecting the variables. Our multivariate dependency question may not relate to functions, however, but to the degree of *association* between one or more variables on one side and a set of variables on the other. Then multiple correlation (Definition 3–12)[6] or canonical

---

2. Assuming, of course, that the data meet or approach the assumptions of the mathematical model underlying the technique employed.

3. Regression is employed here as a generic term encompassing least squares *regression analysis* of stochastic variables with random error assumed to be in the dependent variable (Definition 3–11), *structural analysis* with random error in both variables, and *functional analysis* with nonstochastic variables. See Kendall and Stuart (1961, Chapter 29) for a mathematical discussion of these distinctions and for further references.

4. An applied example is Cutright (1963).

5. For an example of canonical analysis applied to connect two factor spaces, see Berry (1966). Canonical factor analysis is based on the canonical analysis model (Section 5.5).

6. Applied examples are Flinn (1964), Lerner (1957), and Tanter (1965).

correlation can be employed.[7] If the dependency question is concerned only with presence or absence of association, analysis of variance[8] might be applied.

Besides dependency and properties (the latter being the same as in the univariate case), the multivariate question may be concerned with data *interrelationships*—their interconnectedness. Since this concern leads to the factor analysis question itself, a discussion of this *form* will be deferred until the next section. Some definition, range, description, characterization, and delineation levels of a research question have been sketched. As shown in Fig. 8–2, there remains one more level—the significance of the data. This level is concerned with the reliability of the data delineations. It has only one form: How probable is it that the findings of the previous level occurred by chance? This probability is measured as the likelihood of the chance deviation of the findings from a null hypothesis of no dependency, no association, no correlation, random values, etc.[9] Whether the researcher carries the research question to the *significance level* depends on his data. If dealing with the universe of cases rather than a sample, he may wish to remain at the previous levels.[10] This points up a facet of the typology in Fig. 8–2. All levels need not be transversed, although each level presupposes a question at the previous one. There are three natural stopping levels for a question within the typology. It may stop at the *description level*, as do data books like the *Statistical Yearbook* and *Demographic Yearbook* of the United Nations. The question may stop

7. Rozeboom (1965) discusses the relationship between multiple correlation, canonical correlation, and factor analysis.

8. Cattell (1952a, pp. 10–12, 18–20, 364–67, 380–83) and Burt (1941, pp. 271–80) compare analysis of variance and factor analysis. Royce (1963) considers analysis of variance to be a bridge between the multivariate factor analysis approach and univariate designs. Guttman (1958b) relates factor analysis to Fisher's designs and shows that a common factor can be one of the Cartesian products (interaction) terms of analysis of variance. Stephenson (1953) argues for a combined Q-factor analysis approach (Section 8.3, below) and analysis of variance, as does Royce (1950). For a discussion of the relationship of analysis of variance to regression analysis see Chapter 23 of Ezekiel and Fox (1959). Analysis of variance is also useful for comparing effects of different experimental conditions or subgroups of a sample on one or two variables. It may therefore be employed at the univariate or bivariate data range. For bivariate application to nations, see Cutright (1965).

9. See Chapter 2 of Johnson and Jackson (1959). A more advanced discussion is given in Chapter 7 of Dixon and Massey (1957). For a general and sometimes delightful collection of readings on probability, see Parts VII–VIII of Newman (1956).

10. For an interesting discussion on applying significance tests when one does not have a sample, i.e., when the population (universe of cases) is being analyzed, see Gold (1964).

at the *delineation level*, as with traditional qualitative studies in sociology, anthropology, and political science, with studies on a universe of cases rather than a sample, and with studies whose only aim is to clarify the structure of the data at hand. Or the question may be carried to the *significance level* as is done in many statistical studies in the social sciences.

8.2.2 THE MULTIVARIATE INTERRELATIONSHIP QUESTION

The interrelationships or interdependencies among a multitude of variables is the basic concern of the factor analysis question.[11] This is a distinctive characteristic that sets the factor question apart from those focusing on dependency and properties. Indeed, an interest in interrelationships rather than dependency has been suggested as a criterion for applying factor analysis instead of regression analysis (Kendall, 1957). The interrelationship question does not necessarily lead to factor analysis, however. As can be seen in Fig. 8–2, there are at least four alternative *delineations* of *interrelationships* available at the next level: scale, cluster, linkage, and factor.

One delineation of *scale interrelationships* involves an ordering of the variables such that their values represent a continuum of some sort.[12] In Guttman scale analysis, the variables are so ordered (ranked) that the high values for cases (individuals, nations, etc.) on one variable assume high values for the same cases on all higher ranking variables. This scaling procedure perhaps may be best understood in terms of nation votes on UN issues. If all the issues put to a vote in the United Nations in a particular session can be ordered so that a yes vote on all other issues rank above it, the interrelationships among the variables (issues) form a Guttman scale.[13] Scaling of interrelationships among variables need not be limited to one continuum of values. Several

11. Hotelling (1957) argues that some, though not all, of the purposes for which factor analysis has been employed can now be accomplished by other procedures, such as multiple regression, multiple correlation, and analysis of variance.

12. On scale analysis, see Stouffer *et al.* (1950) and Green (1954).

13. For such an application of Guttman scaling to UN voting, see Reiselbach (1960). For comparison, see the factor analysis of UN voting by Alker (1964). Burt (1953) compares Guttman scaling and factor analysis and concludes that the scale is completely reproducible from the factor analysis model—that they have essentially the same results. Horst (1965, p. 515) says, however, that a factor analysis of perfectly scalable Guttman data (dichotomous data) has dimensionality equal to the number of distinct values of the column sums. Kaiser (1963, pp. 165–66) argues that image factor analysis presents a means of adjudicating between factor analysis and Guttman scaling.

continua may be assumed to exist[14] as in multidimensional scaling or dimensional analysis (Section 22.3).

Scaling delineates the interrelationships between a number of variables in terms of continua or a continuum underlying their values. *Clustering*, however, delineates these interrelationships into groups of highly interrelated variables. Clustering techniques[15] usually group variables on some measure of relationship between variables, such as a correlation coefficient or distance coefficient (Definition 3–26). The criterion for clustering may vary, but usually involves minimizing the within-group variance of the variables and maximizing the variance between groups. Further discussion of clustering as a method of grouping cases on their distances in multidimensional space is given in Section 22.2.

Linkage analysis is an extension of clustering. It delineates the clusters of interrelationships in terms of increasingly higher levels of relationship and displays the connection—links—between the various groups at different levels.[16] The nature of these links can be exemplified by the international political system. The most general cluster group of nations is the world system. Within this global group are the East, West, and Neutral subgroups; within them can be discerned the Moscow, Peking, and intermediary Eastern subgroups, the Anglo-Saxon, European, and Latin American Western subgroups, and the African and Asian Neutralist subgroups. Within each, further divisions and connections can be made.

The fourth delineation of multivariate relationships is *factor analysis*. The concern is with the dimensions of variation in the variables as in component factor analysis (Section 5.3), or with the dimensions of the common parts of the variables as in common factor analysis (Section 5.2).

14. See Lingoes (1962), who develops multiple scales for 100 dichotomously scaled variables (issues). He also factor-analyzes these issues for comparison and finds 77 per cent agreement of factors with scales. He further applies his scale technique to the analysis of 88 senators of the 83rd Congress (1963). On multiple scales, see also Coleman (1957).

15. Factor analysis texts occasionally include mention of cluster analysis in their introductory chapters. See Fruchter (1954, Chapter 2), and Cattell (1952a, pp. 32–33, *passim*). See Banks (1964) for an example of a cluster analysis of the variables in Banks and Textor, *A Cross-Polity Survey* (1963). These results may be compared with the factor analyses of the same data by Banks and Gregg (1965) and Gregg and Banks (1965). On clustering sociometric data, see Coleman and MacRae (1960).

16. Hierarchical decomposition is a form of linkage analysis. See Alexander (1964). For a full-scale application to international relations, see Brams (1966) and Russett (1967a).

Factoring is not the same as scaling, although multidimensional scaling may yield continua similar in many respects to factors. Scaling focuses on the multivariate relationships of variables that allow them to be ordered; factor analysis focuses on linearly independent dimensions of variance among the variables. It is possible for variables forming a perfect Guttman scale that is "unidimensional" to yield more than one factor upon factor analysis.

Factor analysis is mathematically distinct from cluster analysis but may have a similar result.[17] Since factor analysis and rotation can delineate clusters of interrelated variables, the definition of cluster analysis as determining groups of highly interrelated variables is often applied to factor analysis. The concept of grouping is simple and facilitates communication with readers unfamiliar with the methodology. The analogy to clustering can be pushed too far, however. This first factor of the principal axes factor technique, for example, is fitted to the variables to account for a maximum amount of their total variance. The factor-dimension may, therefore, lie between clusters of variables instead of defining any one cluster.[18] Rotation of the initial factors maximizes (if simple structure is employed[19]) their fit to each cluster. It is through rotation that the clustering analogy to factor analysis gains most of its substance.

Factor analysis may also overlap with linkage analysis. The rotated simple structure factors appear to delineate the different groups *at one level* of the linked hierarchy of variables. The subgroups and vertical connections between levels do not appear clearly revealed by the factor analysis. Moreover, the level delineated in the hierarchy seems to depend on the degree of interrelationship in the variables.[20]

Figure 8–2 highlights the *form* of the factor analysis question at various *levels* of the typology. Factor analysis is concerned about a number of variables, about their interrelationship, as distinct from their properties or the dependency of any one variable on the others, and about the factors accounting for these interrelationships. If desired, the question may be taken to the final level of significance.

17. Tryon (1959) places factor analysis and cluster analysis in a general category of multidimensional analysis. He treats them as specific decisions of a domain-sampling method. See also Tryon (1958).

18. A graphic example of this possibility is shown in Fig. 16–3.

19. See Section 16.2.2.

20. Research is required to clarify the relationship between the levels of linkage analysis, as defined by the techniques of hierarchical decomposition, and the factors of factor analysis.

8.3 The Data Cube

Any research question requires specification of the cases and variables to be analyzed. Will they be years? Nations? Votes? Attributes? Moreover, considering only nations and attributes: Which will be the variables and which the cases? Understanding the possible alternative specifications helps to answer questions such as these. Although, in the discussion to follow, we will focus on the factor analysis question, the alternatives to be considered are general to most research questions.

Any phenomena can be described along three dimensions.[21] One is a dimension defining the *entities* involved, whether atom, house, planet, menu, lawyer, pencil, international crisis, vote, or whatever. A second dimension defines the *characteristics* of the entities. These are their attributes or behavior that describe and distinguish the entities. For example, an entity such as an international crisis has such characteristics as intensity, scope, geographic location, threats, warnings, informal and formal diplomatic signals, risk of escalation, etc. The third dimension of any phenomenon is *occasion*. It defines the time when the phenomenon occurs.[22]

These dimensions of *entity*, *characteristic*, and *occasion* delimit the three-dimensional data cube illustrated in Fig. 8–3. Each phenomenon is a datum cell defined by the intersection of row (entity) and column (characteristic) for an occasion. Although phenomena are thus three-dimensional, only two dimensions at a time are factor-analyzed.[23] The specification, therefore, consists of cutting a slice out of the data cube. *This slice will then define the data matrix to be analyzed.*

21. The data cube described in this section is similar to Cattell's (1952a, 1952b). His dimensions are persons by variables by occasions. Horst (1965, pp. 8–14) discusses a data cube of entities by attributes by occasions. For the geographer's data cube of characteristics by places by times see Berry (1964a). For a data cube of characteristics by cultures by times for anthropology, see Berliner (1962). For a places by topics by times data cube of historians, see McClelland (1958).

22. A fourth dimension, *operationalization*, might be added to describe the nature of the measurement of the phenomena within a datum cell. A fifth dimension could index how the data were determined—the *instrument*. These additional dimensions present new avenues of applied and methodological research. For example, in determining the reliability of data on threats (characteristic) for nations (entities), the researcher might factor a nation by data source (instruments) by threat matrix. On such additions to the data box, see Cattell (1961, 1963) and Horst (1965, pp. 8–14).

23. Section 9.2.4 discusses factor-analyzing the three data dimensions simultaneously. For applied examples, see Triandis (1964). For some preliminary methodological research on factoring a three-dimensional data matrix, see Tucker (1963).

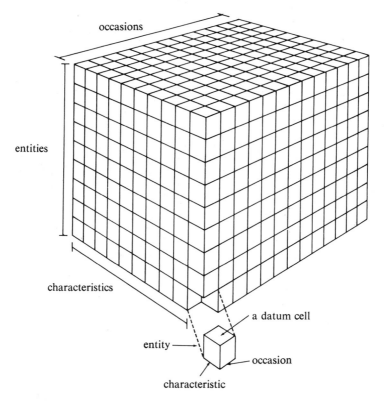

Figure 8–3. The Data Box.

According to our prior treatment of data matrices (Definition 3–14 and Table 3–1), the columns of the matrix are the variables factor-analyzed; the rows are the cases. We will adhere to this usage while pointing out that the *variables* analyzed can be attributes, entities, or occasions, and that the *cases* for which the data are collected can also be attributes, entities, or occasions.

Figures 8–4-6 show three basic ways the data cube may be sliced. A *cross-sectional* (spatial) cut can be made for any occasion.[24] The resulting matrix (the slice) of phenomena for a particular occasion can be analyzed as in Fig. 8–4. The variables (columns) are the characteristics; the rows are the entities. This is the most commonly analyzed matrix of applied factor analysis; factoring this matrix is called R-factor analysis (R-technique; R-analysis). It should be clear that this is

24. A pertinent discussion of cross-sectional analysis is given in Duncan *et al.* (1961).

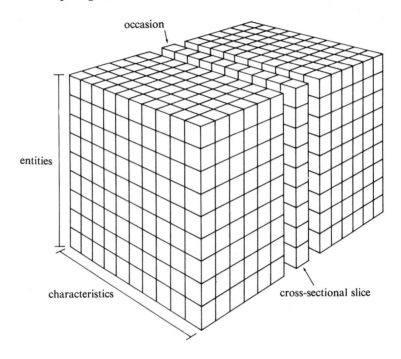

occasion

entities

characteristics

cross-sectional slice

Figure 8–4

not a factor model or a technique of factor extraction but only the factor analysis of a specific slice of the data cube.

> *Definition 8–1.* R-FACTOR ANALYSIS consists of factor-analyzing a matrix with the *variables* (columns) referring to the characteristics of entities; the *cases* (rows) are the entities themselves. The data are all for the same occasion.
>
> *Example 8–1.* Some applied examples of R-factor analy-sis are Godfrey *et al.* (1958), Wood (1961), and Schmid (1960). Godfrey *et al.* factored variables of company success and country economic structure for U.S. com-panies (entities) on 1949–55 (occasion) data. Wood analyzed socioeconomic variables on New Jersey munici-palities for 1955. In trying to determine the components of Seattle crime, Schmid factor-analyzed variables on crime and socioeconomic characteristics of Seattle census area tracts for 1949–51.

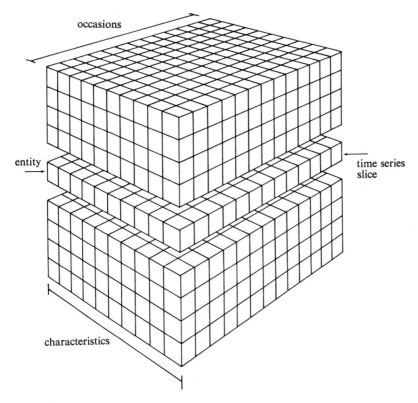

Figure 8–5

Example 8–2. The data in Table 3–1 for 10 political characteristics has been R-factor-analyzed. The unrotated results are displayed in Table 6–4. Figure 8–7 shows the data cube from which this data slice was cut.

If the *cross-sectional* slice of Fig. 8–4 is transposed, the entities become the columns and the characteristics the rows: the entities are now the variables factor-analyzed. Analysis of this matrix is called Q-factor analysis (Q-technique; Q-analysis).[25]

25. The relationship between the results of R- and Q-analysis, or more generally between the dimensions of a matrix and its transpose, are discussed in Section 9.2.2. See Stephenson (1953) for a clear and extended discussion of the philosophy and methodology of Q-analysis of individuals, and Rinn (1961), who writes on the problems of applying Stephenson's methodology. Burt (1937) should be consulted as one of the forerunners with Stephenson in the development of the Q-analysis methodology.

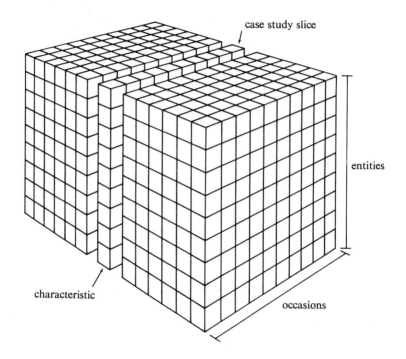

case study slice

entities

characteristic

occasions

Figure 8-6

Definition 8-2. Q-FACTOR ANALYSIS consists of factor-analyzing a matrix in which *variables* refer to entities, and the *cases* (rows) are their characteristics. The data are all for the same occasion.

Example 8-3. Schuessler and Driver (1956) factored 16 primitive societies (entities treated as variables) across 2,500 characteristics of their primitive period (occasion). The factors grouped the tribes as to their similarity on these characteristics. Grumm (1963) factor-analyzed Kansas state legislators (variables) on their roll call votes (characteristics) for 1957–59 (occasion).

Only one cross-sectional slice can be made of the data cube. However, parallel with the occasion dimension, two kinds of slices are possible. As illustrated in Figs. 8–5 and 8–6, the cube may be cut horizontally or vertically along the time axis. Both cuts are longitudinal in involving a number of occasions.[26] But one differs from the other according to whether the data all refer to one characteristic or to one entity.

26. On longitudinal analysis, see Harris (1963) and Duncan *et al.* (1961).

1955

nations

political characteristics

matrix of Table 3–1

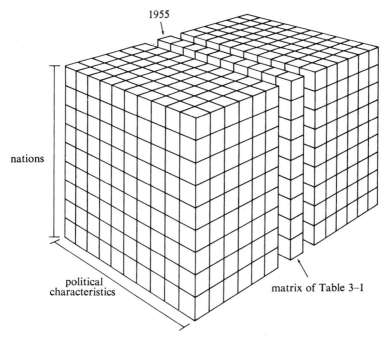

Figure 8–7

For the horizontal slice of Fig. 8–5, the data are for the character-istics of one entity on a number of occasions. This will be termed the *time series* slice. The time series slice, or matrix, may be analyzed in one of two ways: (1) characteristics by occasions or (2) occasions by characteristics. Since longitudinal analysis may not be as familiar to the reader as cross-sectional, the characteristics by occasions matrix is illustrated in Fig. 8–8, the occasions by characteristics in Fig. 8–9. Each cell of the two matrices will give the value of a characteristic for an occasion for the entity of concern.

> *Example 8–4.* Let a time series slice be for the annual characteristics of the United States for 100 years. Then the matrix of Fig. 8–8 will contain the values of each charac-teristic as they change from year to year. Say one of the characteristics is the size of the federal government's budget and the 100 years are 1837–1936. The matrix cells of the row for this characteristic will give the annual budget for 1837, 1838, 1839, . . . , 1936.
>
> *Definition 8–3.* O-FACTOR ANALYSIS consists of factor-analyzing the matrix of Fig. 8–8 with *variables* referring to

occasions

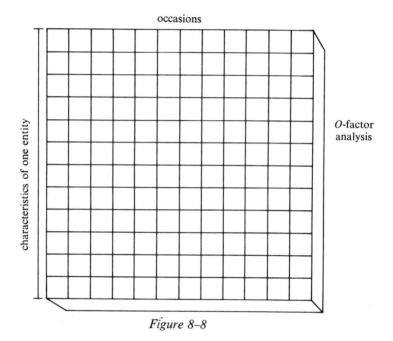

O-factor
analysis

characteristics of one entity

Figure 8–8

the occasions and *cases* to the characteristics of a single entity.

An O-factor analysis will determine the relationships between occasions for an entity. Such findings are relevant, for example, in measuring systematic change or periodic divisions marking changes in an entity.

Example 8–5. If one is concerned about different international systems across time, an O-factor analysis can be done by setting up a matrix of international system characteristics (total trade, number of nations, wars, conferences, total population, treaties, international organizations, etc.) for each of, say, 200 years. A factoring of this matrix should reveal some major systematic changes within international relations.

Definition 8–4. P-FACTOR ANALYSIS consists of factor-analyzing the matrix of Fig. 8–9 with *variables* referring to the characteristics of a single entity and *cases* to occasions.

P-factor analysis delineates the relationships between the characteristics of an entity as they change over time.[27] The factors measure

27. This slice of the data matrix is also employed in the time series analysis

characteristics of one entity

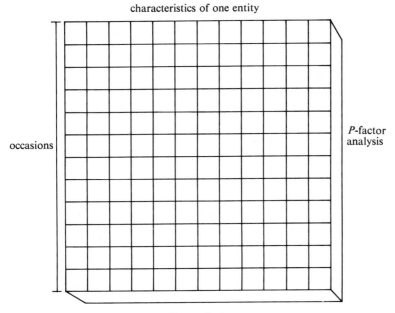

occasions

P-factor analysis

Figure 8–9

the independent components of change in the characteristics for an entity and enable those characteristics changing similarly to be defined.[28]

> *Example 8–6.* Cattell and Adelson (1951) applied P-factor analysis to determine the factors of social change for the United States, 1845–1942.[29] Cattell (1953) similarly factored British characteristics, 1837–1937, and Gibb (1956) did the same for Australia, 1906–46. All three studies found a large economic or technological growth factor and an independent factor reflecting the change in characteristics associated with participation in war.

The third slice of the data cube, shown in Fig. 8–6 above, is vertical along the time axis. It limits the phenomenon of concern to one characteristic and will be called the *case study* slice. The two ways of viewing the case study slice are given in Figs. 8–10 and 8–11. The first

of the economist. For a general nontechnical discussion of time series analysis (unrelated to factor analysis), see Goldfarb (1960).

28. For a recent consideration of P-factor analysis, see Cattell (1963). Cattell (1957) shows the extensive use that has been made of P-factor analysis in measuring personality. Anderson (1963) presents a tight, methodological analysis of the problems of P-factor analysis.

29. See also, Adelson (1950).

occasions for a characteristic

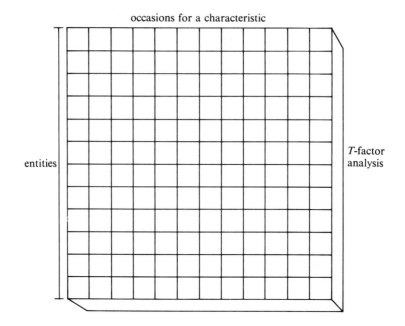

entities

T-factor
analysis

Figure 8–10

is an entities by occasions matrix. This comprises the values over time
of a number of entities for a particular characteristic.

> *Example 8–7.* Let the characteristic of interest be war.
> The matrix of Fig. 8–10 might indicate the number of
> wars for each nation for each year over the last two
> centuries. Matrices of this form are fairly common in
> statistical data sources. As a case in point, in the 1961
> *Statistical Yearbook* of the United Nations there is a
> matrix of wheat production values for the world's nations
> over a number of years (p. 83) and a similar matrix of
> rye production (p. 85).

A factor analysis of the data in the matrix in Fig. 8–10 will determine
the minimum periods or occasions needed to describe the changes in
the values for the entities on the characteristic. Moreover, the answer
would indicate the years that saw similar changes and those between
which there was a jump, or qualitative-quantitative shift. The analysis
of the entities by occasion matrix is called T-factor analysis.

> *Definition 8–5.* T-FACTOR ANALYSIS consists of factor-
> analyzing the matrix of Fig. 8–10 with *variables* referring
> to occasions for a single characteristic and *cases* to entities.

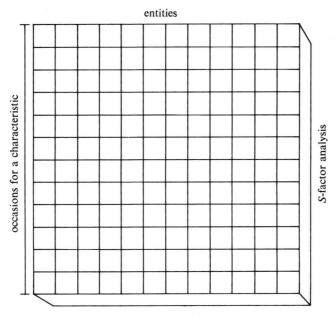

Figure 8–11

Example 8–8. Imagine an analysis of a case study slice involving the total trade (characteristic) of nations for 1900–65. T-factor analysis might reveal five dimensions of these occasions, two of which may index the impact of World Wars I and II on trade. The remaining three dimensions might delineate the post-World War I boom in world trade, the effects of the interwar depression, and post-World War II growth.

Figure 8–11 shows the transpose of the case study slice. This is an occasion by entity matrix, the study of which is called S-factor analysis.

Definition 8–6. S-FACTOR ANALYSIS consists of factor-analyzing the matrix of Fig. 8–11 with *variables* referring to entities and *cases* to occasions for a single characteristic.

Example 8–9. Consider the previous trade example. An S-factor analysis of the years by nations matrix of total trade would delineate those clusters of nations whose trade similarly changed over the period and would help pinpoint the differential national effects on world trade.

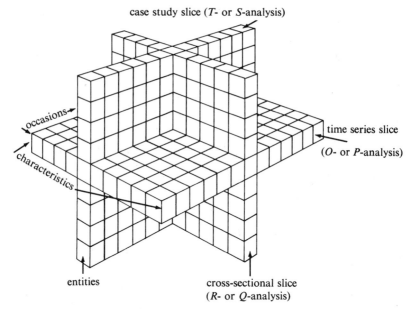

case study slice (*T*- or *S*-analysis)

occasions →

time series slice

(*O*- or *P*-analysis)

characteristics

entities

cross-sectional slice
(*R*- or *Q*-analysis)

Figure 8–12

At this point, the three slices of the data box and their transposes might be reviewed.[30] Figure 8–12 simultaneously shows the cross-sectional, time series, and case study cuts involved. There are, in all, six possible ways in which the phenomena may be oriented when the two possible matrices for each slice are considered. The posing of the factor analysis question, therefore, requires a conscious selection from among these six alternative perspectives.[31]

Appendix 8.1
Factor Analysis and Multiple Regression

Multiple regression is a model often used in the social sciences and bears a striking resemblance to the factor model. For that reason, several comments are appended to this chapter on the similarities and dissimilarities between the two.

30. The O, P, Q, R, S, and T designations for the analysis of the six alternative slices from the data matrix were developed by Cattell. See Cattell (1952a) for a discussion of these slices in the context of factor analysis.

31. Given that almost all factor analyses employ R-factor analysis-type matrices, with a very small scattering of Q and P types, and with no O, S, or T to my knowledge, one might suspect that the six possible ways the data may be sliced have not been fully appreciated.

The regression model for a set of variables $X_1, X_2, \ldots, X_j, \ldots, X_m$ states that any one of the variables, X_j, is a linear function of the others plus a variable X_u, which measures the unique variance of X_j. From Definitions 3–8-11,

$$X_j = \alpha_r + \beta_1 X_1 + \beta_2 X_2 + \cdots + \beta_k X_k + \cdots + \beta_m X_m + X_u,$$

where $k \neq j$. The variable X_j is considered the dependent variable, and the variables to the right of the equality, with the exception of X_u, are the independent variables. The elements of X_u are the residuals, or errors, of the regression. The coefficients, β_k, are the well known regression co-efficients, and the first coefficient, α_r, is termed the intercept or constant coefficient. The intercept is of no significance here and will be dropped from further discussion.

Necessary for the application of the regression analysis are data for the variables on both sides of the equations, with the exception of the residual variable X_u. The purpose of regression analysis is to find values for the coefficients that will *maximize* the linear fit (Definition 3–8) of the data on X_j to the space defined by the $m - 1$ number of X_k variables and will *minimize* the contributions of the residuals.

The independent variables of a regression analysis define a vector space (Definition 3–34) with a dimensionality equal to their number. Translating from "variable" to "vector" terminology, the regression co-efficients then measure the containment of a vector, X_j, in this space and the contribution of each of the other $m - 1$ vectors to this fit. The squared multiple correlation coefficient times 100 indicates the per cent of dependence (per cent of variance accounted for; per cent of variation in common; percentage fit to the vector space of the independent variables) of X_j on the other vectors. For example, a regression analysis of system style, X_1, of Table 3–1 on the other 9 vectors for the 79 nations has the following results:

System style = 2.15 + .36 (constitutional status)
            − .18 (representative character)
            − .13 (electoral system) − .12 (freedom of group opposition)
            − 1.83 (non-Communist regime) + .31 (political leadership)
            − .22 (horizontal power distribution)
            − .31 (monarchical type)
            + .02 (military participation) + X_u.

The squared multiple correlation is .83, indicating that the proportion of contribution of the unique vector is only 17 per cent. From the equation and this squared multiple correlation, it can be seen that system style has a good fit to the vector space defined by the other nine vectors, with most of the fit being due to the relationship of system style to the non-Communist regime vector.

A comparison of the factor model given in Eq. (5–2) and the regression model should show their virtual identity. Consider the factor model for a set of *m* standardized variables, with the regression model for the same data placed beneath it,

$$Z_j = \alpha_{j1}S_1 + \alpha_{j2}S_2 + \cdots + \alpha_{jl}S_l + \cdots + \alpha_{jp}S_p + \alpha_{ju}S_u,$$

$$Z_j = \beta_{j1}Z_1 + \beta_{j2}Z_2 + \cdots + \beta_{jk}Z_k + \cdots + \beta_{jm}Z_m + Z_u,$$

where $k \neq j$. From this we can see that the factors of factor analysis are the independent variables of regression analysis, that the loadings of the first are the regression coefficients of the second [it is shown later, in Eq. (19–10), that the regression coefficients equal the factor loadings times the inverse of the correlation matrix], and that the unique variance of a variable is equivalent to the residuals. Moreover, the communality, h^2, of a variable in factor analysis equals the squared multiple correlation in regression.

Although the models are similar, the questions asked of the data, and thus the usage, of each model is different. In factor analysis the basic question is: What is the smallest number of linear independent dimensions (factors) that will span the vector space defined by data on a set of vectors, $X_1, X_2, \ldots, X_m$? Thus, one has no knowledge of either the loadings for the right side of the equation for the factor model or the elements (factor scores) of the vectors denoting the dimensions. One does have the data for a number of vectors for the left side of the equation, however, and from these a set of dimensions (independent variables) can be generated on which they will have the maximum linear dependence. The discussion of the factor model following Notation 5–3 may be helpful on this point.

In regression analysis the basic questions are: How well will the data for a particular vector fit into the vector space defined by a set of vectors, and what will be the dependence of the particular vector on each vector of the set? With the exception of X_u, there are data on the vectors for *each side* of the equation of the model. The object is to determine the coefficients of dependence and the squared multiple correlation coefficient.

The loadings and regression coefficients of both models are of primary concern. For the factor analyst, however, loadings identify the number and nature of the *unknown* dimensions. In regression analysis, coefficients identify the contribution each *known* dimension makes toward the fit of a vector to this space.

9. Operationalization

Operationalization procedures are perhaps the most difficult aspect of a factor research design. They involve translating the factor analysis question into the procedures of the subsequent research steps. This numerical translation must be effected without introducing distortion or spurious elements into the results and in a fashion to maximize the retranslation back from the numerical findings to the original question.

The considerations involved in the operationalization step are shown in Fig. 9–1. For convenience they may be grouped into *data operationalization* and *design operationalization* considerations. These will serve as the two major sections of this chapter. The first section will cover four primary aspects of data operationalization: *defining phenomena, selecting phenomena, measuring phenomena,* and *observing phenomena.* The design operationalization section will discuss *charting the design* and additional *design considerations.*

STEP

3

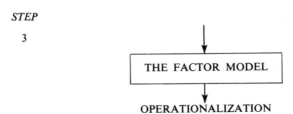

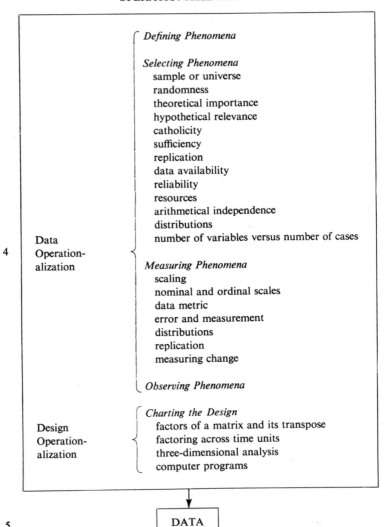

THE FACTOR MODEL

OPERATIONALIZATION

Data
Operation-
alization

Defining Phenomena

Selecting Phenomena
 sample or universe
 randomness
 theoretical importance
 hypothetical relevance
 catholicity
 sufficiency
 replication
 data availability
 reliability
 resources
 arithmetical independence
 distributions
 number of variables versus number of cases

Measuring Phenomena
 scaling
 nominal and ordinal scales
 data metric
 error and measurement
 distributions
 replication
 measuring change

Observing Phenomena

Design
Operation-
alization

Charting the Design
 factors of a matrix and its transpose
 factoring across time units
 three-dimensional analysis
 computer programs

DATA

4

5

Figure 9–1

9.1 Data Operationalization

9.1.1 DEFINING PHENOMENA

Defining the substantive focus of a design involves specifying the data slice of the three-dimensional data cube (Fig. 8–3). The discussion in Section 8.3 of the last chapter is quite relevant here.

9.1.2 SELECTING PHENOMENA

Once the phenomena are defined, the number of rows and columns of the data matrix must usually be reduced to a tractable number.

> *Example 9–1.* If the rows of the matrix are defined as years (*occasions*) and the columns as *characteristics* for the U.S., as in the P-factor analysis of Cattell and Adelson (1951), we cannot deal with all characteristics of the U.S. for all years. Obviously, a selection of years and of characteristics is required.

For some phenomena, however, a selection need not be made. The number of phenomena may be naturally limited to a manageable size.

> *Example 9–2.* In analyzing a matrix of nations (entities) by roll call votes (characteristics) in the UN, as Alker (1964) did, there was no selection problem for nations. All UN members could be included.

9.1.2.1. *Sample or Universe.* A first problem in selecting phenomena, therefore, is to decide whether to analyze a sample or the universe of cases. The answer will depend on the particular phenomena defined by the question. When the entities are defined as nations, members of the Senate, states, counties of Ohio, or chiefs of state, for example, the universe of such entities may well be included. Where such entities as small groups, individuals, legislators, politicians, and concepts are concerned, however, some mode of selection is necessary.

In the case of the characteristics dimension of the data cube (Fig. 8–3), the universe of phenomena can seldom be included. There are exceptions, however, as in possible studies of *all* roll call votes (characteristics) of *all* senators (entities) in the 22nd session of Congress (occasion), or *all* treaties deposited with the Secretary General of the UN (characteristics) of *all* nations for the post-World War II period (occasion). Likewise, for the occasion dimension of the data cube, the universe of phenomena can rarely be included.

When all entities, characteristics, or occasions cannot be included, selection must be made; where selection is necessary, criteria are implied.[1] The following subsections will discuss these criteria at the most general level—with reference to entities, occasions, or characteristics. The reader may perhaps be more familiar with these criteria applied to a particular dimension of the data cube, as with the randomness criterion for entities or with the independence criterion for characteristics (variables). These criteria should not be so limited here, since entities, characteristics, and occasions can be defined in innumerable ways; for each definition establishing a specific three-dimensional data cube, there are six possible modes of analysis (Section 8.3).

9.1.2.2 *Randomness.* Probably the most employed criterion in the social sciences for selecting from a universe of phenomena is that of randomness.[2] This criterion maximizes the probability of the sample reflecting the general properties of the universe and minimizes bias in the sample selection process.[3]

One technique for randomly selecting a sample from the universe involves defining the set of all members in the universe, tagging each member numerically, and then selecting from the universe in a manner that will give each member an equal probability of being selected.

> *Example 9–3.* In one analysis (Rummel, 1966c, Phase II) it was necessary to select from a universe of 3,321 pairs of nations for 1955 a random sample of 160 such pairs. To select pairs, the 82 sovereign nations for that period were ordered alphabetically and numbered 1–82, and a five-digit random-number table was used. Then: (1) a coin was tossed to determine the page of random numbers to begin with; (2) a pencil point was blindly placed on the page; (3) the first three digits of the closest number were used to indicate the line of the page to begin with, and the last two digits to determine the column; (4) a coin was tossed to ascertain which two digits of the five digit random numbers would be used (the last two were thus

1. Cattell (1952a, pp. 331–32, 344–46) considers sampling variables and several criteria for their selection, such as research focus, representativeness, universe of phenomena, number of variables, and defining other findings (marker variables).

2. Not all factor analysts consider a random sample desirable for factor analysis. Thurstone (1947, pp. 324 ff.) argues for a selected sample to display the range of deviation in the data and to bring out the greatest differences.

3. On the universe and sample see Dixon and Massey (1957, Chapter 4). On sampling in general, Wilson (1952, Chapter 7) is pertinent. The seventh edition of Fisher's classic work (1960) is relevant throughout. For those wishing a more precise treatment of random samples, see Feller (1962, Chapter 1).

selected); and (5) the last two digits were paired for successive random numbers (e.g., 17 paired with 53) until 160 pairs of 2 digit random numbers were chosen (any two digits greater than 82 were passed over and the next random numbers taken). By transforming these pairs of digits to nations according to the previously made numerical listing of nations, the sample of dyads was determined.

To select a sample randomly assumes that the nature and membership of the universe can be defined. This can usually be done for such entities as individuals or cities, such characteristics as votes, or such occasions as years. Nevertheless, the universe of small groups, socioeconomic characteristics, and conflict behavior, to name but a few possibilities, is not at all clear. When faced with phenomena lacking a definable universe or when random sampling is not desirable for other reasons, some other criteria of selection are necessary. These may be *theoretical* or *hypothetical importance, catholicity, sufficiency, replication, data availability, reliability,* or *resources.* In any case, whether randomness or several of the other criteria are employed, phenomena must be selected with an eye to their *arithmetical independence, scaling, distributions,* and *degrees of freedom.* These four considerations will be discussed after the other criteria have been considered.

9.1.2.3 *Theoretical Importance.* Once randomness is inapplicable as a criterion for choosing along at least one dimension of the data cube, then a useful criterion of selection is theoretical importance. Phenomena will be preferred as they relate to theories in the substantive area.

> *Example 9–4.* A factor study of the dimensions of variation in small group behavior may well want to include leadership characteristics because of the stress put upon their importance in the small group literature.

> *Example 9–5.* Cross-national factor studies, such as Cattell (1949a), Berry (1960), and Russett (1967b), have included measures of economic development. This phenomenon has loomed large in the analysis of nations and has been recommended as a basic indicator.[4]

9.1.2.4 *Hypothetical Relevance.* Phenomena may be singled out to index interesting hypotheses about interrelationships in a domain. Although the purpose of analyzing these phenomena may not be to test such hypotheses, their inclusion may make the results as widely useful as possible, fit them in better with current concerns, and promote the value of the findings to researchers with varying interests.

4. See, for example, Deutsch (1960) and United Nations (1954).

Example 9–6. In an 82 nation by 236 variable (characteristics) factor analysis of Rummel (1969), some of the many hypotheses guiding the selection of national characteristics were (1) Economic development, communication, and political development are interrelated; (2) desire for achievement is related to level of economic development; and (3) international and domestic politics form a common dimension.[5]

9.1.2.5 *Catholicity.* The phenomena may be selected to be as widely representative as possible of variations in the substantive area.[6] This will insure that the major patterns of variation are indexed and that the primary dimensions of the area being studied will be delineated. In applying this criterion, one may first wish to divide the area into substantive domains and then to select phenomena out of each domain without allowing any one domain to be overly represented in the final sample.

Example 9–7. Since the purpose of the analysis of Example 9–6 was to determine the major dimensions of cross-national variation, catholicity was one of the most important criteria. In applying the criterion, 28 domains spanning the many characteristics of nations were defined. Seventeen of them were internal to nations and covered domains of agriculture, arts and culture, communication, demography, domestic conflict behavior, the economy, education, geography, health, history, the military, the political system, resources, science and technology, the social system, transportation, and values. Ten domains referred to external characteristics in terms of collaboration, colonialism, international communication, diplomacy, international organizations, international politics, foreign conflict behavior, political geography, population movements, and trade. One final domain was methodological and involved measurements of possible error in the data. During the selection of characteristics for the analysis phase, these 28 domains functioned as reminders of the number and kinds of substantive phenomena that needed consideration.

5. The results were positive for hypothesis (1) and (3), negative for (2).
6. In a different terminology, vectors might be selected to span the vector space of concern.

Example 9–8. Cattell's (1949a) selection of 72 characteristics of nations for factor analysis was explicitly guided by the catholicity criterion. His final data matrix thus included diverse phenomena, measuring such aspects of a nation as its politics, foreign conflict, values, economy, and culture.

9.1.2.6 *Sufficiency.* This criterion avoids either substantive or statistical redundancy. In its substantive aspects, the criterion overlaps with the idea of catholicity—with selecting phenomena to span the area of concern. *Substantive sufficiency*, then, means that only one phenomenon will be selected from any potential set of phenomena whose definitions vary in minor ways.

Example 9–9. In a general analysis of cross-national variation, assume the following set of production-type variables: radio production, wool yarn production, lumber production, and butter production. To include a number of such production characteristics at the expense of other economic and more varied characteristics, like unemployment and taxes on wealth, would likely weight the analysis along a high–low production dimension. One characteristic, say manufacturing production, might be selected as a sufficient measure of the other production characteristics.

Statistical sufficiency, on the other hand, means that only one or two phenomena from a cluster of highly intercorrelated known phenomena are included. If many phenomena potentially available for analysis have high correlations with each other, the investigator may wish to avoid the possibility of forcing a factor defining this cluster of relationships to appear in the results. Such an a priori factor may be desirable with regard to some research questions, for example, a set of known intercorrelated phenomena might be included to determine what other phenomena relate to the resulting factor and where the factor is located in the space of all the phenomena of concern. In other cases, however, the study may be limited to mapping only the unknown relationships, thus eliminating dimensions that can be predicted to occur.

Example 9–10. In determining the dimensions of characteristics of cities and towns, as did Moser and Scott (1961), a nest of correlated characteristics would be area (incorporated), population, income, taxes collected, dwellings, paved roads, and so on. Although *substantively* dissimilar and thus likely candidates under the catholicity criterion, these characteristics have a known dimension of *size* underlying their high intercorrelations.[7] These correlated phenomena will be included if we wish to define a size factor in relation to other factors that may appear. On the other hand, if we wish to avoid the more obvious, we may work into more uncharted territory by including only one or two size-related phenomena or by dividing these phenomena by a measure of size (possibly incorporated area).

9.1.2.7 *Replication.* If it will eventually be desired to compare results with those of other studies or to hedge against the possibility that such comparisons may be wanted in the future, *marker variables* should be included in the analysis. Variables, in this sense, can be entities, characteristics, or occasions, depending on the data matrix of concern. A marker variable indexes the dimensions or factor scores of other studies. Including marker variables ensures that there is sufficient overlap between the contemplated analysis and completed studies to enable systematic comparisons. How many marker variables to include depends on the total number of variables to be analyzed. A rule applied in some studies (Rummel, 1969; Cattell and Gorsuch, 1965) and recommended in the literature (Guilford, 1963) is to include at least three marker variables indexing each of the factors from other studies.

9.1.2.8 *Data Availability.* If the phenomena are equal on other relevant criteria, those phenomena for which the most data are available should be selected. Applying this criterion may take some foreknowledge of data sources, however. A preliminary list of phenomena to be analyzed should therefore be drawn up. Then a check through available data sources or a pilot data collection operation should cull from the list phenomena undesirable because of either the presence or the amount of missing data.

9.1.2.9 *Reliability.* The notion of reliable variance has already been presented (Section 5.1) and will be discussed further in Section 9.1.3.4, below, and in the next chapter (Section 10.1.3). As a criterion of selection, phenomena for which the most reliable data are available should obviously be included. If the data are low in reliability, phenomena that have *random* and not *systematic* errors (Section 9.1.3.4) should be included as much as possible.

7. As a matter of fact, a size factor has consistently appeared as a major factor for small groups, organizations, cities, counties, states, and nations. Size might therefore be called a *basic dimension of all social systems.*

9.1.2.10 *Resources.* It is clear that time and availability of assistants will circumscribe the number and kinds of phenomena to be included. In addition, the computing facilities, whether hand, desk calculator, or computer, and the expense in time and funds of using each will set natural upper limits on the range of the analysis. If resources allow for the use of a computer center, further constraints are present. The availability of factor analysis computer programs is one constraint (Section 9.2.5). Another is the restrictions built into the programs as to the number of variables and cases that may be analyzed. These restrictions should be determined before the selection of phenomena for analysis is complete.

The criteria discussed in Sections 9.1.2.1–10 are methodological. They relate to good research practice, but their invocation is not crucial to using the factor models. A mathematically sound factor analysis can be computed, whether the phenomena factored have been selected for their theoretical or hypothetical importance, catholicity, or reliability—to name only a few of the criteria. Sections 9.1.2.11–13, will discuss criteria that are involved in the mathematics of the analysis. Their consideration by the researcher should help ensure rigorous results.

9.1.2.11 *Arithmetical Independence.* Ordinarily, phenomena should be included that are arithmetically independent of each other.[8] Phenomena that are derived from each other through addition, subtraction, multiplication, or division of the basic data may be *necessarily* related or, depending on the arithmetical operations, unrelated in the final result. That is, *the choice of arithmetically related phenomena may produce either general or orthogonal factors that are functions of the arithmetical operations on the data and not of the empirical data themselves.*

To see this, denote some of the variables that may be selected on a dimension of the data cube as X_1, X_2, X_3, X_4, and X_5. There are three relevant arithmetical combinations of data:

(1) $\quad X_1 \pm X_2 = X_3,\quad$ *additive* variables;

(2) $\quad X_1 X_2 = X_4,\quad$ *multiplicative* variables;

(3) $\quad \dfrac{X_1}{X_2} = X_5,\quad$ *ratio* variables.

For *additive* phenomena, it may be a question of including X_1, X_2, or X_3 in the data matrix. If all three are included and the variance

8. For some research purposes, a number of variables with known arithmetical dependence may be included in an analysis. This may be done, for example, to determine which of the arithmetically dependent variables best represents the others.

(Definition 3–2) of X_2, say, is much greater than X_1, there will be a necessarily high positive relationship between X_2 and X_3.[9] If a number of these arithmetically related phenomena are included in the analyses, factors that are only artifacts of additive phenomena may be forced into the result (Thurstone, 1947, Chapter XIX).

> *Example 9–11.* In analyzing the characteristics of nations there may be a choice between including exports, imports, and trade. Since the trade of a nation equals its exports plus imports, there is an additive arithmetical relationship between the phenomena. We therefore might seriously consider including only two of the three possibilities.

Such examples as the above are especially frequent in aggregative statistical data at the state, national, and international levels. It behooves the researcher in these areas, therefore, to be alert when it comes to including data that are arithmetical combinations. One more example might be warranted.

> *Example 9–12.* National income plus depreciation and indirect business taxes equals gross national product. Since depreciation and indirect taxes make up only around 10 per cent of a nation's GNP, national income and GNP are necessarily highly correlated. As a consequence, one or the other would ordinarily be included in factor analysis but not both.

Multiplicative phenomena are of equal concern. There is a tendency in the social sciences to form *ad hoc* indices or measures of concepts such as power, economic development, leadership, or conflict. Generally these indices are formed through the addition of variables but occasionally they are created by multiplying phenomena together. Here also, if

9. The artifactual nature of this relationship can be seen with regard to the correlation coefficient. Given that $X_3 = X_1 + X_2$, the product moment correlation between X_3 and X_2 (from Definitions 3–5 and 3–6 and through algebraic manipulation) is

$$r_{23} = \frac{C_{23} + C_{13}}{\sigma_2 \sigma_3 + \sigma_1 \sigma_3},$$

where C is covariance, and σ is standard deviation. Now, if the variance (σ_2^2) of X_2 is increased while that (σ_1^2) of X_1 is decreased, the greater specificity of r_{23} to the relationship between X_2 and X_3 can be seen from the above formula. The limiting case is when $\sigma_1^2 = 0$. The correlation between X_2 and X_3 will be 1.00, then, since without variance X_1 must be a constant, and adding a constant to a variable does not change its correlation.

for the product $X_1X_2 = X_4$ the researcher includes X_1, X_2, and X_4, or X_2 and X_4, where the variance of X_2 is much greater than that of X_1, artifactual correlations can result.

> *Example 9–13.* In his field theory of international relations, Quincy Wright (1955) proposed population by energy production as a measure of a nation's power (capabilities). If we were to include this measure in a factor analysis of nations along with separate population and energy production variables, there would be a necessary relationship between the product and the multiplier with the higher variance.[10]

Among the three possibilities, ratio phenomena are perhaps most often employed. Usually, they are in the form of percentages or increments, or they are data divided by some magnitude measure such as area, population, or gross national product. In selecting ratio phenomena, one may wish to include in the analysis a number of ratios with the same denominator or a ratio and its denominator separately. Raymond Cattell (1952a, p. 321) has remarked on the dangers of including ratios with the same denominator:

> One must...beware of situations where various ratios are used as variables, some elements in the numerator or denominator of the ratios being common to several of them. For example, if from a timed test we take one variable which represents the fraction of attempted answers that the person gets wrong and another the time he takes to answer each item, a spurious correlation is likely to arise between them because "number attempted" is common to the denominator of both ratios. This is likely to issue in a spurious doublet factor.

When including X_5 (where $X_5 = X_1/X_2$) and X_2, necessary orthogonality (Definition 3–28) may be introduced between the two variables. To divide a measure, such as GNP, by another, such as population, is to remove a certain amount of the variance of the former associated with the latter.[11] In terms of GNP and population, this is analogous (the closer to standardized variables they are, the better the analogy) to linearly regressing (Definition 3–8) GNP on population and (dealing with the residuals) GNP per capita. Thus, the inclusion of GNP per capita and population as separate variables may necessarily result in

10. If the variances of the two measures are unequal, they may be adjusted to equality by standardizing (Definition 3–4) the distribution for each measure.

11. "If constructed properly, a ratio, in the sample in which it is developed, is essentially a special case of a residual, i.e., the value in the numerator variable less that part which is correlated with the denominator variable. Accordingly, a ratio should correlate .00 with denominator variable." (DuBois, 1957, p. 68.)

their loading highly on separate factors. If a large number of such arithmetically independent phenomena were included, at least two independent factors might be forced into the results.

9.1.2.12 *Distribution.* For many studies, the frequency distributions of the data may be of little concern at the variable selection stage. Univariate distributions (see Section 11.2) that are nonnormal and bivariate distributions that are nonlinear may be transformed at step 6 of the design. Moreover, extreme values that may bias or distort the analysis may also be transformed then. If, however, the substantive area is such that many of the phenomena that are candidates for inclusion are *ordinal* or *nominal* (dichotomous) in scaling, one should be aware of the following considerations in selecting phenomena: *extreme frequencies, restriction of range,* and *underlying distribution.*

Extreme frequencies result when a value on a variable measured on an ordinal scale has a frequency greatly exceeding that for the other values.

> *Example 9–14.* In a study of the dimensions of foreign conflict of nations (Tanter, 1965, 1966), a phenomena considered for inclusion was measured as $0 =$ no war and $1 =$ war. Before war measured in this fashion could be included, however, the number of nations in the analysis having a 0 or 1 had to be determined. If out of the 83 nations to be included in the analysis only two or three nations had war (for 1958–60), then war could not be one of the variables. To have included war as a variable as measured would have caused any relationships found between war and other variables to hinge on these few occurrences. In fact, seven nations had war and this was deemed a sufficient frequency by Tanter to include the variable in the study.

> *Example 9–15.* On an ordinal scale of 0, 1, 2, and 3, the frequencies of occurrence for each value may be 103, 3, 1, and 2, respectively. One may seriously wish to question including such a measure in the analysis when there are only 6 cases with nonzero values and 103 cases with zeros.

Unequal frequencies for dichotomously scaled data are often referred to as unequal *marginals* or unequal *splits*. Split refers to the percentage or proportion of cases having one value as against the other. Before selecting variables for analysis, we may wish to establish a maximum allowable split for dichotomously scaled data. In some studies, I have used 90–10 per cent (Rummel, 1963, 1969). Variables on which cases had a frequency for one value greater than 90 per cent were omitted.

Restriction of range is a problem arising when a product moment correlation matrix (Definition 3–6) is factored. Whenever a variable is measured so that more than one case can have the same value, the -1.00 to $+1.00$ range of the correlation coefficient may be *restricted*, that is, the maximum positive correlation for a perfect relationship may be less than $+1.00$ (say .9, .8, or even .6), and the maximum negative correlation may be similarly restricted. This restriction will depend on the distributions of the two phenomena being correlated and the number of identical values in each distribution. If one of the distributions is skewed in a direction opposite to the other, the positive range of the correlation coefficient will be restricted; if both distributions are skewed in the same direction, the negative range will be reduced.[12]

> *Example 9–16.* Carroll (1961, p. 369) presents two hypothetical distributions for two variables, X_1 and X_2, measured on a five-point ordinal scale (0, 1, 2, 3, and 4). Data on these two variables for 50 individuals have the following frequency distributions:
>
> | X_1 Scale Values | Frequency | X_2 Scale Values | Frequency |
> |:---:|:---:|:---:|:---:|
> | 0 | 5 | 0 | 8 |
> | 1 | 10 | 1 | 8 |
> | 2 | 15 | 2 | 20 |
> | 3 | 12 | 3 | 10 |
> | 4 | 8 | 4 | 4 |
>
> As can be seen, the two distributions are nearly similar in that low frequencies appear at the tails, and high frequencies appear for scale value 2 in each case. These similarities notwithstanding, the different frequencies for each scale value (e.g., a frequency of 5 for X_1 versus 8 for X_2 for the zero scale value) and the number of identical values (e.g., 12 scale values of 3 for X_1) restrict the positive

12. This discussion of the range leans heavily on the work of Carroll (1961). See his Fig. 1, p. 350, which shows the bivariate and marginal distributions for two phenomena skewed in opposite directions. Table 1 (p. 351 of his work) shows the correlation coefficient for these *perfectly* correlated phenomena to be .60! Appendix A of Carroll's study describes a technique for ascertaining the range restriction on the correlation coefficient for any set of data. Guilford (1963) compares a number of correlation coefficients for their restriction of range on 0–1 data.

range of the product moment correlation coefficient to
.928. *Were* X_1 *and* X_2 *perfectly correlated in the positive
direction, .928 would be the value of their correlation
coefficient.*

The possibility of restricting the range of the correlation coefficient
is a consideration that seriously enters into the distributional transformations at step 6 of the factor analysis design. It should be a consideration also when selecting variables for analysis. One may be faced
with several variables measurable on different scales and with different
distributions. Other criteria being equal, one may then wish to select
those phenomena that are most continuous or have the larger number
of scale values (e.g., interval-scaled variables are more desirable than
variables measured on only four values; variables with nontied rankings
are desirable over those with tied rankings; variables measured on
three values are desirable over dichotomous variables). For variables
similarly measured, one may wish to select those variables with the
highest frequencies for the central scale values, i.e., those whose
distributions most closely approach normality. In the case of variables
with only three or four values or in the case of dichotomous variables,
one may wish to select those with the most rectangular distributions.[13]

The *underlying distribution* refers to the actual or hypothetical
distribution on the substantive concept, say threats, size, or democracy,
hopefully measured by a variable.[14] If the underlying distribution of a
concept is not taken into consideration, variables selected to measure
the concept may not span the potential range of data for the concept
and, in the extreme, may be limited to one or the other end of the
underlying distribution.

> *Example 9–17.* Consider the concept of "foreign con-
> flict." Let a measure of foreign conflict be, as with Richard-
> son (1960a, 1960b), the number killed in foreign conflict.
> Now the problem with this variable is that it samples
> only one end of the potential range of foreign conflict
> behavior. In rough order of increasing intensity, the conflict
> behavior of a nation can move from no conflict behavior
> through accusations, protests, threats, negative sanctions,

13. A rectangular distribution has the same frequency for each value.

14. On this point also I wish to express my indebtedness to Carroll (1961).
The problem of the difference between values on a measure and the underlying
distributions stimulated the development of latent structure analysis. See Lazarsfeld (1954). For a discussion of latent structure analysis as a form of measurement
in the social sciences and in relation to factor analysis, see Ahmavaara and Markkanen (1958, Chapter 2, Section 3).

troop movements, mobilization, and limited military action to full-scale military action. It is only in the last two stages that deaths will occur. Thus, the zero value on the deaths measure of foreign conflict would encompass no conflict as well as a whole range of conflict behavior. Most importantly, the *difference* between zero deaths and one death would be assumed the same as between one and two deaths. The transition from zero deaths to one death is a tremendous qualitative shift in conflict behavior as compared to a shift from one death to two deaths from hostilities.

Let the data on the number killed variable have a world average of 13 deaths. Nations with less than 13 deaths will appear on the nonconflict side of the average and nations with one death will have virtually the same influence on any correlation of this variable with others as nations with zero deaths. Factors resulting from the correlation of this variable with others could hardly be described as delineating the interrelationships of foreign conflict, although this may have been the intent of the analysis. Rather these factors would describe "intense violent foreign conflict" behavior—a concept far more restrictive than foreign conflict alone.[15]

9.1.2.13 *Number of Variables versus Number of Cases.* This refers to the number of variables that may be selected for a given number of cases. The importance of this question derives from the following mathematical relationships: (1) the rank of the data matrix is less than or equal to the smaller side of the data matrix (Section 4.4) and, (2) the rank of the matrix is equal to the number of factors that can be delineated [Eq. (5–15) and discussion following]. In other words, if the number of variables exceeds the number of cases, then no more factors than this number of cases can be extracted.

> *Example 9–18.* Consider a data matrix of 20 cases. No more than 20 factors can be extracted from these data, regardless of the number of variables included. If the variables number 5, then no more than 5 factors exist, since the rank of a matrix is limited to the smaller side.

15. To see the effects of improperly measuring the underlying distributions in bivariate relationships, see Fig. 2 of Carroll (1961, p. 352). His discussion of the sources and correction of such improper measurements takes up the bulk of his discussion, beginning on p. 352.

It is crucial, therefore, that a sufficient number of variables and cases be included in an analysis to enable the major factors in a domain to emerge. In any case, should one ever analyze a data matrix containing more variables than cases? The answer depends on the specific research question.

When the interest is only in *describing* data variability, then a factor analysis will yield such a description regardless of variables exceeding cases in number.[16] Analyzing 30 variables for 5 cases will still allow up to 5 independent factors to appear. And these 5 or less factors will still divide the 30 variables into major patterns of relationship for the 5 cases.

> *Example 9–19.* There have been published R-factor ana-
> lyses on 69 nations for 72 characteristics (Cattell, 1949a),
> on 40 nations for 72 characteristics (Cattell *et al.*, 1951),
> on 82 nations by 236 characteristics (Rummel, 1969),
> and on 82 nations by 94 international relations charac-
> teristics (Rummel, 1967b). For the most unequal 82
> nation by 236 characteristics case, comparison with other
> studies in which nations exceeded characteristics (Berry,
> 1960; Russett, 1967b; Schnore, 1961; Cattell and Gorsuch,
> 1965) showed the same major dimensions to have been
> extracted.[17]

When the interest is in inference from sample results to universal factors, however, the number of cases should exceed variables. The interrelationships among the variables are assumed to reflect—to represent—those in the universe. To impose a necessary dependence on these interrelationships, due to the number of cases being less than the number of variables, may bias the inferences that can be drawn. What rule of thumb to use for component or common factor analysis in determining the *minimum* allowable ratio of cases to variables for inference is still a matter of research taste. Cattell (1952a) suggests a 4-to-1 rule of thumb, e.g., 40 cases for 10 variables. At any rate, until statisticians define the ratio for these models, the number of cases to variables should be as large as practical. For canonical factor analysis (Section 5.5), however, a significance test does peg inferences to the number of cases.

16. One qualification must be given. In *image analysis* (Section 5.4) the inverse of the correlation matrix is required. If the number of cases is less than the number of variables, then the correlation matrix is *singular* and an inverse does not exist. For image analysis, therefore, the number of cases must be at least as many as the number of variables.

17. See also the factor comparisons in Russett (1967a).

9.1.3 MEASURING PHENOMENA

The above subsections have discussed several criteria for selecting variables. A second concern in data operationalization is measurement.[18] This concern need not be put aside until the variable selection process is finished. Indeed, the process of selection should be simultaneous with that of measurement, since the application of several of the criteria, such as those having to do with arithmetical independence and distributions, imply that measurement has been considered. With regard to applied factor analysis, we might divide the problem of measurement into six overlapping elements: *scaling, data metric, error, bivariate distributions, replication,* and *change.*

9.1.3.1 *Scaling.* As used here, a scale refers to the measurement properties of the numbers attached to phenomena.[19] In measuring phenomena we establish a one-to-one relationship between observations (however defined) and numbers. The arithmetical relationships between the numbers that represent meaningful relationships in the phenomena define the appropriate scale. There are essentially four types of scales of concern[20]: *nominal, ordinal, interval,* and *ratio.*

A *nominal scale* is the lowest rung of the measurement ladder. When measured on this scale, the numbers identify different set memberships—different classifications or categories—but establish no relationship between the sets. The numbers label different things but have no other property. Social scientists are quite familiar with the use of nominal measurement for coding data for storage on IBM cards and for purposes of cross-classification.

18. Burt (1941, pp. 115–38) presents a useful discussion of various problems of measurement and factor analysis.

19. Horst (1965, Chapter 15) discusses several aspects of scaling in relation to factor analysis.

20. The classic paper by Stevens (1946) on scales is still rewarding reading. Coombs (1964), Torgerson (1958), and especially Suppes and Zinnes (1963) revise and expand on Stevens in the light of current developments. Senders (1958) orders a discussion of statistical indices and measures in terms of their scales and is well worth consulting. A clear and concise presentation is given in Siegel (1956, pp. 21–30). For a general and clear discussion, see Kemeny (1958, Chapter 8). On measurement in science, see Campbell's informative essays in Newman (1956, pp. 1797–1813, 1814–29). On measurement in social science, see Lazarsfeld and Barton (1951). On measurement in sociology, see Coleman (1964, Chapter 2); in political science, see Alker (1965a, Chapter 2); in geography, see Duncan *et al.* (1961, Section 3.2). Although not explicitly related to scales, the discussion by Driver (1961) is instructive on measuring anthropological data. For a significant analysis of measurement related to factor analysis, see Ahmavaara and Markkanen (1958, Chapter 2).

Example 9–20. The religion of respondents to a question-naire survey in the U.S. can be coded: 0 = unknown, 1 = Protestant, 2 = Catholic, 3 = Jewish, 4 = none, and 5 = unclassified. These numbers form a nominal scale. Nothing is implied by the numbers about the relationship between religions for individuals other than that respondents with the same number have the same religion, and those with different numbers have different religions.

An *ordinal scale*, however, establishes a relationship between things with different numbers such that they can be ordered in terms of having more, the same amount, or less of a property.[21]

Example 9–21. Five nations, the United States, Japan, Argentina, U.S.S.R., and the United Kingdom, may be ordered in terms of their military power:

United States	1
U.S.S.R.	2
United Kingdom	3
Japan	4
Argentina	5

The rank order then forms the ordinal scale. A nation with order 4 thus has less power than a nation with order 1, or 2, or 3, but it has more power than a nation with order 5.

Example 9–22. Ph.D. dissertations graded according to honors are measured on an ordinal scale by their degree of excellence. Letting honors = 2, satisfactory = 1, and unsatisfactory = 0, one might measure dissertations to assess the correlation of their excellence with other attributes of the candidate, say age, duration of study, and financial support.

An *interval scale*, in addition to the ranking property of the ordinal scale, also has a meaningful interval between the numbers identifying set members. Thus, the relative scale position *and* the scale distance of cases conveys information. Moreover, an interval scale assumes that there is a meaningful unit of measurement and that the position of a case on the scale indicates the number of such units that the case possesses. Scale values therefore can be added and subtracted.

21. Ordinal scales can be divided into *simple ordinal*, or ranking of cases, *ordered metric* scales, which give also the ranking of cases between adjacent scale values, and *higher ordered metric*, which measure the complete ordering of the cases on and between all scale values (see Coombs, 1964). Cattell (1957, pp. 353 ff.) implies that the scales usually factored by psychologists are ordinal.

Example 9–23. Historical events of all kinds may be compared in terms of their date. The year is the unit. On this scale event *A* may have occurred in 1066, as compared to event *B* which occurred in 1648 and event *C*, in 1914. In addition to the ordinal property that *A* is earlier than *B*, and *B* is earlier than *C* in time, the interval nature of the scale allows one to say that *B* is not only later but 582 years later than *A*. In the ordinal scale of Example 9–21, however, one cannot say that the U.S.S.R. (with a rank order of 2 on the scale) has 3 "more of power" than Argentina (with a rank order of 5) and 2 more of power than Japan (with a rank order of 4).

A *ratio scale* includes the properties of the interval scale in addition to a meaningful zero value. Not only can scale values be added or subtracted, as with the interval scale, but they can also be multiplied and divided.

Example 9–24. The measurement of people (or nations) in terms of income forms a ratio scale. If *A*'s income is $4,000, *B*'s $6,000, and *C*'s $8,000, *B* not only has $2,000 more of income than *A*, but, because of the meaningful zero point for the dollar unit, one can also say that *A*'s income is $4,000/$6,000 = 2/3 of *B*'s, and that *C*'s income is twice as great as *A*'s.

The difference between interval and ratio scales can be fixed clearly in mind by remembering that the property that an interval scale measures is invariant under addition or multiplication by a constant. The interval scale *position* is arbitrary (since there is no meaningful zero point). Values on an interval scale of 3, 8, and 10 (or—adding the constant 2 to each—of 5, 10, and 12) have the same interval relationships, e.g., the last scale position is 7 more units than the first. In ratio measurement, however, addition of a constant can change the ratio relationship between values. If ratio scales values are 3, 8, and 10, and a constant of 2 is added to each, the *ratio* between the end numbers will change from 10/3 to 12/5, or from $3\frac{1}{3}$ to $2\frac{2}{5}$.

The recognition of the nominal, ordinal, and interval scales helps one to understand the flexibility of factor analysis as a descriptive instrument and to apply it within substantive domains that have yet to develop interval or ratio scales.[22] The next section will further explore this point.

22. As contrary to common sense as it may appear at first, it is possible to transform a matrix of ordinal-scaled data into a matrix of ratio-scaled data.

9.1.3.2 *Nominal and Ordinal Scales.* Ordinal measurements can be of diverse kinds. They may be rank positions of phenomena on some attribute or three-point ratings like 0, 1, or 2. Nominal measurement, however, is restricted (for factor analysis, multiple regression, and correlation) to only two scale positions It does not matter whether the nominal scale values are 0 and 1, or 5 and 10, or -6 and 4, as long as only two alternative nominal values are employed to measure an attribute. One of these values will usually measure the presence of some property and the other the absence.[23] In this sense, all qualitative knowledge, information, or data in any domain can be potentially factored.[24]

> *Example 9–25.* In analyzing the dimensions of college success, we may employ ratio-scaled data on years of college completed, family income, hours of employment, and so on. We may also have nominal data on religion and race. As nominal measures, religion and race may be included by treating each religion category and racial classification as a "dummy variable."[25] Each religion could be made a separate variable measured by: 0 = not of that religion (absence); and 1 = of that religion (presence). Similarly, each racial category could be treated as a separate variable, each measured as to presence or absence. A factor analysis of all these measurements, including the ratio-scaled data, should show how different religion and racial characteristics interrelate with the indicators of college success.[26]

When phenomena are measured on a nominal scale and factored, the interpretation of the resulting factor loadings may not be clear. For

---

Data reduction techniques are available that concentrate the diluted ratio scale information contained in ordinal data. These techniques are new but already promise a breakthrough in measurement theory and application. See Shepard (1962, 1963, 1965) and Coombs (1964).

23. Krause (1966) presents criteria for employing factor analysis to construct ordinal scales from a set of dichotomous variables.

24. See Burt (1950, 1953), who argues that factor analysis is applicable to qualitative data.

25. On the meaning and use of dummy variables in regression analysis, see Suits (1957) and Johnston (1963, pp. 221–28).

26. Gouldner and Peterson (1962) factor the traits of primitive societies measured on a zero-one nominal scale. For the inclusion of some dummy type measures in cross-national factor analyses, see the variable lists of Cattell (1949a) and Rummel (1969).

example, what does a loading of .56 mean for a variable measured 0–1 on a nominal scale?

Such loadings may be interpreted as are regression coefficients when *dummy variables* are employed in multiple regression (Definition 3–11). The regression coefficient of X_1 regressed on X_2, when each is measured as 0 or 1, can be interpreted as the likelihood of X_1, given X_2—that is, the probability (ranging from 0 to 1) that X_1 will be present when X_2 is present. Thus, a regression coefficient of .6 would imply that the probability of X_1 equaling 1 when X_2 is .6. Analogously, in factor analysis[27] a loading for 0–1-scaled variables can be interpreted as the probability of its presence (if the loading is positive) or absence (if negative), given that the factor exists.[28]

> *Example 9–26.* In Rummel (1969), the colonialism of a nation is measured by: 0 = has no colonies; 1 = has colonies. This characteristic loads .46 on an economic development factor. This loading may be interpreted three ways: as the probability that a highly developed nation has colonies; as the probability that a nation with colonies will be highly developed; or as the probability that colonialism and economic development go together.

The use of nominal and ordinal scales in factor analysis must be done with caution. Their distributions must be checked to determine whether the proportion of cases for any one scale value does not get too large. The frequency distributions should not be unduly skewed if the range of the correlation coefficient is not to be restricted. Moreover, the use of these scales may require a special type of correlation coefficient.[29]

9.1.3.3 *Data Metric.* The metric refers to the scale values on which phenomena are measured.[30] In many substantive areas, the particular metric assigned to phenomena may be quite arbitrary.[31] The rank

27. The loading plays the role in factor analysis of the regression coefficient in multiple regression.

28. For a discussion of the effect of zero–one measurements on Q-analysis, see Guilford (1963).

29. See Section 12.3, which discusses the different kinds of correlation coefficients and some criteria for selecting among them.

30. See Horst (1965, Section 4.6).

31. The discussion of data metric should not be confused with *metric analysis*. The latter refers to analysis employing interval or ratio scales; *nonmetric analysis* is of ordinal or nominal scales. On metric and nonmetric analyses, see Shepard (1965). Shepard also discusses the development of a nonmetric factor analysis that would delineate dimensions for ordinal data that are the same as those that would be found were the data to be interval- or ratio-scaled. See Section 22.3.

ordering of phenomena may be meaningful, but whether their rank positions are assigned values such as 1, 2, 3, 4, or 100, 110, 301, 400, or 5, 6, 8, 25 is arbitrary as long as their rank order is preserved. Unfortunately, however, the product moment correlation coefficient depends[32] on the characteristic of the data metric. The arbitrariness of the data metric and the sensitivity of the correlation coefficient may be reconciled by transforming the metric to accord with some notion of what desirable properties the correlation matrix should have. For example, while preserving rank order of cases and linearity of the bivariate distributions, the data metric may be changed so that the maximum (or minimum) correlation is achieved within the arbitrary limits of the original metric. The factor analysis of such a matrix should then define factors that best delimit the maximum (or minimum) intercorrelations in the data. For further discussion and computational techniques, the reader is referred to Cattell (1962c) and the more technical presentation of Guttman (1959).

9.1.3.4 *Error and Measurement.* Data error may be a result of the data source used, the instrument or methodology employed in measuring the data, or simply clerical error. The concern here is not with the cause of data error, however, but with the characteristics of such error and the measurement and methodological techniques that might be employed to compensate for the error.[33] Section 10.1.3 of the next chapter will consider controlling for error in the data collection process.

Data error may be classified as *random* or *systematic.* To make the discussion more precise, let the error in the data x_{ij} on variable X_j for case i be denoted by e_{ij}. Let the true value (the value if no error were present) be x_{ij}^*. Then

$$x_{ij} = x_{ij}^* + e_{ij} \text{ and } X_j = X_j^* + e_j. \qquad (9\text{--}1)$$

> *Definition 9–1.* For data on any set of variables, X_1, $X_2, \ldots, X_j, X_k, \ldots, X_m$, the error, e_j, in a variable X_j is RANDOM ERROR if the e_j is uncorrelated with the true values, X_k^*, of the other $m - 1$ variables and with their errors, e_k.[34]

Random error will always have this meaning in this book.

32. The correlation is influenced by the univariate distributions, extreme values, and linearity of the bivariate distributions. See Section 12.3.4.

33. Most of the discussion here is more formally developed in Rummel (1968b). An advanced consideration of the statistical nature and controls for data error is in Kendall and Stuart (1961, Chapter 29) and Madansky (1959). On the kinds of error entering into economic data, see Morgenstern (1963).

34. Random error is usually defined as e_j being uncorrelated with X_j^*. That is,

The random error *variance* of a variable is discussed in Section 5.1 with regard to the factor model. In Section 5.2, it has been shown [Eqs. (5–3) through (5–12)] that the variance that is factored, whether common or random error variance, can be controlled by the estimates selected for the principal diagonal of the correlation matrix. The insertion of reliabilities (however determined) will limit the factors to delineating the reliable variation among the variables.[35] Besides the reliability or communality estimates inserted in the principal diagonal of the correlation matrix, there are three other ways to compensate for random error[36]: adjusting the factor loadings, adjusting the correlations, and adjusting the data.

To consider these approaches requires a brief discussion of the effect of random error on correlations and a factor analysis.[37] As shown in Rummel (1966), the influence of random error in the data on two variables is to reduce their correlation coefficient to a lower absolute value than it would have for the true values.[38] That is, the correlation coefficient between data with random error is always a low estimate of the true correlation.[39]

Mosier (1939) has experimentally investigated the result of factoring a matrix consisting of such attenuated correlation coefficients. Contaminating a data matrix of known factors and dimension with random error, he found that the factor analysis and rotation reproduced the

---

the correlation between the true data and its error is zero. This definition, however, can be misleading in the multivariate case where, although the true values and their errors are uncorrelated with each other, the errors may still be correlated with the true values or errors of the other variables included in an analysis.

35. Limiting the dimensions to those that are reliable is connected with the problem of the correct number of factors to extract from a given matrix. See Sections 13.1 and 15.1. Cattell (1958) presents an extended and largely nontechnical discussion of several techniques for assessing and removing random error factors from an analysis. Because of his extensive applied experience with factor analysis on the most diverse kinds of data, Cattell's technical writing generally contains many helpful observations and practical suggestions.

36. The problem of random error in factor analysis is usually discussed with regard to the problem of *attenuation*—the effect random error has on the correlation coefficient. On attenuation and its correction, see Thurstone (1947, pp. 146–47), Cattell (1952a, *passim*), and Thomson (1951, p. 37). Hotelling (1933), in his development of the principal component factor analysis, has much to say on attenuation and on reliability estimates.

37. See Cattell (1952a, Chapter 17), Saunders (1948), and Aleamoni (1966).

38. See also, DuBois (1957, pp. 143–44).

39. For an interesting and informative exchange on random error in cross-national data, see Banks's (1965) review of the data and correlations of Russett *et al.* (1964), and Russett's reply (1965).

proper factors, but with slightly reduced loadings. Other methodologists, such as Cattell (1958) and Saunders (1948), have discussed this attenuating effect of random error on factor loadings.

The influence of random error can be compensated for by adjusting the loadings in the factor matrix. This can be done by factoring the data to the point where all the reliable factors have been extracted.[40] Then the resulting factor loadings can be corrected for random error by normalizing (Definition 3–25) each row vector of the factor matrix to unit length. That is,

$$\alpha_{jl}^* = \frac{\alpha_{jl}}{\left(\sum\limits_{l=1}^{p} \alpha_{jl}^2\right)^{1/2}}, \tag{9-2}$$

where α_{jl} is the loading of variable X_j on factor S_l, and α_{jl}^* is the adjusted loading. Normalizing the loadings will lengthen all the row vectors to unit length in the space defined by the factors.[41]

Instead of altering the factor matrix, the adjustments for error can be made on the correlation coefficients that are factored. Thurstone (1947, p. 146) presents the formula usually employed for this purpose:

$$r_{jk}^* = \frac{r_{jk}}{(r_{jj}r_{kk})^{1/2}}, \tag{9-3}$$

where r_{jk} is the unadjusted correlation between variables X_j and X_k, r_{jk}^* the adjusted correlation, and $r_{jj}r_{kk}$ the product of the reliabilities of the two variables. The reliabilities may be determined through such techniques as the split-half reliability coefficient[42] or the correlation between independently collected data on the same phenomena.[43]

Whether correcting the factor loadings or correlation coefficients for random error, the correction itself introduces error into the analysis. It may therefore be desirable to adjust loadings or correlations only if the required adjustment is relatively small and the reliabilities are good approximations. In any case, a third alternative corrections or control for random error is available. To carve away the unreliable variance in the data, the cases may be rank-ordered or grouped. Moreover, instrumental variables may be employed as a control for error.

40. On determining the reliable number of factors, see Chapter 15.

41. Guilford and Michael (1950) present a formula useful for altering loadings relative to data reliabilities.

42. For examples of its use, see Cattell (1949a) and Cattell and Gorsuch (1965).

43. Cattell (1957, Chapter 9) gives a general discussion of validity and reliability in the context of personality factors. See his Table 9–2, p. 352, which classifies a variety of reliability coefficients.

If data are measured on an interval or ratio scale and the random error range is not so great as to alter the ranks of the cases on the variable from the true ranking then the data might be rescaled to measure only rank positions.

> *Example 9–27.* Consider the following 1960 crude birth rates (per 1,000 population) for six nations (*Statistical Yearbook* of the UN, 1961, p. 43):
>
> | | Rate | Rank |
> |---|---|---|
> | Belgium | 16.9 | 4 |
> | Czechoslovakia | 15.9 | 5 |
> | Finland | 18.4 | 2 |
> | West Germany | 17.7 | 3 |
> | Hungary | 14.6 | 6 |
> | Netherlands | 20.8 | 1 |
>
> Because of the problems in the comparability and reliability of such statistical data, the figures may not measure the *precise rate* for these nations, but nonetheless they do index their *correct rank*. Accordingly, the ranks might be used as data for analysis rather than the rates themselves.

The level of measurement for the data should depend on the reliable information the data contain. In the above example, the unwanted error component of the data was shaved off by reducing the level of measurement to ranks. If the error is large enough to distort even rank positions, however, then a grouping procedure might be used. At the very extreme, one might divide the cases of the previous example into three groups by putting the three high-ranking cases in one group, the three low-ranking cases in another, and the middle-ranking cases in a third. Then the third (or middle) group might be omitted from the analysis. All members of the first group would be given a value of 0 and the remaining group a value 1. This dichotomous measure would then enter into the analysis only the variance in which the researcher has confidence. Of course, the grouping need not be so severe. If the investigator has a reasonable estimate of the error in his data (say 10 per cent), he can group and omit cases until the intervals separating groups exceed twice the error per cent in the values of the cases in each group.

> *Example 9–28.* Consider again the data of Example 9–27. Assume that the maximum random error in such data is $\pm.5$, e.g., the correct value for Hungary is 14.6 $\pm$ .5. This much error could change the ranks of some nations,

such as Belgium (16.9 ± .5) and Czechoslovakia (15.9 ± .5). Given this margin of error, the nations might be grouped as follows:

	Rate	New Value
Netherlands	20.8	1
Finland	18.4	2
West Germany	17.7	omit
Belgium	16.9	3
Czechoslovakia	15.9	omit
Hungary	14.6	4

By omitting West Germany and Czechoslovakia and transforming to new values, the random error has been removed and only reliable values are being analyzed. Regardless of the error for a nation, if the ±.5 maximum error estimate is correct, its new value will not change.

In place of ranking or grouping procedures, *instrumental variables* might be used. The poor data on a variable, say X_j, are replaced by those on another, say X_k, which has a very high correlation with the true values of X_j. If variable X_k can be measured more reliably and has this high correlation with the true values of the variable with error, one should consider replacing the errorful variable with X_k. The substitute variable X_k is called an instrumental variable. Several instrumental variables may be used to converge on the true values of interest.

Example 9–29. Let the data of interest be the gross national product of nations. Because of currency conversion problems, such as pegged rates, and the problem of comparability between Communist and non-Communist economies, GNP is a highly errorful variable. Instrumental variables to replace it might be energy consumption or electrical consumption, for which the data do not have as severe measurement problems. Of course, we must have prior evidence or assume that those instrumental variables are highly correlated with the true values for GNP.

Error that is not random is *systematic*.

Definition 9–2. For data on any set of variables, X_1, $X_2, \ldots, X_j, X_k, \ldots, X_m$, the error, e_j, in a variable, X_j, is SYSTEMATIC ERROR if e_j is correlated with the true values, X_k^*, of the other variables or with their errors, e_k.

The effect of systematic error in the variables is to either raise or lower their correlations over those between the true values. The factor loadings may accordingly be raised or lowered and the factor structure itself may be distorted. Of the two types of error, systematic error[44] obviously has the most undesirable effect.

The techniques for trying to gain some control over systematic error involve grouping, instrumental variables, and error measures. The grouping and instrumental variable approaches have been discussed above with regard to random error. The idea is the same with regard to error measures, with the difference that error measures are neither corrections of the original data nor distinct variables correlated with the true values of the error-laden variables. Rather, they are attempts to index the possible sources of systematic error and to gauge their effect on the analysis. If it is suspected that systematic error may be entering the analysis,[45] measures of this error might be isolated or developed and used in three ways:

1. Error measures may be included in an analysis to assess their correlation with the substantive variables and their location in the factor structure. Variables highly correlated with the error measures might be excluded from the analysis as being contaminated with systematic error. If they are allowed to remain in the factor analysis, then factors containing highly loaded error measures should be interpreted with caution.

> *Example 9–30.* In an analysis of 22 conflict behavior characteristics for nations based on 1955–57 data (Rummel, 1963), 1958–60 data (Tanter, 1966), 1955–60 data (Tanter, 1965), and 1946–59 data (Rummel, 1966b), there was concern that censorship within a nation and the degree of world interest in a nation (influencing the flow of news of that nation) would be systematically related to their conflict data. Accordingly, two measures were employed to gauge systematic error. One was a three-point ordinal

44. The influence of the multivariate selection of data according to the values of a particular variable is like that of systematic error. Thomson and Ledermann (1939) present a theorem showing the distorting effects of such selection on the correlation coefficients. Rydberg (1962) presents several formulas that, depending on the nature of the data, will correct correlations for restriction of range due to selection on a variable.

45. Systematic error enters much cross-national data through politically motivated statistics and the simple relationship between a nation's wealth and the capabilities and reliability of its statistical offices. Intranational data are not immune either. Crime statistics, for example, are influenced by the social status of the offender.

scale rating nations as to their degree of censorship. The second measure was a ratio scale giving the number of embassies and legations in a nation as a measure of the world importance of that nation. In the analyses these two measures came out as a separate dimension, indicating that as possible sources of systematic error they were independent of the interrelationships delineated among the conflict data.[46]

2. Error measures may not only be employed to assess error but also to remove error. They may be used as independent variables in a regression analysis. Each substantive variable may be regressed on the set of error measures. The residuals of the regression may then form a "purged" set of substantive measures, with the variance of the error measures removed by regression. This purged set can then be the data analyzed.

Alternatively, the analysis can be carried out to the point of determining the factor structure of a data matrix including both substantive variables and error measures. Then the first factors can be rotated to maximize loadings for the error measures; the following factors can be rotated orthogonally to these. Since these subsequent factors should contain only high loadings for substantive variables and since they are orthogonal to the factors highly loading the error measures, they can be interpreted as factors with much of the systematic error partialled out of the data.

3. The third approach to using the random error measures is to subdivide (partition) the cases according to their values on the error measures. This partitioning may be done most efficiently by factoring variables and error measures and rotating to determine the systematic error factors as described in the above paragraph. Then compute the factor scores of the cases on these error factors and partition the cases (high, medium, or low) on these factor scores. Finally, do a separate factor analysis on each of these subsamples. Similarity in the results of factoring each subsample suggests that systematic error, as indexed by the measures, has not affected the factor structure.

9.1.3.5 *Distributions.* The effect of distributions on the analysis has been discussed above in Section 9.1.2.12 as a criterion and will be considered from the point of view of transformations in Section 11.1.5. Accordingly, only the most salient considerations will be summarized here.

46. The methodology underlying the assessment of error in nonconflict cross-national data analyses is similar (Rummel, 1968b and 1969).

1. Measurements are preferred that give each case a distinct value (i.e., the frequency of occurrence of each value is one) so as not to restrict the range of the correlation coefficient.

2. Measurements are preferred that maximize normal distributions. This tends to minimize the distorting influence of skewed marginal distributions on the correlations.

3. If ordinal or dichotomous nominal scales are included, measurements are preferred that do not bunch a disproportionately high frequency of cases in one category, as for example 95 per cent zeros and 5 per cent ones on a nominal scale, or 80 per cent zeros, 15 per cent ones, 0 per cent twos, and 5 per cent threes on a four-point ordinal scale. This would give a few cases added weight in the analysis.

4. Unless a reason exists to the contrary,[47] ordinal equal-interval scales are most desirable. If some cases are not to be accorded undue weight, they should be rated on something like a 0, 1, 2, 3 scale, rather than on an unequal-interval ordinal scale such as 0, 1, 3, 10, or 0, 5, 6, 7. The 0, 1, 3, 10 scale would give more weight to the cases with the value 10; the 0, 5, 6, 7, scale would give more weight to the zero position.

5. Measurements should index the full range of the underlying distribution if distortions due to selection at one or the other end of the distribution are not to be introduced.

9.1.3.6 *Replication.* The research design may involve the replication of a previous study or, while no replication is formerly involved, factor comparisons may be anticipated. In either case, measurements between studies should be made as similar as possible.

Another aspect of replication has to do with the use of meaningful units. Psychologists usually have dealt with arbitrary scales and units, and their dependence upon factor-analyzing the correlation matrix reflects this (Cattell, 1962c). The correlation coefficient standardizes the data on which it is calculated and thus, in a sense, washes out the units of the data. In nonpsychological domains, however, the unit of measurement may be quite meaningful. Such units,[48] like length, may have physical standards against which phenomena can be calibrated. Examples of such units used to measure data in the social sciences are: energy units (kilowatt-hours, coal-tons), demographic units (deaths, population), area units (acres, square miles, hectares), time units (years), currency units (dollars, pounds), geographic distance units

47. One may wish to weight certain phenomena, for example, or reduce the effect of extreme values.

48. Although written for natural scientists and engineers, the work of Ipsen (1960) is clear and informative. See especially Chapters 1, 2, 3, 8, and 10.

(meters, miles), temperature[49] units, and food units (calories, protein content).

One may wish to employ a common unit for all the data, that is, to measure, if possible, all data in kilowatt-hours (if dealing wholly with economic production data) or persons (if analyzing a demographic domain) and either factor the data directly (Section 14.3.5) or factor the covariance matrix. The unit magnitudes will then be reflected in the resulting factor structure. The import of this is that the results will contain more information and that factor comparisons with other studies using the same units will determine more about the similarity or dissimilarity of the respective domains. Factor comparisons of factor results based on correlations are only comparisons of *interrelationships between patterns of phenomena;* comparisons of factor results derived directly from the data or based on covariances are comparisons of *pattern and magnitude interrelationships.*

As the level of measurement, development of units, and quantitative theoretical knowledge within a substantive area increase, one may avoid the common and component factor analysis models (Sections 5.2 and 5.3) based on correlations and instead apply one of the scale-free models (see Table 5–2) or direct factor analysis. Alternatively, the covariance matrix rather than the correlation matrix could be factored.

9.1.3.7 *Measuring Change.* Within many designs, the change of a characteristic between two periods (or two individuals) may be measured and included in an analysis of other variables. Measures like population growth rate, GNP growth rate, and per cent growth in urban populations are often employed. The questions to be discussed here are related to the alternative measures of change that may be employed and the features of each.[50]

Following the typology of Duncan *et al.* (1961, Section 3.6), four types of change measures may be identified: *incremental, relative, positional,* and *deviational.*

Notation 9–1. ΔX_j = incremental change in variable X_j.

---

49. Temperature has been employed as a central social variable by Huntington (1945).

50. Two excellent books on the nature and problems of measuring change in social science data are Harris (1963a) and Duncan *et al.* (1961, Section 3.6). The essays by Bereiter (pp. 3–20) and Lord (pp. 21–38) in Harris (1963b) are especially relevant here. The Harris book, moreover, contains essays by Tucker, Harris, Kaiser, and Cattell that discuss factor analysis as a technique for assessing change. Horn and Little (1966) have recently published a discussion and comparison of several approaches to the study of change that is especially pertinent to isolating change patterns by factor analysis.

The use of the symbol Δ for incremental change will be distinguishable from the use of Δ for determinants of matrices (Notation 4–2) by context and by restricting our application of the notation to variables.

> *Definition 9–3.* If a variable X_j is measured at two different time intervals, t_1 and t_2, then the INCREMENTAL CHANGE in X_j is $\Delta X_j = X_{jt2} - X_{jt1}$.

If ΔX_j is to be the index of change, the data must be measured on an interval or ratio scale: The intervals between the scale values must be meaningful. The change measure, moreover, assumes no ceiling on X_j. If there is an upper limit on X_j (as there would be if X_j is literacy rate, for example, since literacy rate cannot exceed 100 per cent), then the value on the measure of change must become necessarily smaller as X_{jt1} approaches the ceiling. Nations with 98 per cent literacy have little room for change compared with those having 15 per cent. Thus, to include ΔX_j in a factor analysis with the values for X_{jt1} may result in an artificial negative relationship between X_{jt1} and the measure of change. If X_{jt1} is not included in the analysis, there may still be an artificial relationship between ΔX_j and any phenomena correlated with X_{jt1}.

> *Example 9–31.* Let the growth in literacy rate for nations, measured according to Definition 9.1.3.3, be included in an analysis of nations. Also include measures of economic development, such as GNP per capita. Since GNP per capita is correlated over .80 (Rummel, 1969) with literacy rate, *economic development must be negatively related to change in literacy rate* by virtue of the measure of change used. Since a necessary consequence of the measure of change employed, this finding would not usually be substantively interesting.

If no natural ceiling exists for X_j, there may still be a *regression effect*. This effect results from very large X_j having a greater tendency to larger negative and smaller positive change than very small X_j.[51] Therefore variables may accidentally be included in the analysis that are related to the absolute change measures only because they are related to the initial values, X_{jt1}. This may be substantively interesting, but if so, we need only include X_{jt1} in the analysis rather than ΔX_j. If we wish

---

51. This may appear contrary to reason. The skeptical reader is referred to Lord (1963) for a more complete discussion with examples.

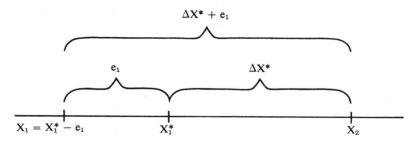

Figure 9–2

to find phenomena related to change independent of values of X_{jt1}, however, we might adopt a different measure of change.

For some phenomena, the regression effect may be negated and in fact reversed. Large initial values may lead to larger incremental changes than do smaller values. Population is, of course, an excellent example of this. Regardless of the direction of the effect, however, the high correlation between X_{jt1} and ΔX_j remains.

Two other consequences of using ΔX_j can be mentioned. If X_{jt1} and ΔX_j are included in the same analysis, their errors are negatively correlated -1.00. To illustrate this consequence, the notation will be simplified so that $X_1 = X_{jt1}$ and $X_2 = X_{jt2}$. Then, Figs. 9–2 and 9–3 show how the errors become negatively correlated.

Moving right to left, the scale of Fig. 9–2 represents the values X_2, true value X_1^*, and observation X_1 which is a combination of X_1^* with negative error e_1. As can be seen, addition of negative error to X_1^* as in Fig. 9–2 adds positive error to ΔX^*; addition of positive error to X_1^* as in Fig. 9–3 adds negative error to ΔX^*. The result of this in an analysis is to increase, as the variance of e_1 to X_1^* gets larger, the

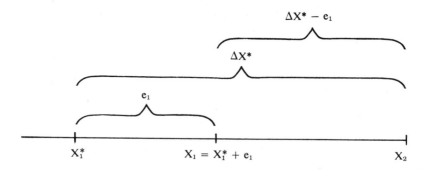

Figure 9–3

negative correlation between $X_1 = X_1^* \pm e_1$ and ΔX. Coupled with the ceiling and regression effects, therefore, the results of including X_1 and ΔX in the same analysis could be quite misleading.

Two final problems with ΔX_j should be mentioned. For some kinds of data, say attitudinal, questionnaire, opinion poll, or voting-type data, *the higher the correlation between* X_{jt1} *and* X_{jt2}, *the more unreliable* ΔX_j *may be*. In the limiting case of a correlation of 1.00, the variance in ΔX_j *can be entirely due to random disturbances*. Before determining the ΔX_j for voting or attitudinal shifts, one can assess the correlation between X_{jt1} and X_{jt2} or otherwise make sure that the ΔX_j is meaningful.

Finally, a *zero boundary* problem plagues the use of this measure for much social science data. The range in values on X_j may be between zero and some indefinitely large figure that does not constitute a ceiling. Negative ΔX_j for small X_{jt1} are necessarily smaller than ΔX_j for large values of X_{jt1}, while whether X_{jt2} is small or large does not restrict the range of the positive ΔX_j.

The problems of ΔX_j have been considered in some detail because many of them carry over to *relative change*, the second and most popular measure of change.

Notation 9–2. $R(X_j)$ = relative change in variable X_j.

Definition 9–4. If a variable, X_j, is measured at two different time intervals, t_1 and t_2, then the RELATIVE CHANGE in X_j is

$$R(X_j) = \frac{\Delta X_j}{X_{jt1}}.$$

$R(X_j)$ may be measured in different ways:

$$R(X_j) = \frac{\Delta X_j}{X_{jt1}} = \frac{X_{jt2} - X_{jt1}}{X_{jt1}} = \frac{X_{jt2}}{X_{jt1}} - 1. \tag{9-4}$$

By multiplying $R(X_j)$ by 100 we get the well-known *per cent rate of change*. For our purposes we can consider $R(X_j)$ to refer to a class of change measures including per cent rate of change as well as X_{jt2}/X_{jt1}.

While the change measure ΔX_j assumes interval- or ratio-scaled data, $R(X_j)$ requires that the data be measured on a ratio scale. $R(X_j)$ is dependent on the scale values: Adding or subtracting a constant, as is permissible in interval-scaling, would alter the value of $R(X_j)$.

All the ills associated with ΔX_j are equally a problem with $R(X_j)$. The relative change measure is susceptible to a *ceiling effect* within an analysis if X_{jt1} has an upper limit. A *regression effect* can influence

$R(X_j)$ for high and low values of X_{jt1}; and *artifactual correlation* due to the necessary correlation between errors can influence an analysis involving both $R(X_j)$ and X_{jt1}. Moreover, the more correlated X_{jt1} and X_{jt2} are, the more unreliable is $R(X_j)$.

The *zero boundary* problem is especially severe for the $R(X_j)$ measure. This effect is clearest with regard to X_{jt2}/X_{jt1}. When $R(X_j)$ equals 1, no relative change has taken place. Values smaller than 1 imply negative change; values larger than 1 imply positive change. The problem is that *$R(X_j)$ values for positive change can range between 1 and infinity, while those for negative change must lie between 0 and 1*. The distributions of $R(X_j)$ values can be very highly weighted in a positive direction, therefore. Since 1 is the midpoint of $R(X_j)$, the measure is skewed with unequal ranges on the positive and negative change sides. The effect of such measures on correlations (and consequently on factors) is to cause the correlation of $R(X_j)$ with other variables or measures to be overweighted by those cases with high positive change and under-weighted by those with high negative change.

Example 9–32. Consider the following values:

Case	X_j at time 1	X_j at time 2	X_{jt2}/X_{jt1}
A	5	100	20.00
B	10	5	.50
C	20	20	1.00
D	40	60	1.50
E	100	10	.10
		Total	23.10
		Mean	4.62

Note that two cases increased (A and D), two cases decreased (B and E), and C remained the same and that for the two cases that decreased, B decreased by 50 per cent and E by 90 per cent. Yet D, which *increased* by 50 per cent, is far below the mean change. Hence, whenever D has above-average values on variables being correlated with $R(X_j)$, D's value on $R(X_j)$ would contribute to a negative correlation coefficient even though it has positive change. Moreover, although A increased by only a few more units than E decreased, A will have far greater weight in any correlation.

Incremental and relative change measures are simple to compute and often used. The next two measures to be discussed, *positional change* and *deviational change*, are neither simple to compute nor often applied.

Positional change requires the data be first standardized; deviational measures require that the data first be regressed on each other.

> *Notation 9–3.* $P(X_j)$ = positional change in variable X_j.
>
> *Definition 9–5.* If a variable X_j is measured at two different time intervals, t_1 and t_2, then POSITIONAL CHANGE in X_j is $P(X_j) = Z_{jt2} - Z_{jt1}$, where Z_j is the standardized variable (Definition 3–4).

What $P(X_j)$ measures is the *incremental change* in the standard score position of a case. It takes account of the *ceiling effect* that can influence ΔX_j and $R(X_j)$ "insofar as the 'ceiling effect' results in an equal contraction of intervals all along the scale" (Duncan *et al.*, 1961, p. 163). The same observation holds for the *zero boundary* problem as well. Although potentially mitigating these biases, $P(X_j)$ is still plagued with the *regression effect*, necessary correlations between error, and unreliability due to any high correlation between X_{jt1} and X_{jt2}.

The *deviational change* measure, however, not only accounts for the ceiling and zero boundary effect, without the necessity for equal contraction of range, but also compensates for the regression effect, correlation of error problem, and unreliability with high correlation of X_{jt1} and X_{jt2}.

> *Notation 9–4.* $D(X_j)$ = deviational change in variable X_j.
>
> *Definition 9–6.* If a variable X_j is measured at two different time intervals, t_1 and t_2, then DEVIATIONAL CHANGE in X_j is
>
> $$D(X_j) = X_{jt2} - \hat{X}_{jt2},$$
>
> where $\hat{X}_{jt2}$ is the regression estimate (Definition 3–10) of X_{jt2} regressed on X_{jt1}.

In other words, the $D(X_j)$ values are the deviations (residuals) around the line of best fit[52] between the plot of cases on X_{jt1}, and X_{jt2}. $D(X_j)$ measures how much a case has over- or under-changed *relative to the change of all cases.*

> *Example 9–33.* Faced with the problem of measuring economic growth for nations, D. C. McClelland (1961, pp. 87–89, *passim*) employed the $D(X_j)$ measure of change. This mitigated the effect on his results of a high correlation between initial level of national economic development and amount of growth.

---

52. The regression can be curvilinear or linear.

9.1.4 OBSERVING PHENOMENA

So far the definition, selection, and measurement aspects of operational-izing phenomena have been discussed. After determining the units and scales for variables, one is prepared to collect data. Data collection may involve any combination of procedures,[53] including techniques of historiography (Barzun and Graff, 1957; Bloch, 1953) content analysis (Berelson, 1952; North *et al.*, 1963; Pool, 1959), simulation (Guetzkow *et al.*, 1963; Brody, 1963), sample surveys (Hansen *et al.*, 1953; Hyman *et al.*, 1954; Hyman, 1955), field research (Moore, 1961), or experimentation (Sidman, 1960; Selltiz *et al.*, 1959).

To discuss these approaches to generating data in detail would take us too far afield. It must suffice to say here that data collection procedures for each approach entails a methodology that is as important and as complex as that associated with analysis. Actually, the *research process* might be divided into three interacting but analytically distinct components. One is *theory*, or the formal-analytic structure, be it mathematics or logic, in which the research is embedded.[54] The second is *analysis*, or the methodologies, methods, and techniques by which theory and observation are connected. The third is *data collection*, with attendant methodologies spanning such diverse procedures as taking a rock sample, photographing a cloud, creating a chemical reaction, counting hostile diplomatic symbols or asking respondents if war is likely this year.

9.2 Design Operationalization

9.2.1 CHARTING THE DESIGN

Chapter 7 discussed the factor analysis research design and sketched its major elements, and Fig. 7–1 delineated the full design. Charting the design involves laying out the design steps for the factor analysis. A number of design decisions must now be made as to the alternative paths the analysis will follow.

It must first be decided what factor *model* to employ and whether *communalities* will be estimated and, if so, how. A decision as to factor *comparison* and possible *new data cycles* must also be made here.

---

53. Of course, one will not first define and select appropriate measures and only then begin to think of research procedures. Definition, selection, and research procedures are interwoven. Operationalization is a constant iteration among them until there is convergence on the best data for the task at hand.

54. So-called atheoretical or exploratory studies still employ theory, although the theory is implicit and sometimes subliminal.

Moreover, the *technique* of factor analysis should be selected at this stage. For further discussion of the design itself and the alternatives available at each step, the reader is referred back to Chapter 7.

Several considerations are relevant to the charting of the design and the operationalizations of the data: relationship between dimensions of a matrix and of its transpose, autocorrelation in P- and S-factor analysis, three-dimensional factor analysis, and computer programs.

9.2.2 FACTORS OF A MATRIX AND ITS TRANSPOSE

The cross-sectional, time series, and case study slices of the data cube have been discussed in Section 8.3. Each of these slices constitutes a data matrix. For each of these matrices, the interrelationships between the column vectors or, by transposing the matrix, the interrelationships between the row vectors may be analyzed. In the case of the cross-sectional slice, these alternative analyses are called R- and Q-factor analyses.

A question often raised is: What is the relationship between the factors of a matrix and those of its transpose? Since most factor analyses have been of the R or Q types, the question is usually discussed in the literature[55] in terms of the relationship between R- and Q-factor analyses.[56] The conclusions of these discussions are applicable to the time series and case study slices as well.

A simple answer to the question cannot be given. Much depends on the characteristics of the raw data matrix and the type of matrix transformations (Chapter 12) applied. To develop answers to the question, we will have to review some notations and present some new ones.

A = a slice (matrix) of the data cube.
A' = transpose of the data slice.
C = covariance matrix.

55. Sometimes the problem is discussed under the category "correlating persons."
56. A seminal article on this topic is that by Burt (1937). Thomson (1951, Chapter 17) evaluates Burt's conclusions in detail. See also Cattell (1952a, 1952b), Stephenson (1953, Chapter 3), Horst (1965, Chapter 12, Section 14.4, and p. 324), and Eysenck (1953). The exchange between Broverman (1961, 1963) and MacAndrew and Forgy (1963) is very useful for clarifying the relationship between data transformations and R- and Q-factor analyses. Those unfamiliar with the normative-ipsative scale distinctions mentioned in the above exchange might read Broverman (1962) and Cattell (1952a). Section 12.1.1, below, also discusses these terms. A mathematical consideration of the problem in the general case is contained in Higman (1964, Chapter 11, especially pp. 160–61).

R = correlation matrix.

A_c = *centering* the columns of A by subtracting the column means from each column value.

$_cA$ = *centering* the rows of A by subtracting the row means from each row value.

$_cA_c$ = centering first one way and then another. *The rows and columns of $_cA_c$ will all sum to zero.*

A_s = standardizing columns of A.

$_sA$ = standardizing rows of A.

$_sA_s$ = a doubly standardized matrix produced by standardizing by columns and then by rows and by repeating these operations until the row and column standard deviation of $_sA_s$ converge upon unity within acceptable limits.

F_A = factor matrix of A or of any of its scalings, A_c, A_s, etc.

$F_{A'}$ = factor matrix of A' or of any of its scalings, A_c, A_s, etc.

Answer 1. The *rank* of a matrix (see Section 4.4) is not altered when it is transposed. That is, rank of A = rank of A'. Moreover, the rank of A is unaltered by elementary transformations (Hohn, 1958, Section 4.2) such as multiplying a column or row by a constant or pre- or post-multiplication by itself (which yields C or R). Finally, the rank of a matrix is equal to the *number* of orthogonal factors that can be extracted from the data. Accordingly, *insofar as the number of factors are concerned*, the results of factoring a matrix and its transpose are the same, regardless of whether the original data, the correlation matrix, or the co-variance matrix is factored, and regardless of the elementary transformation.

Answer 2. If A is symmetrical, that is $A = A'$, then $F_A = F_{A'}$.

Answer 3. Let A be asymmetrical, as are almost all data matrices. Moreover, directly factor (Section 14.3.5) A, A_c, $_cA_c$, A_s, or $_sA_s$. Then, in general, the interpretation of the factors of F_A will be different from the interpretation of $F_{A'}$.

Answer 4. If A is asymmetrical and is scaled to $_cA_c$ or $_sA_s$ prior to computing, then there is a transposable relationship between the factors of F_A and $F_{A'}$ (Burt, 1937).[57] The interpretations of the factors of F_A and $F_{A'}$ therefore should be the same.

Answer 5. The computation of R automatically involves standardizing A. Therefore, if a matrix A is standardized by rows only and R is computed on the resulting $_sA$, the consequence is the same as if R

57. For empirical demonstrations of this similarity, see Broverman (1961, pp. 77–73) and Thomson (1951, Chapter 17).

had been computed on a doubly standardized matrix, $_sA_s$. The answer in this case, then, will be the same as answer 4, above. If, however, R is computed for A unscaled and for $_sA'$ (what were the columns of A are now the rows of A' and are standardized), the results will be the same in the unrotated case *except for the first factor of* F_A that accounts for the variation standardized out of $_sA'$, *and the last factor of* $F_{A'}$ that delineates the new variation introduced into A by the standardization procedure. This last factor is minor and would not be interpreted in any case. So essentially, *except for the first factor of* F_A, the interpretable factors of A are similar to those of its transpose A' standardized by rows across the direction of correlation.

To summarize the above answers, the *number* of factors is unaltered by factoring a matrix or its transpose. As to the content of the factors, their similarity hinges on the symmetrical property of the raw data matrix and the matrix transformations applied. If the matrix is symmetrical and factored directly, the two sets of factors are the same. If the matrix is not symmetrical, the two sets of factors are similarly interpretable when calculated from the correlation matrix of doubly centered or doubly standardized data. If only the transposed data matrix is standardized by rows and the factor results are similarly interpretable except for the first unrotated factor of the untransposed matrix.

One question remains. The above discussion is general to the three data slices. In the case of the cross-sectional slice, it should be clear that factoring the transposed matrix refers to Q-factor analysis. What, however, are the transposed matrices for the other two slices (see Figs. 8–8-11)? For the time series slice, the O-factor analysis matrix is the transpose, since occasions are being analyzed across characteristics, as with entities across characteristics in Q-analysis. In each case, the units of measurement for the characteristics may vary. For the T- and S-factor analysis, either matrix may be considered the transpose, since the measurement unit is the same throughout the matrix.

9.2.3 FACTORING ACROSS TIME UNITS

In P- or S-factor analysis the interest is in the interrelationships of characteristics or of entities over time units (see Figs. 8–9 and 8–11). The peculiar nature of time units presents several problems for such analyses. These problems may be classified as *serial correlation, dependence of errors*, and *loss of information*.[58]

58. A clear and comprehensive analysis of the mathematical issues involved in P-analysis is contained in Anderson (1963). Anderson, moreover, presents an informative discussion of the factor analysis model in general and in comparison

Serial correlation results from the lack of statistical independence between the sequential values for many variables. Often the magnitude of a variable at a specific time, say t_1, will be directly related to its magnitude for the previous time, t_0, and subsequent time, t_2. The magnitudes at successive intervals will display some kind of trend movement instead of sharply alternating between the extremes of their possible range.

> *Example 9–34.* The level of gross national product of nations for successive years will vary, but within small increments between adjacent years. Large changes may occur, but only as an accumulation of many small changes over many time units.

Many phenomena of interest to scientists manifest this statistical interdependency.[59] Change between successive states requires a movement over time. If the time units are too short, *then the time positions of the movement itself will be included in the analysis.* The result of factor-analyzing, over time, a number of characteristics or entities that manifest this serial correlation is that an artifactual trend factor may emerge, indexing the statistical interdependence of the changes in a number of phenomena—the trend movements themselves.

One way of handling this problem is to define the unit time intervals so that they are long enough to incorporate the trend changes. Thus, the data on the characteristics of a nation, might be factored for decades or quarter-centuries, rather than for years; in factoring the characteristics of a person, month or year units might be used rather than days.

Another way of approaching this is to orthogonally rotate the factor solution so that the first factor defines the serial correlation, or trend in the data. The subsequent factors may then be interpreted as defining interrelationships in the data with the influence of serial correlation removed.

The *dependence of errors* problem is similar to that of serial correlation. A number of chance effects unrelated to the substantive concern of the investigator may similarly influence phenomena over time. Such

---

with multiple regression. On the problems of P-analysis, Cattell (1952b, 1957, 1963) should also be read.

59. Economists have long been aware of problems of autocorrelation. For a technical description by an econometrician, see Johnston (1963, Chapter 7). An advanced general mathematical treatment is given in Rosenblatt (1963, Part 1).

happenstances as bad weather, sunspots, or earthquakes may similarly influence the characteristics or entities over a number of time units, thus tying—correlating—these phenomena together. Instrument or data source error may similarly produce spurious common variance.

We must be on guard against possible extraneous influences that may cause such statistical interdependencies. If we have reason to suspect their existence, we should change the time units or introduce into the study measures of such systematic sources of error so as to gauge and control their effects (Section 9.1.3.4).

Loss of information results from the nature of the factor models. It is assumed that the rows of the data matrix (when interrelationships among column vectors are being analyzed) can be shifted around arbitrarily. That is, they form no order. In analyzing an entity by characteristic matrix, it does not matter which row refers to what entity. But, when the rows refer to time units as in P- and S-factor analysis, then the ordering of the rows is important—the time sequence *is* meaningful.

A way of trying to overcome this problem is to include in the P- or S-factor analysis a measure of time numbered sequentially. Since this measure will be correlated 1.00 with time, its loading on the factors should indicate which factors, if any, are themselves time sequence or progression dimensions. If we have reason to believe that cyclic phenomena are involved we may wish to make the time measure a sine or cosine function.[60]

Besides losing the order of events, the factor analyses may not catch any *lag relationships* that exist. The relationships between phenomena may take several time units to manifest themselves, as would, perhaps, a relationship between technological change and change in sociopolitical institutions. To check out this possibility we can run a number of factor analyses on data that have been lagged behind each other for different time units.

> *Example 9–35.* To determine whether technological measures have a 25-year relationship to change in institutions, the data on the technological measures for a year and that for institutions 25 years later can be inserted in the *same row* of the data matrix—as though they had occurred for the same year.

60. A measure of time has no error of measurement. According to Anderson (1963), since the factor analysis model assumes that all variables are measured with some error, a contradiction is created and several statistical consequences ensue. This issue, however, does not appear to be significant in application. Those wishing to pursue this question should consult Anderson.

9.2.4 THREE-DIMENSIONAL ANALYSIS

One of the problems faced by many analysts is that of collapsing data available along all three dimensions of the data cube (Fig. 8–3) to a two-dimensional data matrix.[61] One solution, not altogether desirable, is to sum the data along one dimension of the cube and factor the resulting aggregate data for the other two dimensions. Another approach, used, for example, by Triandis (1964), is to factor each of the three combinations of two dimensions possible out of the three and compare the results.[62]

Another solution is possible, however, and since it does not appear to be mentioned elsewhere, it will be discussed briefly here in terms of an illustration.

Assume that data are available for 100 nations for a number of characteristics over 100 years. Let the problem be to determine the factors of change over these years for *all* these nations, rather than for just one nation as in P-factor analysis. Let the columns of the data matrix be the characteristics; order the rows so that the first 100 rows refer to the 100 years for the first nation, the second 100 rows to the second nation, and so on for the 10,000 rows. Now, if this matrix is analyzed as is, the variance in the characteristics for nations will be confused with that due to the variance over time on a characteristic for each nation. In different terms, the between-nation variance on characteristics will confound the within-nation variance on time.

To bring out the within-nation variance on the characteristics over the 100 years for each nation and to generalize this across the 100 nations, we must standardize each characteristic across the 100 years for each nation separately. That is, data on characteristic X_j for nation A will be standardized, over the 100 years, then data for the same characteristic for nation B will be separately standardized, and so on for all nations on these characteristics. Similarly we will standardize the data for each nation separately on the other characteristics.

These separate standardizations within nations will remove from the analysis the variance on the characteristics *between* nations due to, say, the different magnitudes of such nations as the United States and Yemen on a number of characteristics. The remaining variance will

61. Osgood *et al.* (1957), for example, faced this problem in the analysis of semantic data.

62. Recent effort has been directed at simultaneously factoring the data cube to define a factor matrix summarizing variance along the three data dimensions. See Tucker (1966) and Levin (1963, 1965). Horst (1965, Section 14.1) considers ways of simultaneously factoring the data cube. His results, however, are influenced by different within-group and between-group variance. He suggests in Section 14.2 a transformation of scale to overcome this.

define the interrelationships between changes in the characteristics over the 100 years generalized across the 100 nations. This standardization method of collapsing a data cube to two dimensions is quite general and may be employed in many problems.

9.2.5 COMPUTER PROGRAMS

The computer programs available at a computing center depend on the type of computer available, the center's philosophy about its service function to the research community, and the computing demands placed upon the center. Factor analysis programs and connecting routines for screening data, computing matrix transformations, and doing rotations may cover all possible techniques and research needs. On the other hand, a center may have only one factor analysis program and the one may be limited in terms of the amount of data it can analyze, estimation of communalities, acceptance of missing data, and so on.

It is important, therefore, to survey the limitations and availability of needed computer programs before a research design is charted and resources invested in collecting data. If the required programs are not locally available, they often may be acquired from other centers and (usually with some effort) adjusted to the local computer. If necessary, arrangements can be made to run the data at another center where the proper programs exist.

Those having little or no acquaintance with computing facilities may wonder what computations can be expected from a center's library programs.[63] A fairly good computing center library should have programs available to aid in the following:[64]

1. Processing data to determine the amount missing (if any), extreme data values, distribution plot, chi-square fit to normality, kurtosis and skew, mean, standard deviation, and range;

63. Harold Borko's (1962) collection is especially valuable for those uninitiated in computer usage. The essay in this book by Fruchter and Jennings (1962) describes factor analysis generally and in relation to computers. See also Cooley and Lohnes (1962).

64. It should be mentioned for the benefit of those unfamiliar with a computing center that the full range of statistical and mathematical techniques may be employed through programs already written and on file in the center's library. These programs are written as general instructions to the computer and can be accommodated to different sets of research data and needs. The user need not know how to write programs; he need only punch up a few instruction cards indicating the nature of the data, their location on the data decks, and his selection of the options the program may allow. Assistants are usually on duty at a center to help with even this limited requirement.

2. Transforming the data distributions, using any one of a dozen or more of the most desirable transformations, and punching the transformed data on a new set of cards;
3. Calculating covariances or correlations with or without missing data, and punching results on cards;
4. Factor-analyzing the input data, either raw data (in which case the program itself will carry out the distribution transformations and calculate correlations) or the covariance or correlation matrix from another program, allowing a number of options for communality estimate and limiting the number of factors extracted (a program employing the principal axes technique should be available);
5. Rotating to an orthogonal varimax solution;
6. Rotating to oblique solutions;
7. Computing factor scores;
8. Comparing factors;
9. Computing distances between cases in factor space.

These programs may be linked into one program or they may be distinct programs. In any case, by employing one or another of these programs, it should be possible to complete almost any factor analysis design through existing computing facilities.

10. Data

The previous step of the research design concerned operations for translating the phenomena of concern, whether brickbats, kitchen sinks, or man's inhumanity to man, into a matrix capable of being factor-analyzed. This chapter will discuss the content of that translation —the data. The focus will be on some of the procedures that are involved in moving from the operational considerations of the last chapter to a data matrix ready for the subsequent steps of the factor design.

As shown in Fig. 10–1, these procedures involve data processing, data coding, and handling missing data. Within each of these procedures, moreover, a number of considerations are important, such as the collection of the data proper, the coding of data, and data card punching. Each of the set of procedures listed in Fig. 10–1 and considerations will be discussed separately.

10.1 Data Collection

The great diversity of phenomena that may be factored and the many different modes of collecting data that are possible allow for a discussion

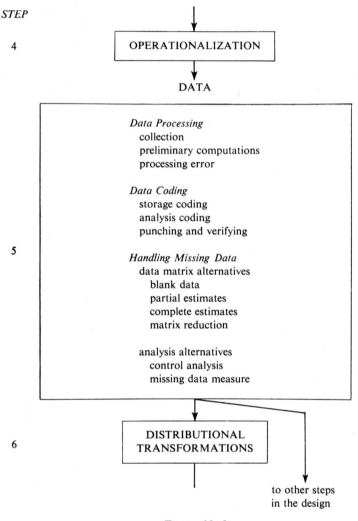

Figure 10–1

of only the most general considerations. These considerations, however, may be overlooked in applying factor analysis. They are particularly important in large-scale analyses in which such a mass of data is involved that some kind of data management procedures have to be established. For small-scale studies, say a data matrix on the order of 10 rows by 8 columns, the proverbial back of an envelope might be adequate, although it is not recommended.

10.1.1 COLLECTION PROCEDURES

Regardless of the mode of data collection and the sources employed, there must be a means of coding the data. For some data, the coding may be done directly on computer cards,[1] like answers to questionnaires or data already tabulated in a source. For most data, however, a set of data collection sheets will be needed. These will organize the data prior to card punching and should allow for the recording of qualifications for each datum and the source from which it was obtained.

Although the data collection sheets will be a permanent record of the data and relevant information, they will also be employed in punching the data onto computer cards. Consequently, the format of the collection sheet should facilitate both functions.

Figure 10–2 presents the format of a data collection sheet that may be useful. The number of columns on the sheet are the same as for a computer card and are numbered accordingly. Each row of the sheet would be data for one computer card. Columns on the sheet are set aside for identification of cases, footnote qualifications, and card numbers. Appendix 10.1 of this chapter includes a set of instructions for research assistants using such a data collection sheet.

10.1.2 INITIAL COMPUTATIONS

Often the data will exist in raw form and will have to be converted to ratios, percentages, or some other combined measure selected at the operationalization stage.

> *Example 10–1.* Data on the national income of nations is usually given in domestic currency. The researcher wishing to compare nations on national income must therefore convert the currencies according to the exchange rates to some standard currency prior to analysis.

If the data matrix is relatively small, one may carry out these initial computations of ratios, percentages, and so forth, by hand or on desk calculators. If, however, the data matrix is large and if the data are amenable to such a procedure,[2] the factor analysis computer program or a preliminary correlation program may be used for such a purpose.

1. It is assumed in this and the following section on data coding that a computer will be used to analyze data and that the data will be punched on computer cards. For a book that discusses many of the problems of computer processing of data, card punching, and coding, see Janda (1965).

2. In some cases, as with some of my data, the numerator and denominator may have to be matched by year, with the year varying for each case and variable. In such cases, even for large matrices the desk calculator may be more efficient for preliminary computations.

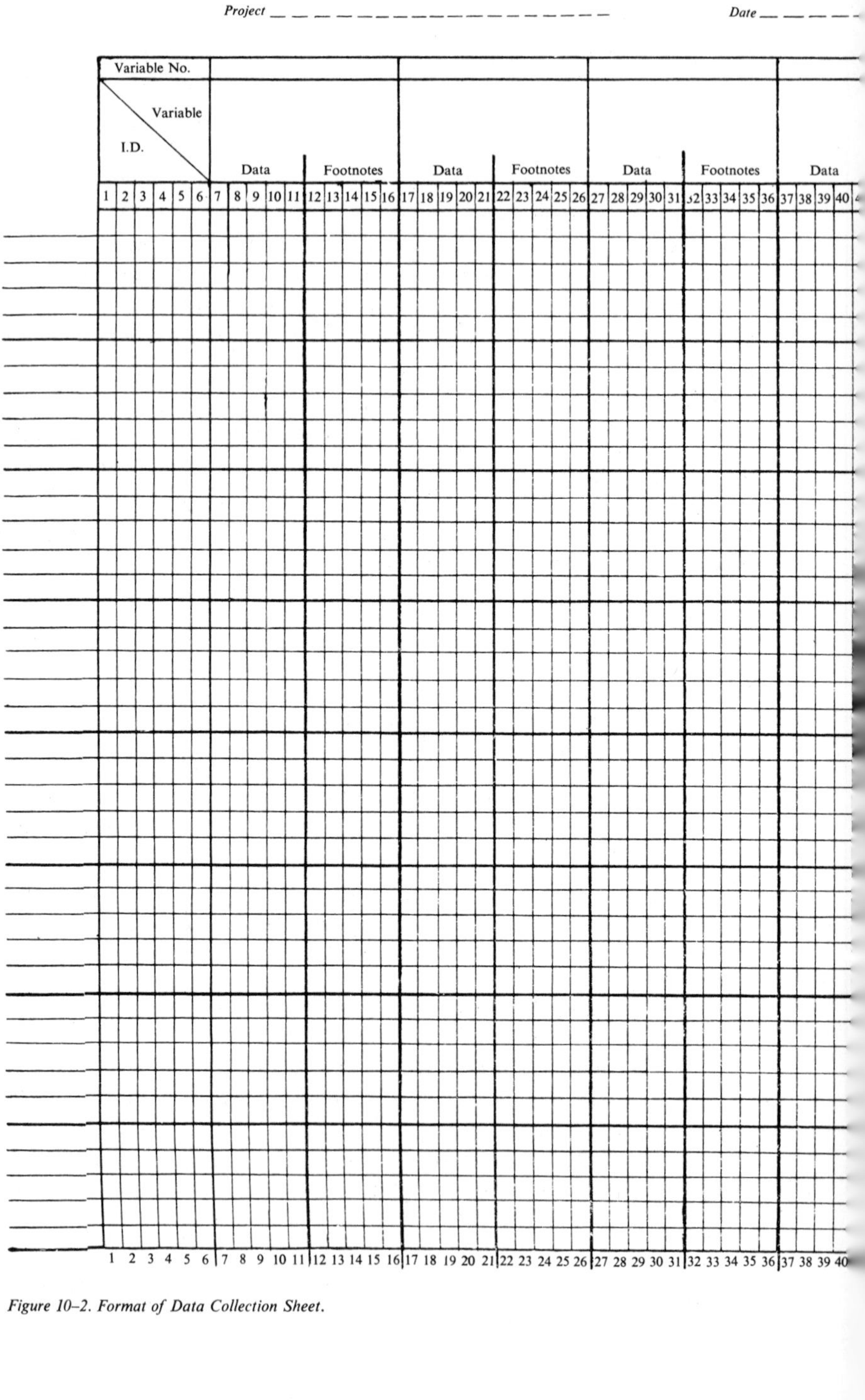

Figure 10–2. Format of Data Collection Sheet.

Page_ _ _ _ _ _ _ of _ _ _ _ _ _ _ _ _ _ _ _ _ _

Footnotes	Data	Footnotes	Data	Footnotes	Data	Footnotes	Card No.
42 43 44 45 46	47 48 49 50 51	52 53 54 55 56	57 58 59 60 61	62 63 64 65 66	67 68 69 70 71	72 73 74	75 76 77 78 79 80

42 43 44 45 46 | 47 48 49 50 51 | 52 53 54 55 56 | 57 58 59 60 61 | 62 63 64 65 66 | 67 68 69 70 71 | 72 73 74 | 75 76 77 78 79 80

Green check = visually screened for clerical error

Red check = double checked against source
Blue check = ratios, etc., calculated twice

Name

To do this, data on components entering into the computations may be collected and punched as though separate variables. Then, when the data are analyzed through the computer, so-called transgeneration cards may be prepared that instruct the computer to combine the components in the desired way into new variables and to delete the data on the components from the analysis.

> *Example 10–2.* Let one of the measures for an analysis of social groups be the group fund (treasury) per group member. Data on group treasuries and members will usually be found separately rather than as a ratio. To use the computer to form the ratio of fund amount per member, these two components can initially be treated as separate variables. Then, in factoring the matrix containing these components (or in employing a data screening or correlation program), transgeneration cards may be prepared instructing the computer to (1) divide fund by membership, (2) erase fund data and replace them with data for the ratio, and (3) delete membership data from the analysis.

Preparing transgeneration cards is a simple procedure, and most available programs contain provisions for so combining variables. If such an option is not available or if deletion of variables is not possible when desired, there should be a transgeneration program available that will allow a wide range of transformations and combinations of the variables and that will punch the results on a new set of cards. These cards may then be input to a factoring program.

10.1.3 PROCESSING ERROR

It is difficult and expensive to employ procedures for eliminating all clerical error from a large-scale data collection process.[3] Although most such errors that enter the data matrix will probably be random and thus only depress the strength of the relationships formed (Section 9.1.3.4), it is desirable to hold such errors to a minimum. Each investigator will develop his own checking procedures as he gains experience in data collection and processing. The techniques that I have found useful may be of some help in this regard. They are embodied in the following list.

---

3. The experience of the U.S. Bureau of the Census in this regard is instructive, and the techniques they are developing for controlling clerical error are potentially useful on a smaller scale. See Fasteau *et al.* (1962, 1964).

1. *Checking the raw data collection*
   1.1. *A* (where *A* denotes one assistant and *B* the other) records the data from the source.
   1.2. *B* reads aloud the recorded data as *A* checks the source. This controls:
      a. legibility of *A*'s recording of data so that those punching computer cards from the raw data will not be faced with an ambiguous figure;
      b. the accuracy of the recording;
      c. the accuracy of the footnotes;
   1.3. Footnotes for each recorded variable give:
      a. variable name and number;
      b. units;
      c. source for each datum if sources differ (if one source is used for all data it is so indicated);
      d. definition;
      e. important qualifications for a datum where relevant.
   1.4. Data are scanned by the research director to locate unreasonable values that may be in error.
   1.5. After punching, data are screened through a program that lists data of more than a specified number of standard deviations from the mean, say 2.5 or 3.0 standard deviations. These extreme values are then checked for accuracy.
2. *Checking the presence of all required information on data collection sheets*
   2.1. All data collection sheets have been checked by *A* with respect to:
      a. proper ID number in proper place for all cases;
      b. right justification (e.g., if a case has a value of 23 on a 6-column variable, then the 23 must be preceded by four *blank columns*);
      c. same units for all data on the same variable.
3. *Checking control of variables on computer cards and during computer runs*
   3.1. For each data collection sheet a variable record sheet has been made, consisting of a vertically and horizontally ruled 8×15 inch sheet. Each variable record sheet corresponds to a data collection sheet. On it is recorded:
      a. variables used in ratios as components, those used as is, and those already in ratio form (those to be transgenerated are recorded in separate columns and on separate rows);
      b. each variable's digit places, sample size, and column

numbers on the computer card (recorded in separate columns).

3.2. About 10 columns of space are left to the right of the variables in which to record the variable number that a variable will have as it is run through the machine for a particular analysis. The column heading will thus contain the analysis number, and the column itself will contain the numbers of the variables entering into the analysis.

4. *Checking accuracy of preliminary calculations*

4.1. All of *A*'s calculations on the data, such as computing ratios, are checked by *B* independently, and the results are re-computed.

5. *Checking safety of data*

5.1. All punched data are reproduced on computer cards twice to give:

a. one master deck;

b. one deck for computer use;

c. one deck to keep separate in case of fire or some act of God.

10.2 Data Coding

Those familiar with the use of computer cards in computer analyses may wish to omit this section. It is safe to assume however, and probably will be for many years to come, that a large majority of students and social scientists have yet to be initiated into the mysteries of computer data processing. For these researchers, the first coding of computer cards may be traumatic if certain elementary rules are not known. Most computer centers have manuals on such coding available for reference. Here we might note that computer cards have two basic purposes: data storage and data analysis.

10.2.1 DATA STORAGE

The types of codes that are convenient for data storage may not be the best for data analysis. It is often a practice to use codes that classify cases on a variable as well as describe the availability or nature of the data.

> *Example 10–3.* The number of political parties of a nation may be coded: $0 = $ no data, $1 = $ ambiguous, $2 = $ one party, $3 = $ two parties, $4 = $ multiparty.

> *Example 10–4.* Religion for respondents to a question-
> naire may be coded: 0 = unknown, 1 = Catholic,
> 2 = Protestant, 3 = Jewish, 4 = other religion, 5 = ag-
> nostic, 6 = atheist.

Although codings such as those given in the examples are quite common, aside from cross tabulation they do not allow for bivariate and multivariate analysis through the computer. For one thing, the codings of Example 10–4 do not form an adequate scale of measurement (Section 9.1.3). Secondly, the mixture of data and information about data (e.g., unknown, ambiguous) in the same coding scheme even when there is an underlying ordinal scale for most of the codes, as in Example 10–3, makes meaningful multivariate analysis difficult, if not impossible.

In coding for data storage, of course, data and information about data can be mixed. When these stored data are to be used later for analysis, the card sorter or a transgeneration program may be used to separate the codes or to create a number of dichotomously scaled variables out of the codes.

10.2.2 DATA ANALYSIS

If some precautions are taken, the data may be coded in a form amenable to immediate analysis as well as long-term storage. Some rules for doing this are listed below.

1. Code data on an ordinal, interval, or ratio scale on columns separate from information about data, such as "ambiguous," or "nonapplicable." Then when analyzing the data, the computer can be instructed to read only the data while skipping over the columns with information about the data.

> *Example 10–5.* The codes of Example 10–3 can be put
> in two columns of the card. One column should contain
> the data, coded 2, 3, or 4. The other columns can contain
> a 0 or 1, depending on the absence of data or the ambiguity
> of available data.

2. If the data form a nominal scale as in Example 10–4, set aside separate columns for each label (e.g., Catholic) and code as to presence or absence. These variables are then dichotomously scaled and may be factor-analyzed along with other variables.

3. When data are missing or nonapplicable, or for some other reason a value cannot be given to a case, leave the relevant data column

blank. Many computer programs have a provision for reading blanks as missing data and excluding the particular case from the analyses for that variable.

10.3 Handling Missing Data

Often we are faced with an incomplete data matrix. Perhaps some of the variables are not applicable to some of the cases, or these data would be prohibitively expensive to determine or track down. When confronted with this problem, one may try any of a number of alternatives for treating such missing data in the matrix.[4] In addition, or alternatively, some controls for missing data may be employed in the factor analysis itself. These two not mutually exclusive sets of possibilities will be discussed below in Sections 10.3.1 and 10.3.2.

10.3.1 DATA MATRIX ALTERNATIVES
Essentially four practical options are available for treating missing data: Leave them blank; partially estimate the missing data; make complete estimates; or reduce the order of the data matrix.

10.3.1.1 *Missing Data.* The data matrix may be analyzed with the missing data cells left blank. Computer programs that make a provision for missing data usually specify this in their write-up. It should be noted that only when the factor analysis will be applied to the covariance or correlation matrix of the data is it possible to leave missing data as blank. If factor analysis is to be applied directly to the data, some means of completely estimating missing data must be determined.

When the correlation (or covariance) matrix is calculated for data matrices with blanks, those cases that have a missing datum on one or both of the variables entering into a particular correlation coefficient are omitted from the computation. The means and standard deviations for the variables are adjusted accordingly.

---

4. The problems of analyzing incomplete data have been getting increased attention. Horst (1965, Chapter 11) presents several factor solutions for cases of unreliable or missing covariances or correlations. The component analysis model has been used by Dear (1959) to estimate missing data for multiple regression. Factor analysis also has been employed as a general missing data estimation method by Woodbury *et al.* (1963). Statistical inference from samples with incomplete data has received some attention at least as early as three decades ago (Wilks, 1932; Yates, 1933). Some of the more recent literature includes Anderson (1957), Hartley (1958), Matthai (1951), Nicholson (1957), Lord (1955), Rao (1956), Trawinski and Bargmann (1964), and Wilkinson (1958).

Example 10–6. Let three variables X_1, X_2, and X_3 have the following data:

Case	X_1	X_2	X_3
A	5	8	
B	7		8
C	4	6	4
D			6
E	7	7	3
F	2	10	4

If the correlation between X_1 and X_2 is calculated, only the data on cases A, C, E, and F will be used; the means and standard deviations for this correlation will be computed from cases A, C, E, and F. When the correlations between X_1 and X_3 are assessed, however, the cases to be used will be B, C, E, and F, and the means and standard deviations for only these four cases will be employed in computing the correlation coefficient.

When missing data are left as blanks in the data matrix, computing the correlations between variables as above has an important effect on the factor loadings and communalities (h^2). To discuss these effects, some preliminary remarks about the relevant mathematical properties of the factor analysis model should be made.

Most factor models uncover the basic structure of the correlation matrix by determining its eigenvalues and eigenvectors (Section 4.5). Now, the correlation matrix is theoretically *Gramian* (Definition 4–16). The relevant property of a Gramian matrix is that its eigenvalues are zero or positive. Thus, the square root of the eigenvalue is a real number and can be used to scale the eigenvectors to determine the factor loadings [as in Eq. (5–14)]. This Gramian property of a correlation matrix will be preserved as long as the principal minors of the matrix are greater than or equal to zero.

When the correlations between variables that have blank data are calculated, the particular values of a variable that enter into the correlations with the other variables change as a function of the missing data on the other variables. Thus, the correlations calculated across blank data are not dependent on the same set of data for any variable. A rereading of Example 10–6 may help to make this clearer.

Example 10–7. Consider three variables X_1, X_2, and X_3. If there are no missing data, a perfect correlation of 1.00 between X_1 and X_2 implies that the correlation between X_1 and X_3 must be the same as that between X_2 and X_3.

If there is missing data, the correlation between X_1 and X_3 on the one hand and X_2 and X_3 on the other can be quite different even though that between X_1 and X_2 is 1.00.

The consequence of missing data is to allow some of the principal minors of the correlation or covariance matrix to be less than zero, *and this results in negative eigenvalues*. Since the square root of the eigenvalue is used in scaling the eigenvectors [as in Eq. (5–14)], a negative eigenvalue results in an *imaginary number*.

On the basis of this preliminary discussion, several points about the effect of missing data can now be made.

1. Missing data can result in negative eigenvalues.

2. When the eigenvalues are ordered by size (i.e., the first eigenvalue and eigenvector account for the most variance in the data, the second account for the second most, etc.), the negative eigenvalues will be the last ones extracted from the data.

3. An eigenvalue measures the amount of variance accounted for by an eigenvector. Negative eigenvalues measure what I will call *imaginary variance*.[5]

4. The more missing data there are in the data matrix, the more imaginary variance there is.[6]

5. Since the total variance of a variable is unity if correlations are factored (Section 5.1), the total amount of variance extracted from a data matrix cannot exceed the number of variables. That is, when there is imaginary variance due to missing data, the positive plus imaginary variance must sum to the number of variables.[7]

6. With missing data, *the positive variance extracted* (*the positive eigenvalues and their eigenvectors*) *will be inflated* to compensate for the imaginary variance, since both positive and imaginary variance added together must equal the number of variables.

7. With the inflation of the positive variance—presuming that the number of factors extracted is limited to those with positive eigenvalues

5. At first, I used the term negative variance for that variance associated with negative eigenvalues. By Definition 3–2, however, variance is only positive. Although negative variance is only meant to refer to variance associated with negative eigenvalues, the term can be more confusing than its use justifies. Therefore, I will call this variance imaginary, realizing that I have not done away completely with the problem but that I still need some term that intuitively reflects what is involved.

6. A mathematical relationship has yet to be established in this regard. What factor analyses I have done across missing data indicate, however, a clear monotonic relationship between the amount of missing data and imaginary variance.

7. Harman (1960, p. 187) discusses this point.

—the loadings on these factors will be larger than they should and the communality for the variables may exceed 1.00.

8. Those variables with the most missing data appear to have the most inflated loadings and communalities.[8]

> *Example 10–8.* In an analysis of 94 international relations variables for 82 nations (Rummel, 1967b), the over-all missing data amounted to about 17 per cent. The percentage of 4,371 correlations between these variables that fell within the following ranges for the sample size used in computing the correlation were: 21–30 nations—1.6 per cent; 31–40 nations—7.1 per cent; 41–50 nations—15.3 per cent; 51–60 nations—24.2 per cent; 61–70 nations—16.9 per cent; and 71–82 nations—34.8 per cent. Four correlations involved between 10 and 20 nations. Sixteen factors with positive eigenvalues were extracted from the 94-variable correlation matrix. The subsequent factors had negative eigenvalues. The communality on the first 16 factors for the variables involved in those 4 correlations with the lowest sample size were:
>
> | No. | Variable | n | h^2 |
> |-----|----------|-----|-------|
> | 19 | Aid received | 47 | .81 |
> | 75 | Immigrants/migrants | 33 | .86 |
> | 20 | Aid received/GNP^2 per capita | 43 | 1.29 |
> | 74 | Emigrants/population | 43 | 1.11 |
>
> The n refers to the number of nations having data on these variables out of a possible 82. It can be seen that the inflation of the variance accounted for by factors caused two of the variables to exceed the theoretical upper limit of 1.00 for h^2. Had all the imaginary variance for these variables also been extracted, the h^2 would have decreased to 1.0 or less.

The effect of missing data on a factor analysis begs an answer to the question "How much missing data can be allowed?" No methodological work on this problem seems to have been published. An answer depends on how the missing data will decrease the sample size (n) for the correlations. Two data matrices, each with 15 per cent missing data, may result in correlation matrices of vastly different average sample size. This hinges on whether the missing data are generally

8. Here, also, no mathematical relationship has been established. Nor can the statement be made more precise, since it is based only on my experience in factor-analyzing several matrices with missing data.

for the same cases or are spread randomly through the data matrix. In the former case, the average sample size for the correlations will be higher.

10.3.1.2 *Partial Estimates.* This involves the use of expert judgment in estimating some of the missing data. It is assumed that the factor analyst is not without some knowledge of what he is analyzing, and, although specific data on some variable may be missing, an estimate may be made based on his familiarity with the domain. Such an estimate may not be possible in all cases, but general knowledge sometimes makes it possible to override a mechanical inability to collect all the data.

> *Example 10–9.* Consider the following 5×5 matrix with missing data treated as blanks.

Above World Average on Ratio of Female Employment (*yes* = 1; *no* = 0)	Roman Catholic %	Prot- estant %	Mos- lem %	Liter- acy %
U.S.	0	43	54		
Denmark	1	00	98		98
Yemen					
China	1	00			
Japan	0	00	00		99

> Data for all nations on these variables are not easy (if possible at all) to find. (I actually could not find data on the 1955 U.S. literacy rate or that for adjacent years in UN statistical sources.) Based on my general knowledge, estimates (underlined) for the missing data are filled in below. Almost all readers would probably agree with these estimates to within a margin of, say, ± 2 per cent, which is more than sufficient for analysis.

Above World Average on Ratio of Female Employment (*yes* = 1; *no* = 0)	Roman Catholic %	Prot- estant %	Mos- lem %	Liter- acy %
U.S.	0	43	54	00	97
Denmark	1	00	98	00	98
Yemen	0	00	00	99	
China	1	00	00		
Japan	0	00	00	00	99

10.3.1.3 *Complete Estimates.* One may not be willing to muddy factor analysis results with the effects of missing data or may wish to employ a factor analysis program that does not allow for missing data. Consequently, all the missing data must be estimated. Where possible, the matrix should first be filled in with those estimates that can be safely made on the basis of general knowledge. The remaining missing data may be estimated through the techniques of *average value, rating, measurement scale reduction, multiple regression*, or *factor analysis*.

Estimating with the *average value* technique involves calculating the average on available data for a variable and inserting this average in place of the missing data for that variable. This may well be the most popular approach. Unfortunately, the simplicity of the technique must be weighed against the effect it has on the analysis. Inserting the average will *lower* the correlations or covariances of the variable. The more averages inserted in the matrix, the more the over-all correlations or covariances will *underestimate* the true values. The effect on the factors extracted will be to attenuate their loadings and, moreover, the analysis may stop short of identifying all the meaningful factors existing in the data. That is, the effect of inserting averages is to deflate the positive variance.

A second approach to estimating missing data is that of *rating*. This may be likened to the partial estimates approach, except that here one is willing to accept a larger margin of error. The rationale is essentially that averages should be used only in cases of complete ignorance of a case and the variable. Where some knowlege exists, one should be able to judge whether a case is one, two, or three standard deviations above or below the mean. The estimate inserted would then locate a case in the appropriate part of the data distribution.

> *Example 10–10.* Assume the average log GNP per capita for nations in 1955 was 2.42 with a standard deviation of .42. Let data on this measure be missing for Yemen, China, Albania, South Vietnam, and East Germany. Readers may agree in estimating the number of standard deviations below the mean for Yemen as 3.0 (i.e., a value of $2.4 - 3 \times .42$); for Albania, 2.5; and for China and South Vietnam, 2.0 each. East Germany is a more ambiguous case, but might be estimated at half a standard deviation above the mean.

Measurement scale reduction, the third approach to estimating missing data, involves transferring the data to an ordinal or dichotomous scale that enables a more reliable estimate of missing data. Data measured on an interval or ratio scale can be divided into groups either above or below the data mean or into groups falling into particular ranges of the data, such as deciles or quartiles. Those groups into which cases with missing data should fall may then be estimated. Often quantitative data for a case may be missing, but verbal descriptions are available from which the researcher may be able to place a case on an ordinal or dichotomous scale.

The *regression* and *factor analysis* approaches to estimation are attempts to avoid the judgmental bias latent in the previous techniques. In regression analysis, the available data on each variable are regressed on the available data on the other variables to determine regression estimates (Definitions 3–10 and 3–11) for the missing data. A number of regression equations equal to the number of variables with missing data are thus computed (a relatively simple task if a computer is available) to determine regression estimates for all missing data. The equations may be recomputed, including the missing data estimates this time, to generate a new set of estimates. These recomputations may be carried through several cycles until the estimates converge to stable values for the missing data.

As long as many of the variables in the data matrix are highly inter-correlated, regression estimation appears to be an efficient and fairly reliable approach. If, however, the correlations between all the variables are low or zero, then the estimates for the missing data may be quite unreliable and may increase the margin of error above that of the more judgmental approaches discussed above.

The *factor analysis* approach to estimation is an extension of the regression technique. The missing data may be filled in first with some arbitrary estimate, perhaps the average or a rating discussed above, and a factor analysis is then computed to determine the factor loading and factor score matrices. Using the factor model, new missing data estimates are calculated from the factor results. The data are thus rerun through the computer a number of times until the estimates converge to a stable value. Convergence will not occur in the case of all estimates, however, and considerable research is needed to determine the best and most efficient initial estimates for convergence. In the meantime, the use of factor analysis in this fashion in conjunction with averages and rating estimates of initial values should probably determine the best estimates that might be made.[9]

10.3.1.4 *Matrix Reduction.* Finally, another feasible approach is to

9. Woodbury *et al.* (1963) have applied and tested this approach on biological data. An interesting finding of theirs is that the stable estimates to which factor analysis converges indicate the approximate number of factors for the data matrix.

remove a combination of rows and columns from the data matrix until the reduced matrix has no missing data. This is a simple approach, but drastic if the missing data is spread throughout the matrix. Once data are collected, it is unlikely that a researcher would remove rows or columns of useful information from the matrix because of a few missing data cells. If, however, the missing data is concentrated in a few rows or columns, this may appear to be the most expedient alternative.

10.3.2 ANALYSIS ALTERNATIVES

We have considered in the previous section some possible approaches to handling missing data in the data matrix. Here our concern is with some modes of dealing with missing data in the analysis itself. The question is: Given that the analysis is carried out on missing data, how can one gauge its effect?" Two major alternatives seem possible. A *control analysis* may be carried out, or a *measure of missing data* may be employed.

10.3.2.1 *Control Analysis.* A complete factor analysis may be run on the data matrix containing missing data. Additional factor analyses may then be computed for the data either with estimates for missing data or with the matrix reduced to eliminate missing data. The first analysis may then be systematically compared (Chapter 20) with the control runs.[10] If the results are similar, one may conclude with more confidence than otherwise that factors invariant of the missing data have been found.

> *Example 10–11.* Cattell's (1949a) 69 nation by 72 characteristics study involved missing data. A later "refined" run was made by Cattell *et al.* (1951) on 40 nations by the same 72 characteristics to determine more reliable dimensions. The initial 69-nation matrix was reduced by omitting the 29 nations with the most missing data. Subsequent agreement between the two studies was found.

> *Example 10–12.* The 82 nation by 236 characteristics matrix (Rummel, 1969) contained about 17 per cent missing data. The factors delineated in this data were

10. Rather than compute control analysis, one might compare the missing data results with the factor analyses done by others within the substantive domain. A substantial agreement among the studies should increase one's confidence in the independence of the results from possible distorting effects of missing data. This assumes, of course, that the distribution of missing data, if any, differed between studies.

compared with those of a 71 nation by 153 characteristics matrix resulting from removal of nations and characteristics with the most missing data. The comparison showed virtual identity for the major factors, thus increasing our confidence in the first and more extensive results.

10.3.2.2 *A Missing Data Measure.* This involves counting the number of blank cells in each row of the data matrix and making the resulting figures for each case an additional variable to be included in the analysis. This variable then is employed as a systematic error measure as described in Section 9.1.3.4.

The rationale of this approach is this: If the amount of missing data of the cases on all the variables is statistically independent of the major interrelationships found in the substantive data, then the missing data itself has had little influence on their determination. Such independence is evidenced by a low loading for the missing data measure on the factors defining these interrelationships. If the measure has a high loading on a factor, three alternatives are available.

First, when the factors are given interpretation and use, the one with the highly loaded missing data measure should be handled with caution. The factor may be a major substantive factor in the domain being analyzed. On the other hand, it may be a spurious result of missing data.

> *Example 10–13.* In the analysis of 236 characteristics of Example 10–12, a missing data measure was included. The result was that it loaded −.63 on an economic development factor and +.52 on a totalitarianism one. That is, the amount of missing data for a nation is inversely proportional to the wealth of a nation and proportional to its totalitarianism. Nations with richer and more open societies publish more data on themselves. The loading of the missing data measure on these two factors could compromise their reliability except that the factors were also found in the 153-characteristics study mentioned in Example 10–12 and in cross-national studies of similar data by others.[11]

Second, the cases can be divided into those with high and low factor scores on that factor with a high loading for the missing data measure. Factor analysis can then be carried out *within* each group to test the factor stability. The results will then be independent of the amount of missing data.

11. See the factor comparisons in Rummel (1969) and Russett (1967a).

And third, the factors can be orthogonally rotated so that the first factor is colinear with the missing data measure.[12] The subsequent factors can be interpreted as independent of the amount of missing data.

Appendix 10.1
Data Collection Procedures for Assistants

I. *Data Collection Sheets*

A. Data are to be filled in on the data collection sheets (Fig. 10–2). These sheets have a format to ease the transference of data from the sheets to computer cards.

B. The location of each variable's data on the sheet is indicated in a variable list. For example, data on economic aid will go in columns 7–11.

1. Five columns are alloted for the data, including sign and decimal point, if needed, for each variable. Therefore, before you write in the data for a particular case, scan the data for all the cases in the sample to see which case has the largest figure. This figure will indicate the units in which the data should be recorded. For example, if the variable of interest is economic aid, you might find that the largest figure is for the case U.S.–France, say $140,000,000 for 1955. Since you have only five columns in which to record the data (one digit, decimal, or sign to a column), you will have to record the data as 14000 (commas are not recorded). The unit is 10 thousands of U.S. dollars ($0,000). Once you have the largest figure fitted into the columns allotted, you must put the data on the same variable for the other cases *in the same units* and with the *unit places in the same columns.* For example, if the U.S., in addition to France, gives the following amount of aid to other countries:

Case	Data	Data Recorded				
U.S.–France	$140,000,000	1	4	0	0	0
U.S.–U.K.	85,000,000		8	5	0	0
U.S.–Brazil	1,890,000			1	8	9
U.S.–Peru	78,466					8

The data are rounded off if necessary as in the case of U.S.–Peru above.

12. In factoring a correlation matrix, an orthogonal factor is colinear with a variable when its loading squared equals its communality.

2. If the data have decimal points, as in per cent figures (e.g., 82.3 per cent), the decimal point itself must go into a column, and the decimals for all the figures for this variable for all the cases must be in the *same column*. For example:

Case	Actual Data			Data Recorded			
A	82.3%	8	2	·	3		
B	3.4		3	·	4		
C	5.6		5	·	6		
D	19.5	1	9	·	5		

The % sign is not recorded with the data. It is given as the data unit on the footnote sheet and at the head of the columns discussed below.

3. If the data have negative signs, these signs must all go in the same column. Plus signs need not be recorded but are assumed to be in the same column as the minus signs. For example:

Case	Actual Data				Data Recorded			
A	72.3			7	2	·	3	
B	−14.6	−		1	4	·	6	
C	.8					·	8	
D	1.6				1	·	6	

4. Record all data beginning with the rightmost column of the five allotted for a variable. For example:

Case	Actual Data		Data Recorded	
A	5			5
B	16		1	6
C	7			7
D	0			0

5. Record the variable number, as given in the variable list, in the appropriate place at the head of the columns. In the space provided at the head of the columns also put the variable name and underneath (in parentheses) the units. For example:

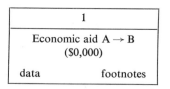

1
Economic aid A → B ($0,000)
data   footnotes

C. Along the left side of the data collection sheets are lines for you to write in the case. Write the names or abbreviations for the cases on these lines, but be sure your writing does not cross over into column 1.

All the data you put in the same row on which you have written a case's name will refer to this particular case.

D. Put in columns:
    1–3: The case ID number, with the one-digit number going in column 3, the two-digit number in columns 2–3, and the three-digit number in columns 1–3;
    5: The card number for the case if more than one card (row) is necessary to record all the variables.
  76–79: The year of the data, e.g., | 1 | 9 | 5 | 5 |.

II. *Data Description and Footnote Sheets*

A. For each variable for which you collect data you must fill out a data description and footnote sheet.

B. It is especially important that you give the units correctly and that you completely specify the primary source of your data, including author, if there is one, publisher and city, and year of publication. A primary source is defined as one from which over 50 per cent of the data for a variable are taken.

C. For your footnotes you may use the numerals 0–9, the letters A–Z, and the following symbols:

$$. \quad = \quad , \quad) \quad (\quad * \quad - \quad + \quad /$$

D. Write the letter O with a bar through it, Ø, and the letter Z with a line, Z. The location of the footnotes for each variable is indicated on the data collection sheet. The footnotes for a datum should begin in the leftmost column of those allotted for the footnotes. Only one footnote is to go in a column. Since there are five columns allotted for footnotes for each variable, it is possible to have as many as five footnotes for a datum. Experience indicates that this is more than ample.

E. You should footnote for each datum:

1. Its source (with complete citation including table number and page from which the data were taken) *if other than the primary source* (if there is no primary source, then all the data sources will be footnoted);

2. Significant changes in definition or principles of classification that may be indicated in the source;

3. Major qualifications about the scope or reliability of a datum as indicated in the source;

4. Reliability codes given in the source;

5. Any interpolations or extrapolations, with the values used;

6. Estimates of values not specifically given but inferred from source context or from your special knowledge of the variable or the case (when such estimates are made, write "project estimate" on the footnote sheet and put your last name in parentheses after it).

11. Distributional Transformations

With the completion of the data collection and estimation of missing data, if needed, the research design may require that transformations be made of the data. These may be applied to the *distributions* for each variable to bring each distribution in line with some design criteria or with assumptions of the techniques to be applied later, or the transformations may be applied to the *data matrix* itself. The basic difference between distributional and matrix transformations is that, for the former, different transformations may be used for each distribution to maximize the criteria of concern, whereas, for the latter, the same transformations are uniformly applied to all the variables in the matrix.

The focus of this chapter will be on the criteria for making distributional transformations, the kind of distributions of concern, and the major distributional transformations that may be made. Figure 11–1 presents the content of this research step. The next chapter will discuss the matrix transformations.

STEP

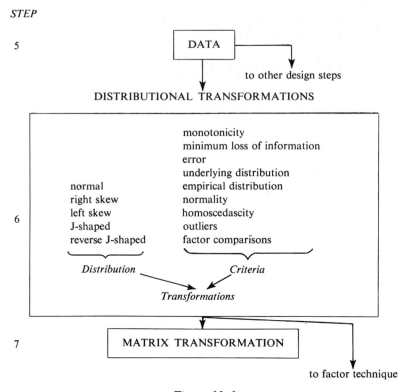

Figure 11–1

11.1 Criteria for Distributional Transformations

The reader may well ask, "Why transform at all?" It may seem that the simplest and best course is to analyze the data without going through the difficulty of transformations.

Distributional transformations have two important objectives. First, they are made to maximize the fit of the data to the mathematical assumptions and requirements of the technique of analysis. Otherwise, the substantive interpretation of the results may be quite at variance with their actual meaning. In order to realistically relate the empirical findings to the initial research question, the data and method have to be matched as perfectly as possible. Second, the chance, unique, or unrepresentative variance in a data matrix that may distort the interpretation of the results may be minimized in its influence through the choice of an appropriate transformation. These two objectives of distributional transformations will be made clear by a discussion of the criteria for selecting transformations. The criteria are *monotonicity, minimum loss of information, errors, underlying distribution, empirical distribution, normality, homoscedasticity, outliers,* and *factor comparisons.*

11.1.1 MONOTONICITY

The transformation should be such that the relative *rank* positions of cases are not altered; it will change the values for cases, but not the order of the cases based on these values. This seems to be a universally accepted criterion. It defines a limit to the kinds of transformations that one may apply.

There is another aspect of monotonicity, however, that is not so rigidly adhered to. The effect of a transformation is usually to contract or expand the intervals between cases in the data proportional to the values for a case. Figure 11–2 may make this clear. The dots along

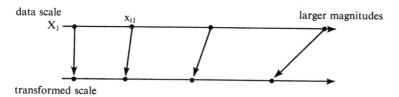

Figure 11–2

the scale stand for the different values of the cases. As can be seen, the particular transformation exemplified has contracted the intervals between the data; the intervals between the larger magnitudes are proportionally more contracted than intervals between the smaller magnitudes. That is, the amount of expansion or contraction of intervals is a monotonic function of the values. This criterion has a strong practical basis. In conjunction with the necessity for maintaining rank invariance of case, it insures that the maximum amount of information about the distance between cases will be preserved in the transformed data.

Occasionally, due to an overriding necessity to normalize a distribution (Section 11.1.6), a transformation may be applied in which the expansion or contraction of intervals is not monotonic. While maintaining rank invariance, the values may be shifted around until the distribution is normal. Although this may be legitimate for certain research designs,[1] it is prudent to be aware of the consequent loss of information.

1. Such a design might be one dealing with a sample for which the underlying distributions on the variables can be assumed normal and the analysis of which will involve significance tests.

11.1.2 MINIMUM LOSS OF INFORMATION

Except to make it explicit, little need be said about this criterion. The researcher is faced with two needs. One is to utilize to the maximum information contained in the data matrix. The other is to maximize the applicability of the techniques and design selected to the nature of the data. A good transformation is one that does both.

11.1.3 ERROR

The problem of error permeates the entire research process. From the selection of variables for analysis (Section 9.1.2.9) and their measurement scales (Section 9.1.3.4), through the factor analysis (Section 14.1.6) and rotation (Section 16.2.4) to the interpretation of the design (Section 21.1.2), error is of the utmost concern. In the choice of transformation, an assessment of error is necessary to determine whether the degree of expansion or contraction of scale intervals can be allowed. If the small differences among cases in a distribution *are less than the range of error in the data,* then a transformation is undesirable if it gives these small differences greater effect in the analysis than they would otherwise have.

> *Example 11–1.* Consider Fig. 11–3. Now, let an assessment of error in the data indicate that the very small intervals between the four dots on the left of the scale are within the margin of error, while the larger intervals between such cases as the two dots on the right of the scale are greater than would be due to error. That is, the ordinal position of the values on the left may be in error while the ordinal position of those on the right is reliable. The transformation of this data shown in Fig. 11–3 has the unfortunate effect of expanding the intervals on the left relative to the intervals on the right and thus giving greater weight to the former. Error will play a larger role in the result than would otherwise be the case.

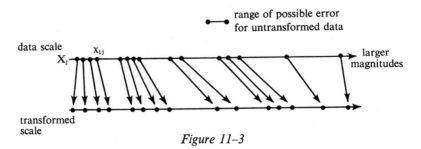

Figure 11–3

11.1.4 UNDERLYING DISTRIBUTIONS

For a sample of cases the distribution of data may vary from the distribution for the universe. The selection of a transformation will then be guided by the researcher's knowledge or guess as to the nature of this underlying distribution. The objective will be to bring the sample data distributions in line with that for the universe of cases, other criteria of concern being equal.

The distribution underlying a variable is also important (Section 9.1.3.5). If the data are not at one end or another of the potential distribution for a variable, such as conflict, then the choice of transformation should be one to minimize the effect that this censuring of the underlying distribution will have on the analysis.

11.1.5 THE EMPIRICAL DISTRIBUTION

The nature of the actual distribution of data on a variable is of primary concern in selecting a transformation. The transformation that satisfies the various criteria for one distribution may not do so for another. *To apply a transformation, such as the logarithm, across the board without checking the empirical distribution may result in transformations that satisfy the criteria less than the original data.*

11.1.6 NORMALITY

Although normal (Section 11.2) univariate or marginal distributions are not sufficient for the bivariate distribution[2] to be normal, they increase the likelihood. A *bivariate* normal distribution has the useful property that the relationship between the two variables is linear (Kendall and Stuart, 1958, vol. 1, p. 383). Linearity in the bivariate interrelationships of the data is a basic assumption of the factor model, and we want to satisfy this assumption as well as we can.

Besides increasing the possibility that relationships will be linear, transformations to normal distributions help ensure that the range of the product moment correlation, if used, will not be restricted (Section 9.1.2.12) by highly disparate marginal distributions. A correlation matrix involving correlations with different ranges other than the theoretical range of ± 1.00 can introduce distortions into the analysis. Although such restrictions in range may be compensated for by dividing each correlation by its maximum value, such as with the phi-over-phi-max correlation, this in turn involves an assumption about

2. A univariate or marginal distribution refers to the frequency distribution of data on a variable. A bivariate distribution is the frequency distribution of the points plotted in a Cartesian coordinate system for two variables. For a useful example of marginal normal distributions *not* resulting in bivariate normality, see Carroll (1961, p. 360, Fig. 5).

the underlying distribution that we may not wish to make. Accordingly, transformations of all the data to normality may be the best course.

Besides the assumption of linearity, the product moment correlation assumes that a zero correlation measures statistical *independence* of the variables (Kendall and Stuart, 1961, vol. 2, p. 283).

> *Example 11–2.* Figure 11–4 plots a hypothetical correlation between age and wealth. Since the regression line is parallel to the age axis, the best predictor of wealth for any age would be average wealth. This implies that the correlation coefficient between age and wealth for this data would be zero. Yet, as can be seen from the figure, as age increases, the variability in wealth also increases— that is, for these hypothetical data, the older person is either richer or poorer than the younger. Consequently, taking the zero correlation as a measure of statistical independence for this type of data would be misleading.

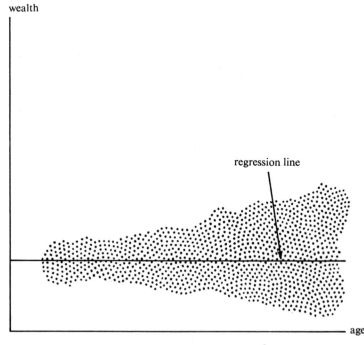

Figure 11–4

Including in a correlation matrix a number of zero or near-zero coefficients that mask relationships of the type in the above example may have misleading results when factored.

A *sufficient condition* for the correlation coefficient to be a true measure of statistical independence between two variables is that the *bivariate* distribution of the variables be normal (Kendall and Stuart, 1961, p. 288). To rephrase this, if the *marginal* distributions of the variables are normal, then the correlations between them are more likely to index statistical independence when zero. Thus, another reason for normalizing distributions through transformation has been indicated.

Finally, and what perhaps most researchers consider the most important rationale for normal distributional transformations, applications of tests of significance to the results of the factor analysis assume that the distributions of the variables are all normal. Consequently, if we are planning tests of significance, we may wish to transform the data to distributions as near normal as possible.

The previous paragraphs beg the question as to how one can test for the adequacy of a transformation to normality.[3] One method is to determine the *kurtosis* (peakedness) and *skew* (concentration of data on one or another side) of a distribution,[4] and then test the significance of their deviation from the kurtosis and skew of the normal distribution.

A second method, and one that requires much less computation, is to compare the frequency grouping of the data with what it should be were the data normally distributed. The significance of the deviation from that for the normal distribution can be determined by the chi-square test.

11.1.7 HOMOSCEDASTICITY

This refers to the variability in one variable for a given value of another.[5] The variability of wealth with increasing age in Fig. 11–4 illustrates the homoscedasticity of the two variables. The distributions of two variables are *homoscedastic* if the variability in one variable for specific values of the other has the same standard deviation. If not, they are heteroscedastic.

3. This is the problem of testing the "goodness of fit" of one distribution (the raw or transformed) to another (the normal). An advanced treatment of this is given by Kendall and Stuart (1961, vol. 2, Chapter 30, especially Section 30.63 and the references therein).

4. Statistics for their computation have been derived by R. A. Fisher (1958, pp. 74–79) and are exemplified in application by P. O. Johnson (1949, pp. 153–57).

5. A brief but rigorous discussion of homoscedasticity in relation to regression analysis is given in Johnston (1963, pp. 207–11). His Fig. 8–1 is particularly helpful to the reader who may wish a visual representation of the concept.

As discussed in the last section, but in different words, the correlation coefficient is not a measure of statistical independence between variables if the distributions are heteroscedastic. Homoscedastic distributions can only be guaranteed if the marginal distributions of the variables are normal. Accordingly, the criterion of homoscedasticity merges with that of normality. It has been given a special section here, however, since texts occasionally mention homoscedasticity as a rationale for transformation.

11.1.8 OUTLIERS

Elsewhere (Section 9.1.2.12), it has been pointed out that extreme values[6] in the data can influence the results. An application of transformations, then, is to decrease the effect of outliers by proportionally contracting or expanding the scale intervals of the data.[7] The procedures for doing this will be discussed in Section 11.2, below, on distributions and transformations.

In the meantime, a technique for determining an outlier might be discussed.[8] A precise measure of the extremeness of the values on a variable is the number of standard deviations each case is from the mean value for the distribution. This measure for each case is given by the standard score (Definition 3–4). A way of checking the data for outliers, therefore, is to standardize the distribution and then identify those cases with standard scores exceeding, say, an absolute value of 3.00.

6. The term "extreme values" should not imply that the outliers will always be at the higher magnitude of the distribution. A distribution may have extremely low, rather than high, values.

7. One may argue that, if he is concerned only with describing the data itself through factor analysis and not with making inferences from his sample to the universe of cases, he should not transform outliers. The outliers, the argument may continue, are actual data and should not be arbitrarily altered. They represent the way the world is, and not the way the world should be, as implied by the transformation. This is a legitimate point, but in invoking it the consequences of its application should be realized. An analysis of data for which one case has extreme values will yield factors that are descriptive of two groups. One group will be composed of the one case with the outliers; the other group will be composed of all other cases. In essence, then, the analysis is on a sample of two. Presumably, the reason many cases were included in the original sample was to arrive at factors that were descriptive of all the cases, with each case having nearly equal weight, rather than to consider only one case versus all the others. Transformations, therefore, are justified to reduce the influence of outliers and, accordingly, to ensure that the results maximally relate to the research question and the rationale for the sample selection.

8. For a more extensive discussion of outliers than that given here, see Dixon (1953), Anscombe (1960), and Finetti (1961).

No precise standard score can be given for the case in which a value becomes an outlier. This limit depends on the taste of the investigator and the nature of his data. If the distribution is normal, one guideline is a table of areas for the standard and normal distribution. In such a table the area under a normal curve for cases less the particular standard score is tabulated, and from such a table the probability of a case falling between, say, $+2.00$ and -2.00 standard scores, can be determined (see the discussion following Definition 3–4).

It should be noted that the standard score values for a distribution should be recalculated after each transformation of outliers. The transformation of one outlier may so change the mean and standard deviation of a distribution that other outliers are created. These will in turn have to be corrected. Although the computations for this way seem laborious, most computer centers may have in their program libraries a data screening program that will identify outliers at given standard scores and compute requested transformations.

11.1.9 FACTOR COMPARISONS

The measurement scales employed, normality of distributions, and outliers have a great impact on a factor analysis.[9] It is quite possible that a factor analysis of data with distributional transformations applied can delineate substantively different dimensions from an analysis on the same data without transformation.[10] If we wish to compare results, we should determine what transformations, if any, to apply to our data on the basis of what has been done in the other studies to

9. Horst (1965, p. 295) writes that "in general the factor analytic results will vary for a given data matrix according to what is done about the problem of origin. The importance of this is not as widely recognized as it should be." See his numerical example (1965, pp. 298–303) as an illustration of this. What holds true for the origin is equally valid for the distribution.

10. If this statement seems extreme, consider the effect on the product moment correlation coefficient of a hypothetical outlier for case F on the following:

Case	X_1	X_2
A	1	5
B	2	4
C	3	3
D	4	2
E	5	1
F	100	100

The correlation for cases A–E on X_1 and X_2 is -1.00. But when case F is included, the correlation shifts to .67. In other words, an extreme outlier can cause the correlation to shift from perfect negative to high positive.

be used for comparison. Otherwise, divergence in factor structures between studies might be a result of transformations having been applied in one study and not in the other, rather than a consequence of real substantive differences in the data.

11.2 Distributions and Transformations

The normal distribution for a variable X_j is shown in Fig. 11–5. It is a bell-shaped curve symmetrical about the mean. Its great importance as a goal of transformations[11] has been discussed above.

One transformation that may be applied involves *grouping* the data. The grouping transformation is useful for transforming to normality,

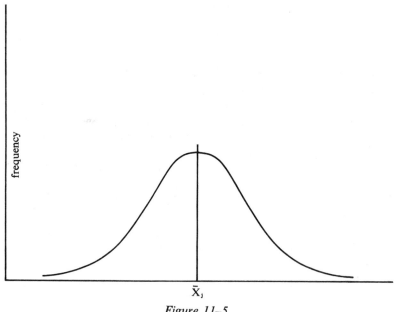

$\bar{X}_j$

Figure 11–5

11. An advanced discussion of transformations is given in Kendall and Stuart (1958, pp. 163–75). Johnson (1949, pp. 155–66) gives a more elementary treatment of transformations especially of interest in applied work. See also Hald (1952, Chapter 7) for a thorough consideration of skew distributions and their transformations, and Snedecor (1956, pp. 314–21). For consideration of transformations of probability distributions, see Anscombe (1948). For examples of application of most of the transformations to be considered, see Rummel (1969).

for compensating for *error*, or for the characteristics of the *underlying distribution*, or for eliminating *outliers*.

Through grouping, any distribution of ordinal data with many scale positions, or interval- and ratio-scaled data, can be transformed to a *normal distribution*. The procedure is to determine the frequency of cases that would lie between particular values of standard scores on the normal distribution. Then, working from one end to the other of the distribution, the same frequencies for the raw data distributions are transformed by giving them the value at the midpoint of the two standard scores defining the frequency for the normal distribution.[12] An example should make this clear.

> *Example 11–3.* Divide the normal distribution for standard scores into 10 equal frequencies. That is, the first 10 per cent of cases appear between negative infinity and -1.282, the next 10 per cent between -1.281 and -0.842, and each successive 10 per cent between: -0.841 and -0.525; -0.524 and -0.253; -0.252 and -0.000; $+0.000$ and 0.252; 0.253 and 0.523; 0.524 and 0.841; 0.842 and 1.281; 1.282 and infinity. Working from the negative to the positive end, assign successive numbers to each range, e.g., a number 1 to the range from negative infinity to -1.282 standard scores, a number 2 to the range -1.281 to -0.842 standard scores, etc. The transformation then consists of assigning the number given the range of standardized values to the cases falling within that range.

The problem with this grouping transformation is that, although it may preserve monotonicity of rank value of the cases, it does not often preserve the monotonicity of the data intervals. That is, the intervals between the values in the raw data are not proportionally constricted or expanded with size of the value.

> *Example 11–4.* Let the data be given by the raw data scale of Fig. 11–6. A hypothetical grouping transformation to normality is shown on the bottom scale. It can be seen that the intervals between some data are widened and some are lessened without regard to their actual values on the scale.

A result of applying a grouping transformation, therefore, is that whatever meaningful information is contained in the scale intervals

---

12. The "probits" technique can be useful in simplifying the grouping to normality. See Johnson (1949, pp. 160–62).

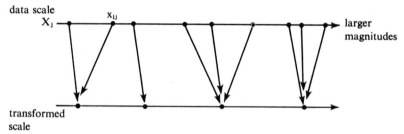

Figure 11-6

between cases is lost. If the data are ordinal-scaled to begin with, such information is not important. If, however, the data are on an interval or ratio scale, the intervals are significant, and the researcher may wish to apply another transformation—one that will uniformly and minimally affect scale intervals.

Besides transforming to normality, the grouping procedure can be used to control for random or systematic error in the data. Since the procedures here are analogous to adopting the measurement scale to such error as was discussed previously, the reader is referred to Section 9.1.3.4. With regard to using the grouping transformation to compensate for censuring of the underlying distribution, the discussion of Sections 9.1.2.12 and 9.1.3.5 is relevant.

The problem of *outliers* can be handled through grouping if other transformations fail. The value of the outlier is changed while values for the other cases in the distribution remain the same (if other criteria are satisfied). In increasing order of loss of information, three techniques for reducing the outlier may be employed. One technique is to reduce the outlier to that value that will yield a just acceptable standard score, perhaps an absolute value of 3.0 or 3.5. The distorting effect of the outlier on the analysis will be reduced while still allowing the analysis to take cognizance of the large value for the particular case. The difficulty with this approach is that several values for the outlier may have to be tried, and each time new standard scores for the whole distribution will have to be calculated until the just acceptable standard score for the outlier is found.

A second technique is to reduce the outlier to some value greater than the next highest one.[13] This next highest value may be one unit or scale interval higher or as many units higher as that between the second and third highest values. The third approach to reducing outliers is to

13. The discussion throughout is in terms of one outlier. The technique, however, can easily be adapted to those situations in which two or more outliers appear.

give the outlying case the same value as the next highest. This is the most drastic, but may be justified by the particular outlier being judged a random or unnatural case.

Grouping transformations appear to be most often employed by psychologists. For social data, the most often applied transformation may be the logarithm to the base 10 (to be denoted, henceforth, by log X_j).[14] This is justified because so many of the distributions dealt with are right skew, as in Fig. 11-7A. The log X_j transformation constricts the intervals of the data as the values increase in size. The consequence on the distribution is that the right tail is drawn in while the values at the left of the distribution are moved away from the mean, thus tending to normalize the distribution.[15]

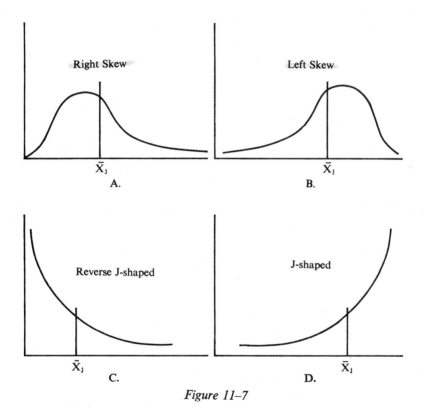

Figure 11-7

14. For one of the best extensive treatments of the logarithm transformation, see Aitchison and Brown (1963). For examples of its application to cross-national political data, see Russett *et al.* (1964, Part B).

15. Lewis F. Richardson has employed the log transformation extensively

There is a danger in applying the log X_j transformation without checking the distribution of the transformed data. Occasionally, the log X_j transformation will be too strong. It will pull the right tail in too far and may create outliers on the left side of the distribution. When this occurs, a weaker left skew transformation is warranted. The $(X_j)^{1/2}$ or $1/X_j$ are such transformations. They may normalize a left skew distribution when the log X_j tends to constrict the higher data values more than necessary.

Besides normalizing and reducing outliers, these transformations may also improve the homoscedasticity of the distribution. The log X_j transformation is especially powerful in this regard and is often employed for this specific purpose.

Before trying to employ transformations for any of the above purposes, however, the data may have to undergo a preliminary arithmetical transformation to satisfy certain restrictions on the data imposed by the transformation. In terms of the three transformations discussed, the log X_j transformation requires that all values of the data be greater than zero. This can be satisfied by making the transformation $\log (X_j + C)$, where C is either the largest absolute negative data value plus 1, or 1 itself if there are no negative values.

The second transformation, $(X_j)^{1/2}$, has the restriction that there be no negative values. To satisfy this, the data can be altered by $(X_j + C)^{1/2}$, where the constant C is the largest absolute negative data value.

The $1/X_j$ transformation assumes, when applied as a right skew transformation, that the data are greater than zero. Accordingly, the transformation should be $1/(X_j + C)$, where C is determined as in the case of $\log (X_j + C)$.

The appropriate normalizing transformations for the left skew distribution shown in Fig. 11–7B consist of any of the powers of X_j greater than 1.0, e.g., X_j^2, X_j^3, X_j^4, etc. The most often employed of these perhaps is the square (X_j^2) transformation. The third or fourth powers may be tried and are, of course, more powerful. By raising the data to some power, these distributions tend to pull the left tail of the distribution in and to lengthen that on the right. The larger the exponent employed in the transformation, however, the more the loss of information from the original data (given, of course, that the intervals in the data were meaningful to begin with).

The restriction on the data involved in employing these exponential transformations is that X_j must be nonnegative. A constant C that is the

---

to compensate for the errors in data on the number killed in wars. See Richardson (1960b, Chapter 1, Part 4, especially p. 6).

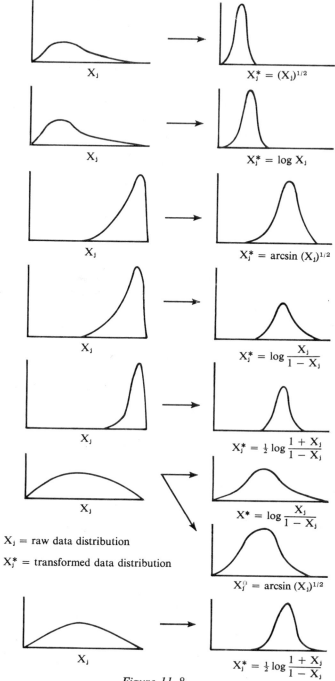

X_j = raw data distribution

X_j* = transformed data distribution

Figure 11–8

largest absolute negative value, if one exists, can be added to all the data to satisfy this requirement.

Less-well-known transformations, but very useful in normalizing highly left-skewed distributions, are $\log [(X_j)/(1 - X_j)]$ and $\frac{1}{2} \log [(1 + X_j)/(1 - X_j)]$. The latter is the more powerful of the two. The values of X_j should be $0 < X_j < 1.0$ for the first transformation and $0 \leq X_j < 1.0$ for the second. If X_j does not already lie in these ranges, the addition of the largest absolute negative value to X_j and the division of the result by the largest value plus 1 (or 0.1 if the range of X_j is small) will scale X_j to the appropriate range.

An additional strong transformation applicable to the left-skewed distribution is the arcsin $(X_j)^{1/2}$ transformation.[16] In order to apply the transformation, the values should be in the range $0 \leq X_j \leq 1.0$. The data can be initially transformed to conform to this restriction by adding the absolute value of the largest negative value, if any, to all the other values and then dividing the data through by the largest resulting positive value.

If the distribution is J-shaped, or reverse J-shaped, as in Figs. 11–7C and 11–7D, there is no simple nongrouping transformation that will normalize the distribution. Transformations may still be applied, however, to eliminate or reduce the size of outliers. For a reverse J-shaped distribution, the same transformations employed for the right skew distributions may be used; likewise, the left skew transformations for the J-shaped. As discussed in previous sections, the use of these transformations entail certain restrictions on the data that can be satisfied through preliminary scaling by an appropriate constant.

Figure 11–8 displays the kinds of transformations applicable to the various distributions.[17]

16. Guilford (1954, pp. 574–76) gives a table of arcsine values for the transformation.

17. I wish to express my appreciation to Michael Haas for passing on to me the set of transformation charts from which Fig. 11–8 was derived. For graphs of the distributions of 70 cross-national variables, see Russett *et al.* (1964, Part A).

12. Matrix Transformation

In applying factor analysis it has been the custom to transform the data matrix to a correlation matrix, which is then factored.[1] This custom has often been justified by (1) the arbitrary units and scales of the data usually factored,[2] and (2) the application of the Spearman-Thurstone common factor analysis model (Section 5.2) based on the correlation matrix [Eq. (5–15)]. With the growth of factor analysis outside the field of psychology, where data with arbitrary units abound, and the increasing application of the method to data with meaningful units and scales,[3] it may be time to consider the correlation transformation as only one of a number of possible transformations that can be

1. One of the most cited factor analysis texts (Harman, 1960) assumes throughout that it is a correlation matrix that is factored. This assumption is largely maintained in Harman's (1967) revision.

2. Factor analysis has been predominantly applied to test or questionnaire items administered to samples of individuals.

3. Much of the data of the social sciences can be measured on ratio scales in terms of such units as people, currency, geographic distance or size (miles, kilometers, hectares, etc.), kilowatt-hours, votes, or years.

applied as the data, factor model, or requirements of factor comparison warrant.[4]

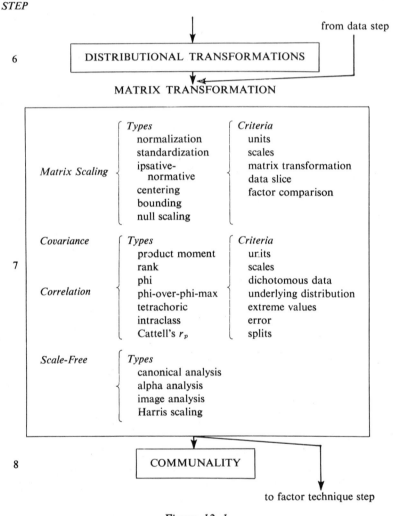

Figure 12–1

4. An unfortunate aspect of the great historical emphasis on the correlation transformation is that almost all factor analysis computer programs compute or require a preliminary correlation matrix transformation. It may be expected that this will soon change, however, as is evidenced by the computer programs listed in Horst (1965), which directly factor the data matrix or employ matrix transformations other than the correlation.

In research designs employing data with meaningful units and scales, there is no reason why these data should not be included. By factor-analyzing these data, the resulting factors can be rooted more directly in observation, and factor comparisons can better test the invariance of the findings. The ideal is to determine factors and factor scores that are based on some physical unit precisely defined and intersubjectively determinant. In practice, however, the researcher may often have data that fall short of the requirements of direct factor analysis (Section 14.3.5). For example, he may have meaningful units, such as dollars, people, and miles, but they may not be comparable from one variable to another. Consequently, he may have to scale or transform the matrix prior to factor analysis.

In this chapter, three alternative ways of transforming the data matrix will be considered. The first is the covariance matrix transformation. The second is the correlation matrix transformation, which will be discussed at length because of its extensive application. The third involves matrix transformations that yield results invariant of the scale of original data. Often, for one or several possible reasons, which will be mentioned later, a preliminary matrix *scaling* transformation will be done on the data matrix. This preliminary transformation will be discussed first.

The alternatives and considerations involved in the matrix trans-formation step of the factor analysis research design are shown in Fig. 12–1. They are the subjects of the various sections of this chapter.

12.1 Matrix Scaling

Matrix scaling procedures are often employed to transform the data to a form more consonant with the matrix transformation to be applied. Matrix scaling is distinguished from the distributional trans-formations of the last chapter by being applied equally to all data in the matrix. The scaling can therefore be represented as a series of matrix operations.

12.1.1 MATRIX SCALING PROCEDURES
There are six major types of matrix scaling procedures relevant here: *normalizing, standardizing, centering, ipsative-normative scaling, boun-dary scaling*, and *null scaling*. Each will be discussed in turn.

12.1.1.1 *Normalization.* This involves transforming each column vec-tor (variable) of the data matrix by dividing each element by the square root of the sum of the squared elements [Definition 3–25, Eq. (3–5)].

It should be clear that a normalization scaling procedure is quite different from a normalizing distributional transformation (Section 11.1.6). Normalizing the variable scales the data so that the sum of their squares equals unity. Normalizing the data distribution on a variable, however, transforms the distribution to a normal curve (Fig. 11–5).

Scaling a data matrix by normalizing the column vectors contracts or lengthens the vectors in space so that they all have a magnitude of 1 —a unit length. A consequence of analyzing this "unit-space" is that the inner product (Definition 3–22) of all normalized vectors equals the cosine between them (Definition 3–27). Consequently, the matrix of inner products of all the normalized column vectors[5] will give a matrix of cosines between the vectors that has the same mathematical properties for factor analysis as does the correlation matrix: The matrix willl be symmetrical, *Gramian,* and, for empirical data, *non-singular.*

If the data units from vector (variable) to vector (variable) are noncomparable, as with dollars, people, and miles, normalizing the vectors will make their data comparable. It does so by equating vector magnitudes, but without equating the means and standard deviations between the vectors (as does the standardization transformation to be discussed below). A normalized vector thus retains a maximum amount of scale information from the original data.

Normalizing of vectors has not often, if at all, been applied as a scaling transformation prior to factor analysis. It has been employed extensively, however, in transforming factor matrices prior to and during orthogonal and oblique rotation and has been used in factor comparison.

12.1.1.2 *Standardization.* The standardization transformation subtracts the mean of the data for a variable[6] from the original data and then divides by the standard deviation (Definition 3–4). The effect of the transformation is to remove the difference in means and deviation between variables from their covariance. The data are reduced to *common units* of deviation around the mean—*standard score units.*[7]

---

5. If $A^*_{n \times m}$ is the data matrix of normalized column vectors, then $A^{*\prime}_{m \times n} A^*_{n \times m}$ is the matrix of inner products.

6. In the terminology developed in this book, "variable" and "column vector" have been employed interchangeably when discussing the data matrix. When referring to normalization to unit length, the term "vector" is customarily employed in the literature, however. When referring to standardization and the other scaling transformations to be considered, the term "variable" is used. This practice will be followed here.

7. If the original data have a mean of zero, then data normalized to unit length equal the standardized data times the square root of the sample size [Eq. (3–7)].

This is a powerful transformation. It enables the comparison not only of data that have different units, such as dollars and people, but also of data on different measurement scales. The extensive usefulness of the product moment correlation coefficient, for example, has been due to a formula [Definition 3–6, Eq. (3–1)] that involves standardizing the data on each variable when computing their correlation.

A *doubly standardized* matrix is one that is standardized both by column (variable) and by row (case).[8] This removes variation in the matrix associated with variable as well as case differences. The variance remaining for comparison is that *within cases*. If an entity by characteristic data matrix is doubly standardized, then, variation of entities on a particular characteristic is removed, and what remains is the variance of *each* entity across its characteristics. The result of factor-analyzing such a matrix is to delimit *intra*-entity and not *inter*-entity factors.

Doubly standardized data have been labeled *ipsative* by Cattell (1944) in contrast to *normative* data—data standardized by variable.[9] I have not seen ipsative scaling of matrices outside of psychology, but potentially the transformation has wide application in the social sciences. It makes possible the determination of interrelationships within (rather than among) entities, characteristics, and occasions.

> *Example 12–1.* Consider a city by socioeconomic characteristic matrix. *Normative scaling*—standardization by variable—would make the units and scales of the characteristics comparable. Each city would have a standard score on a characteristic depending on how it compared with all other cities on *this* characteristic. An analysis of this data would then show which characteristics were interdependent in terms of cities scoring high or low on these characteristics *relative to each other*. If the data are *ipsative*, however, a city's score on a characteristic now only measures whether a city is high or low relative to its

8. Doubly standardizing a matrix is an iterative process. Standardizing rows after standardizing columns upsets the column standardization so that columns have to be restandardized. Restandardization then upsets the row standardizations. Therefore, one has to work back and forth between column and row standardizations until the standard deviations for columns and rows converge within some acceptable limits of unity.

9. On normative and ipsative data in psychology, see Broverman (1962). Horst (1965, Section 13.2) discusses ipsative data and considers some ways in which such double standardization may arise (Section 13.2.2). He defines ipsative scores as those for which the rows of the matrix sum to the same constant (1965, p. 293). Ipsative data so defined would also include doubly centered matrices as discussed in the next section.

own values on the *other* characteristics. An analysis of this matrix would now show which characteristics were interrelated in terms of cities being high or low on them relative to *their own values on the other characteristics*. In the normative case, between-city factors of wealth and size might appear. In the ipsative case, to make a rough guess, the within-city factors might be tax structure and segregation.

12.1.1.3 *Centering.* The variables (or cases) of a data matrix are centered by subtracting their means. If all the variables (or cases) are centered, the columns (or rows) of the scaled matrix will sum to a constant: zero. The effect of centering is to remove the covariance associated with the different means while retaining that resulting from different deviations around the means.[10] Since standardization removes covariance associated with both mean and deviation differences, centering retains more information in the data than does standardization. Centering transformations, however, do not retain as much information as does the normalization transformation, which merely contracts the column vectors to unit length.

If both variables and cases have their means subtracted, i.e., both columns and rows sum to a constant, the matrix is called *doubly centered*.[11] As with the doubly standardized matrix, the *intercase* variation in means has been removed. The remaining variation is for a case across the variables, that is, the *intrarow* variance. In terms of a doubly centered entity by characteristics matrix, the intra-entity deviations around the entity mean for the characteristics is what will determine the factors of the analysis. The intra-entity analysis for a doubly centered matrix differs from that for a doubly standardized matrix in that the deviations around the means for each entity are not equated. Entities with larger differences in their characteristics can thus have greater influence on the results.

12.1.1.4 *Bounding.* This type of transformation scales the range of values within a matrix to within certain bounds. This is done by

10. Centering the rows of a matrix reduces the rank of a matrix by one (Horst, 1965, p. 294) when the number of variables is less than or equal to the number of cases.

11. If only the columns are centered, and, without further transformation, the rows sum to a constant, the matrix is still doubly centered. That is, columns sum to one constant and rows to another. Dubois (1957) calls such matrices "closed systems" and points out that such "systems" may create difficulties of interpretation in Q-factor analysis. Horst (1965, Section 13.1) discusses centered matrices and develops (pp. 295–314) methods of deriving the factors for one scaling of the data matrix from the factors of a different scaling of the data matrix.

similarly increasing or decreasing the magnitude of the data without equating their different means and standard deviations. The purpose of such a transformation may be to allow easier interpretation of the factors resulting from a direct factor analysis or to satisfy certain mathematical requirements of the computer programs or factor techniques involved.

Example 12–2. Consider a trade matrix in which rows and columns refer to nations, and the matrix elements are the total trade between them. The matrix is symmetrical, since the total trade of nation A with B equals that of B with A. Let the research design specify a direct factor analysis of this matrix without going through a correlation matrix transformation.[12] If the only factor analysis program available is one requiring a correlation matrix, then this program can be employed to do the direct factor analysis. First, apply a bounding transformation that would uniformly reduce the trade figures to a range of values similar to the correlation coefficient. Second, input the transformed trade matrix *as a simulated correlation matrix* to the factor analysis program. The resulting factors will define the patterns of trade links between the nations.

Two alternative boundary transformations are possible for the trade matrix. The first alternative is to reduce the range of the trade data to between 0 and 1, where 0 means no trade between two nations, and 1 means the highest trade of all. In this case the boundary transformation would be done by dividing all trade values by the largest one in the trade matrix. The second alternative is to transform to values lying between -1.00 and $+1.00$, where zero would be the mean trade value in the matrix. The transformation then would be done by subtracting the mean[13] trade value from all trade data and dividing the result by the largest absolute trade value minus the mean. For the first alternative, the factor analysis would delimit uncorrelated trading blocs. For the second, the analysis

12. We may wish to delineate factors defining interdependent groups of nations in *both* magnitude and pattern of trade. The correlation matrix transformation would restrict the groups delineated to those with similar trade patterns only. See Section 12.3.3, below.

13. Of course, the geometric mean, median, mode, or other such descriptive statistic of central position might be employed.

would distinguish trading blocs with more within-trade than the average from trading blocs that are bipolar in terms of little between-bloc trade.

12.1.1.5 *Null Scaling.* The null, or so-called transaction matrix transformation,[14] rescales the data to deviations from expected (null) values. The matrix is thus transformed according to a null statistical model so that significant deviations from the null model can be ascertained.

A null matrix transformation may be used to alter the interrelationships identified by the factor analysis. For a null-scaled matrix, the factors will identify those variables (nations, if a trade or transaction matrix is employed) that cluster in terms of large deviations of their values from expectation.

12.1.2 SELECTING THE MATRIX SCALING TRANSFORMATION

In the previous sections a number of criteria for selecting a matrix scaling transformation have been implied but not discussed. These are *factor comparison, data slice, matrix transformation, measurement scales,* and *data units.*

How previous factor studies have scaled the data matrix will have an influence on the scaling procedure selected. Otherwise, as with the selection of the measurement scales themselves, differences found in *factor comparison* may be due as much to different methodologies in the studies as to actual data dissimilarity.

The *data slice* selected for analysis will also help determine the matrix scaling procedure adopted. If the slice is a characteristics by entity (Q-factor analysis) or characteristics by occasion (O-factor analysis), we may scale the data by rows to remove interrelationships resulting from data unit (i.e., scale or *species*) differences in the rows of data.

> *Example 12–3.* Consider a characteristics by cities matrix. That is, the variables to be analyzed are cities, and a Q-factor analysis is to be done. If the cases (rows) are average taxable income, population, birthrate, and other such measures, the *first* factor will define between-variable relationships due to the differences in data units between the cases. Wealth, for example, will be measured in dollars and will have a different row mean and standard deviation than that for population. The first factor will extract this variance.

14. See Section 7.7, footnote 3.

Centering the rows will help remove the variance due to mean differences but not that from unequal deviations, as between population and birthrate. Rather than being centered, consequently, the rows should be standardized to equate mean and standard deviation.

Example 12–4. Consider the matrix in the last example, but add a row consisting of a three-point ordinal measure of segregation. Since the scale intervals and integers selected to index the ordinal values are arbitrary, the only variance worth comparing with the other measures is that around the scale mean. The rows should therefore be standardized to remove from the analysis the variance due to different scale units and means.

Example 12–5. Let the characteristics of a characteristics by cities Q-factor analysis matrix be private income, city budget, school expenditures, tax rate per $1,000, and average family income, all measured in dollar units. An analysis of this matrix would produce a *species factor* as the first factor, resulting from the large differences in row means and standard deviations that create an inter-relationship between the columns. The following hypo-thetical data for cities A, B, and C should help make this clear.

	City A	*City B*	*City C*
Private income	$194,000,000	$53,000,000	$17,000,000
City budget	4,500,000	1,400,000	743,000
School expenditures	2,300,000	700,000	513,000
Tax rate per $1,000	42	53	31
Average family income	3,800	47,300	3,200

As can be seen, there is similar variation down the columns due to the vastly different magnitudes for each characteristic. The variance resulting from these different magnitudes will produce a factor defining this intrinsic difference. A normalization or standardization of rows will remove this *species* variance.

A third consideration in selecting a matrix scaling procedure is the matrix transformation to be applied. Covariance and correlation transformations vary, as discussed below, in their requirements about the data units and measurement scales. Matrix scaling can be employed to alter the data consonant with the nature of the matrix transformation.

The kinds of units and types of measurement scales, themselves, are considerations in selecting a matrix scaling transformation. If the units are noncomparable, as with horses and houses, then the data will have to be scaled by some procedure that makes the means and variations around the means comparable. The normalization transformations would do so by contracting (or expanding) the vectors to the same length. The standardization transformation would also make the units comparable by converting them to the same standard deviation units. If the scales are also noncomparable in that ordinal scales with different scale values are employed, then the standardization transformation would be most appropriate.

12.2 Covariance Matrix Transformation

The covariance matrix transformation is given in Eq. (4–10). The mean of each variable is subtracted from its data prior to the matrix multiplication of the transposed data matrix by itself. The transformation thus removes covariance associated with differences in magnitudes between variables and measures only their covariance around the mean.

The covariance matrix transformation has not often been employed, although factor analysts have long recognized its possibilities. Cyril Burt, in particular has pointed out some of the advantages of covariance over correlation (1941, pp. 280–88) and has given examples of its use.[15]

12.3 Correlation Matrix Transformation

It is safe to say that almost all factor analyses have been preceded by some variant of a correlation matrix transformation. Accordingly, since our primary concern is applied factor analysis, a discussion of different types of correlations might be helpful. The product moment will be considered first. The following sections will concentrate on (1) alternative coefficients to the product moment, (2) pattern magnitude coefficients, and (3) selecting the proper coefficient.

12.3.1 PRODUCT MOMENT
The formula for the product moment matrix transformation is given by Eqs. (4–11) and (4–12). The product moment is certainly the most often

15. See also Thomson (1951, Chapters 17 and 21).

employed transformation. Perhaps reflecting this popularity, most computer programs of which I am aware compute the product moment matrix transformation as the only correlation option prior to factor analysis. As will be shown in Section 12.3.4, this transformation may not always be desirable.

12.3.2 ALTERNATIVE CORRELATION COEFFICIENTS

The *rank* correlation coefficients, such as those of Spearman or Kendall (Siegel, 1956, pp. 202–23) offer one alternative to the product moment. Using scalar notation, the Spearman correlation coefficient, r_s, between rank order data on variables X_j and X_k is

$$r_s = 1 - \frac{6}{n(n^2 - 1)} \sum_{i=1}^{n} (x_{ij} - x_{ik})^2, \qquad (12\text{--}1)$$

where x_{ij} and x_{ik} are rank orders of case i on variables X_j and X_k.[16] The Kendall rank correlation coefficient, r_k, is

$$r_k = \frac{2S}{n(n - 1)}, \qquad (12\text{--}2)$$

where S is the sum of the number of pairs of ranks that are in their natural order on X_k, when cases are ranked in ascending order on X_j, minus the number of pairs that are not in the proper order.[16]

Example 12–6. Consider the following data:

Case	X_j	X_k	Ranked X_j	Ranked X_k
A	15	4	4	2
B	4	7	3	3
C	3	18	2	4
D	2	1	1	1

Order the ranked data in ascending order for X_j:

Case	Ranked X_j	Ranked X_k	(1) Number of cases below this one that have larger ranks	(2) Number of cases below this one that have smaller ranks	S_i (1) − (2)
D	1	1	3	0	3
C	2	4	0	2	−2
B	3	3	0	1	−1
A	4	2	0	0	0
					$\sum_{i}^{n} S_i = S = 0$

16. See Siegel (1956, pp. 207–10, 217–19) for the adjustments to be made if several ranks are tied.

Now, considering each case in turn, count the number of cases below it (in rank order on X_j) that have higher ranks and the number of cases with lower ranks. These two values can be put in adjacent columns. The latter value should be subtracted from the former to form S_i for each case. The sum of the S_i values is then S in the formula. In this example, $S = 0$, and $r_k = .00$.

The Spearman and Kendall rank correlation coefficients utilize the same amount of information, although not as much as the product moment.[17] Both allow significance tests for the correlations, and partial correlations can be computed for the Kendall coefficient. The Spearman and Kendall coefficients give *different values* for the same data, however, and are therefore not directly comparable. The remaining correlation coefficients to be considered are applicable to dichotomous data—data on two variables that can be distributed in a fourfold table. These are the *phi*, *phi-over-phi-max*, and *tetrachoric* coefficients.

The phi coefficient is the product moment applied to dichotomous data.[18] Let the two values on the dichotomous scale be 0 and 1. Then the two-way table for variables X_j and X_k is shown in Fig. 12–2.

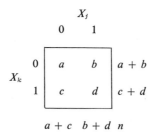

Figure 12–2

The letters a, b, etc., stand for the joint frequency of the values for variables X_j and X_k. The coefficient phi is then:

$$\phi = \frac{ad - bc}{[(a + b)(c + d)(a + c)(b + d)]^{1/2}}. \qquad (12\text{–}3)$$

17. When calculated on data which can be assumed to be from a bivariate normally distributed population, both have an efficiency equal to 91 per cent of that of the product moment (Siegel, 1956, pp. 213, 223). The Spearman rank correlation is the product moment applied to rank-ordered data.

18. On the phi coefficient, see Guilford (1954, pp. 431–33).

An alternate way of computing ϕ is through the chi-square of the fourfold table, viz.:

$$\phi = \left(\frac{\chi^2}{n}\right)^{1/2}. \tag{12-4}$$

This close relation of phi to chi-square allows for a test of significance of correlation. The range of phi is between -1.00 and $+1.00$ if the margins $(a + b, c + d, a + c,$ and $b + c)$ of the fourfold table are equal. For unequal marginals the range of phi is restricted. The maximum value, ϕ-max, of the phi coefficient for a given set of marginals is (Guilford, 1954, p. 359; Carroll, 1961, p. 350):

$$\phi\text{-max} = \left(\frac{p_s q_l}{p_l q_s}\right)^{1/2}, \tag{12-5}$$

where $p_l =$ the *larger* marginal proportion to n of the row sums $(a + b)$, $(c + d)$, and $p_l + q_l = 1$; and $p_s =$ the *smaller* marginal proportion to n of the column sums $(a + c)$, $(b + d)$, and $p_s + q_s = 1$. If the marginal proportions are equal, ϕ-max $= 1$.

Because of the restriction on the range of phi as indicated by phi-max, an alternative correlation coefficient often employed is called *phi-over-phi-max*. It is derived by dividing ϕ by ϕ-max (E. E. Cureton, 1959).

In addition to the phi and phi-over-phi-max coefficients of correlation for dichotomous data, the *tetrachoric* (r_t) coefficient might be used. Although there appears no simple equation for computing r_t, "abacs" (graphical aids) for approximating r_t have been published.[19] The tetrachoric coefficient estimates the value of the product moment correlation, *if the dichotomized data are drawn from a normal distribution*. The basic assumption of the tetrachoric, therefore, is that the underlying distribution of the data is normal. It should be noted, however, that in contrast to the phi coefficient, the tetrachoric does not have its range affected by unequal data marginals.

12.3.3 PATTERN-MAGNITUDE COEFFICIENTS

The correlation and alternative coefficients discussed in the last section measure the *pattern* similarity of the values for two variables. In some research designs, however, it may be preferable to employ a matrix transformation that measures both pattern and *magnitude* similarity.

19. A mathematical development of the tetrachoric is given in Kendall and Stuart (1961, Section 26.27); see especially pp. 306–7 for references to methods of approximating r_t. Guilford (1954, p. 431) gives an "abac" for graphically determining the phi when the data are split evenly.

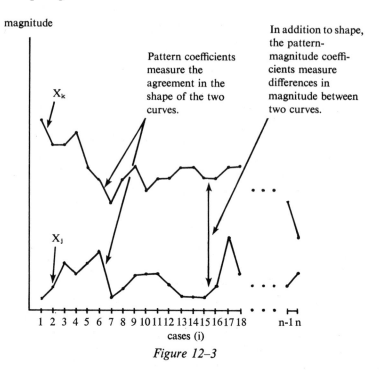

Figure 12-3

Figure 12-3 may help to make the distinction between pattern and magnitude clear. The need for a pattern-magnitude coefficient often appears when a Q-factor analysis research question (Definition 8-2) is being asked.

> *Example 12-7.* Consider a data matrix of 20 ratio-scaled characteristics by 30 nations—that is, a Q-factor analysis data slice. A correlation transformation of this matrix involves intercorrelating nations across their characteristics. Presumably, to avoid a species factor (Section 12.1.2, Example 12-3), the characteristics have been standardized by rows. A product moment coefficient will measure the similarity in pattern for these nations, based on their characteristics, and the factor analysis will delineate the most interrelated patterns and the nations manifesting them. The researcher may not wish to employ a product moment matrix transformation, however. The resulting factors might lump together nations like Yemen and England, which are very dissimilar in magnitudes of size, economic development, density, and proportion of Catholics but

which have a similar *pattern* of change in magnitude across characteristics. Referring to Fig. 12–3, X_k and X_j can indicate those patterns for England and Yemen, respectively. The "cases" along the horizontal axis are the characteristics, measured in standard score units. Now it can be seen how the similarity in the shapes of their curves could group England and Yemen together, in spite of their different data magnitudes. Accordingly, the matrix transformation for this data might more appropriately be one to measure both the shape and the *coincidence* of the curves.

Cattell (1949b) has been particularly concerned about pattern-magnitude measures and has developed one, the r_p coefficient, which he has applied.[20] A number of other pattern-magnitude coefficients have also been developed (Muldoon and Ray, 1958). Moreover, coefficients that have been primarily derived from different analyses for comparing factors (Section 20.2.3) measure both pattern and magnitude and might be accordingly considered as transformations for the data matrix.

One coefficient that appears particularly appealing in its similarity to the analysis of variance is the *intraclass correlation coefficient* (Kendall and Stuart, 1961, vol. 2, Section 26.25).[21] The intraclass can be applied to any number of variables, but for our purposes we will restrict its consideration to bivariate relations. As an analysis of the variance coefficient, the intraclass divides the variance on two variables into two parts. One part is the variance of each case on the two variables and is called the *within-class variance*. If the two values for a case on the two variables are the same, this variance is zero. A measure of this variance for a case is the squared deviation of the two values from the mean of the values:

$$\text{within-class variance} = (x_{ij} - \bar{X}_i)^2 + (x_{ik} - \bar{X}_i)^2,$$

where $\bar{X}_i = (x_{ij} + x_{ik})/2$. The *total* within-class variance, which we will denote as W, generalized across all n cases on the two variables, is

$$W = \frac{\sum_{i=1}^{n} [(x_{ij} - \bar{X}_i)^2 + (x_{ik} - \bar{X}_i)^2]}{n}.$$

20. Cattell and others call such measures *pattern* or *pattern similarity* coefficients. Labeling notwithstanding, they measure both shape and magnitude similarity. Muldoon and Ray (1958) have compared six pattern coefficients, among them the r_p coefficient, for their effects on factor analyses of the same data. See also Gaier and Lee (1953) and Cattell (1957, pp. 374, 402 ff.).

21. See also Haggard and Gupta (1958) and Blalock (1960, pp. 268–69).

If each case has the same two values on the two variables, $W = 0$. W therefore measures the *magnitude* similarity of two variables.

The second part of the variance of two variables is that down the columns (remembering that variables are column vectors of a data matrix). This is the *between-class variance* and measures the variance between the cases on the two variables. The variance is determined by computing the joint mean of all the data on X_j and X_k and summing the squared differences of this joint mean from the means, $\bar{X}_i$, of the two values of each case. Denoting this variance as B,

$$B = \frac{\sum_{i=1}^{n} (\bar{X}_i - \bar{X}_{jk})^2}{n - 1},$$

where B = between-class variance, $\bar{X}_i = (x_{ij} + x_{ik})/2$, and $\bar{X}_{jk}$ = mean of all the data on X_j and X_k [$\bar{X}_k = (\bar{X}_j + \bar{X}_k)/2$].

With W and B defined for two variables, we can now specify the intraclass correlation coefficient, r_i:

$$r_i = \frac{B - W}{B + W}, \qquad (12\text{–}6)$$

where r_i is computed for n cases on *two* variables.

For bivariate relationships, r_i will vary between -1.00 and $+1.00$.[22] In the latter case, all the X_j, X_k values for each case are identical: All the variance is between cases. When $r_i = -1.00$, all the variance is due to different values for each case on X_j and X_k, while the mean values on the two variables for each case are the same. When $r_i = 0$, both within-case and between-case variances are equal.

In terms of Fig. 12–3, W measures the variation in distance between the two curves, X_j and X_k, while B measures the variation along the curves. If $W = 0$, the curves are congruent, $X_j = X_k$, and $r_i = 1.00$. If $B = 0$, the curves are perfectly negatively correlated, $X_j = a - X_k$, and $r_i = -1.00$. When the variation along the curves about equals the varying distance between the curves, r_i is near zero.

12.3.4 SELECTING THE CORRELATION TRANSFORMATION
The large number of coefficients available for the matrix transformation may cause confusion and despair, leading perhaps to the use in all

---

22. The intraclass correlation coefficient may be computed on more than two variables. If it is computed on m variables with m values for each case, the maximum negative value the coefficient can attain is $-1/(m - 1)$. For two variables we have two values for each case, and the maximum negative correlation is $-1/(2 - 1) = -1.00$.

cases of the most familiar and most often employed product moment. The general application of the product moment (or any of the coefficients discussed above) may lead to spurious or misleading factors if certain requirements of the data are not satisfied. The purpose of this section is to make explicit major criteria for selecting an appropriate correlation transformation.[23] These criteria are related to the *units and scales, data slice, splits, error, distributions,* and *underlying distributions* of the data.

12.3.4.1 *Units and Scales.* The product moment and alternative coefficients, such as the rank, phi, and tetrachoric, can be applied to data measured in different units and on different scales. The pattern-magnitude coefficients, on the other hand, are appropriately sensitive to unit and scale differences. If the data in a matrix are not in common units, standardizing by *row* will enable the coefficients to be applied. If data were standardized by column, then the very magnitude differences the coefficients are meant to assess will be washed out of the data.

12.3.4.2 *Data Slice.* The data slice (Section 8.3) will determine whether a pattern-magnitude coefficient should be employed. In R-factor analysis, the variables are characteristics, and the differences in magnitudes for an entity across these characteristics are not usually of concern. Nor are these differences meaningful, since they are the result of non-comparable units (e.g., GNP, population, area). In Q-factor analysis, however, the differences in standard scores of characteristics across entities is important information. Information about these differences may be entered into the analysis through a pattern-magnitude measure, such as the *intraclass.* Example 12–7, above, is relevant here.

12.3.4.3 *Splits.* If the data are measured as dichotomies, and similarity of pattern *and* magnitude is not of concern, the phi, phi-over-phi-max, or tetrachoric coefficients may be used. The splits in the data, that is, the proportion of cases with one value of the dichotomy, can produce artifactual factors if the proportions deviate from .5 and if these proportions vary from variable to variable.

These artifactual factors are often called *difficulty factors* in the literature. The name arose from the application of factor analysis to psychological tests of the yes-no variety. These tests may have disproportionate

---

23. Carroll's (1961) essay is most salient to this section and should be read by anyone considering alternative correlation coefficients. Cattell (1952a) discusses different correlation coefficients and their effects on a factor analysis. Guilford (1963), although mainly concerned with the difficulties of the Q-factor analysis of dichotomized data, makes a relevant comparison of a number of correlation coefficients for such data. Comrey and Levonian (1958) make an empirical examination of the effects of the differences in phi, phi-over-phi-max, and the tetrachoric.

yes-no answers resulting from the varying level of difficulty of each test. Since difficulty is intrinsic to the tests and the analysis is concerned with characteristics of the sample and not the tests, there has been some concern over avoidance of difficulty factors—factors resulting from the covariance of different proportions of dichotomous values within the data matrix (Ferguson, 1941; Carroll, 1945; Wherry and Gaylord, 1944; Cattell, 1952a, pp. 321–26; Horst, 1965, pp. 513–16).[24]

The problem of artifactual factors resulting from splits in the data is related to the choice of correlation coefficient. The phi coefficient, if used, can only realize its full range of -1.00 to $+1.00$ if the split in the data is even. Otherwise its range will be restricted. The different phi coefficients calculated on data with different splits will have their ranges restricted to varying degrees.[25] These phi coefficients with different ranges *will accordingly not be directly comparable,* and the variation entering the factor results from these different ranges may produce artifactual ("difficulty") factors (Cattell, 1952a, p. 326).

Because of this very problem, the phi-over-phi-max coefficient has been proposed. By dividing the phi for two variables by its maximum range for their data, the phi coefficient is made more comparable, and the possibility of an artifactual factor resulting from this variance is removed. The phi-over-phi-max, however, makes a strong assumption that the underlying bivariate distribution in the data is *rectangular* (Carroll, 1961). The researcher may not often be willing to make this assumption about his data. Moreover, the phi-over-phi-max has an increasingly steep approach to 1.00 (perfect correlation) as the splits in the data become more disproportionate,[26] thus introducing a different source of noncomparable variance in place of that which it eliminates.

In contrast to the phi and phi-over-phi-max, the tetrachoric is not influenced by disproportionate splits in the data. Its range will remain -1.00 to $+1.00$ even for highly disparate splits, but it also makes a strong assumption that the underlying distribution is *bivariate normal* (Kendall and Stuart, 1961, pp. 304–5).

It is unfortunate that methodologists have not arrived at a consensus on the best coefficient for dichotomous data. Wherry and Gaylord (1944) consider the tetrachoric the best, and Cattell (1952a, pp. 326–27)

---

24. McMurray (1964) discusses at length "difficulty" factors, resulting from dichotomously scaled political data. He concludes, too pessimistically, that the problem is so severe that factor analysis should not be applied to such data.

25. See Carroll (1961) for a discussion of restrictions in range relative to phi, phi-over-phi-max, and tetrachoric coefficients.

26. This is graphed in Figs. 7 and 8 of Carroll (1961).

favors the phi-over-phi-max. Carroll (1961) feels that phi-over-phi-max leaves too much to be desired and that the tetrachoric is most suited to dichotomous data. Horst (1965, p. 515), on the other hand, states that the use of the tetrachoric on dichotomous (which Horst terms "binary") data is not warranted.

Much methodological[27] and empirical research on this issue yet remains to be done. One of the few empirical analyses of the three coefficients was published by Comrey and Levonian (1958). Comparing factor analyses of different coefficients applied to the same data—Minnesota Multiphasic Personality Inventory (MMPI) items—they found strong evidence that phi, phi-over-phi-max, and tetrachoric result in the "same major factors, although the absolute values of the loadings and the nature of minor factors may be expected to vary" (1958, p. 752). They conclude that the phi coefficient is the most reasonable choice because the phi-over-phi-max and tetrachoric lead to overly high communalities, and artifactual factors resulting from the phi may also appear with phi-over-phi-max and tetrachoric.

12.3.4.4 *Error.* The nature of data error as discussed in Section 9.1.3.4 is relevant here. If the data contain random and systematic error, the product moment correlation may not be the best matrix transformation, since it will enter the reliable and unreliable variance (Section 5.1) into the factor analysis.[28] When such error exists, one may select a correlation matrix transformation consonant with the degree of error. If the data errors are not so large as to distort ranking of cases, the rank correlation coefficients can be used. If, however, even rankings are unreliable, then the data can be dichotomized (a distributional transformation) and the phi, phi-over-phi-max, or tetrachoric matrix transformation applied, as other criteria dictate.

12.3.4.5 *Distribution.* The product moment can be calculated for any two variables regardless of their distribution. If, however, the product moment coefficient is going to be used *inferentially*—if tests of significance are to be applied—then a bivariate normal distribution

---

27. Horst (1965, Chapter 22) has developed three promising techniques for overcoming the problem of splits. His approach is to partial out the variability in the data due to unequal splits from the determination of the factors. One of the three approaches, for example, constructs a Guttman-type data matrix of the data and separates the dispersion due to this matrix from the data. The residual variance is then factored.

28. If the data have only *random* error, then the product moment correlation transformation is justified for the *common factor analysis* model, with communality or reliability estimates in the principal diagonal of the correlation matrix. See Section 5.2. The common factor model results, however, can be distorted by *systematic* error.

is assumed.[29] When tests of significance are applied to the factor results, the usual assumption is of a *multivariate* normal distribution.

In factor designs that will use the results descriptively rather than inferentially, the characteristics of the distributions are still important. Variables with tied values and disparate marginal distributions will restrict the range of the product moment (Section 9.1.2.12). Moreover, the product moment will be unequally weighted by skewed distributions with extreme values. Accordingly, if the distributions in the data depart from normality and cannot be transformed to normality as discussed in Chapter 11, then a correlation matrix transformation not dependent on normality should be used.[30]

The *nonparametric*[31] correlation coefficients may be employed if the data distributions are largely nonnormal. The nature of the distribution and existence of outliers (Section 9.1.2.12) will not affect the Spearman or Kendall rank correlation coefficients, and, if many tied values (causing tied ranks) exist, there are correction formulas (Siegal, 1956, Chapter 9). When many of the values are tied or the data are dichotomies, the correlation coefficients for dichotomies are appropriate.

The computation of phi, phi-over-phi-max, or tetrachoric can be done on any dichotomous distribution. The descriptive ability and usefulness of the phi, however, decreases as the split in the dichotomies departs from one-half because of the effect on its range. While the ranges of the phi-over-phi-max and tetrachoric are not influenced by splits, the phi-over-phi-max approach curve to 1.00 (perfect correlation) is highly influenced by these marginal proportions. The tetrachoric appears to be the coefficient most free from effects of the distribution of dichotomous data.

12.3.4.6 *Underlying Distribution.* The problem of the underlying distribution has now been discussed in a number of contexts (Sections 9.1.3.5 and 11.1.4). With regard to the selection of an appropriate correlation coefficient, the underlying distribution that may be assumed

---

29. Kendall and Stuart (1961, Chapter 26). Those who have difficulty "visualizing" a bivariate normal distribution are referred to Fig. 11.4 of Dixon and Massey (1957, p. 199).

30. The role of normality of distributions in computation of the product moment and in evaluating the coefficient descriptively and inferentially has been extensively discussed in the literature (Carroll, 1961; Goldfried and Drasgow, 1964; Heath, 1961; Nefzger and Drasgow, 1957; Norris and Hjelm, 1961; LaForge, 1958; Binder, 1959).

31. Nonparametric statistics are those that do not involve assumptions about the parameters, such as the mean and standard deviation, of the distributions for the universe from which the sample of data was taken. See Siegel (1956, p. 3).

Table 12–1. Selection Criteria for Correlation Matrix Transformation

Matrix Transformation	Assumptions[a]									
	Comparable Units between Columns	Comparable Scales between Columns	Comparable Units and Scales between Rows[b]	Normal Distribution	Bivariate Normal Underlying Distribution	Bivariate Rectangular Underlying Distribution	No Extreme Outliers	No Error	No Rank Distorting Error	Equal Proportional Splits for Dichotomies
Product moment	No	No	Yes	Yes	No[c] Yes[d]	No	Yes	Yes[e]	Yes	Yes[f]
Rank correlation	No	No	Yes	No	No	No	No	No	Yes	—[g]
Pattern-magnitude correlation	No	No	Yes	No[h]	No[c] Yes[i]	No	Yes	Yes	Yes	?
Phi	No	No	Yes	No	No	No	No	No	No	Yes
Phi-over-phi-max	No	No	Yes	No	No	Yes	No	No	No	Yes[j]
Tetrachoric	No	No	Yes	No	Yes	No	No	No	No	No

a Assumptions are for descriptive and inferential analyses.
b Relevant to Q-factor analyses.
c Results used descriptively.
d Results used inferentially—tests of significance to be applied.
e For random error in the component factor model and systematic error in all factor models.
f Becomes the phi coefficient when computed on dichotomous data.
g Cannot be calculated for dichotomous data.
h For intraclass coefficient.
i Results of the intraclass to be used inferentially.
j Due to effect on the approach (to +1.00 or −1.00) values.

is important.[32] For the product moment, the underlying distribution is assumed to be bivariate normal if the results of the analysis are to be employed inferentially. If the product moment and factor results are to be employed descriptively, then no assumptions about the underlying distribution are involved.

With the rank correlation coefficients and the phi coefficient for dichotomous data, no assumption about the underlying distribution is made. As shown by Carroll (1961), however, the phi-over-phi-max assumes an underlying rectangular bivariate distribution. The tetrachoric coefficient, on the other hand, assumes a bivariate normal distribution *when used descriptively* as well as inferentially.

12.3.4.7 *Summary Table.* A number of different correlation matrix transformations and various criteria for selecting among them have been discussed. Table 12–1 summarizes this information in a compact form for easy reference and comparison.

12.4 Scale-Free Matrix Transformations

The methodology of factor analysis is going through a computer revolution. One indication of this (Horst, 1965) is the break-away of factor analysis from the constraints of being considered only a statistical technique and from traditional reliance on the correlation matrix transformation. A component of this revolution, auguring a new period in the theoretical and empirical use of factor analysis, is the ongoing development of scale-free solutions (Section 5.8). Even though much methodological work and practical testing needs to be done, the development has progressed sufficiently far for at least one factor methodologist to call Harman's (1960) factor analysis text an "historical document" only four years after it was published (Harris, 1964b, p. 193).

Although scale-free transformations may contain burrs yet to be worn down by application, the transformations are presented in this book because of their great potential. Consider that many social phenomena are measured on arbitrary scales and in arbitrary units. A profession of ignorance of the best units and scales is made when the researcher scales his data by many of the matrix scaling techniques of Section 12.1. Moreover, different matrix transformations lead, with trivial exceptions, to different factors for the same data. This presents a dilemma. Units and scales may be necessarily arbitrary, but different selections of arbitrary units and scales will result in different factors, depending on the matrix scaling techniques and transformation applied.

32. Carroll (1961), particularly, addresses his discussion to this problem.

No wonder, then, that in psychology, where the problem of meaningful units and scales may be most severe, the standard approach is to employ a correlation matrix transformation that in effect reduces the data to standard score units before measuring the relationship between them.

The virtue of scale-free matrix transformations is that they result in factors that (within a scaling constant) *are invariant of the original units and scales of the raw data. That is, the same interpretable factors and the same number would be found regardless of the matrix scaling techniques applied to the data and regardless of whether the covariance or correlation matrix transformation were applied.* Scale-free matrix transformations thus lift the factor results out of their traditional dependence on the data scales and the matrix transformation.

Once the basic principles associated with scale-free transformation are known, a number of different types of such transformations may be developed. Three that seem particularly exciting and that have been presented in Chapter 5 are *canonical factor analysis, alpha factor analysis,* and the *Harris variant of image factor analysis.* Table 5–2 compares a number of these models. One may also wish to refer to the sections of Chapter 5 in which these models are discussed.

13. Communality

The communality research design step has been of great concern in the methodological and applied psychological literature. Outside of the field of psychology, however, the meaning, and indeed importance, of communality has been little appreciated. It is not uncommon to see published factor studies of social or political data that neglect to mention the factor model or communality estimate employed. Yet, as illustrated below, the decision or lack of decision on communalities may markedly alter the interpretation and number of factors delineated.

A discussion of this communality problem is given in Section 13.1. A subsequent section will describe techniques for determining communality, and a final section will discuss some of the major considerations in selecting the communality approach or estimate. The content of these sections is outlined in Fig. 13–1.

310

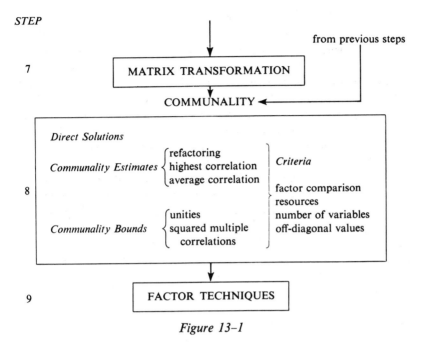

Figure 13-1

13.1 The Problem

The communality problem[1] arises when the *common factor analysis* model is selected for the research design. From Eq. (5–15), the fundamental theorem of common factor analysis is

$$R_{m \times m} - U^2_{m \times m} = F_{m \times p} F'_{p \times m},$$

where R is an m variable correlation matrix, U is a diagonal matrix of *unique* variances for each variable, and F is the factor matrix of factor loadings.

Now, we know that $U^2_{m \times m} = I_{m \times m} - H^2_{m \times m}$, where $H^2_{m \times m}$ is the diagonal matrix of *common* variances for each variable.[2] Therefore,

$$R_{m \times m} - (I_{m \times m} - H^2_{m \times m}) = F_{m \times p} F'_{p \times m},$$
$$R_{m \times m} - I_{m \times m} + H^2_{m \times m} = F_{m \times p} F'_{p \times m}.$$

1. Thurstone (1947, Chapter 13) presents a still helpful, although somewhat outdated, discussion of the communality problem. Harman (1967, Chapter 5) is excellent and presents some considerations not covered in Thurstone. For a concise statement of the communality problem, see Cattell (1965a, pp. 198–202).

2. A rereading of Sections 5.1, 5.2, and 5.3 might be helpful at this point.

Since $R_{m \times m}$ is a correlation matrix, it has unities in the principal diagonal. Subtracting the diagonal identity matrix $I_{m \times m}$ from $R_{m \times m}$, therefore, leaves zeros in the principal diagonal, and addition of the diagonal matrix of communalities $H^2_{m \times m}$ has the effect of inserting communalities into the principal diagonal of $R_{m \times m}$. Figure 13–2 displays this result.

The problem is that in common factor analysis the communalities, h^2_j, cannot be known until the common factors are defined. The delineation of these factors, however, depends on the correlations and the communality values in the principal diagonal of the correlation matrix. This inability to determine precisely the communalities is a basic indeterminacy in the common factor model. The traditional procedure for dealing with this indeterminacy—this communality problem—is to insert in the principal diagonal of the correlation matrix some *estimates* of the communality values. The analysis can then proceed to the determination of the common factors. Of course, since communality estimates are used, the resulting common factors themselves can only be estimates, to some degree, of the true common factors for the data.

$$
\begin{bmatrix}
1 & r_{12} & r_{13} & \cdots & r_{1m} \\
r_{21} & 1 & r_{23} & \cdots & r_{2m} \\
r_{31} & r_{32} & 1 & \cdots & r_{3m} \\
\vdots & \vdots & \vdots & \ddots & \vdots \\
r_{m1} & r_{m2} & r_{m3} & \cdots & 1
\end{bmatrix}
-
\begin{bmatrix}
1 & 0 & 0 & \cdots & 0 \\
0 & 1 & 0 & \cdots & 0 \\
0 & 0 & 1 & \cdots & 0 \\
\vdots & \vdots & \vdots & \ddots & \vdots \\
0 & 0 & 0 & \cdots & 1
\end{bmatrix}
$$

$$
+
\begin{bmatrix}
h^2_1 & 0 & 0 & \cdots & 0 \\
0 & h^2_2 & 0 & \cdots & 0 \\
0 & 0 & h^2_3 & \cdots & 0 \\
\vdots & \vdots & \vdots & \ddots & \vdots \\
0 & 0 & 0 & \cdots & h^2_m
\end{bmatrix}
=
\begin{bmatrix}
h^2_1 & r_{12} & r_{13} & \cdots & r_{1m} \\
r_{21} & h^2_2 & r_{23} & \cdots & r_{2m} \\
r_{31} & r_{32} & h^2_3 & \cdots & r_{3m} \\
\vdots & \vdots & \vdots & \ddots & \vdots \\
r_{m1} & r_{m2} & r_{m3} & \cdots & h^2_m
\end{bmatrix}
$$

Figure 13–2

It must be clear that communality estimates and the common factor analysis model of Section 5.2 go together. The *component analysis* model has no communality estimates. The researcher inserts unities or, more correctly, leaves unities in the principal diagonal of the correlation matrix, and that is the end of it. For the *image analysis* model, the squared multiple correlation coefficient of each variable with the others is the precise communality value. No estimate is needed. In the *canonical* and *alpha factor analysis* models, communality estimates (or estimates of uniquenesses) are employed, to be sure, but the best estimates are known (Sections 5.5 and 5.7 and Table 5–2). The analyses begin with these estimates, which are then converged to *stable values*. Moreover, in two historical approaches to common factor analysis—the two-factor and bifactor approaches yet to be discussed (Sections 14.2.1 and 14.2.3) —no communality estimate is required. For these models and approaches, therefore, the communality problem is solved. For common factor analysis, however, no best estimates giving convergence to stable and to proper communality values are known.

The only operational difference between the common factor analysis and component analysis models is the values in the principal diagonal of the correlation matrix. These values are unities for principal components and communality estimates for common factor analysis. But even for these diagonal values, the operational difference between the models may disappear if unities are also used for communality estimates in common factor analysis. Therefore, one should know what model one is using *apart* from what is in the principal diagonal of the correlation matrix if the proper interpretation is to be given to the factors.

A question often arises as to whether what is inserted in the principal diagonal makes much difference in the factor loadings anyway. The answer is that the values in the principal diagonal *can* alter the factor loadings and the number of factors defined for the data.[3] The factors delineate the interrelationships between the variables of the correlation matrix. As the number of variables in the matrix decreases (holding the size of the off-diagonal correlations constant), the contribution of the principal diagonal elements to the measurement of the interrelationships between the variables increases.

The practice outside the field of psychology of leaving unities in the principal diagonal (when the common factor analysis model is involved) can have an especially great influence on the results if the off-diagonal correlations are small. Then the principal diagonal values become *extreme values*, having a disproportionate weight in measuring the interrelationships between the variables.

> *Example 13–1.* Consider two hypothetical variables, X_1 and X_2, of a six-variable correlation matrix. The large size of the 1.00 in rows 1 and 2 will have a far greater effect on measuring the interrelationship between X_1 and X_2 than will the correlations in the remaining rows.

3. Thurstone (1947, p. 285) presents the factor results for three different sets of elements in the principal diagonal of a three-variable correlation matrix. The factor structures differ remarkably.

$$
\begin{array}{c|cccc}
 & X_1 & X_2 & \cdots \\
\hline
X_1 & 1.00 & .13 & \cdots \\
X_2 & .13 & 1.00 & \cdots \\
X_3 & .08 & .14 & \cdots \\
X_4 & .03 & .21 & \cdots \\
X_5 & .16 & .00 & \cdots \\
X_6 & .00 & .02 & \cdots \\
\end{array}
$$

Example 13–2. As an empirical example, the correlation matrix of Table 13–1 for 1962–63 data on 10 domestic conflict variables has been factored with communality estimates of unities and again factored with squared multiple correlation (SMC) estimates (Notation 3–10). The results are shown in Table 13–2.

Table 13–1. Correlation Matrix for 1962–63 Domestic Conflict Behavior Data[a]

Variables	(1)	(2)	(3)	(4)	(5)	(6)	(7)	(8)	(9)	(10)
1. Demonstrations	.33									
2. Major government crises	.16	.25								
3. Purges	.11	.32	.47							
4. Riots	.53	.30	.21	.53						
5. Bombings	.25	.30	.31	.53	.71					
6. Small-scale terrorism	.05	.17	.22	.35	.71	.75				
7. Small-scale guerrilla war	.01	−.02	.13	.04	.15	.49	.40			
8. Plots	.08	.21	.64	.16	.23	.16	.11	.44		
9. Coups	.11	.37	.36	.18	.17	.07	.00	.39	.29	
10. Number killed in domestic conflict	.22	.06	.20	.37	.19	.52	.51	.15	.19	.55

[a] Product moment correlations are given for 105 nations. The elements in the principal diagonal are squared multiple correlations. From Rummel (1965a).

13.2 Estimating Communality

In common factor analysis, the only factors wanted are those defining the common variable interrelationships. The 1.00 correlation of a variable with itself is not of interest, and the influence of this correlation on the results should be avoided. In other words, we want to determine the common factors and rank (Section 4.4) of the matrix of off-diagonal correlations, leaving the principal diagonal elements blank. With the definition of these common factors and this rank, the diagonal elements

Table 13–2. Common Factors of 1962–63 Domestic Conflict Behavior[a]

Variables	h_j^2 estimate = 1.00				h_j^2 estimate = SMC			
	1	2	3	h^2	1	2	3	h^2
1. Demonstrations	−.03	.01	(.77)	.59	.01	.07	(.54)	.30
2. Major government crises	−.06	(.51)	.40	.43	.01	.39	.33	.26
3. Purges	.19	(.81)	.06	.70	−.16	(.72)	.11	.55
4. Riots	.21	.13	(.84)	.77	−.18	.15	(.73)	.59
5. Bombings	.45	.24	(.58)	.60	−.40	.22	(.63)	.61
6. Small-scale terrorism	(.83)	.10	.27	.77	(−.81)	.09	.32	.76
7. Small-scale guerrilla war	(.83)	.00	−.17	.71	(−.66)	.03	−.09	.44
8. Plots	.14	(.82)	−.04	.69	−.12	(.71)	.03	.51
9. Coups	−.02	(.70)	.14	.51	−.01	.54	.15	.31
10. Number killed in domestic conflict	(.73)	.09	.19	.59	(−.64)	.13	.18	.46
Per cent total variance	22.2	21.7	19.6	63.6	17.3	15.7	15.1	47.9

[a] Varimax orthogonally rotated factors. For the h_j^2 estimate = 1.00 analysis, factors with eigenvalues ≥ 1.00 were rotated. The same *number* of factors were then rotated for the h_j^2 estimate = SMC analysis, although application of the same eigenvalue criterion would have resulted in only two factors. The sum of per cent total variance figures do not exactly equal the sum of h^2 values (× 100) due to rounding errors.

can be filled in with the communalities computed from the common factors [Eq. (5–17)]. When inserted in the principal diagonal, these proper communalities would not alter the factor results. This description of the problem actually summarizes a set of solutions for determining communality that may be termed *direct solutions*. Another set of solutions tries to insert, prior to common factor analysis, the best *estimate* of the communality for each variable. And a third set of solutions tries to insert values that are the *bounds* on the communalities.

13.2.1 DIRECT SOLUTIONS

One technique is to hypothesize that the correlation matrix has a certain rank, say of one or two.[4] The communalities for a small number of variables can be computed if the off-diagonal correlations satisfy certain conditions. These conditions, called the *tetrad criterion* for rank one and the *pentad criterion* for rank two, and the technical details for solving the communalities are fully discussed in Harman (1960, Sections 5.3 and 5.4). A numerical example for two factors and eight variables is also given by Harman (1960, Section 5.6).

An analogous solution has been proposed by Albert (1944a, 1944b).[5] Assuming that the matrix is of a given rank, Albert presents an algebraically unique solution to the communalities. A problem related to this approach and to that in the previous paragraph, however, is that the rank of the correlation matrix must be known in advance. Moreover, for Albert's solution a basic condition for a unique solution to the communalities is that the rank be less than half the number of variables. This is a restrictive assumption, since in empirical data random variation from perfect measurement alone should cause the rank of the correlation matrix to exceed this limit.

If the rank assumption involved in the direct solutions is correct, the communalities will lie between zero and unity. When any of the communalities computed by a direct solution for rank one exceeds unity, the result is called the *Heywood case* (Thurstone, 1947, pp. 289–90). All this result indicates is that the assumed rank of one is too low for this correlation matrix. One can then increase the size of the assumed rank until the offending communalities are brought within the proper bounds.

4. See Guttman (1958a), who seriously questions whether a correlation matrix can be assumed to have a low rank.
5. A brief discussion of Albert's solution is given in Harman (1967, p. 78). Thurstone (1947, pp. 314–18) reviews in detail and exemplifies Albert's technique. Gibson (1963) generalizes Albert's solution, making a stringent assumption about the vector configuration of variables.

13.2.2 COMMUNALITY ESTIMATES

Harman (1960, Sections 5.8, 5.9, and 5.10) lists several approximations to communality, among which are the *average correlation* of a variable, the *highest correlation*, and communality through *refactoring*.

The *refactoring* approach is to employ an initial estimate of communality, such as the average correlation of a variable or the SMC discussed below, factor the matrix, and compute new communalities from the factors. These new communalities are then inserted in the correlation matrix, and the matrix is refactored. The procedure can be iterated until the successive communalities converge on a stable value. As quoted by Harman (1960, p. 89), Charles Wrigley has found through empirical investigation that SMC's are the best initial estimates for convergence. Guttman (1956, p. 275), however, cautions that mathematical proof has not been given of convergence to the proper communalities for minimum rank, and that the final stable value may vary with the initial estimate used.

Instead of refactoring, the communalities might be estimated by the *highest correlation* for a variable. As each successive factor is extracted from the correlation matrix by the centroid or principal axes technique, the highest residual correlation for the variable can be inserted in the diagonal. Such an estimation procedure has been favored by Thurstone (1947, pp. 299–300, 318).

A simpler approach is to estimate the communalities by the *average correlation* of a variable with the others. Although the estimate appears useful, it has not found much application, nor has it found any champions in the literature.

13.2.3 COMMUNALITY BOUNDS

Rather than try to estimate the communalities directly, it might be more meaningful to insert in the principal diagonal of the correlation matrix the upper or lower communality bounds. The *upper bound* on a communality is unity. If a variable were completely contained in the common factor space of the other variables, i.e., completely predicted or generated by the common factors, then its communality would equal unity.

Some empirical investigation of unity estimates has been done. In a study by Tyler and Michael (1958) a comparison of the results of 6 factorings of 12 variables indicated to them that unities were a good estimate. Although this study suggests that unities may be an appropriate estimate for some data, as a rule one may not wish to use unities for small sets of variables, say fewer than 10.

The *lower bound* of the communality has been shown to be the squared multiple correlation of a variable with all the others (Guttman, 1940, 1956, 1957b). We have established the notation that SMC is the squared multiple correlation of variable X_j with all the others (Notation 3–9) and that h_j^2 is its communality (Notation 5–1). Then,

$$\text{SMC}_j \leq h_j^2. \tag{13–1}$$

The SMC's have a number of important theoretical properties.[6] One is that they may actually equal h_j^2 in some cases. Another is that they are a function of the number of variables. As the number of variables increases, SMC_j approaches h_j^2 in the limit. Specifically, if the ratio of the number of common factors p to the number of variables m approaches zero as m approaches infinity, i.e.,

$$\lim_{m \to \infty} \frac{p}{m} = 0, \tag{13–2}$$

then,

$$\text{SMC}_j = h_j^2. \tag{13–3}$$

The SMC values themselves help to determine whether the data are adequate for *common* factor analysis. If they are low and not close to h_j^2 for the data, then Eq. (13–2) may not hold, or the variables are a poor sample from the substantive domain (Kaiser, 1963, p. 160; Guttman, 1956, p. 274). In this case *the same factor may have alternative factor scores that have little correlation with each other* (Guttman, 1956, p. 276). Thus, the SMC lower bound may be used to decide if a common factor analysis should be used.

Occasionally, the SMC estimates may lead to factor matrices with communalities and some orthogonal loadings exceeding 1.00. This is due to the SMC's being a lower bound—underestimating the true h_j^2 and causing the correlation matrix for some data to lose its Gramian properties. The result is the same as when the correlation matrix is computed for variables with missing data (Section 10.3.1.1). This consequence of employing SMC's, however, seems to decrease with the increasing number of variables analyzed.

13.3 Selecting the Communality Estimate

The investigator's choice of communality estimate for the common factor analysis model will depend on the estimate adopted by other factor

6. Guttman (1940, 1953, 1956) is the best source on these properties. Most of them are briefly discussed by Harman (1967, pp. 86–88).

studies against which results might be compared, on existing computing facilities, on the number of variables, and on the size of the off-diagonal values.

The choice of communality estimate will have to be guided by the choice made in other studies. Presumably, the researcher will wish to compare his factor structure with others to determine the stability of his common factors and the degree of convergence of all relevant studies to sound empirical propositions. Especially in the case of small variable studies, the findings are partly a function of the estimate adopted. Example 13–2 exemplifies this. Moreover, in an empirical study directed in part at this question, Bechtoldt (1961, p. 424) found that "comparable analysis for the several sets of data of this study indicate that differences in the stability of factor loadings do result both from the method of factoring and from the diagonal values used as communality estimates as well as from the characteristics of the data." The partial dependence of the factor results on communality estimates strongly suggests that these estimates be kept as constant as possible in the case of small sets of variables when factor comparisons are contemplated.

If the number of variables in the analysis is small, then the factor analysis may be computed by hand or on a desk calculator. This may be necessary if computer facilities are unavailable or computer programs do not allow for principal diagonal values other than unities. Computer program availability and options should therefore be investigated before making a final selection of estimates.

At several points throughout this chapter the number of variables has been mentioned as important. The number of diagonal elements of a matrix is m, the number of variables. But the number of off-diagonal elements in the matrix is

$$m^2 - m = m(m - 1). \tag{13–4}$$

Therefore, an approximate measure of the proportional influence the diagonal elements have is the ratio

$$\frac{m}{m(m - 1)} = \frac{1}{m - 1}. \tag{13–5}$$

As the above equation indicates, the larger the number of variables, the smaller the approximate effect of the diagonal elements on the factor results.

Equation (13–5) should not be considered alone in determining the influence of the diagonal elements. Also important is the size of the off-diagonal correlations. The larger the average absolute correlations in the off-diagonal cells, the less influence diagonal values of unity have for a given number of variables. This results from the increasingly larger variance contribution of the diagonal values with decreasing size of the off-diagonals. Whether the balance between number of variables and size of off-diagonal correlations is sufficient to meaningfully affect the analysis is a question that can only be answered in the extremes. Perhaps if the number of variables is greater than around 70 or so, the off-diagonal elements may be so numerous relative to the diagonal values that the factor structure and interpretation is invariant of choice of estimate. This is an empirical question, however. *With the speed of the computer at his disposal, the investigator might try a couple of estimates to see if they make any difference for his purposes.*

At any rate, the best estimate on theoretical and empirical grounds appears to be the SMC for each variable.[7] This estimate may not always be possible to employ, however, because of the lack of computing facilities or missing data.[8] In such a situation the researcher may employ as his estimate for a final solution the highest correlation in a column for a variable.

7. Howard and Cartwright (1962) found that of three communality estimates investigated (unities, h_j^2 resulting from a factor analysis with unities in the diagonal, and SMC's), the SMC estimate was most stable and was that estimate toward which other estimates tended to converge.

8. DuBois (1957) presents charts for shorthand computation of multiple correlation coefficients.

Part Four · The Analysis

14. Factor Techniques

The heart of a factor analysis design is the factor technique. It is the computational means by which the matrix resulting from the previous steps in the research design can be reduced to its factor dimensions. A number of such techniques will be discussed in terms of their logic and characteristics. As these techniques are adequately presented in Thurstone (1947), Cattell (1952a), Fruchter (1954), and Harman (1967), precise computing instructions and derivations will not be given.[1] Here, as elsewhere in this book, the emphasis is on the alternatives available, their characteristics, the criteria for selecting an alternative, and an explanation of the concepts involved in the process.

The first section will suggest criteria for selecting among three approaches: *two-factors*, *bifactors*, and *multifactors*. These approaches will be discussed in the second section. The subsequent section focuses on the multifactor approach through several techniques for arriving at a

---

1. Cattell (1952a, Chapter 21) treats fully of the strategy and tactics of economy in computing factor analyses.

multifactor solution. A summary table of these various approaches and techniques is presented in the final section.[2]

The content of this chapter as a factor analysis research design step is shown in Fig. 14–1.

14.1 Criteria for Selecting Approach and Technique

With the profusion of procedures available for determining numerical values on the factors, it might be useful to establish at the outset a number of relevant criteria to which a discussion of approaches and techniques can be explicitly related. Ten criteria appear especially pertinent: grouping requirements, number of factors, complexity of

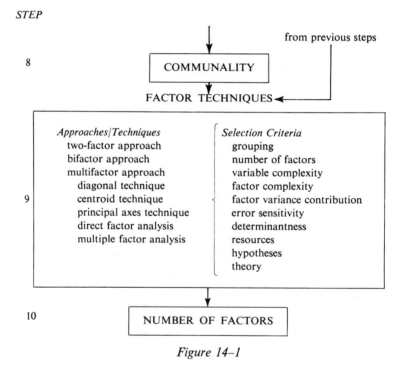

Figure 14–1

2. Burt (1941, Chapter 9) divides factor techniques into two major classifications, one depending on whether or not the whole correlation matrix is factored and the other on whether the factors are computed through a simple summation (centroid) or weighted summation (principal axes) method. The classification employed in this chapter adopts his point of view that distinctions should be made on the basis of mathematical characteristics. See also Solomon (1960).

variables, factor complexity, factor variance, error sensitivity, determinantness, resources, hypotheses, and theory.[3]

14.1.1 GROUPING REQUIREMENT
Some procedures require a preliminary grouping of interrelated variables. This grouping, if done visually, adds a certain amount of subjectivity to the factoring process. Techniques requiring grouping may compensate for this subjectivity by being computationally fast. If a computer is at the disposal of the factor analyst, however, ease of computation will have little bearing on choice of technique.

14.1.2 NUMBER OF FACTORS
The factoring technique itself may determine the number of factors for the data. On the other hand, we may wish to assume that only one general factor or a general factor plus group factors (Section 14.1.4) exists, in which case we would use the two-factor or bifactor approach. If the existence of a single general factor is a viable hypothesis within the content area, such techniques may be applied to see how well they fit the data

14.1.3 VARIABLE COMPLEXITY
Complexity refers to the *number of factors* upon which a variable has moderate or high loadings. What the investigator deems moderate—whether loadings are above an absolute .50, .20, or even .10—depends on the assessment of error in his data, the overall interrelationship between the variables, and the findings of other factor studies in his substantive domain. As with the previous criteria, the choice is between allowing the factor technique to identify all factors relevant to a variable or to select a technique that will restrict the number of factors to no more than one or two for a variable.

14.1.4 FACTOR COMPLEXITY
Complexity of factors refers to the *number of variables* that have moderate or high loadings. Three types of factors can be identified in terms of their complexity: general factors, group factors, and specific factors.

3. Harman (1967, Section 6.2) describes 10 criteria: grouping of variables, factor model, frame of reference, parsimony, factor contribution, linear, planar, hyperplanar, and ellipsoidal geometric fit, and simple structure principles. See also Cattell (1952a, pp. 141–42), who lists factor complexity, algebraic process, number of factors, desirability of rotation, ease of computation, and completeness and accuracy of numerical values.

A *general factor* has moderate or high loadings for all the variables. It delineates the general pattern of relationships among the variables.

A *group factor*, however, has moderate or high loadings for only a subset of two or more, but not all, of the variables. A factor loading for two variables is a special instance of a group factor and is called a *doublet*, or *doublet factor*. If the loadings of the *group factor* are such that there are both high positive and negative loadings, it is called, understandably enough, a *bipolar factor*. When all the variables loading a *group factor* load only that factor, it is called a *nonoverlapping group factor*.

A *specific factor* has been discussed in relation to the common factor model and unique variance (Section 5.2). Here, we can loosen our

Group factors

Variables	General factor		Bipolar factor	Doublet factor	Specific factor
	1	2	3	4	5
1.	×	×			
2.	×		×		
3.	×	×	×		
4.	×		×		
5.	×	×			
6.	×	×			×
7.	×		− ×		
8.	×		− ×		
9.	×			×	
10.	×			×	

Nonoverlapping group factors

Variables	1	2	3
1.	×		
2.	×		
3.	×		
4.		×	
5.		×	
6.		×	
7.			×
8.			×
9.			×
10.			×

× = meaningful loading

Figure 14–2

definition of *specific factor* to say that it is any factor with only *one* high loading.

These distinctions in terms of factor complexity are illustrated in Fig. 14–2.

The various approaches and techniques of factor analysis generate different configurations of factor complexity. It may be wise, therefore, to determine beforehand whether the particular computing procedure contemplated uncovers the factor complexity suitable to the data or the research hypotheses.

14.1.5 FACTOR VARIANCE CONTRIBUTION

The column sum of squared factor loadings for an (orthogonal) factor define its contribution to the total variance in the data [Eq. (6–2)]. The proportion of variance accounted for by a factor measures the overall correlation of the variables with the factor. If we imagine that these proportional figures for successive factors determined by some technique are plotted on a graph, with the vertical axis indicating the proportion of variance and the horizontal axis the number of the factor extracted, then we can identify three possible graphs.

One graph can define those techniques that yield factors in order of *decreasing proportional variance*. The first factor will account for proportionally the most variance, the second for the second most, and so on. Each successive factor defines less variance than the previous one. Another graph can classify those techniques that delineate factors with approximately *level proportional variance*. Each factor will be nearly as important as any other in contributing to the variance of the raw data. The third graph can index those techniques giving factors that contribute *step-level proportional variance*. They determine a first factor, of more proportional variance than any other, and secondary factors of less, but level, proportional variance among themselves. All factors except the first account for about the same amount of variance.

14.1.6 SENSITIVITY TO ERROR

Some techniques will be more sensitive to data error or poor communality estimates than others. If the data are errorful, therefore, this may be a crucial criterion for choosing between, say, the diagonal and centroid techniques.

14.1.7 DETERMINATENESS

This criterion relates to the uniqueness of the factor solution for a given set of data. Some techniques, such as the centroid, are not mathematically determinate. For the same set of data a different investigator may arrive at a slightly different configuration of factor loadings. For the principal axes technique, however, only one solution is possible.

14.1.8 RESOURCES

If we have access to a computer center with a wide variety of programs, computing time or labor may figure little in choice of technique. If, however, the choice of programs is highly limited or the "computing facilities" consist of a desk calculator or hand-operated adding machine, then the ease of computation of the various techniques will play a dominant role in their choice. This is one reason the computationally easy centroid technique has dominated applied factor analysis prior to the computer. With the computer, however, there has been a shift to the more computationally difficult principal axes technique.

14.1.9 HYPOTHESES

As discussed in Section 2.5, factor analysis may be used for a number of purposes, including the testing of hypotheses. The content of these hypotheses as they relate to variable and factor complexity or the number of factors may well be a deciding element in selecting a technique. If these hypotheses are based on prior factor studies, then it will be desirable to select a factor technique comparable to that used previously.

14.1.10 THEORY

The same considerations above that involve the hypotheses in the selection of the factor technique are applicable to the substantive theory governing the research. An additional consideration here is the structure of the theory. If the theory has a geometric structure (or is geometrically interpretable), then the technique selected should be consonant with the geometric assumptions made. Geometric fit will be discussed below as relevant to the various techniques.

14.2 Approaches to Factor Analysis

With regard to the number of factors and complexity criteria, three approaches to the data can be discerned: two-factor, bifactor, and multifactor.[4]

14.2.1 TWO-FACTOR APPROACH

This approach involves a theory that there is one basic *common* factor underlying the variation in the data (or in the substantive domain of

4. Guttman (1957a) reduces all possible factoring methods to necessary and sufficient formula, differing only in choice of weight matrices.

which the data are a sample). All other variation is ascribed to specific factors defining the unique variance of each variable. Figure 14–3 displays the theoretical two-factor matrix for the data. Moderate or high loadings are indicated by crosses, near-zero loadings by blanks.

Variables	F_1	F_2	F_3	F_4	F_5	F_6	$\cdots$	F_p
1	×	×						
2	×		×					
3	×			×				
4	×				×			
5	×					×		
⋮	⋮						⋱	
m	×							×

Figure 14–3. Two-Factor Approach.

This factor analysis approach was initiated by Spearman (1927) in psychology. Spearman theorized that there was a general intelligence factor (denoted *g*) underlying ability and that *g* was hereditary. The specific factor (denoted *s*) was then the unique environmental experiences of the individual. Ability tests were therefore thought of as containing only *g* and *s*—that is, *two* factors.

Spearman's theoretical approach is now mainly of historical interest in psychology. In other social science domains analogous theories continue to exist, however. Single-factor explanations of war (capitalism), of societal change (technological development), and crime (poverty), and many other phenomena have at one time or another been defended. A systematic testing of such theories through the two-factor approach is possible.

The computational procedures[5] involve a prior examination of product moment correlations between the variables to determine if the correlations meet a proportionality criterion called the vanishing of the *tetrads*. The correlations can be accounted for by a general factor if the columns of correlations (ignoring the principal diagonal) stand in nearly the same proportions to each other. Variables that do not meet this criterion are removed from the matrix until only variables satisfying

5. A brief but clear discussion of the approach and procedure is given by Fruchter (1954, pp. 6–9). For those with more than passing interest in two-factor theory, Thomson's (1951, Part I) extended and excellent treatment is recommended.

it are left. Those remaining then contain only general and specific factors. No estimate of communality is needed. If the tetrad criterion is satisfied, the rank of the *reproduced* correlation matrix (Definition 6–1) is one and from this knowledge the communalities can be computed directly.[6]

14.2.1.1 *Characteristics:*

1. The two-factor approach involves a theoretical stance, namely, that an explanation of the data in terms of one general factor and a specific factor for each variable is appropriate.

2. The correlation matrix must be screened to eliminate variables not satisfying a so-called tetrad criterion. Therefore, what is in essence a grouping procedure must be applied to the data.

3. The variable complexity is one (two, if the specifics are included).

4. The factor complexity is one: one general factor.

5. The proportional variance contribution of the factors is in terms of one general factor accounting for the most variance.

6. The communality need not be estimated, since it can be exactly solved for if the tetrad criterion is satisfied.

7. The screening of the correlations may be laborious for large matrices. Once it has been determined whether the tetrad criterion is satisfied, however, the computation of the factor loadings for the general factor is relatively simple.

8. The geometric fit of the approach is *linear*. If the variables are considered a configuration of vectors in space, the general factor is fitted into this space through the origin in such a way that the product of the projection of any two vectors on the factor will equal their correlation.

14.2.2 BIFACTOR APPROACH

This is a revision of the two-factor approach[7] and involves a significant shift in theory. Whereas two-factor theory has a *general* and a *specific* factor explaining the variance of each variable, the bifactor approach alters the specific factors to *group* factors. The general monofactor explanation of the data is elaborated to include one general factor and a number of nonoverlapping group factors.

> *Example 14–1.* A Q-factor analysis of wars on their political and socioeconomic characteristics can be approached by a bifactor theory. It may be hypothesized

---

6. The tetrad criterion can be used apart from the two-factor approach to test for the appropriateness of a rank-one or single-factor hypothesis for a matrix. See Harman (1967, Section 7.2).

7. See Harman (1967, pp. 104–6, Section 7.5).

that there is one general factor of *power politics*. Overlaying this general factor, wars may also cluster along distinct nationalistic, economic, colonial, territorial, and ideological group factors.

The theoretical bifactor matrix is shown in Fig. 14–4. Note that the group factors are assumed to be nonoverlapping. Including the general factor, the complexity of each variable is two.

Factors

Variables	F_1	F_2	F_3	$\cdots$	F_p
1	×	×			
2	×	×			
3	×	×			
4	×		×		
5	×		×		
⋮				⋱	
$m-1$	×				×
m	×				×

Figure 14–4. Bifactor Approach.

The computational procedures[8] allow variables to remain in the correlation matrix even though they do not satisfy the tetrad proportionality criterion of the two-factor approach. The variables are first grouped together—clustered—on the basis of their correlations. Each group is then considered of rank one and the group factor is determined under the condition that the correlation between two variables is equal to the product of their factor loadings. With the group factors thus defined, it is possible to similarly extract the general factor. The communality of the variables can be solved by utilizing the rank two assumption of the approach.

14.2.2.1 *Characteristics:*

1. A theoretical perspective is involved. It is assumed that the correlations can be explained by a general factor common to all the variables in addition to nonoverlapping group factors.

2. Prior to analysis, the variables must be clustered in terms of their

8. The procedures with computational examples are given in Harman (1967, Section 7.5).

correlations. This adds an element of subjectivity, since in borderline cases the inclusion of a variable may be arbitrary.

3. The complexity of the variables is two: a general factor plus one group factor.

4. The factor complexity is one general factor and two or more group factors.

5. The proportional factor variance is step-level. The general factor accounts for the most variance, and the group factors make relatively level contributions.

6. Communalities need not be estimated, since they can be solved for exactly, according to a rank-two assumption.

7. The computations are slightly more complicated than in the two-factor approach but still seem manageable by hand.

8. The geometric fit is planar. Each variable is assumed to be generated along a plane defined by the general factor and one group factor, i.e., two common factor-dimensions.

9. The factors are mutually orthogonal. They measure statistically independent components of variance.

14.2.3 MULTIFACTOR APPROACH

This approach may involve a theory of the data or a profession of ignorance. If a theory is involved it assumes that the variance in a domain is explained by a multiple number of general factors. Within the last couple of decades multifactor explanations have been popular among social scientists, which may partly explain the relative eclipse of the two-factor and bifactor approaches.

As a profession of ignorance, the multifactor approach is concerned with classifying the major factors of covariation, with mapping a domain, or with determining the primary empirical concepts. The interest is in uncovering those factors that are the minimum necessary to reproduce the data.[9] The multifactor technique may be applied, however, with an eye on the two-factor or bifactor theories. If either theory is actually applicable to the data, then the minimum factor approach of multifactor analysis will result in a general factor with either specific or group factors.

There are a number of procedures for computing a multifactor solution: diagonal method, centroid, multiple group, principal axes, direct factor analysis, and multiple factor analysis. These will be discussed in turn and their salient characteristics noted. First, however,

9. This is the conceptual meaning of "basic structure" as used by Horst (1963, 1965).

three general characteristics of the multifactor approach can be listed.

14.2.3.1 *Characteristics:*

1. The approach is one of reducing the data to the minimum number of common factors or factor-dimensions necessary to reproduce the original data.

2. The complexity of the variables may be one (as in the multiple-group technique), two, or greater.

3. The complexity of the factors may consist of general, group, or specific factors.

4. Communalities must be estimated if the common factor model is involved.

14.3 Multifactor Analysis Procedures

A number of techniques of multifactor analysis will be discussed and their salient characteristics indicated. It should be stressed at this point that, with the exception of the multiple factor approach, these techniques may only involve a preliminary solution. A rotation of the factors to a more satisfactory fit with the data may be computed, *and this may alter the characteristics of the preliminary solution* (e.g., by decreasing variance). The characteristics to be listed, therefore, refer to the unrotated factors. The nature of the change in these characteristics through rotation and the criteria for applying a particular rotation are discussed in Section 16.2. Of course, rotation need not be done if the characteristics of a particular multifactor technique are found desirable.

14.3.1 DIAGONAL TECHNIQUE

The diagonal factoring procedure is the simplest and most straightforward to employ and can be applied to a symmetrical matrix of any size.[10] The factor matrix developed by the diagonal technique has the configuration of loadings shown in Fig. 14–5. The blanks refer to zero loadings. The factor matrix resembles a Guttman scaling matrix (Torgerson, 1958, pp. 307–17), where the nonzero loadings form a lower triangular matrix.

The technical procedures begin by selecting a pivot variable (variable 1 in Fig. 14–5) through which the first factor is projected. This variable will have a high loading on the first factor and zero loading on the

10. Fruchter (1954, Chapter 5) presents very clear computing instructions. Thurstone's (1947, Chapter 4) description of the diagonal technique is not as computationally clear, but his examples are more useful, and he discusses rotation of the resulting factor matrix.

Factors

Variables F_1 F_2 F_3 F_4 F_5 $\cdots$ F_p

Variables	F_1	F_2	F_3	F_4	F_5	$\cdots$	F_p
1	×						
2	×	×					
3	×	×	×				
4	×	×	×	×			
5	×	×	×	×	×		
⋮	⋮	⋮	⋮	⋮	⋮	⋱	
m	×	×	×	×	×	$\cdots$	×

Figure 14–5. Diagonal Method.

remaining factors; its loading on the first factor will then equal the square root of its communality. From the assumption that the correlations of the pivot variable with the other variables is equal to the sum of the cross products of their factor loadings [Eq. (5–17)], the loadings of the other variables on the first factor can be determined. For the second factor, a second variable is taken as pivot (variable 2 in Fig. 14–5) and its loadings on the second factor can be calculated from its first factor loading and communality. By successive pivoting and the use of loadings on previous factors and the communalities, loadings for all variables on all factors can be computed.

The diagonal technique has apparently been little used outside of psychology. Besides serving as a rapid computing technique, however, it can serve useful functions within a research design. The characteristic of making the first factor colinear with a selected pivot variable allows one to test a causative model and to determine, for example, whether the other variables are necessary and sufficient conditions for the occurrence of the pivot variable. If this is the case, the other variables should all load highly. Moreover, one may use the orthogonality characteristic to partial out the variance associated with specific variables by making them the first pivot variables.

> *Example 14–2.* If we wish to partial the influence of race from an assessment of the interrelationship of socioeconomic variables, we can make race the first pivot variable. Since the first factor will be colinear with the variable, the subsequent orthogonal factors define influences statistically independent of race.

This approach may also be useful for partialling out systematic error (Section 9.1.3.4) or holding conditions, such as time, constant.

14.3.1.1 *Characteristics:*

1. There is no prior grouping of variables, but the selection of pivot variables is arbitrary in the absence of a theoretical or design rationale.

2. The number of factors depends on the rank of the data matrix.

3. The complexity of a variable depends upon the factor for which it is used as a pivot. The first, second, third, etc., pivot variables have maximum complexity of 1, 2, 3, etc., while those that are not pivot variables have maximum complexity equal to the number of factors extracted.

4. The factor complexity is one general factor, the first, and group factors of successively fewer variables. The group factors may be bipolar.

5. The variance contributions of the factors are of successively decreasing magnitude. The first factor accounts for the most, the second for as much of that remaining as possible, the third for as much as possible after the first two factors are partialled out, and so on.

6. For the common factor analysis model, this technique is highly sensitive to the communality estimate. This is due to the computation of the loadings for the pivot variables being a function of the communalities.

7. The factor matrix is not uniquely given for a set of data but is a function of the pivot variable selected.

8. Computations are relatively simple.

9. Factor loadings are not generally orthogonal to each other, although factor scores are mutually uncorrelated.

14.3.2 CENTROID TECHNIQUE

This has certainly been historically the most popular procedure for computing the factor matrix. Although with the advent of the computer the favorite technique may now be the principal axes method described in the next section, the long and great popularity of the centroid approach has apparently created some confusion, at least outside of psychology. This confusion is evident in the number of current social science factor analysis studies that have calculated centroid solutions through computers. The centroid technique is only a mathematical approximation to the more computationally laborious principal axes procedures. If a computer is available, then the principal axes procedure should be used. If hand computation must be done, then the centroid approximation is a time-saving alternative.

Except for computational ease, the centroid results add nothing to the qualities of the principal axes factors while losing their mathematical uniqueness and orthogonality. The centroid factors approach orthogonality but are not precisely orthogonal (Horst, 1965, pp. 158–59) and are not mathematically determinant (Jöreskog, 1963, pp. 121–22). Alternative centroid factors for the same correlations are possible.

The computational procedures[11] involve summing the columns of the correlation matrix to be factored. Negative sums are reflected (their signs are changed), and the diagonal element or communality estimate is added to the sum. Then all the column sums are themselves added to get a grand sum. Each column sum is now multiplied by the reciprocal of the square root of the grand sum to determine the first centroid factor loadings. Reflecting the loading of those variables that had the sign of their sum changed then gives the final loadings on factor one. From Definition 6–1, the reproduced correlation matrix is computed from the first centroid factor and then subtracted from the original matrix. This residual correlation matrix is then factored, as was the original matrix, to get the second factor. The correlation matrix reproduced from the second factor is in turn subtracted from the first residual correlation matrix, and so on. Successive application of the procedure will yield the complete centroid factor matrix.

Geometrically, the first factor is placed through the centroid of the *row* vectors of correlation coefficients. (Since a correlation matrix is symmetrical, its row and column vectors are equal.) The row of sums of *columns* is the resolution vector—the centroid vector—for the vectors. Dividing the centroid's elements by the reciprocal of the square root of the grand sum then scales the vector so that its elements will range between +1.00 and −1.00 and produces the first centroid factor. This first factor is used to reproduce the correlation matrix, which, when subtracted from the original correlation matrix, projects the vectors (of correlations) onto a plane through the origin which is near orthogonal to the first factor. The centroid of these projections is the second factor. Reproducing the correlation matrix from the first and second centroid factors, subtracting these correlations from the original matrix, and finding the centroid of the resulting vectors determines

11. Cattell has done extensive applied work with the centroid technique and goes to great pains to present clear and extensive instructions (1952a, Chapter 10). Thurstone (1947, Chapter 8) and Harman (1967, Section 8.9) describe and exemplify the procedures; Fruchter (1954, Chapter 5) presents a brief but sufficient step-by-step guide. Horst (1965, Chapter 5) gives the mathematics and computational instructions; he lists the computer programs for the centroid technique involving three alternative communality estimates.

factor three. In a similar manner, the remaining centroid factors are defined.

14.3.2.1 *Characteristics:*

1. The centroid technique is an approximation to the more computationally difficult principal axes procedure.

2. Complexity of variables and factors, and variance contributions of the factors are the same as the principal axes procedure.

3. The centroid factor loadings will not always be mutually orthogonal as with principal axes factors. Factor scores are uncorrelated, however.

4. The centroid factors are not unique for a given matrix (Horst, 1965, p. 114; Cattell, 1952a, pp. 131 ff.).

5. The geometric fit is approximately ellipsoidal. That is, the centroids of the vectors approximate the principal axes of an ellipsoid in p dimensions, where p is the number of centroid factors of the space.

6. The computations involve a relatively small number of computationally easy steps.

14.3.3 MULTIPLE-GROUP TECHNIQUE

This is a variation of the centroid technique that is computationally easier for large matrices and results in characteristically different factors. Because the multiple-group factors are different, the technique should not be used to approximate centroid or principal axes results. The primary importance of this technique is in enabling the researcher to determine statistically independent *group* factors. These may be useful in classifying data into distinct categories or as a test of a theory or hypothesis about the group factors within a domain.

The procedure[12] consists of partitioning the correlation matrix into linearly independent sets of variables, either visually or through some technique like cluster analysis. Then the sums of the columns (or rows) of correlations are computed by group, and a simultaneous determination is made of their centroids. These centroids, scaled, are the factor solution. The major computing virtue of the technique is that the centroids can be determined without having to compute the residuals of the correlation matrix after each factor is extracted.

14.3.3.1 *Characteristics:*

1. The technique is a method for classifying variables into groups or testing for the existence of specified group factors in a domain.

12. Harman (1967, Chapter 11) presents background material on the technique and should be consulted for examples of its use. Fruchter (1954, Chapter 6) gives a clear and brief step-by-step set of computational instructions. Horst (1965, Section 6.5) can also be consulted on the specifics.

2. On the basis of their correlations, the variables must be clustered into linearly independent sets. This requirement makes the technique most useful when there is prior knowledge or theory as to what these groups should be (Fruchter, 1954, p. 87).

3. The number of factors depends on the rank of the correlation matrix, i.e., the number of linearly independent groups of variables.

4. Each variable tends toward a complexity of one, i.e., a loading on only one factor.

5. The factor complexity is in terms of bipolar group factors, with a tendency toward these factors being nonoverlapping.

6. The variance contributions of factors are approximately level.

7. The procedure is sensitive to the grouping of the variables, since an *unrotated* solution may be altered by changing the prior grouping of variables.

8. Because of the possible combinations of variables and the indeterminateness inherent in the centroid itself, the multiple-group solution is not unique for a correlation matrix.

9. The computational labor is less than that for the centroid technique for large matrices.

10. The technique extracts all the factors at once.

11. The factors may be mutually *oblique*.

12. The factors are a linear fit to each of the linearly independent sets of variables.

14.3.4 PRINCIPAL AXES TECHNIQUE

This is a mathematical technique long used to determine the principal axes of an ellipse in two or more dimensions. In factor analysis, the technique is useful to map the empirical concepts of a domain, reduce data to a smaller set of independent variables, or test hypotheses about major sources of covariation.

The principal axes (Definition 4–25) are the *minimum* orthogonal dimensions required to linearly reproduce (define, generate, explain) the original data. As a theoretical tool, the principal axes technique is significant for mathematical model building. A mathematical structure isomorphic with the field of linear algebra enables results to be integrated with this deductive system. Secondly, each step of the technique can be given geometric justification and interpretation, with the great conceptual and heuristic power that this entails. Third, the basic mathematics of the technique involve solving for the eigenvalues and eigenvectors of a matrix (Section 4.5). The natural scientist and the engineer often has to deal with eigenvalue-eigenvector problems and has even made eigenvalues a basic ingredient of some of his theory, as in quantum theory (Margenau, 1950, Chapter 17). The use of principal axes thus allows the researcher to exploit theoretical analogies from other areas to build his own theory or to suggest potential application. Finally, principal axes are generally employed in the derivation of factor analysis models [e.g., Eqs. (5–9) through (5–15)].

The computations can either solve for one factor at a time[13] or all factors simultaneously.[14] A procedure that can be employed was developed by Hotelling (1933). The computations are begun with a set of trial values. These are transformed iteratively by using successive powering of the correlation matrix until they stabilize within a specified range. From these, the first eigenvalue and eigenvector can be determined and the first factor loadings calculated. The reproduced correlation matrix is calculated from this first factor and then subtracted from the original correlation matrix. The iteration procedure is duplicated for the residual correlation matrix, the second factor is extracted, and a new reproduced correlation matrix is calculated from the first and second factors. In this fashion, the iteration procedure is successively applied to smaller and smaller residual correlation matrices to extract factors until the residuals are small enough to be ascribed to random error or insignificant variation.

A geometric interpretation[15] of the technique may be helpful. In plotting the relationship between two variables, an orthogonal coordinate system is usually set up with one variable denoted by the abscissa and the other by the ordinate. The plot of the cases in terms of their data on these two variable-axes then indicates the strength of relationship between the two variables. If the points representing the cases fall on a straight line, as in Fig. 14–6A, the correlation is perfect. If the points form an ellipse, as in Fig. 14–6B, there is some correlation. And if the points form a circle, as in Fig. 14–6C, there is no correlation.

For more than two variables, say m variables, the n cases can still be interpreted as a swarm of points plotted on m variable-axes. These axes are at 90° to each other and form an m-dimensional space in which the configuration of points (cases) is ellipsoidal (unless the data

13. Harman (1967, Chapter 8) gives an excellent presentation of the procedures. For those who wish a brief listing of the steps involved, Fruchter (1954, Chapter 6) is recommended.

14. Horst (1965, Chapter 8) presents procedures for extracting all the factors at once, as well as computer programs for their computation.

15. Perhaps the clearest geometric interpretation given in factor analysis texts is that of Thomson (1951, Chapter 6). In elementary mathematics texts, the simplest, clearest, and most extended description of the geometry of eigenvalues, eigenvectors, and principal axes is by Owen (1961, pp. 121–64).

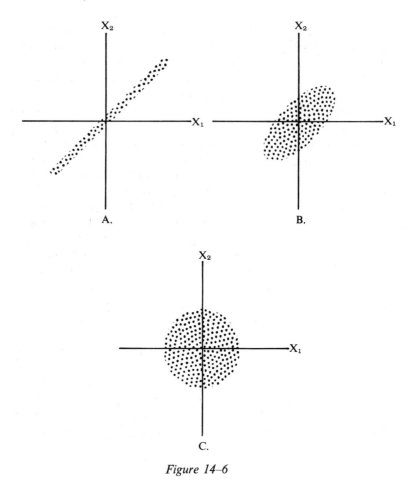

Figure 14–6

are all statistically independent), as in the two-dimensional example of Fig. 14–6B. For conceptual simplicity we can concentrate on the two-variable example to illustrate principal axes. A geometric interpretation for three or more variables would be analogous, although not as easy to visualize.

Figure 14–7A shows again the ellipse of Fig. 14–6B, describing the configuration of points representing cases. The configuration is outlined only, and the points are not shown. The origin of the two axes is at the point of symmetry of the ellipse, and the major and minor principal axes of the ellipse are shown. As can be seen, these principal axes measure two orthogonal components of variance in the data. The *major* principal axis is similar to a regression line (Definition

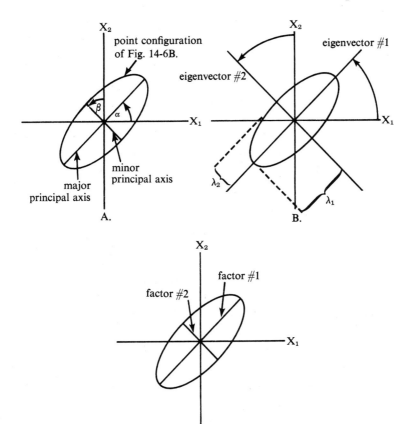

Figure 14–7

3–8) in measuring the greatest common variance among the two variables. The *minor* principal axis then measures the variance at right angles to the first, i.e., statistically independent of that described by the major principal axis. The degree to which the major principal axis accounts for the variance in the points measures the correlation between the two variables. The minor principal axis then measures the residual variance independent of that common to the variables. As the correlation between two variables *increases*, the length of the minor principal axis decreases relative to the major axis. For perfect correlation, the minor principal axis disappears altogether, and the configuration of points can be completely measured along one line. As the correlation between the variables *decreases*, the minor axis approaches the major axis in length. When they are equal, the ellipse has degenerated into a circle, and the two variables are statistically independent. In this degenerate case, the major and minor axes have no unique position and can be rotated to any direction within the circle and may even lie along the variable axes.

For a given data matrix the principal axes problem is this: *What transformation will rotate the variable axes so that they lie colinear with the principal axes?* It can be seen in Fig. 14–7A that the variable axes for X_1 and X_2 will have to be rotated counterclockwise α and β degrees, respectively, for them to lie along the major and minor axes. For $m = 2$ variables, the solution is given in terms of

$$E_{m \times m}^{-1} R_{m \times m} E_{m \times m} = \lambda_{m \times m}, \qquad (14\text{–}1)$$

where $E_{m \times m}$ = matrix of m columns of eigenvectors, $R_{m \times m}$ = correlation matrix of m variables of rank p, and $\lambda_{m \times m}$ = diagonal matrix of m eigenvalues, $m - p$ of which are zero. The *rows* of normalized $E_{m \times m}$ are the transformation coefficients for the variables that rotate the variable-axes so that they lie along the principal axes. The *columns* of $E_{m \times m}$ are the principal axes. The eigenvalues measure the length of the principal axes,[16] as shown for two eigenvalues in Fig. 14–7B. By scaling each of the eigenvectors by its associated eigenvalue,

$$R_{m \times m} = (E_{m \times m} \lambda_{m \times m}^{1/2})(\lambda_{m \times m}^{1/2} E_{m \times m}'), \qquad (14\text{–}2)$$

we reduce the length of the eigenvector proportional to the principal axis it measures. *The results are the factor we are after,* as illustrated in Fig. 14–7C. What was said about the major and minor principal axes when the variables are perfectly correlated or statistically independent holds for the factors. With regard to the two-variable example—for perfect correlation, factor 2 would disappear and factor 1 would be sufficient to measure all the variation in the data. That is, the variation of the two variables could be accounted for by one factor.

For empirical data, which will usually have some random variance, a configuration of points on m variables describe a hyperellipsoid in m

16. The correlation ellipse for m variables, standardized data, and a multivariate normal distribution is

$$Z_{n \times m} R_{m \times m}^{-1} Z_{m \times n}' = k,$$

where k is a constant, and R is the correlation matrix for the m variables of the standardized data matrix Z. Let the length of the lth principal axis of R^{-1} be $1/\gamma$. Since the eigenvalues of a symmetric matrix are the reciprocal of the eigenvalues of the inverse of the matrix [Eq. (4–33)], then $1/\gamma = \lambda_l$, where λ_l is the lth eigenvalue of R. Thus, λ_l is the length of the lth principal axis of the correlation ellipse of R^{-1}. The principal axes of R^{-1} are the same as those for R, since R is symmetric. On this point, see Hotelling (1933, especially Sections 2 and 3) and Thomson (1951, Appendix 7).

dimensions. The principal axes technique rotates the variables so that the first eigenvector measures the largest component of variance (the longest length of the hyperellipsoid), while successive eigenvectors measure decreasing orthogonal lengths of the hyperellipsoid. If the hyperellipsoid can be described by fewer eigenvectors than there are variables, we have a parsimonious reduction of the original data without loss of information. Such a reduction of three variables to two factors is shown in Fig. 14–8. In most cases, however, there will be as many factors as variables.

The technique of principal axes fits eigenvectors to decreasing orthogonal components of variance along the ellipsoid. Therefore, the first several factors will describe the major variance in the data, leaving

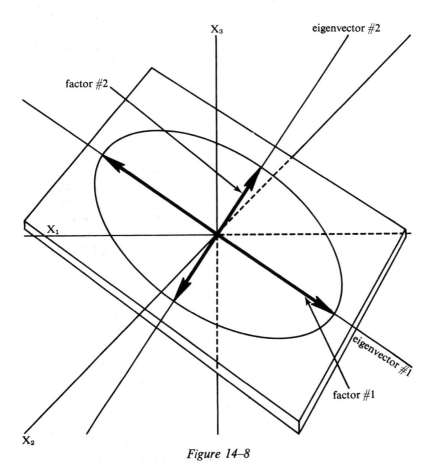

Figure 14–8

only minute portions of variance for the last factors. These last factors may thus be disregarded in the final result.

One final geometric interpretation should be mentioned. In Chapter 5 the factor models are described in terms of variable-vectors projected into the space of the cases that are the coordinate axes of the space. The angles between the vectors are the correlation they have with each other, and the factors are the basis dimensions of this vector space. The geometric interpretation given in this section is of variables as coordinate axes and cases as points plotted on them. Either geometric interpretation is applicable to the factor models. They are alternative representations of the data.

Consider again the representation of cases as a swarm of points plotted on the *m* variable-axes and forming a hyperellipsoid in *m* dimensions. Recall that the variable axes are at right angles. Now, if the variable axes are moved obliquely to each other until the angles between them are equal to their correlations, then the configuration of points representing cases will change from a hyperellipsoid to a hypersphere, and *lines* drawn from the origin to each point will be at right angles. Each of these mutual orthogonal lines from origin to point can now represent the coordinate axes and the oblique variable-axes can now represent the vectors in the geometric interpretation of Chapter 5. The cases then become axes on which the variables are plotted as vectors and the principal axes of the data matrix are the *basis* dimensions (Definition 3–33) of the space. We can thus move geometrically from one representation to another, depending on our theoretical or conceptual requirements. From one point of view, the principal axes technique extracts the orthogonal components of variance in the data. From another point of view, it delineates the basis dimensions of the vector space defined by the data matrix.

14.3.4.1 *Characteristics:*

1. The technique is useful for determining the minimum orthogonal factors required to reproduce the data matrix. These factors may be interpreted as classifications, causative agents, basic variables, or basis dimensions of the data.

2. Both factor loadings and factor scores are orthogonal.

3. The number of factors depends on the rank of the data matrix.

4. The variable complexity is limited only by a variable's communality. This communality may be spread across the factors or accounted for by one factor.

5. The factor complexity tends toward all general factors, with factor loadings on all but the first factor tending toward bipolarity.

For some data with high positive and negative correlations between the variables, the first factor may also be bipolar.

6. The variance contributions of the factors are decreasing. The first factor measures the most variance, and successive factors will account for decreasing proportions of variance.

7. Sensitivity to random error or communality estimates appears low, relative to other techniques. The principal axes are a weighted function of all the data.

8. The principal axes are mathematically unique for a data matrix in which the data are not all statistically independent. Although the principal axes factors may be *rotated* to an infinite number of solutions, this indeterminateness of rotation should not be confused with the uniqueness of the principal axes themselves. As discussed in Section 14.3.6 below, rotation is what is done to the principal axes, once they have been extracted. The principal axes themselves have only one position in space and that is fully determined by the correlations in the data (assuming distinct eigenvalues, which will usually occur in application).

9. The computation of the principal axes is laborious, even for moderately sized matrices. Until the computer made the principal axes solution practical, the centroid approximation to the principal axes was more often used.

10. The geometrical fit of the factors is ellipsoidal, as explained in the last section.

14.3.5 DIRECT FACTOR ANALYSIS

This technique is directly applicable to a data matrix for the component factor analysis model. No covariance or correlation matrix need be calculated.[17]

Two sets of factors are extracted from the data—one set for the variables and the other for the cases. In other words, the technique extracts the factors of the data matrix and of its transpose simultaneously. With regard to the three data slices of the data cube (Section 8.3), the technique determines both O- and P-factors (or R- and Q-factors or S- and T-factors, depending on the slice the data matrix represents).

17. Horst's (1963, Chapter 17) development of the "basic structure" of a matrix is clear and identical to the mathematics of direct factor analysis. See also Horst (1965, pp. 98–100) for application of rank reduction theorem (direct factor analysis) to a data matrix. Horst gives the computational instructions and FORTRAN writeups for the direct factor analyses methods he presents. Since he uses the same data for examples throughout his book, the direct factor analysis results of his Section 12.3.4 may be compared with the factors extracted by other techniques.

As researchers begin to realize the versatility of factor analysis and to release themselves from the traditional adherence to the correlation matrix, which Horst (1965, p. 258) terms "perhaps unfortunate," the use of direct factor analysis will probably increase. Direct factor analysis enables the investigator to view the factors of both sides of his data matrix and to remain close to the units of his raw data. Within the range of application of the technique are matrices of roll call votes, sociometric or social choice matrices,[18] transaction matrices,[19] similarity matrices,[20] and rank-order data matrices.[21]

For the computation of a direct factor analysis of a nonsymmetrical matrix, the reader is referred to Saunders (1950) or Horst (1965, Chapter 12).

14.3.5.1 *Characteristics:*

1. The direct factor analysis technique is applied directly to the raw data and extracts a set of factors for the variables and another set for the cases.

2. In number of factors, variable complexity, factor complexity, factor variance, uniqueness, and computational labor, the direct factor analysis and principal axes techniques are similar.

14.3.6 MULTIPLE FACTOR ANALYSIS

The researcher may employ any of the above multifactor techniques to extract a preliminary solution. He may not be concerned with the complexity and factor variance characteristics of the technique, but rather with arriving at a set of more or less determinant factors that may be then rotated to a more desirable solution. Although any number of criteria can be used to rotate the preliminary factors, the most commonly applied criteria result in what is called a *simple structure solution* (Section 16.2.2). *Multiple factor analysis* as here defined, then, involves the application of a multifactor technique to yield a preliminary solution that is rotated to simple structure.

The mathematical and conceptual meaning of rotation and considerations involved in opting for a rotation are decreased in Section 16.1. Here it should suffice to list the characteristics of multiple factor analysis.

18. Wright and Evitts (1961) do a direct factor analysis of a sociometric choice matrix, try to explain the resulting factors through multiple regression, and compare R- and Q-type factors to show congruence of chosen and choosers. See also Wright and Evitts (1963), and MacRae (1960).

19. See Russett (1967a)

20. Ekman (1955) determined directly the principal axes of a symmetrical similarity matrix.

21. See Berry (1960, 1961b).

14.3.6.1 *Characteristics:*

1. Multiple factor analysis involves determining a factor matrix through some multifactor technique and rotating the result to simple structure.

2. The number of factors may be less than the preliminary solution, since the researcher may decide to rotate only meaningful, significant, or interpretable factors.

3. The complexity of the variables tends toward 1.

4. The complexity of the factors tends toward overlapping nonbipolar group factors.

5. Factor variance tends toward a level contribution by the factors.

6. For moderate-sized factor matrices, rotation is a computationally laborious procedure. Fortunately, however, the more popular rotational criteria have been programmed for computers.

7. The geometric fit of the final solution is usually hyperplanar. The factors are rotated so that each variable-vector falls as nearly as possible within a space defined by fewer factors than the number rotated.

14.4 Summary Table

Several characteristics of a number of factor analysis approaches and techniques have been presented. These are briefly summarized in Table 14–1.[22]

22. A table along similar lines is given by Harman (1967, Table 6.1, p. 108).

Table 14–1. Characteristics of Factor Analysis Approaches and Techniques[a]

Approaches and Techniques	Prior Grouping or Screening Required	Communality Estimates[b]	Number of Factors[c]	Complexity of Variables	Complexity of Factors	Factor Variance Contribution	Mathematically Unique	Computational Labor	Geometric Fit	Orthogonal	Prior Hypothesis or Theory Required	Comments
Two-factor approach	Yes	No	1	1	One general and m specific	Step-level	Yes	Moderate	Linear	Yes	Yes	Single common factor theory.
Bifactor approach	Yes	No	≤ m	2	One general and group factors	Step-level	No	Moderate	Planar	Yes	Yes	Revision of above to allow for non-overlapping group factors.
Multifactor approach Diagonal technique	No	Yes	≤ m	≤ p	One general and group factors	Decreasing	No	Low	—	Yes	Yes	Requires selection of pivot variable.
Centroid technique	No	Yes	≤ m	≤ p	All general	Decreasing	No	Moderate	Ellipsoid	Appr.	No	Approximate principal axes.
Multiple-group technique	Yes	Yes	≤ m	Tends to 1	Nonoverlapping group	Level	No	Low	Linear	No	No	All factors extracted simultaneously.
Principal axes technique	No	Yes	≤ m	≤ p	All general	Decreasing	Yes	High	Ellipsoid	Yes	No	Each factor is colinear with a principal axis of the data.
Direct factor analysis	No	—[d]	≤ m	≤ p	All general	Decreasing	Yes	High	—	No	No	Extract two sets of factors—one for variables and the other for the cases.
Multiple factor analysis	No	—[d]	≤ m	Tends to 1	Overlapping group	Level	No	High	Planar	—[e]	Yes[f]	Involves rotating multifactor results to another solution.

[a] m = number of variables; p = number of factors.
[b] For the common factor analysis model.
[c] Assuming $n \geq m$, where n = number of cases.
[d] Not applicable.
[e] Depends on whether rotation is orthogonal or oblique.
[f] Yes in terms of selecting a criteria of rotation.

15. Number of Factors

One major uncertainty in factor analysis that has already been discussed concerns the proper *communality estimate* to be used in common factor analysis. A second source of uncertainty for all factor models concerns the *number of factors* that will be sufficient or adequate for the research design and data—that is: When should one stop extracting factors?

The first section of this chapter will describe the problem and argue that for many research designs the problem does exist and is worthy of careful consideration. The following two sections will deal with the statistical and mathematical approaches, respectively, to deciding the issue. The fourth section will consider some of the rules of thumb that are suggested in the literature, and the final section will make a few concluding observations. Figure 15–1 defines the major content of this factor analysis research design step.

15.1 The Factor Number Problem

At the outset it might be helpful to review some mathematical considerations bearing on the number-of-factors problem. The factors delineated by a factor analysis describe the independent sources of variance in the data matrix. The number of such sources equals the number of factors one can extract from the data, and this in turn is equal to the *rank* of the matrix (Definition 4–21). A problem with empirical data matrices is that their rank is usually equal to (or one less than) the number of cases or variables, whichever is smaller. Usually, this is the

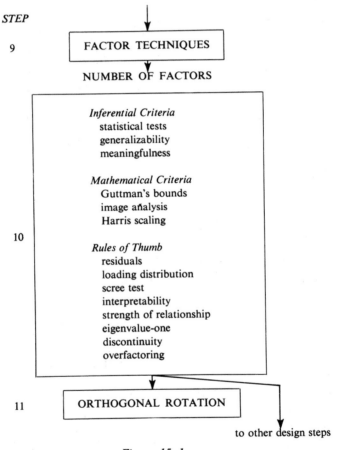

Figure 15–1

number of variables. Being able to extract as many or nearly as many factors as variables hardly implies the parsimonious or data reduction solution often sought.

Fortunately, factor techniques like the centroid, principal axes, and direct factor analysis extract the factors that account for decreasing variance. We can thus stop factoring the data when we reach factors accounting for only trivial variance. But what is trivial? How is it operationally defined for a given data matrix?

There are a number of aspects to this problem that should be identified. If we wish only to *describe* the given data through a multifactor solution, no rotation of these results need be contemplated. In this design the number of factors is least problematical. The investigator extracts factors until the level of variance or the factor loadings drop below that acceptable for the description or use to which the factors will be put. Since in the unrotated solution the previous factors extracted will be unaffected by the retention of subsequent factors, the data can be exhaustively factored and the cutoff point determined by inspection of the proportional factor variances and factor loadings and by the application of the rules of thumb described in Section 15.4, below.

For the unrotated solution, however, the concern may be with *inference* from the findings to the population of cases or with *generalization* to the universe of content. More care must be exercised in discarding trivial factors, for they may be a faint reflection of major factors existing in the population or universe that have been imperfectly tapped in the sample. Something more than subjective judgment is needed to disentangle these small but meaningful factors from those that may be ascribed to random error.

The unrotated factors, however, may be considered to be only preliminary to a multiple factor—a rotated—solution. Rotation can have distorting consequences if insufficient attention is given to selecting the "best" number of factors. Whereas in the unrotated case the decision to accept or reject the factors accounting for the smaller variance has no effect on the factor structure delineated by the larger factors, in rotation the inclusion or exclusion of one small factor may change the rotated factor structure. In other words, the loading and interpretation of all rotated factors may differ for the same data, preliminary solution, and rotation criterion by virtue of the different number of factors rotated. Due to this sensitivity of rotation, a very careful consideration of the best number of factors for rotation is crucial regardless of whether the intent of the analysis is description, inference, or generalization.

The sensitivity of rotation to factor number is apparently not well known outside of psychology. A larger number of factor studies in the social sciences have published rotated factor results without justifying or even mentioning the criteria for the specific number rotated. Those familiar with these applications may wonder, then, if the sensitivity of rotation to the number rotated is being exaggerated here. Two examples

Table 15–1. Oblique Rotated Factors of Domestic and Foreign Conflict Behavior[a]

Variables	Five-Factor Oblique Rotation[b]					Six-Factor Oblique Rotation[c]					
	F_1	F_2	F_3	F_4	F_5	F_1	F_2	F_3	F_4	F_5	F_6
1. Assassinations											.70
2. General strikes		.80				.85					
3. Guerrilla war											.74
4. Major government crises				.55		.59					
5. Purges		.70				.68					
6. Riots		.71				.74					
7. Revolutions		.74				.70					
8. Antigovernment demonstrations		.63				.63					
9. Number killed in domestic wars		.84				.72					
10. Antiforeign demonstrations										.59	
11. Negative sanctions										.64	
12. Protests	.59						.60				
13. Severed diplomatic relations					.73					.77	
14. Expulsion and recall of ambassadors											
15. Expulsion and recall of lesser officials			.70						.76		
16. Threats	.78						.68				
17. Military action	.81						.71				
18. Wars	.74						.93				
19. Troop movements	.56		.50						.52		
20. Mobilizations	.75						.68				
21. Accusations	.79						.73				
22. Number killed in foreign wars	.87						.95				
23. Censorship				.68				.61			
24. Embassies and legations			.54	.57				.78			
Sums of squares	5.10	4.18	2.19	1.85	1.56	3.79	4.67	1.92	1.85	2.10	1.61

[a] For clarity in distinguishing different structures, loadings < |.50| are not shown. Unrotated and orthogonally rotated factor matrices are given in Rummel (1963, Table 9).

[b] Biquartimin primary pattern matrix. Solution took 60 major cycles and 5,240 iterations.

[c] Biquartimin primary pattern matrix. Solution took 60 major cycles and 3,099 iterations. All program parameters were made identical to the five factor run.

Table 15–2. *Orthogonally Rotated Factors of Ten Political Variables*[a]

	Two-Factor Rotation		Three-Factor Rotation			Four-Factor Rotation			
	1	2	1	2	3	1	2	3	4
1. System style	.63	.92		.92			.95		
2. Constitutional status	.89	-.71	.61	-.71			-.71		
3. Representative character	.69		.78			.67			
4. Electoral system	.61	-.62	.63	-.64			-.63		
5. Freedom of group opposition		-.74		-.79			-.76		
6. Non-Communist regime		.93		.95			.91		
7. Political leadership	.78		.72						.83
8. Horizontal power distribution	.81		.68	-.52			-.51		
9. Monarchical type	-.63				.96			.97	
10. Military participation	-.66		-.95			-.95			
Per cent total variance	41.8	37.3	35.2	38.8	15.4	22.4	37.4	15.1	17.7

[a] For clarity in distinguishing different structures, loadings < |.50| are not shown. The first three unrotated factors are given in Table 6–4. Table 4–1 presents the correlation matrix. Rotations are to an orthogonal varimax solution.

of an alteration in factor structure due to rotating different numbers is given below. The first is for oblique rotation; the second is for orthogonal rotation. Other examples might have been selected. In fact, experience with dozens of oblique rotations indicates that number-dependent shifts in factor structure are the norm rather than the exception.

> *Example 15–1.* Table 15–1 gives the oblique rotated factors for 22 domestic and foreign conflict variables and two error measures given in Rummel (1963). The factor structure between the five- and six-factor solutions are different, as indicated by the shift in loadings for all factors and the creation of two different factors (F_5 and F_6) in the six-factor rotation.

> *Example 15–2.* Table 15–2 gives the orthogonal rotation results for the factors of 10 political variables .shown in Example 6–5. For comparison, two-, three-, and four-factor rotations were done. Note the considerable change in the first factor with increase in number of factors rotated.

The number-of-factors problem has no general solution. Specific solutions, dependent on the choice of factor model, such as alpha factor analysis, however, do exist, and will be discussed below. Moreover, from the practical experience of such factor analysts as Raymond Cattell and Henry Kaiser, a number of rules of thumb have developed that are a general aid to the researcher. These will also be discussed.

15.2 Inferential Approaches

Many more factors may exist for a population of entities, such as nations, or for a universe of content, such as international relations, than can be determined in any one analysis. The size of the sample of cases and variables sets an upper limit on the number of factors that can be extracted. In any such analysis the question is implicit as to how to judge if a small factor may be significant for the population, generalizable to the universe of content, substantively meaningful in its own right, or merely the result of chance covariance in the data matrix. The approaches to the number of factors using tests of significance, generalizability, or meaningfulness will be discussed separately.

15.2.1 STATISTICAL TESTS

Factor analysis statistical tests are based on a particular probability model that makes possible the evaluation of the chance occurrence of a common factor for a given sample size. A common factor found significant is judged to have a greater than chance probability (at the selected level, e.g., $P \leq .05$) of existing for the population of cases from which the sample was selected for the same *variables*. No inference is made as to whether the common factor exists in the larger domain of content from which the variables were chosen.

The maximum-likelihood factor analysis model was developed to allow for such statistical tests. Rao's version, canonical factor analysis (Section 5.5), estimates common factors that have the maximum canonical correlation with the common parts of the data. Factor significance is decided by testing each common factor against the null hypothesis that the subsequent factors are too small to be credited to anything but chance.

Although the number-of-factors problem is statistically solved by the canonical factor model, the characteristics of the statistical solution must be carefully evaluated. Any significance test is dependent on the sample size. With small sample sizes, common factors tying together several variables may be rejected even though the factor is substantively interpretable and accounts for appreciable variance. On the other hand, for very large samples the smallest of common factors can become significant.[1] Moreover, because the number of common factors existing for a population in a domain of content may be very large relative to the rank of a matrix, excluding any factors on the basis of a test dependent on the number of cases results in a near-one probability of an error of the second kind occurring. In other words, the probability of rejecting a common factor that may exist for the population is almost one.[2]

15.2.2 GENERALIZABILITY

Significance tests are one way to objectify an answer to the number-of-factors problem. Another way to answer the problem has been posed by Kaiser and Caffrey (1965). Rather than test for the significance of a sample of cases, they propose looking in the other direction. Their model, termed alpha factor analysis (Section 5.7), attempts to maximize the fit of the common factors for the sample of variables to the factors for the universe of variables in the domain. Employing

1. This point is made, among others, by Harman (1967, Section 9.5) and Kaiser and Caffrey (1965, p. 10).
2. Kaiser (1960a, p. 6) claims that the probability is one.

the alpha coefficient of generalizability, derivable from the Kuder-Richardson reliability coefficient (1937) or Cronbach coefficient (1951; Cronbach *et al.*, 1963), Kaiser and Caffrey derive a scaling and matrix transformation of the data that yields common factors with maximum generalizability to the universe.

In alpha factor analysis, factors are extracted from the data as long as the factor has *positive* generalizability. From the generalizability coefficient, it is shown that a common factor ceases to have this generalizability when its associated eigenvalue is less than or equal to one. Therefore, in the alpha factor analysis model the simple rule for the number of common factors is to extract and rotate factors with eigenvalues greater than one.

While the significance test of the canonical factor model is dependent on the number of cases, that of the alpha factor model is not dependent on the size of the variable sample.[3] As the number of variables increases relative to a given sample of cases, the generalizability of the factors to the universe may or may not increase. Since the eigenvalue measures the variance accounted for by a factor [Eq. (6–7)], the eigenvalue-greater-than-one criterion assures that the common factors extracted define a certain level of variance among the variables. And since the variance of a variable is unity, the cutoff rejects factors that do not account for at lest the variance of one variable. As more variables are added to the data matrix, the eigenvalue of a common factor will increase only if that factor accounts for some of the variance of the new variables. In the case of canonical factor analysis, however, a given nonzero eigenvalue, and therefore its associated factor, will tend toward significance as more cases are added to a sample.

15.2.3 MEANINGFULNESS

Significance and generalizability criteria are dependent on objective measures and relate to *common* factors. Meaningfulness, however, is a subjective probability criterion for deciding the acceptability of a factor, whether a common factor or a dimension of component analysis. Those who are expert in the substance and literature of their domain and familiar with the nuances in their data may reject factors unless the factors have a certain subjective probability of significance or generalizability.

---

3. An exception is that the number of variables sets an upper bound to the number of factors (if cases exceed variables in number). No more factors can be extracted than there are variables, regardless of the approach used for determining the number of factors.

The researcher who uses such knowledge as a screening device, therefore, will first weigh the interpretability of a factor, its consonance with other research findings, the configuration of its loadings, and its proportional factor variance and then decide whether to accept or reject the factor. For the investigator who has considerable practical experience and is substantively grounded in the data area, this may well be the wisest course. It appears foolish to allow an analytic decision criterion to override a "research sense" of the data. If, however, one has not developed this competence, or if a domain has had little benefit of systematic analysis, the analytic decision criteria or rules of thumb discussed below will certainly be helpful.

15.3 Mathematical Approaches

Canonical and alpha factor analysis models are solutions to the number-of-factors problem based on principles of maximum likelihood and maximum generalizability, respectively. In this section, the discussion will be limited to approaches derived from the rank properties of a matrix and the algebraic characteristics of the matrix transformation employed. Louis Guttman has derived the lower bounds on the number of factors and these will be considered first. The subsequent subsections will then discuss the image and Harris solutions to the problem.

15.3.1 GUTTMAN'S BOUNDS

As he later did for communality (1956), Guttman sought to determine the lower bounds that would limit the number-of-factors problem. In 1954 he published in *Psychometrika* derivations that established three such lower bounds on the number of factors.

Let the three Guttman lower bounds be denoted by b_1, b_2, and b_3, the rank (Section 4.4) of a correlation matrix by $r(R_{m \times m})$ and the total number of factors by p. We have established [Section 4.5, Eq. (5–15)] that $p = r(R_{m \times m})$. Guttman shows that for a Gramian correlation matrix with *unities* in the principal diagonal, the first limit, b_1, is

$$b_1 = \text{number of eigenvalues} \geq 1.00, \qquad (15\text{–}1a)$$

and

$$r(R_{m \times m}) \geq b_1. \qquad (15\text{–}1b)$$

This is called Guttman's *weakest lower bound*.

The second limit, b_2, is defined for the correlation matrix with squared multiple correlations as communality estimates in the diagonal. Then,

$$b_2 = \text{number of eigenvalues} \geq 0, \tag{15–2a}$$

and

$$r(R_{m \times m}) \geq b_2. \tag{15–2b}$$

The lower bound, b_2, is called Guttman's *strongest lower bound*.

Bound b_3 is weaker than b_2, but better than b_1. It is associated with a correlation matrix with the highest column correlation for a variable inserted as communality estimate. Then,

$$b_3 = \text{number of eigenvalues} \geq 0, \tag{15–3a}$$

and

$$r(R_{m \times m}) \geq b_3. \tag{15–3b}$$

The relationship between the three bounds and the number of factors, p, is,

$$p \geq b_2 \geq b_3 \geq b_1. \tag{15–4}$$

These bounds[4] are most pertinent to the common factor analysis model. In component analysis of empirical matrices the total number of factors will usually equal the dimension of the smaller side of the data matrix. In the common factor analysis model, however, it is desired to find the number of common factors after adjustments have been made in the principal diagonal of the correlation matrix. This number will ordinarily be less than the rank of the original matrix, *but no less than Guttman's bounds.*

Kaiser (1960b) has empirically investigated the strongest lower bound for a large number of matrices. Invariably he found the number of factors to exceed half the number of variables, which would be an undesirable proportion for many researchers. He also investigated the weakest lower bound and usually arrived at factors equal to between $\frac{1}{6}$ and $\frac{1}{3}$ the number of variables.

Besides yielding a more tractable number of factors and being a lower limit on the total number of common factors, the weakest lower bound (i.e., unities as communality estimates and extracting factors with eigenvalues greater than or equal to one) has additional virtues. Kaiser (1960b) worked out the Kuder-Richardson (1937) formulas for

---

4. Kaiser (1961) has generalized Guttman's bounds to the case in which the communalities, h_j^2, lie in the closed interval $0 \leq h_j^2 \leq 1.00$.

reliability and found that it is necessary and sufficient for the reliability of a factor that its eigenvalue be greater than unity. Moreover, Kaiser asserts (1960b) that the weakest lower bound gave him the most meaningful factors. This last observation was made for psychological data but may be more or less true in other fields.[5]

Perhaps, as a consequence of Guttman's derivation of b_1 as the weakest bound and Kaiser's argument that it is the "best" solution to the number-of-factors problem for a correlation matrix, b_1 has been apparently the most often employed number-of-factors criterion in applied studies outside of psychology.

15.3.2 IMAGE FACTORS

If the image factor model is employed, the number-of-factors problem can be solved in the following way: Extract all factors with eigenvalues greater than zero. This will equal Guttman's *strongest lower bound*, and these factors may be orthogonally rotated (varimax) without the trivial common factors distorting the result (Kaiser, 1963, p. 161). The very small factors may then be left uninterpreted.

15.3.3 HARRIS SCALING

The Rao-Guttman relationship derived by Harris (Section 5.6) is claimed by Kaiser (1964, p. 41) to practically solve the number-of-factors problem. Harris shows a direct proportional relationship between the common factors of a scaled image matrix and the canonical matrix (scaled correlation matrix). The scaled image matrix given in Eq. (5–46) is of particular interest. As pointed out by Harris (1962) and Kaiser (1963, 1964), the factor analysis of this matrix evokes a number of mathematical considerations pointing to an eigenvalue-one factor cutoff. For our purposes it is enough to note that eigenvalues greater than one for the scaled image matrix are equal to Guttman's *strongest* lower bound for the number of common factors.

15.4 Rules of Thumb

Whenever a methodological problem has not been generally solved, practical guidelines always seem to appear. The number-of-factors problem is no exception. Rules of thumb, so to speak, can be quite

5. Based on Guttman's *weakest lower bound*, Horn (1965b) presents a technique of removing the factor from the data that is a result of "sampling error, and least-squares 'capitalization' on this error, in the correlations and the roots."

helpful to a researcher newly carving out the structure of a domain. Although they do not constitute mathematical theorems, they nonetheless embody a considerable amount of practical experience and intimate acquaintance with the factor model. Dozens of guidelines may be listed, but attention here will be focused on those that seem most useful: *residuals, loading distributions, scree test, interpretability, strength of relationship, eigenvalue-one, discontinuity,* and *overfactoring.*[6]

15.4.1 RESIDUALS

For the most popular factor techniques—centroid and principal axes—factors are extracted successively and the reproduced correlations for each factor are subtracted from the correlation matrix. The factoring may be continued until the residual correlations appear to be due to random error or until no residual is high enough to be considered meaningful.[7] Cattell (1952a, pp. 296–301) presents some stopping criteria based on residual correlations, one of which is that they be normally distributed. This rule assumes that, if only random error variance remains, the residual correlations will tend toward a normal distribution.[8]

Another criterion, called *Tucker's phi*, tests for the significance of the decrease in residuals as each factor is extracted. When the decrease becomes nonsignificant, factoring is stopped.[9]

Harman (1967, Section 2.6) suggests a way of determining whether all common factors have been removed from the data. The distribution of residual correlations may be considered the same as that of a correlation for a sample of n cases. The standard error of a correlation, $1/(n-1)^{1/2}$, may therefore be used to gauge the significance of the residuals. If the standard deviation of the residuals is less than the standard error of a zero correlation for the given n, then it may be inferred that no additional significant factors exist. The problem with this approach and Tucker's phi is that, as with inferential tests in general, the significance of a factor hinges on the sample size.

6. Cattell (1952a, pp. 296–301) lists 11 criteria, the most useful of which seem to be (1) a normal distribution of residuals, and (2) discontinuity. For an empirical comparison of five criteria, see Sokal (1959).

7. This is not to imply that random error is like sediment settling on the last residuals. Error is spread more or less evenly across the factors, rather than bunched on the last factors to be extracted (Cattell, 1958).

8. The concept of a normal distribution developed out of early attempts in science to describe the distribution of errors around an observation. This distribution is still occasionally called an error curve.

9. Fruchter (1954, pp. 77–79) gives the formula for Tucker's phi.

15.4.2 LOADING DISTRIBUTION

This criterion assumes that the loadings of a factor will tend toward a normal distribution as the factor taps more random error. A factor that is small and mainly due to random error will then have a mean of zero. Cattell (1958) has suggested that factoring be stopped at this point.

15.4.3 SCREE TEST

The scree test, also proposed by Cattell (1966c), results from the practical observation that the factor variance levels off when the factors are largely measuring random error. Figure 15–2 may help make this idea clear. The number of the factor is plotted against the proportion of variance it extracts. The curve fitted to the plot of these factors will have a decreasing negative slope (the difference in variance between successive factors will decrease) until the random error factors—or trivial factors—are reached. Then the curve will level off and the incremental difference between successive factors will be about the

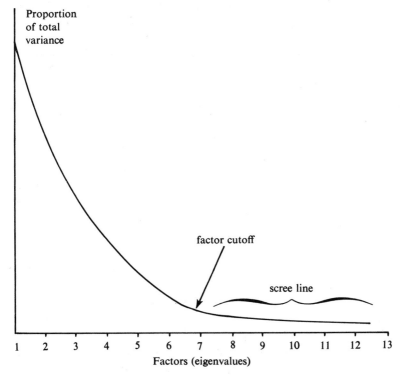

Figure 15–2

same. Cattell calls this the scree test, since the random error factors in a plot like that of Fig. 15–2 resemble scree—the debris that has fallen or been eroded off a mountain and that lies at its base.

15.4.4 INTERPRETABILITY

This criterion is similar to meaningfulness (Section 15.2.3). The smaller factors are retained only if they have sufficient substantive meaning to be interpretable. Unfortunately, it is the smaller factors that may tap conceptually new or unsuspected influences in a domain. The larger factors are usually already known by experienced observers[10] aside from systematic research, while the smaller factors are masked by these larger interdependencies. Throwing away a strange factor, therefore, may toss out an important discovery.

15.4.5 STRENGTH OF RELATIONSHIP

This criterion depends on the size of the factor loadings. In the case of orthogonal factors, the factor loading squared is the proportion of variance of a variable explained by the factor. Factors may be excluded as trivial if their highest loadings account for no more than 5 or 10 per cent of the variance of any one variable.

In order to have some basis for not setting the variance requirement below that which may possibly result from random error, a practical guide can be obtained by including a variable of random numbers in the analysis. This random variable should have a communality across the factors less than any of the substantive variables. The highest loading of the random variable provides a bench mark for gauging the acceptability of the high loadings on the small factors.

Besides the size of the loadings, the specificity of a factor to a variable may constitute an additional criterion. Only common factors are desired in common factor analysis. Therefore, if a small factor has a high loading for only one variable and very low loadings for the others, it might be discarded as a *unique* factor not of concern. This will insure that only factors defining common variance are rotated.

15.4.6 EIGENVALUE-ONE

A criterion that has gained wide popularity for common factor analysis is that of retaining unities in the principal diagonal of the correlation matrix and limiting the factors to those with eigenvalues greater than unity.

Kaiser (1960b) originally proposed this criterion as the " best" answer to the number-of-factors problem. Its original conception was based

10. This is true, for example, of dimensions of economic development and size for nations.

on Guttman's *weakest lower bound* [Eq. (5–19)], on excluding factors not accounting for at least the total variance of one variable, and on psychological interpretability. The criterion has been subsequently buttressed by the convergence of a number of algebraic derivations, as discussed in Section 15.3.3 above.[11]

Guttman (1954, pp. 154–55) had made several comments on the frequency distribution of eigenvalues that are salient to the number-of-factors problem and especially the eigenvalue-one criterion. The sum of the eigenvalues is equal to the sum of the principal diagonal elements of the matrix factored. If the matrix factored is a correlation matrix with unities in the diagonal, the sum of the eigenvalues will equal the number of variables, m [Eq. (4–31)]. The average eigenvalue will therefore be unity, i.e., m/m. With a trivial exception which should never occur in applied research,[12] at least one eigenvalue must therefore be greater than unity and at least one eigenvalue less than unity. For a Gramian matrix, moreover, all the eigenvalues must range between 0 and m in value. Guttman (1954, p. 155) then states that the m eigenvalues of the correlation matrix "have an asymmetric frequency distribution about the mean of unity." This implies that if there is sufficient correlation in the data for a couple of eigenvalues to be much larger than unity, then a greater number of eigenvalues less than unity must exist to maintain an average eigenvalue of unity.

The eigenvalue-one criterion is a neat and easy one to apply. It should not be employed, however, without certain precautions. In some cases the criterion may discriminate between factors that have little difference in eigenvalues. One factor may have an eigenvalue of 1.02 and the subsequent factor one of .96. For a study in which the eigenvalues may range, say, from 14.6 to 0.0, this small variance difference between the factors appears hardly meaningful, yet one factor is retained and the other dropped.

Regardless of the previous factor's eigenvalue, consider a not in-frequent case in which a factor is barely under the 1.00 cutoff—.987 for example. Disregarding such a factor by applying an across-the-board cutoff risks missing important factors. Small data errors, applying one distributional transformation versus another, unequally skewed distributions, and various design decisions (e.g., tetrachoric versus the product moment correlation coefficient) can shift the eigenvalues that are close to unity from above-one acceptability to below-one unacceptability, and vice versa. Given the effect that various design

11. See also Kaiser (1963, pp. 162–65).
12. This is a matrix of mutually uncorrelated variables.

decisions can have on the eigenvalues, it seems foolhardy to apply the eigenvalue-one criterion mechanically.

15.4.7 DISCONTINUITY

This criterion may be used by itself or in conjunction with the eigenvalue-one cutoff. It is based on the belief that, when the last meaningful or substantively important factor is extracted, the eigenvalues will show a discontinuity—a sharper drop than that for adjacent factors. Figure 15–3 illustrates this possibility. Factors subsequent to the discontinuity will then have a fairly constant slope for their eigenvalues, implying that they mainly extract random error as in the scree test.

To my knowledge, no mathematical proof exists for this notion. Cattell (1958, 1966c) has pointed out, however, and I have noticed in my own factor analyses that this discontinuity usually does appear within the neighborhood of the eigenvalue-one cutoff and that it seems to discriminate quite well between common factors on the one

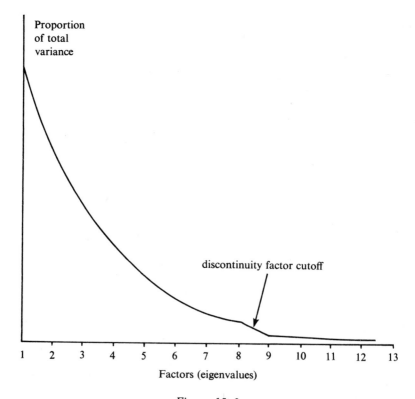

Figure 15–3

hand and unique or substantively meaningless factors on the other. Discontinuity appears, therefore, as a useful criterion to employ when there are several eigenvalues close to unity (e.g., 1.72, 1.31, 1.04, .94, .68, and .59, with the discontinuity appearing between .94 and .68). Then the researcher can seriously consider dropping those factors subsequent to the discontinuity. The eigenvalue-one criterion is thus employed to locate a range of candidates to which the discontinuity criterion, or the scree test for that matter, can be applied.

15.4.8 OVERFACTORING

All factor methodologists seem agreed that extracting *and* rotating *too few* factors to orthogonal or oblique solutions can distort the factor structure. There is disagreement as to what rotating *too many* factors will do, however. Some empirical studies devoted to this question have been done. Mosier (1939), for example, investigated the question for data with four underlying factors. He obliquely rotated different numbers of factors and found that rotating one too few had more effect on the factor structure than rotating two too many.[13]

Cattell, drawing on his great practical experience and citing Mosier, has consistently held that overfactoring is better than underfactoring (1952a). This position is the basis of one of Cattell's (1958) recommended solutions to the number-of-factors problem: Extract factors accounting for 99 per cent of the variance—certainly all substantive factors—and rotate. The trivial factors can then be left uninterpreted. Kaiser, on the other hand, referring to the common factor analysis model, says that rotating both too few and too many can have disastrous results, although less so in the case of too few (Kaiser, 1960, pp. 4–5; 1963, p. 165; 1964, p. 42).

The effect of overfactoring has yet to be clearly resolved, either through empirical research or mathematical proof. In the meantime, although the researcher should apparently err on the side of too many factors if he errs at all, he would probably be wiser to use one of the above rules of thumb in order to stay as close to the "right" number of factors as possible.

15.5 Conclusion

A large number of approaches, criteria, and considerations have been discussed above. The reader may be forgiven if at this point he feels

13. See also Dingman *et al.* (1964), Levonian and Comrey (1966), Kiel and Wrigley (1960), Humphreys (1964), and Howard and Gordon (1963).

Table 15–3. Suggested Criteria for the "Best" Number of Factors

| Model | Best Number of Factors[a] | | | Sensitivity of Rotated Factor Structure to Overfactoring | |
	Description	Significance	Generalizability	Auxiliary Criteria	Orthogonal Rotation	Oblique Rotation
Component	Scree test	Standard error of residuals; Tucker's phi	Eigenvalue-one	Discontinuity; minimum loading	High	High
Common	Eigenvalue-one	Standard error of residuals; Tucker's phi	Eigenvalue-one	Discontinuity; scree test	Moderate?	High?
Canonical	[b]	Chi-square test	[b]	Interpretability	Unknown	Unknown
Alpha	[b]	[b]	Eigenvalue-one	Discontinuity; scree test	Unknown	Unknown
Image	Eigenvalue > 0	[b]	Eigenvalue > 0	—	Small	High?
Harris[c]	Eigenvalue-one	[b]	Eigenvalue-one	Discontinuity; scree test	Small	High?

[a] *Description*: Accounting only for the variance in the data at hand. *Significance*: Making inference from the factors on the sample of cases to the population of cases. *Generalizability*: Making inference from the factors on the sample of variables to the universe of content.
[b] Not applicable.
[c] This refers to the scaling of the image covariance matrix and resulting factors (Section 5.4.1).

more confused about determining the right number of factors than he was a chapter ago. The purpose of this concluding section will be to suggest a strategy that might help to clear up the confusion.

Table 15–3 lays out these suggestions explicitly. How the "best" number of factors is defined is partly a function of whether the approach to the data involves descriptive, significant, or generalizable factors. Each approach may require a different criterion. The major criteria that might be used are indicated in the appropriate column. Auxiliary guides that can be applied are also indicated. These are to enable the researcher to distinguish acceptable factors when one or more factors are close to the criterion. In such cases the difference between the criterion and the factor may be due to data error or to methodological decisions. Auxiliary criteria then help to converge on a cutoff more consonant with the specific data and design. Hopefully, inclusion of auxiliary criteria in the table serves to warn the reader against employing any single criterion in a mechanical fashion.

A very important caveat to Table 15–3, as well as to this whole chapter, must be made explicit. Empirical testing *and* mathematical proofs for most of the entries in the table have yet to be provided. Most of the entries reflect the judgments of researchers and methodologists (including the writer). Those judgments, or my reading of them, may be faulty. Table 15–3, therefore, should not only be looked on as a listing of criteria, but also as a typology upon which further methodological research might focus.

Regardless of the answer to the number-of-factors problem for a particular design, however, *no one study will by itself suffice to establish the best number.* Reanalysis of the same data, involving altered design decisions and replications across cases and variables, will in the long run eliminate factors due to specific design decisions or random influences in the data. Rather than seek a definitive answer to the question of the best number of factors in a single analysis, we should expect the question to be answered like any empirical proposition—by the ultimate convergence of many diverse empirical findings.

16. Orthogonal Rotation

At this point the factor analysis research design may be completed. One of the multifactor solutions of Chapter 14 may be satisfactory by itself; rotation, computation of factor scores, or calculation of distances may be unnecessary. Most often, however, once a multifactor solution has been computed, we will at least want to rotate the factors. This chapter will focus on the considerations involved in such rotation, with particular attention given to orthogonal rotation. Except for a general discussion here, the complexities of oblique rotation will be covered in the next chapter.

The first section of the present chapter discusses the value of rotation[1] and—we hope—clarifies the substantive importance of rotation in a research design. The several alternative goals of rotation are considered in the second section. The third section introduces the restriction of

1. I agree with Jöreskog (1963, p. 18) that "transformation" is more appropriate a term than "rotation" for the operation of determining a factor matrix that is a linear function of the initial solution. The term rotation is so embedded in applied factor analysis that the confusion a shift in terminology would create does not seem warranted by the long-term gain.

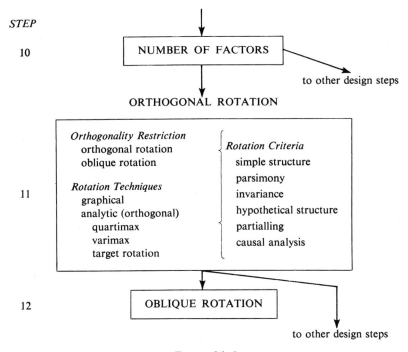

Figure 16-1

orthogonality, and the fourth section considers the graphical and analytic modes of rotation and presents the quartimax, varimax, and target matrix techniques. Figure 16–1 presents the content of this research design step.

16.1 The Rotation Problem

16.1.1 GEOMETRIC PRELIMINARIES
Some of the geometric concepts developed in previous chapters salient to rotation should be reviewed here. Multifactor techniques (Section 14.3) delineate the *basis dimensions* (Definition 3–33)—factors—of the common or total *vector space* of the data. These dimensions are *orthogonal* (Definition 3–28); they *span* (Definition 3–32) the vector space. This means that all the vectors (variables) contained in the common or total space of the data are *linearly dependent* (Definition 3–29) on the dimensions. Another way of saying this is that the dimensions can reproduce the original data.

Now, a vector space has more than one *basis*. Indeed, the number of bases is infinite. Each of these bases of a vector space contains the same number of independent dimensions and each is a *linear transformation* of any one of the other bases. A *linear transformation* is simply, in the orthogonal case, a *rotation* of the dimensions around the origin of the space.

For simplicity, consider a factor matrix of two dimensions (factors) for three variables (vectors), X_1, X_2, and X_3. The matrix of factor loadings α_{jl} is:

	S_1	S_2
X_1	α_{11}	α_{12}
X_2	α_{21}	α_{22}
X_3	α_{31}	α_{32}

Figure 16–2A shows a hypothetical plot of one of these variables, X_1, in this two-dimensional space. To keep the plot simple, the variable is treated as a point rather than a vector.

Let the desired rotation of S_1 and S_2 be to positions S_1^* and S_2^*, as shown in Fig. 16–2B. The angle through which they are rotated is θ degrees. The new coordinates (factor loadings) of the variables in the new coordinate system are determined by the perpendiculars drawn from the points representing the variables to the new dimensions.[2]

The loadings α_{je}^* on the rotated dimensions can be computed through the following linear transformation equations (Harman, 1967, Section 12.3):

variable 1
$$\alpha_{11}^* = (\cos \theta)\alpha_{11} + (\sin \theta)\alpha_{12}$$
$$\alpha_{12}^* = (-\sin \theta)\alpha_{11} + (\cos \theta)\alpha_{12}$$

variable 2
$$\alpha_{21}^* = (\cos \theta)\alpha_{21} + (\sin \theta)\alpha_{22}$$
$$\alpha_{22}^* = (-\sin \theta)\alpha_{21} + (\cos \theta)\alpha_{22}$$

variable 3
$$\alpha_{31}^* = (\cos \theta)\alpha_{31} + (\sin \theta)\alpha_{32}$$
$$\alpha_{32}^* = (-\sin \theta)\alpha_{31} + (\cos \theta)\alpha_{32}$$

These equations can be put in more compact matrix form. First, a notation for a transformation matrix is needed.

Notation 16–1. $T_{p \times p} =$ a linear transformation matrix for p factors.

Now, for p factors and m variables,

$$F_{m \times p}^* = F_{m \times p} T_{p \times p}, \tag{16-1}$$

where $F_{m \times p}^*$ is the rotated factor loading matrix, and $F_{m \times p}$ is the unrotated factor loading matrix.

2. For clarity an orthogonal rotation is employed. The different geometrical concepts introduced by oblique rotation are considered in the next chapter.

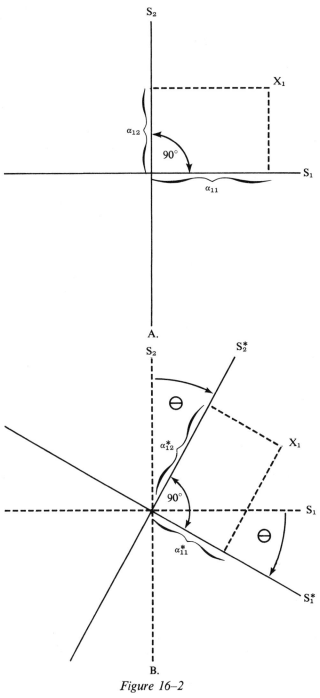

Figure 16–2

In the $m = 3$, $p = 2$ example of Fig. 16–2B, Eq. (16–1) is

$$
\begin{array}{cc} S_1^* & S_2^* \end{array} \qquad\qquad \begin{array}{cc} S_1 & S_2 \end{array}
$$

$$
\begin{array}{c} X_1 \\ X_2 \\ X_3 \end{array}
\begin{bmatrix} \alpha_{11}^* & \alpha_{12}^* \\ \alpha_{21}^* & \alpha_{22}^* \\ \alpha_{31}^* & \alpha_{32}^* \end{bmatrix}
= \begin{array}{c} X_1 \\ X_2 \\ X_3 \end{array}
\begin{bmatrix} \alpha_{11} & \alpha_{12} \\ \alpha_{21} & \alpha_{22} \\ \alpha_{31} & \alpha_{32} \end{bmatrix}
\begin{bmatrix} \cos\alpha & -\sin\alpha \\ \sin\alpha & \cos\alpha \end{bmatrix}
$$

The fundamental problem of rotation is to determine the elements of $T_{p \times p}$ that will yield a rotated matrix with certain desirable properties. However, *the number of transformation matrices that may be chosen for any $F_{m \times p}$ is infinite, and any one of the resulting rotated matrices $F_{m \times p}^*$ is an alternative basis of the common or total vector space.*

Since any data have an infinite number of factor matrices, how is the *unrotated* factor matrix selected from among them? In other words, what enables us to initially select any one basis, $F_{m \times p}$, from among all the others? This is done according to the criteria embodied in each factoring technique. For the principal axes technique (and its centroid approximation), for example, the first factor is fitted to the data to maximize the variance related to it, the second factor is similarly fitted at right angles to the first factor, and so on. Since there is only one $F_{m \times p}$ from among the infinite bases that will satisfy this maximization criterion, $F_{m \times p}$ is uniquely specified.[3]

16.1.2 WHY ROTATE?

If our original factor matrix is uniquely determined by a factoring technique, it seems foolish to open the door to the limitless world of rotated solutions. Yet, perhaps strangely to the mathematician, most factor analysts seem enamored of rotation.

The reason for rotation is that the factoring technique may be adequate to define the minimum dimensionality of the data and a basis of the space, but the original factors are often *substantively* uninteresting. The properties the factors should have to be substantively interesting serve as the criteria to be satisfied by rotation. These criteria will be discussed in the next section.

16.2 Rotation Criteria

Major substantive rotation criteria involve *simple structure* (or a multiple factor solution), *parsimony, factorial invariance, hypothetical structure, partialling,* and *causal exploration.* Before concerning our-

---

3. $F_{m \times p}$ is unique as long as no nonzero eigenvalues are equal. If two or more eigenvalues are equal, the associated eigenvectors (and, consequently, the associated factors) are indeterminant.

selves with these goals, however, it might be helpful to review the salient characteristics of the preliminary factor matrix.

16.2.1 CHARACTERISTICS OF THE UNROTATED MATRIX

For the principal axes, centroid, and direct factor analysis techniques, the factors account for decreasing amounts of variance. The first factors may have high loadings for most of the variables, and, conversely, most of the variables may have high loadings on a number of factors. Most importantly, the first factor is fitted to the data to account for the maximum variance; each successive factor is maximally fitted to the residual variance. *This procedure often locates the first factor between independent clusters of interrelated variables.* These clusters cannot be distinguished in terms of their loadings on the first factor. However, the different clusters will have loadings *different in sign* on the second or subsequent factors (thus producing *bipolar* factors).

> *Example 16–1.* This situation may be illustrated for a hypothetical two-factor, eight-variable case by Figs. 16–3, 16–4, and 16–5. Figure 16–3 displays the vector space of the data. In Fig. 16–4, the first factor falls between the two clusters of variables labeled I and II, since in this position S_1 maximizes the size of its loadings for all eight variables. In terms of the projection (loadings) of these vectors on the factor, however, the different clusters are indistinguishable. Table 16–1 gives the loadings for the eight hypothetical variables on S_1. Figure 16–5 shows the projection of the variables on the second factor, which is placed at right angles to the first; Table 16–1 also gives these loadings. Note that S_1 is a general factor and that S_2 is bipolar. Since the unrotated factors may lie between clusters, it is incorrect to say that factoring a matrix

Table 16–1. Unrotated Factor Matrix

	S_1	S_2
1	.76	.45
2	.83	.53
3	.59	.73
4	.63	.66
5	.77	−.60
6	.64	−.71
7	.72	−.53
8	.81	−.52

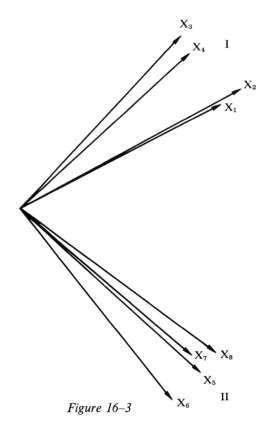

Figure 16–3

delineates clusters. Rather, variance is delineated; *rotation* of these initial factors (to simple structure) defines clusters if they exist.

Substantively, the first unrotated factor delimits the most comprehensive classification, the widest net of pairwise linkages among the variables, or the largest scale applicable to the data. For comparative political data, the first factor might be a political institution's dimension, and the second factor might define democratic versus totalitarian poles. For international relations, the first factor might be participation in international affairs, while the second factor might describe a polarization between cooperation and conflict involvement. For variables measuring heat, the first factor might be temperature while the second delineates hot versus cold. For physiological measurements on adults, the first dimension might be size and the second might reflect a polarization between height and girth.

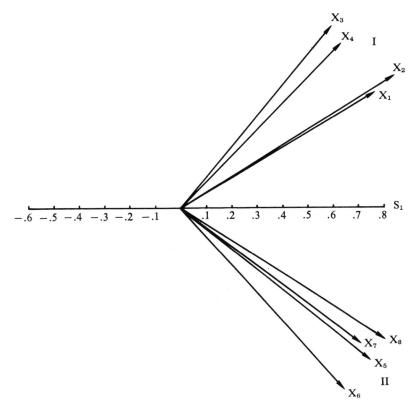

Figure 16–4

Besides maximizing variance, the principal axes, centroid approximation, and direct factor analysis techniques have another characteristic important here. *The factor loadings for each variable are dependent on all the variables included in the analysis.* Remove or add a variable to the data matrix, and the factor loadings shift. The maximization criterion of the techniques locates a factor within the vector configuration as a function of a weighted summation of all the variables.

A final salient characteristic of the unrotated factor solution is that *there is no way to exercise control over the initial location of the factor-axes in the configuration of vectors.* If we want to test a theory that a religious factor exists, say, in the variation among states of the U.S. on their attributes, a religious configuration or cluster of attributes might be obscured by variance associated with income, area, and educational and regional factors. One of the virtues of rotation is

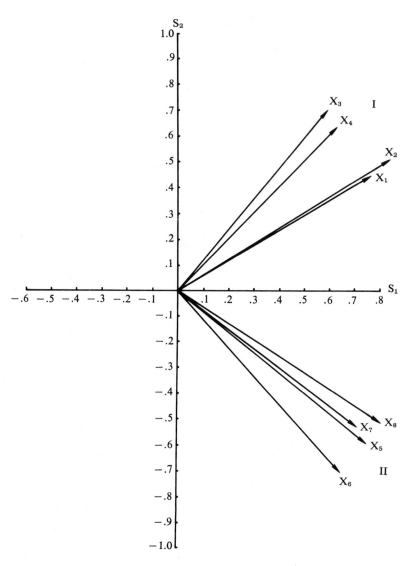

Figure 16–5

that such theories can be explicitly tested by altering the location of the factors.

16.2.2 SIMPLE STRUCTURE

The simple structure goal of rotation, or what is sometimes called the multiple factor solution, is achieved by rotating the factors around the

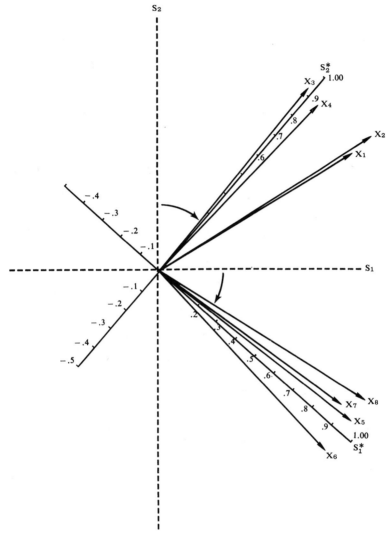

Figure 16–6

origin until each factor is maximally colinear with a distinct cluster of vectors. The shift is from factors maximizing total variance to factors delineating separate groups of highly intercorrelated variables.

> *Example 16–2.* Consider again the initial (unrotated) factor solution shown in Fig. 16–4. A simple structure

rotation would be equivalent to that shown in Fig. 16–6. The new factor positions, S_1^* and S_2^*, clearly define the two clusters. The rotated factor matrix is given in Table 16–2 alongside the unrotated factors of Table 16–1 for comparison.

Table 16–2[a]

	Unrotated		Rotated	
	S_1	S_2	S_1	S_2
1	(.76)	.45	.25	(.85)
2	(.83)	(.53)	.27	(.95)
3	(.59)	(.73)	−.05	(.94)
4	(.63)	(.66)	.02	(.91)
5	(.77)	(−.60)	(.98)	.08
6	(.64)	(−.71)	(.97)	−.08
7	(.72)	(−.53)	(.91)	.09
8	(.81)	(−.52)	(.96)	.15

[a] Loadings $\geq |.50|$ shown in parentheses.

Example 16–3. Consider the 10 political characteristics of Table 3–1. The unrotated factor matrix is given in Table 6–4, and the plot for the first two unrotated factors is shown in Fig. 6–1. Two-, three-, and four-factor simple structure rotations of these factors are given in Table 15–2. Table 16–3 reproduces for better comparison the three-factor unrotated and rotated solutions.

The shift in loadings between the unrotated and rotated factors is from one *general* factor (accounting for 62.5 per cent of the total variance) and two minor *bipolar* factors to two group factors of about equal variance and one minor *specific* factor. The simple structure rotation separates out three clusters of political characteristics. The first might be defined as a *constitutional democracy* dimension characterized by polyarchic tendencies, a competitive electoral system, a tendency toward permitting group opposition, nonelitist political leadership, horizontal power distribution, and, in particular, a neutral military. The second factor might be called a *Communist* dimension, which is loaded by a mobilization system, and by a tendency toward totalitarianism, a noncompetitive electoral system, intolerance of independent groups, and a vertical power structure. The third cluster is a strictly *monarchical* dimension.

Table 16–3. Ten Political Characteristics[a]

Characteristics	Unrotated[b]			Rotated[c]		
	S_1	S_2	S_3	S_1^*	S_2^*	S_3^*
1. System style	(−.69)	(−.62)	−.09	−.11	(.92)	−.11
2. Constitutional status	(.95)	.10	−.05	(.61)	(−.71)	−.15
3. Representative character	(.86)	−.38	−.03	(.78)	−.34	−.41
4. Electoral system	(.93)	−.01	.01	(.63)	(−.64)	−.25
5. Freedom of group opposition	(.95)	.13	.14	.49	(−.79)	−.27
6. Non-Communist regime	(.70)	(.65)	.12	.08	(.95)	.10
7. Political leadership	(.84)	−.24	−.07	(.72)	−.41	−.29
8. Horizontal power distribution	(.92)	−.20	.05	(.68)	(−.52)	−.39
9. Monarchical type	−.25	(.66)	(−.67)	−.11	−.10	(.96)
10. Military participation	(−.54)	.40	(.69)	(−.95)	−.07	−.18
Per cent total variance	62.8	16.7	9.7	35.2	38.8	15.4

[a] Loadings ≥ |.50| shown in parentheses.

[b] From Table 6-4.

[c] Varimax orthogonal rotation.

The attempt to rotate the factors so that they define distinct clusters of intercorrelation has resulted in several explicit simple structure criteria. These were developed by L. L. Thurstone (1947, Chapter 14) more than two decades ago and have since served as the basis for such rotation. There are five requirements that simple structure should satisfy:

1. Each variable should have at least one zero loading in the factor matrix.
2. For a factor matrix of p factors, each column of factor loadings should have at least p variables with zero loadings.
3. For each pair of columns of loadings (factors), several variables should have zero loadings in one column but not in the other.
4. For each pair of columns of loadings (factors), a large proportion of the variables should have zero loadings in both columns.
5. For each pair of columns of loadings (factors), only a small proportion of variables should have nonzero loadings in both columns. (Thurstone, 1947, p. 335.)

These conditions insure that factors will be rotated to positions identifying the distinct clusters of variables. A simple structure rotation then has several characteristics:

1. Each variable is identified with one or a small proportion of the factors. If the factors are considered explanations, causes, or underlying influences, this is equivalent to minimizing the number of agents or conditions needed to account for the variation of distinct groups of variables.

2. The number of variables correlated with (loaded on) a factor is minimized. This changes the unrotated general or bipolar factors to

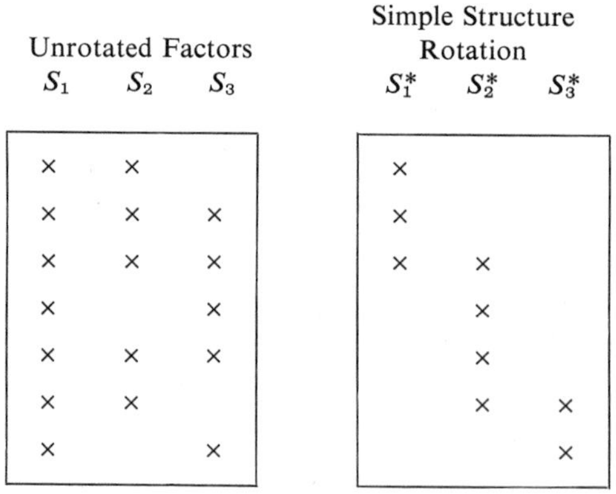

Unrotated Factors			Simple Structure Rotation		
S_1	S_2	S_3	S_1^*	S_2^*	S_3^*
×	×		×		
×	×	×	×		
×	×	×	×	×	
×		×		×	
×	×	×		×	
×	×			×	×
×		×			×

Figure 16–7

group factors, and the requirement that only a small number of variables be loaded on any two factors reduces the overlap of these group factors. The rotation thus attempts to maximize the hypothesis that only a small number of separate factors are needed to account for any particular clusters of relationships, as illustrated in Fig. 16–7. Nonzero factor loadings are indicated by crosses and zero loadings are left blank.

3. The variance accounted for by the major unrotated factors is spread across all the rotated factors. Each of the simple structure rotated factors tends to account for about the same magnitude of variance.

4. Each rotated factor is now more or less identified with a distinct cluster of interrelated variances.

16.2.3 PARSIMONY

One major goal underlying the use of simple structure is to make our model of reality as simple as possible. If phenomena can be described equally well using fewer factors, then the principle of *parsimony* is that we should do so. Simple structure maximizes parsimony by transforming from a solution accounting for the variance of a variable by several factors to a solution accounting for this variance by one, or at most two, factors.

16.2.4 INVARIANCE

Another research goal often involved in an analysis aims at maximizing the generalizability of the factor results. As discussed above (Section 16.2.1), an unrotated factor loading is dependent on all the variables. We may desire, therefore, to alter the solution to one that will not be wholly dependent on the particular mix of variables involved. That is, we may desire an *invariant* factor solution. Invariant factors will delineate the same cluster of variables as long as some variables defining the cluster are included in the analysis, regardless of the inclusion or exclusion of variables unrelated to the cluster.

One of the chief justifications of simple structure rotation is that it determines invariant factors. As long as *marker variables* (Section 9.1.2.7) highly loaded on a simple structure factor are included in a study, that factor should be identified regardless of the other variables involved. This concept of invariance underlying simple structure enables a comparison of the factor results of different studies to be made. Very seldom can different investigators include all of the same variables in their designs, nor would they want to. But where variables overlap between studies and simple structure rotation is employed, then comparison can be made to see if the same factors emerge. Kaiser (1958, p. 195) considers factorial invariance the "ultimate criterion" of rotation. That simple structure achieves this invariance is attested to by Thurstone (1947, p. 440) and is shown by Kaiser (1958).

16.2.5 HYPOTHETICAL STRUCTURE

Rather than guide rotation by simple structure criteria, we may desire to test specific hypotheses or theories. These may involve a factor matrix that is neither a principal axes fit or a simple structure fit to the data.

In order to determine whether the data can be rotated to a hypothesized structure or pattern (i.e., whether one of the bases of the vector space *is* the hypothesized or theoretical basis), four steps can be followed. First, a target matrix can be defined in terms of the appropriate number of factors and the hypothetical loadings of the variables on each factor. These loadings may be specified in binary language (1 = high loading; 0 = low or zero loading), or actual loading coefficients may be posited.

Second, a preliminary factor solution can be determined by one of the appropriate techniques described in Chapter 14. Third, the initial solution can be rotated to a least squares fit to the hypothetical structure (Section 16.4.2.3). If the hypothetical structure is indeed a basis of the data, then the rotated solution should completely fit the hypothetical loading matrix posed in the beginning. In other words, the hypothesized factors will describe the pattern of relationships in the data. As the rotated solution deviates from the posited solution, the adequacy of the hypothesized structure should become more questionable. The fourth step would be to use one of the factor comparison methods of Chapter 20 to test the agreement between the actual and hypothetical factor matrices.

> *Example 16–4.* G. Schubert (1962) determined the factors of agreement of Supreme Court Justices with majority decisions. He then rotated the factors to fit three Guttman scales defining voting on civil rights, economic liberalism, and government fiscal policies. He found the correlations between the fitted factor loadings and the scale loadings to be quite high.

> *Example 16–5.* Van Arsdol *et al.* (1958) used a hypothetical target matrix to test indices that theoretically differentiate cities. They rotated multiple group factors on 6 variables for 10 cities to fit a structure involving

social rank, urbanization, and segregation factors. The fit was very good.

16.2.6 PARTIALLING

One of the useful features of factor analysis is that it can divide the variance in the data into orthogonal components. This characteristic may be employed in a fashion analogous to the partial correlation coefficient (Definition 3–13).

A partial correlation coefficient assesses the correlation between two variables, holding constant the influence of other variables on the relationship (e.g., holding race constant in assessing the correlation between income and education). Factor analysis considerably expands this capability. Once an initial factor solution is obtained, a number of influences may be partialled out of the data through various rotation possibilities:

1. If we desire to remove the influence of a specific variable from the assessment of the relationships between the others, then the first factor may be rotated to a position colinear with the variable,[4] and the other factors orthogonal to it. These remaining factors then delineate effects statistically independent of the specific variable.

> *Example 16–6.* Let the concern be to determine the factors of expenditure (food, clothing, utilities, etc.) for family units. A variable defining climate might then be included, and the first factor rotated colinear with it. The remaining factors will then delimit the desired expenditure factors, holding constant the differential influence of climate.

2. Instead of a variable, a dimension or scale may be partialled from the data. The first factor may be rotated to maximally fit a set of variables representing the effects to be held constant. If there is a Guttman scale of variables whose effects are clouding the desired relationships, then the first factor can be rotated to the scale.

> *Example 16–7.* In a study of *intra*national conflict dimensions we might want to hold constant the opportunity for conflict associated with population size and land area. Consequently, the first factor may be rotated to partial out the effects of a nation-size dimension from the interrelationships.

4. The point representing the variable is now on the factor. The loadings (projections) of the variable on all other factors is then zero in the orthogonal case.

3. The effects of two or more independent variables or factors may be simultaneously partialled from the data. In this case the first and as many subsequent factors as necessary are rotated to define the different variables or dimensions whose influences are to be removed.

> *Example 16–8.* If it is desired to assess the conditions influencing budget expenditures of cities, while holding real estate valuation and municipal size constant, this may be done by rotating the first two factors so that they are as colinear with valuation and size variables as possible. If these variables are correlated, the first factors may be placed so that the variables are embedded in the plane defined by the first two factors. The remaining orthogonal factors will define the independent influences on the budget.

16.2.7 CAUSAL ANALYSIS

Often a research design will evoke a causal theory or hypothesis. Cross tabulation and plotting, correlations, partial correlations, and multiple regression have been favorite tools for testing causal explanations. Although also suited to such a purpose, factor analysis has seldom been employed. In this regard, the freedom that rotation allows for the investigator to try various linear combinations of factors gives more flexibility to causal analysis than do many traditional approaches.

Let the variable we wish to explain be Y, and let one of m hypothetical causal agents be X_j. Once the preliminary factors for the combined data matrix of Y and the mX_j variables have been determined, the first factor may be rotated so as to be colinear with Y. Those variables hypothesized to be causally related to Y should then have high loadings on this factor. If the causal hypothesis specifies that two independent groups of causal variables influence Y, then the first two factors should be rotated orthogonally so that Y lies midway between them. Y will then have high loadings on both factors, and the hypothesized variables should load one or the other factor, depending on which of the two independent causal groups they belong to. This procedure may be followed for a number of presumed causal groups, although we should keep in mind that, as the number of factors involved increases, the loading of Y on any one factor decreases. The restraint is that the sum of squares of the factor loadings for Y is less than or equal to 1.00, the maximum communality.

> *Example 16–9.* Denton and Jones (1966) rotated factors of a P-factor analysis of war, 1825–1946, to test three

causal theories of international or civil wars: Wars result from distribution of power; wars result from colonial-imperialist conflict; or (civil) wars result from political or social oppression. The results lent credence to these theories.

More than one Y may be tested at a time. Moreover, we may hypothesize a causal structure in advance (Section 16.2.5) or include in the causal analysis influences that we want to hold constant (Section 16.2.6).

It is not necessary to pose a causal hypothesis in the beginning. A number of variables may be included that *may be* causally relevant, and various rotations may then be tried until the most parsimonious and theoretically satisfactory combinations of Y and the X_j variables are found. It should be noted that *the spatial configuration of variables defined by the preliminary solution is not altered by rotation.* Rotation changes only the perspective, not the interrelationship between the variables. If no X_j is related to Y in the analysis (i.e., if Y is orthogonal to all X_j and has a communality of zero accordingly), then rotation will not alter this fact. Nor can rotation alter a perfect relationship between Y and some X_j. If there are several variables partially related to Y, however, then through rotation these variables can be combined in various linear combinations to explain Y. Exploratory rotation can try out these combinations in the same fashion as the experimental scientist tries out various combinations of variables to assess their effect on laboratory behavior.

16.3 Orthogonal versus Oblique Rotation

16.3.1 ORTHOGONAL ROTATION

A restriction that may be placed on the factors either in the preliminary analysis[5] or in the rotation is that they be mutually orthogonal (Definition 3–28). The orthogonality restriction ensures that factors will delineate *statistically independent* variation. The orthogonal factors themselves are a mathematically simple description of the data and are amenable to subsequent mathematical manipulation and analysis (e.g., as independent variables in a multiple regression analysis).

Orthogonal rotation has several characteristics of interest:

1. The inner product of the factor *loadings* is zero (Definition 3–22) for the rotation of principal axes factors. The reader should not be

5. The choice of factor techniques will determine whether the resulting factors are orthogonal or not. See Table 14–1.

confused by the orthogonality of factor loadings into assuming that the factor *loadings* are uncorrelated. They may be correlated, even though they are orthogonal. This is possible because the correlation coefficient involves summing the product of mean deviation loadings (Definition 3–6), while orthogonality is determined through a straight sum of products of loadings.

2. The resulting factor *scores* are linearly independent *and* uncorrelated. A correlation matrix of factor scores will be an identity matrix.

3. The communality of a variable is invariant through an orthogonal rotation of an orthogonal preliminary solution. Therefore, a check on rotation accuracy is made to calculate the communality and compare it with that for the unrotated factors.

4. The ordering of the rotated factors may be completely different from the unrotated solution. Factor S_3 in the unrotated case, for example, may be most similar to S_6 of the rotated factors.

16.3.2 OBLIQUE ROTATION

Whereas in orthogonal rotation the final factors are necessarily uncorrelated, in oblique rotation the factors are allowed to become correlated.[6] Orthogonal rotation involves moving the whole factor structure around the origin in a rigid frame (like the spokes of a wheel moving around a hub) until the best fit is obtained. Oblique rotation, however, individually rotates the factors until, in the simple structure case, each factor delineates a distinct variable cluster. The empirical correlation between the clusters will determine the degree of correlation between the resulting factors. Figure 16–8A shows a hypothetical two-factor orthogonal simple structure rotation, and for comparison Fig. 16–8B gives a simple structure oblique rotation to the same clusters.

Orthogonal rotation is a subset of oblique rotations. If the clusters of variables are uncorrelated, then oblique rotation will result in orthogonal factors. The difference between the two modes of rotation, therefore, is not in defining uncorrelated or correlated factors, since the factors of oblique rotation can also be uncorrelated, but in whether this lack of correlation is empirical or imposed on the data by the model.

There has been some controversy over whether orthogonal or oblique rotation is the better approach. Burt, for example, has argued (1941, p. 266) for orthogonal rotation, while Thurstone (1947) and Cattell (1952a) have been among the chief proponents of oblique

6. Coming right after the last section, this point may be confusing. Conventionally, when speaking of factors as being correlated or uncorrelated we are referring to the factor *scores*. When speaking of factors as orthogonal or oblique, however, we are speaking of factor *loadings*. Orthogonal factor loadings imply uncorrelated factor scores. Oblique factor loadings imply correlated factor scores.

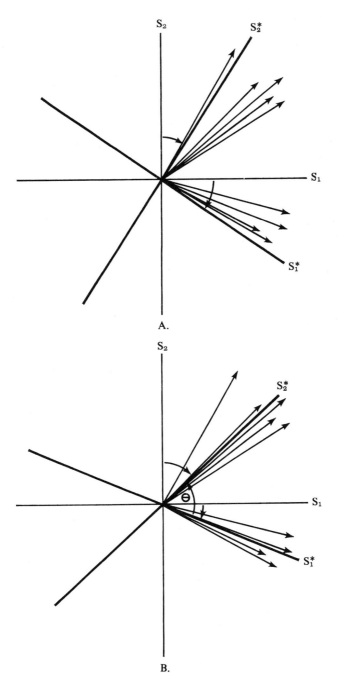

Figure 16–8

rotation. The chief grounds for orthogonal rotation are simplicity, a mathematical elegance in the result, conceptual clarity, and amenability to subsequent manipulations and analyses.

Oblique rotation is usually advocated on two grounds. One is that it generates additional information from the analysis. The clusters of variables will be better defined. There is less possibility of confusion as to variables involved in a cluster, and the central or nuclear members of the cluster can be identified by their high loadings. In orthogonal rotation, variables central to a cluster may not have very high loadings on the relevant factor.

Moreover, information about the correlations between the clusters—the factors—is obtained. These correlations constitute substantive knowledge in their own right and enable the researcher to gauge the degree to which his data approximate orthogonal factors. If, after oblique rotation, the largest correlation between factors is, say, .10, then the simpler orthogonal factor structure might be employed as a final solution with the knowledge that the factors are naturally near orthogonal.

A second ground for justifying oblique rotation is epistemological. It is argued[7] that the world cannot be realistically treated as though basic functional unities represented by the factors are uncorrelated. Phenomena, whether singly or in clusters, are interrelated, and the factors themselves must reflect this reality. Oblique rotation allows this reality to be represented by the factor correlations. Moreover, the correlations between the factors enable the search for patterns of relationship to be carried to the *second order* (Chapter 18). The factor correlations themselves may be factor-analyzed to determine the more general, abstract, and comprehensive functional unities or the more persuasive influences underlying the variation in the data. But if only orthogonal rotation is applied, the investigator closes the door identifying these second-order and higher-order factors.

The question of orthogonal versus oblique rotation need not be phrased in an either-or manner. With computer facilities now widely available, the researcher can try both options, and, with oblique and orthogonal results at hand, he can then commit himself to one of them.

The technical features of oblique rotation are considered in the next chapter. Here, only the major characteristics of oblique rotation will be listed:

1. The factor *scores* will have intercorrelations given by the matrix of factor correlations (Sections 6.4 and 17.1.3).

7. See especially Cattell (1958, p. 309).

2. A clear distinction must be made between factor *structure* and factor *pattern* matrices (Sections 6.3 and 17.1).

3. The factor loadings can be interpreted as correlations between variable and factor only in the cases of the *primary* factor *structure* matrix or *reference* factor *pattern* matrix.

4. In the case of orthogonal factors of a correlation matrix, the loadings can range between $+1.00$ and -1.00.[8] In oblique rotation some of the loadings may increase above an absolute value of 1.00 (Section 17.1).

5. The communality of a variable cannot be computed directly from the oblique loadings as in the orthogonal case.

6. The per cent of variance accounted for by the factors cannot be computed from the column sum of squared loadings as in the orthogonal case.

16.4 Rotation Techniques

16.4.1 GRAPHICAL ROTATION

The historical means of rotating a preliminary factor solution is through various graphical devices. A plot is made of the configuration of variable points in the space of two factors at a time. The two factors are then orthogonally or obliquely rotated to give the desired fit to the points. By measuring the angle of rotation, the investigator can compute the new factor loadings according to Eq. (16–1). Rotating all possible paired combinations of unrotated and newly rotated factors constitutes a cycle—a complete rotation of the initial factor structure. Graphical rotation may be carried through a large number of cycles until the two factor rotations can no longer be improved.[9]

Graphical rotation is time-consuming and subjective, and, because a computer can be employed for most rotation criteria, it is now seldom employed. Nevertheless, graphical rotation is still of considerable value in polishing an oblique computer rotation.[10] Through graphical

8. This assumes that there is no missing data (Section 10.3.1.1) or, more generally, that the correlation matrix is Gramian (Definition 4–16).

9. An excellent source on graphical rotation is Cattell (1952a, Chapters 12 and 15). Fruchter (1954) presents clearly the steps involved. Thurstone (1947) lays out a graphical method for rotating three factors at a time. A technically concise description of graphical rotation is given in Harman (1967, Sections 12.3 and 13.3).

10. There is as yet no generally accepted simple structure oblique computer rotation technique. There are a number of techniques that vary slightly in their results. For a program that will allow visual computer rotation, see Cattell and

rotation, moreover, the effects of particular variables can be partialled from the analysis, causal hypotheses can be tested, and various linear combinations of the factors can be explored.

16.4.2 ANALYTIC ROTATION

Graphical rotation is purely subjective: The final location of the factors is an accumulation of visual judgments. In the sense that experience and finesse play a large role, graphical rotation is more an art than a science. It is possible for investigators to arrive at different simple structure rotations, although in the case of simple structure the criteria are apparently explicit enough for independent graphical rotations to be very similar in result.

Dissatisfaction with the labor and subjectivity of graphical rotation, perhaps combined with a natural inclination to make all aspects of factor analysis mathematically determinant, led to attempts to develop an analytic rotation technique. This involved efforts to reduce Thurstone's simple structure criteria (Section 16.2.2) to the maximizing or minimizing of a mathematical function and led to different solutions for orthogonal and oblique rotation. The next chapter will consider the oblique analytic techniques that were developed. Here, we will focus on the orthogonal approach, particularly the varimax analytic criterion.[11]

Although adequate for graphical rotation, the simple structure set of criteria were not explicit enough to specify a mathematical function. However, because the simple structure criteria involved simplifying variable and factor complexity—that is, they reflected the principle of parsimony—simple structure served as a goal of analytic rotation. This simplification involved two major approaches to a mathematical function: *quartimax* and *varimax*. These will be discussed separately and will be followed by a brief mention of analytic target rotation.

16.4.2.1 *Quartimax Rotation.* A number of analytic orthogonal rotation techniques have been developed by Ferguson (1954), Neuhaus and Wrigley (1954), Carroll (1953), and Saunders (1960). Although these techniques vary in formulation, they all reduce to a maximization of the fourth powers of the factor loadings (Harman, 1967, Section 14.3) and are all equivalent orthogonal solutions. Accordingly, these techniques may be considered a class of *quartimax* rotations.

Foster (1963). One may still wish to use a graphical plotting of the factor space as a check. Analytic rotation may confound factors that the trained eye might discern (Guilford and Zimmerman, 1963).

11. Harman (1967, Chapter 14) presents an excellent historical and technical discussion of analytic rotation techniques.

The rationale underlying quartimax can be seen best in two-factor rotation. As one factor is rotated toward a point, the projection (loading) of the point on the factor increases. As a second factor is moved away from the point, the projection on the second factor decreases. Now, for any two *orthogonal* factors, as one factor is rotated toward a point the other factor must move away. Therefore, the *product* of the loadings squared of a point on two orthogonal factors will decrease as one of these factors is moved toward the point. The product is zero when the point lies on one of the factors. Consequently, it seems reasonable that the complexity of a variable's factor loadings could be decreased by a function *minimizing* the sum of products of all possible pairs of factor loadings for a variable. Summing each of these sums over all the variables would then give one function for simplifying the complexity of the whole factor matrix.

Harman (1967, p. 297) points out that such a minimization of sums of cross products is the same as maximizing the expression

$$Q = \sum_{j=1}^{m} \sum_{l=1}^{p} \alpha_{jl}^4, \qquad (16\text{--}2)$$

where Q is the value to be maximized, and α_{jl} is the factor loading of variable X_j on factor S_l. Since Eq. (16–2) will be at a maximum when each variable has a perfect loading of unity on one of the factors and zero loadings elsewhere, the function has the effect of increasing the high and decreasing the middle loadings for a variable.

The result approximates simple structure[12] but has a bias toward loading more variance on the first factor than would result from graphical rotation. This deficiency is overcome in the varimax rotation method developed by Henry Kaiser.

16.4.2.2 *Varimax Rotation.* Rather than simplify variable complexity, Kaiser (1958) instead proposed a criterion focusing on factor complexity. By simplifying the columns of a factor matrix, the tendency of quartimax toward a general factor is avoided.

The varimax criterion is a function of the *variance* of the column of factor loadings. As there are more high *and* low loadings on a factor, the variance of the squared factor loadings is larger. The highest variance is obtained when the loadings are either zero or unity. Therefore an orthogonal rotation can be computed by maximizing the variance (hence, varimax) of the squared factor loadings. This function is:

$$V = m \sum_{l=1}^{p} \sum_{j=1}^{m} \left(\frac{\alpha_{jl}}{h_j}\right)^4 - \sum_{l=1}^{p} \left(\sum_{j=1}^{m} \frac{\alpha_{jl}^2}{h_j^2}\right)^2, \qquad (16\text{--}3)$$

12. See Harman (1967, Table 14.2, p. 302).

where V = variance of normalized factors, α_{jl} = factor loading of variable X_j on factor S_l, and h_j^2 = communality of variable X_j. Equation (16–3) is called the *normal* varimax criterion. It involves the normalization (note the division of loadings by h_j) of the rows of loadings. Kaiser had originally proposed (1956) a *raw* varimax criterion that achieved better simple structure than quartimax but still did not determine the best possible orthogonal simple structure. The difficulty was due to a differential weighting of the variables as a result of their unequal communalities. The normalization procedure embodied in the normal varimax assigns each variable equal weight.

The term "varimax rotation," now used in the literature, usually means that the *normal* varimax criterion is maximized. Likewise, varimax in this book always refers to the maximization of Eq. (16–3). The computational procedure[13] involves the maximization of this equation for a pair of factors at a time. The angle between the paired factors enables the transformation matrix to be computed; the determination of the transformation matrices for all possible pairs of factors constitutes a rotation cycle. Rotation is iterated through a number of these cycles until differences in successive values of the varimax criterion for the whole matrix achieves a desirable minimum.

For an illustration of the preliminary and varimax rotated solutions, see Example 16–3 above.

The varimax criterion for orthogonal rotation comes closest to the graphical simple structure solution, or, in other words, Thurstone's simple structure goal.[14] Varimax is now generally accepted as the best analytic orthogonal rotation technique (Harman, 1967, p. 311; Harris, 1964b; Kaiser, 1964; Warburton, 1963). Almost all published factor analysis studies doing analytic orthogonal simple structure rotation now employ varimax and the criterion is the basis of all the orthogonal rotation computer programs of which I am aware.

A strong feature of varimax is its ability to discern the same cluster of variables regardless of the number or combination of other variables in the analysis. This invariance property, highly desirable in its own

13. Kaiser (1959) gives the outline of a computer program. Horst (1965, Section 18.2) discusses four variations of Kaiser's method: successive factor varimax, simultaneous factor varimax, successive factor general varimax, and simultaneous factor general varimax. Horst (Chapter 19) also presents a very useful technique for computing the rotated varimax solution directly from the data without going through the preliminary factor solution.

14. See the comparison in Harman (1967, p. 311) of graphical, quartimax, and varimax rotation of 24 psychological variables. Kaiser (1958) presents an interesting comparison of a graphical *oblique* rotation with quartimax and varimax orthogonal rotations for Thurstone's classic box study.

right (Section 16.2.4), was demonstrated by Kaiser (1958) on 24 psychological variables. Using the preliminary centroid loadings for the 24 variables, he successively rotated the factors for the first 5 variables, then 6, then 7, etc., up to the rotation of all 24 variables. A comparison of the shifts in the factors with change in number of variables showed two of four factors invariant from the first, while the other two fluctuated some until they picked up a high loading variable. This property of invariance is mathematically proven to hold for any two-factor matrix (Kaiser, 1958, pp. 194–95) but has not been generalized to cases of more than two factors.

Kaiser's investigation of invariance has led him to assert that this property

> would seem to be of greater significance than the numerical tendencies of the normal varimax solution to define mathematically the doctrine of simple structure. Although factor analysis seems to have many purposes, fundamentally it is addressed to the following problem. Given an (infinite) domain of . . . content, infer the internal structure of this domain on the basis of a sample of m variables drawn from the domain. The possibility of success in such inferences is obviously dependent upon the extent which a factor derived from a particular sample of variables approximates the corresponding unobservable factor in the infinite domain. If a factor is invariant under changing samples of variables, i.e., shows factorial invariance . . . there is evidence that inferences regarding domain factors are correct.[15]

16.4.2.3 *Target Rotation.* Target rotation involves specifying hypothetical factor loadings and rotating the preliminary solution to a maximum fit with these loadings. Hurley and Cattell (1962) have written a program for the analytic rotation of a preliminary solution to a hypothesized factor matrix (Section 16.2.5).[16] The factor loadings and correlations between the factors may be specified in advance. Since orthogonal rotation involves mutually zero correlations, the orthogonality of the data may also be tested. As usual, let $F_{m \times p}$ be the preliminary factor matrix. Let $H_{m \times p}$ be the hypothesized factor matrix and $T_{p \times p}$ the matrix transformation to rotate $F_{m \times p}$ to a best fit with $H_{m \times p}$. By Eq. (16–1), it is desirable to find a $T_{p \times p}$ such that

$$F_{m \times p} T_{p \times p} = H_{m \times p} + \Gamma_{m \times p}, \qquad (16\text{–}4)$$

15. Kaiser (1958, p. 195). Minor editorial liberties have been taken with this quotation to make it conform with the terminology developed in this book.

16. Horst (1965, Section 17.1) presents several methods (with the listing of computer programs) for rotating to a hypothesized structure. See also Digman (1967), who treats target rotation as a class of Procrustes rotations, and Schönemann (1966). Jöreskog (1966) uses the maximum-likelihood factor model to test for a hypothesized simple structure matrix directly without using rotation methods.

where $\Gamma_{m \times p}$ = error of fit, $H_{m \times p} - F_{m \times p}$, and is uncorrelated by columns with $F_{m \times p}$. Left-multiplying both sides of Eq. (16–4) by $F'_{p \times m}$,

$$F'_{p \times m} F_{m \times p} T_{p \times p} = F'_{p \times m} H_{m \times p} + F'_{p \times m} \Gamma_{m \times p}$$
$$= F'_{p \times m} H_{m \times p}. \qquad (16\text{–}5)$$

The best transformation matrix $T_{p \times p}$ is then given by

$$T_{p \times p} = (F'_{p \times m} F_{m \times p})^{-1} F'_{p \times m} H_{m \times p}, \qquad (16\text{–}6)$$

where $F_{m \times p}$ is nonsingular. The resulting $T_{p \times p}$, normalized by columns and applied to $F_{m \times p}$, will give

$$F_{m \times p} T_{p \times p} = H^*_{m \times p}, \qquad (16\text{–}7)$$

where $H^*_{m \times p}$ is the least squares fit of $F_{m \times p}$ to $H_{m \times p}$, and the $H_{m \times p}$ factors may be oblique.[17]

Matrix $H^*_{m \times p}$ can then be compared to $H_{m \times p}$ to determine their correspondence. The method of Hurley and Cattell is fundamentally similar to Ahmavaara's (1957) factor comparison method (Section 20.2.3) and differs only by normalization of columns rather than of rows.

---

17. Note how Eq. (16–6) is similar to Eq. (4–14) for determining the matrix of regression coefficients.

17. Oblique Rotation

Oblique rotation is more complex than orthogonal rotation. Not only do correlations between factors have to be included in the results, but there is no longer one factor matrix to interpret. As discussed in Section 17.1 below, oblique rotation generates a *structure* and a *pattern* factor matrix, both of which have to. be considered in evaluating the rotation. Moreover, the analytic techniques for oblique rotation are varied and technically difficult. No wonder, then, that oblique rotation has caught on slowly among psychologists[1] and seems to be scarcely used in the social sciences.

1. There are notable exceptions to this. Some psychologists, such as Thurstone and Cattell, appear to have applied oblique rotation in all their later studies. Their rationale is that it is unrealistic to expect factors to be uncorrelated in a sample. Verification of their belief can be seen in several artificial experiments. Thurstone's famous box experiment (1947, pp. 140–46), for example, has shown that an oblique solution gives the best definition of the length, width, and height dimensions of boxes. See also Cattell and Gorsuch (1963) and Cattell and Dickman (1962), who have constructed ingenious artificial experiments to show that oblique rotation better enables the delineation of the true functional dimensions operating in the data.

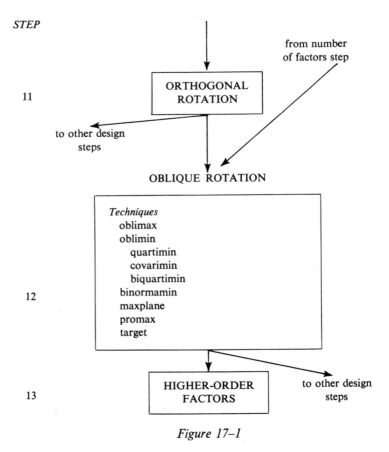

Figure 17–1

The first section below will discuss various types of oblique factor matrices and the oblique factor space. The second section will consider the various techniques that have been developed for analytic oblique rotation. Figure 17–1 displays the various alternatives of this research design step.

17.1 Oblique Space

Whereas orthogonal rotation results in one factor matrix to be interpreted, oblique rotation delineates a *pattern* and *structure* matrix for each of two types of oblique axes. These two types—*primary* and *reference* axes—will be discussed in separate sections.

17.1.1 PRIMARY AXES
In oblique rotation the projection of a variable-point may be determined in two ways. Consider the variable X_j in the space of two oblique

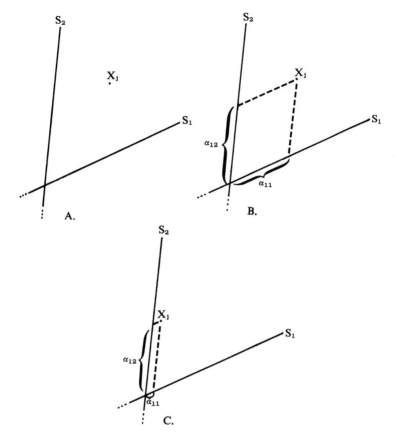

Figure 17–2

factors as shown in Fig. 17–2A. In oblique coordinate systems, the projections (loadings) of a point are determined by lines parallel to the
axes, as displayed in Fig. 17–2B. As a point moves closer to one axis,
its projection on the other axis gets smaller, as shown in Fig. 17–2C.

> *Definition 17–1.* Projections on oblique factors deter-
> mined as in Fig. 17–2B are called PATTERN LOADINGS.
> The matrix of pattern loadings is called A PATTERN FACTOR
> MATRIX.

> *Notation 17–1.* $P_{m \times p}$ = a pattern factor matrix for m
> variables and p factors.

The pattern loadings may be interpreted as measures of the *unique
contribution* each factor makes to the variance of the variables. They

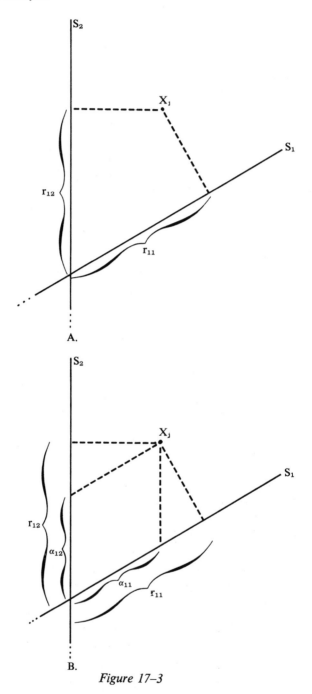

Figure 17–3

measure the dependence of the variables on the different factors (Cattell, 1962b, pp. 679–80), and in this sense they are regression coefficients of the variables on the factors. *For oblique factors, the coefficients α_{jl} of the factor models shown in Eqs. (5–2) and (5–19) are the pattern loadings.*

The projection of a variable-point X_j on the oblique factor-axes may be determined in another way, however. Consider again the point of Fig. 17–2A. As shown in Fig. 17–3A, the projection can be measured by lines from the point *perpendicular* to each axis.

> *Definition 17–2.* Projections on oblique factors determined as in Fig. 17–3A are called STRUCTURE LOADINGS. The matrix of structure loadings is called a STRUCTURE FACTOR MATRIX.

> *Notation 17–2.* $K_{m \times p}$ = a structure factor matrix for m variables and p factors,
> r_{jl} = structure loading of variable X_j on factor S_l, as illustrated in Fig. 17–3A.

The use of r_{jl}, which has already been employed as notation for the correlation coefficient (Notation 3–6) is no oversight. *The structure loadings are the product moment correlations of the variables with the oblique factors.*[2] For comparison, Fig. 17–3B shows both pattern and structure representations of the location of a variable in two-factor oblique space.

In orthogonal rotation the pattern and structure projections of a point onto a factor-axis coalesce. The perpendicular projections drawn from a point to the orthogonal factors and the projections drawn parallel to the other axes are the same. Accordingly, there is only one orthogonal factor matrix and its elements may be interpreted as pattern loadings or as correlations.

In oblique rotation, however, the pattern and structure matrices are different. Both give different perspectives on the data and both should be evaluated. It is ambiguous to report only one oblique matrix without indicating whether it is a pattern or a structure.

The pattern matrix is best for determining the clusters of variables defined by the oblique factors.[3] If a factor-axis is placed through a cluster of variables, the pattern projections of the variables on the other factors will be near zero. This can be seen from Fig. 17–4A, in

---

2. Proof of this is derived in Harman (1967, Section 13.2).

3. Cattell (1962b) and White (1966) consider which of several matrices resulting from oblique rotation are best for interpretation.

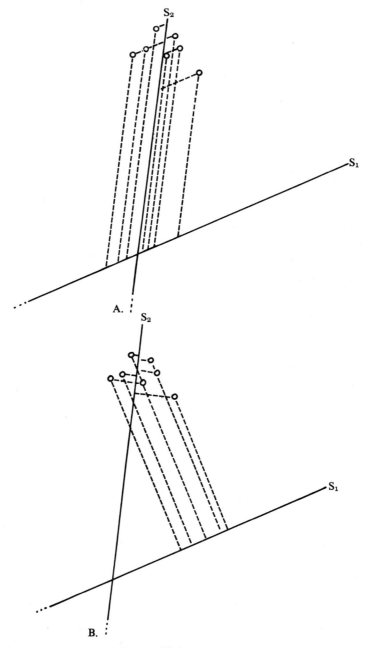

Figure 17–4

which the variables have high loadings on S_2 but near zero loadings on S_1. The pattern matrix, therefore, defines the simple structure configuration and is basic for substantively interpreting the oblique factors.

In contrast to the pattern loadings, the structure loadings do not well delineate simple structure. Consider again the configuration of Fig. 17–4A, then examine the structure loadings as shown in Fig. 17–4B. As can be seen, it is possible for some of the members of the cluster defined by S_2 to have appreciable loadings on S_1. Since the structure loadings are correlations, the structure loading of a variable on two factors measures a variable's *direct* relationship with each factor and *the interaction between the two factors expressed in their factor correlation.* In factor interpretation, it is desirable to discriminate between the independent factor contributions to variation in the variables. The structure matrix is not very useful for this purpose. Its main value is in measuring the variance (structure loading squared) of each variable jointly accounted for by a particular factor and the interaction effects of that factor with the others.[4]

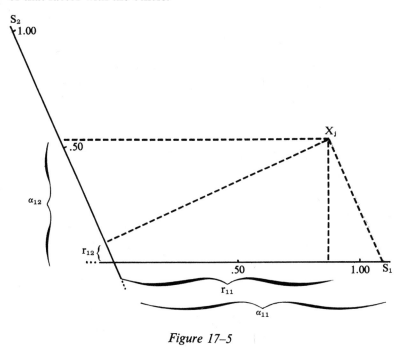

Figure 17–5

4. Harman (1967, pp. 284–85) gives equations for calculating the direct and joint contributions of the oblique factors to the total variance of the variables.

Table 17–1. Correlations of Sixteen Foreign Conflict Variables[a]

Variables	(1)	(2)	(3)	(4)	(5)	(6)	(7)	(8)	(9)	(10)	(11)	(12)	(13)	(14)	(15)	(16)
1. Number of violent acts	100															
2. Number of planned violent acts	100	100														
3. Incidence of violence[b]	36	34	100													
4. Number of discrete military acts or clashes	99	99	32	100												
5. Number of days of violence	91	92	28	89	100											
6. Number of negative acts	25	25	21	25	24	100										
7. Number of diplomatic rebuffs	31	31	08	33	28	48	100									
8. Number of negative communications	44	44	33	44	38	69	35	100								
9. Number of written negative communications	22	22	23	22	19	62	28	91	100							
10. Number of oral negative communications	45	45	34	45	42	69	35	95	77	100						
11. Number of written and oral negative communications	66	66	29	67	49	29	26	54	31	51	100					
12. Number of unclassified communications	16	16	08	13	17	32	15	43	34	47	20	100				
13. Number of accusations	39	39	32	39	32	67	33	99	92	93	50	35	100			
14. Number of representations and protests	34	33	18	36	27	46	26	65	59	57	49	30	57	100		
15. Number of warnings	55	55	36	54	54	65	33	77	54	84	53	34	71	49	100	
16. Number of antiforeign acts	02	01	04	01	01	18	01	15	07	19	14	16	13	16	20	100

[a] For definitions of variables and code sheet, see Rummel (1966a). The sample is 341 directed pairs (e.g., A → B) of nations for 1955 data collected from the daily *New York Times*. Correlations are product moment with decimals omitted. Data distributions are untransformed but have no more than 89 per cent zero values for any one variable.

[b] Incidence of some kind of military violence during year = 1; none = 0.

Table 17–2. *Orthogonal Dimensions of Sixteen Foreign Conflict Variables*

Variables	Unrotated Factors[a]				h^2	Orthogonally Rotated Factors[b]			
	S_1	S_2	S_3	S_4		S_1	S_2	S_3	S_4
1. Violence	(.76)	(−.63)	.01	.01	.98	.19	(−.97)	.00	−.01
2. Planned violence	(.76)	(−.64)	.01	.02	.98	.18	(−.97)	.00	.00
3. Incidence of violence	.42	−.10	.06	(−.62)	.57	.31	−.33	−.11	(−.60)
4. Military acts	(.76)	(−.63)	−.01	.03	.97	.19	(−.97)	−.01	.02
5. Days of violence	(.69)	(−.61)	−.00	.07	.86	.14	(−.91)	.00	.05
6. Negative acts	(.67)	.41	−.12	.23	.69	(.77)	−.12	.09	.29
7. Diplomatic rebuffs	.46	.03	−.37	(.61)	.72	.36	−.28	−.11	(.71)
8. Negative communications	(.90)	.39	−.05	−.10	.97	(.95)	−.27	.07	−.04
9. Written communications	(.71)	(.55)	−.18	−.15	.86	(.92)	−.02	−.06	−.04
10. Oral communications	(.89)	.34	.02	−.06	.91	(.89)	−.30	.14	−.03
11. Written and oral communications	(.71)	−.25	.15	−.04	.59	.36	(−.65)	.17	−.08
12. Unclassified communications	.41	.28	.27	.21	.37	.43	−.07	.40	.13
13. Accusations	(.85)	.42	−.10	−.15	.93	(.94)	−.21	.01	−.07
14. Protests	(.65)	.24	.07	.03	.49	(.63)	−.24	.17	.03
15. Warnings	(.84)	.10	.08	−.01	.73	(.69)	−.46	.17	−.01
16. Antiforeign acts	.16	.19	(.86)	.23	.85	.09	.00	(.91)	−.05
Per cent of total variation	48.2	17.2	6.5	6.0	77.9	34.8	29.8	7.2	6.1

[a] Principal axes technique and component analysis model. Factor cutoff at eigenvalues > 1.00. Loadings ≥ |.50| shown in parentheses.
[b] Varimax rotation.

Table 17–3. Oblique Primary Factors of Sixteen Foreign Conflict Variables[a]

Variables	Structure				Pattern			
	S_1	S_2	S_3	S_4	S_1	S_2	S_3	S_4
1. Violence	.33	(.99)	.00	−.02	.04	(.98)	−.02	−.01
2. Planned violence	.33	(.99)	.00	−.01	.03	(.98)	−.02	.00
3. Incidence of violence	.34	.37	−.12	(−.60)	.29	.27	−.10	(−.60)
4. Military acts	.33	(.98)	−.01	.01	.04	(.97)	−.03	.02
5. Days of violence	.28	(.92)	.01	.04	.00	(.92)	−.02	.05
6. Negative acts	(.79)	.23	.12	.31	(.77)	.00	.04	.27
7. Diplomatic rebuffs	.41	.33	−.08	(.70)	.32	.25	−.16	(.71)
8. Negative communications	(.98)	.41	.09	−.03	(.94)	.12	.01	−.07
9. Written communications	(.91)	.16	−.03	−.02	(.96)	−.13	−.11	−.06
10. Oral communications	(.94)	.43	.16	−.01	(.88)	.17	.09	−.05
11. Written and oral communications	.47	(.70)	.17	−.08	.27	(.61)	.14	−.09
12. Unclassified communications	.46	.14	.42	.15	.42	.00	.37	.11
13. Accusations	(.96)	.35	.03	−.06	(.95)	.06	−.05	−.09
14. Protests	(.67)	.33	.19	.05	(.62)	.14	.13	.01
15. Warnings	(.77)	(.57)	.19	.00	(.64)	.37	.13	−.03
16. Antiforeign acts	.14	.03	(.91)	−.01	.07	−.01	(.91)	−.08
Sums of squares	6.37	5.52	1.19	.99	5.32	4.45	1.09	.99

[a] Biquartimin solution at 100 major cycles and 1,179 iterations. Precision level of criterion at 100th cycle is 4.24×10^{-5}. Loadings and coefficients $\geq |.50|$ shown in parentheses.

The individual loadings of the structure matrix should not exceed an absolute value of 1.00, as can be expected from their being correlations. For the pattern matrix, however, the absolute value of some of the coefficients may be greater than 1.00. This possibility is shown in Fig. 17–5 for a variable X_1. Both the pattern and structure loadings are drawn.

At this point an example of oblique results may be helpful.

> *Example 17–1.* Consider the conflict behavior of 341 *pairs* of nations for 1955 (Rummel, 1967a). Table 17–1 presents the correlation matrix of raw data for 16 conflict behavior variables, and Table 17–2 displays the unrotated and varimax rotated factors for the component analysis model (Section 5.3). Table 17–3 shows the *primary structure* and *pattern matrices* and Table 17–5 of Example 17–3 gives the primary factor correlations.
>
> Except for the first two factors, which have a correlation of .30, the oblique factors are nearly orthogonal. For these data, the oblique pattern shows no dramatic difference from the orthogonal rotation. There are more near-zero loadings, indicating a slight "cleaning up" of the simple structure, but the basic interpretation of the factors remains the same. The major substantive result of the oblique rotation for these data is the yielding of the factor correlations.
>
> The elements of the structure and pattern matrices are shown in Table 17–3 for contrast. Note how much cleaner the pattern matrix is in terms of high and low loadings, thus making possible a better substantive interpretation of the factors.

17.1.2 REFERENCE AXES

Rather than interpret the oblique factor-axes directly, a new coordinate system may be defined by drawing through the origin lines perpendicular to each of the oblique axes. These lines can then represent a new oblique coordinate system. This alternative system was originally proposed by Thurstone to give a slightly better delineation of simple structure. The projections of a variable-point X_j on the reference axes is shown in Fig. 17–6. It is usual to denote the reference axes by Λ. To distinguish these reference axes from the original oblique structure and pattern factors, the latter are called the *primary factors*, or the *primaries*.

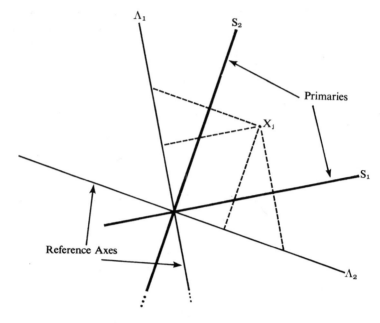

Figure 17–6

Definition 17–3. The PRIMARY OBLIQUE FACTORS, or PRIMARIES, consist of the factor-axes rotated to a best oblique fit to the configuration of variables in the space.

Definition 17–4. The REFERENCE FACTORS consist of the axes perpendicular to each of the *primaries*, as in Fig. 17–6.

As shown in Fig. 17–6, a variable-point may have *pattern* and *structure* projections on the reference axes. In conformity with Harman's notation (1967), the pattern matrix of reference axes will be denoted by W and the structure by V.

Notation 17–3. Λ_l = the lth reference factor,
$W_{m \times p}$ = the reference pattern matrix,
$V_{m \times p}$ = the reference structure matrix.

From Fig. 17–6, an important connection between primary and reference axes is evident: The *pattern* of the primaries is the *structure* of the reference axes, and the *structure* of the primaries is the *pattern* of the reference axes. Therefore, for the $W_{m \times p}$ and $V_{m \times p}$ matrices, *it is the structure matrix $V_{m \times p}$ that yields the pattern coefficients of the variables and defines the simple structure configurations.* The *pattern*

Table 17–4. Primary Pattern and Reference Structure of Sixteen Foreign Conflict Variables [a]

Variables	Primary Pattern				Reference Structure			
	S_1	S_2	S_3	S_4	S_1	S_2	S_3	S_4
1. Violence	.04	(.98)	−.02	−.01	.04	(.93)	−.02	−.01
2. Planned violence	.03	(.98)	−.02	.00	.03	(.93)	−.02	.00
3. Incidence of violence	.29	.27	−.10	(−.60)	.27	.26	−.10	(−.60)
4. Military acts	.04	(.97)	−.03	.02	.04	(.93)	−.03	.02
5. Days of violence	.00	(.92)	−.02	.05	.00	(.88)	−.02	.05
6. Negative acts	(.77)	.00	.04	.27	(.73)	.00	.03	.27
7. Diplomatic rebuffs	.32	.25	−.16	(.71)	.30	.23	−.16	(.70)
8. Negative communications	(.94)	.12	.01	−.07	(.89)	.11	.01	−.07
9. Written communications	(.96)	−.13	−.11	−.06	(.91)	−.12	−.11	−.06
10. Oral communications	(.88)	.17	.09	−.49	(.83)	.16	.09	−.05
11. Written and oral communications	.27	(.61)	.14	−.09	.26	(.58)	.14	−.09
12. Unclassified communications	.42	.00	.37	.11	.40	.00	.37	.11
13. Accusations	(.95)	.06	−.05	−.09	(.90)	.06	−.05	−.09
14. Protests	(.62)	.14	.13	.01	(.58)	.14	.13	.01
15. Warnings	(.64)	.37	.13	−.03	(.61)	.35	.13	−.03
16. Antiforeign acts	.07	−.01	(.91)	−.08	.06	−.01	(.91)	−.08
Sums of squares	5.32	4.45	1.09	.99	4.79	4.04	1.08	.98

[a] Biquartimin solutions. See footnote to Table 17–3.

matrix $W_{m \times p}$ gives the correlations between variables and reference factors. Table 6–5 shows these similarities and differences between the primary and reference axes.

One virtue of the reference axes over the primaries is that the *structure* matrix $V_{m \times p}$ gives a slightly better fit to the zero loading criterion of simple structure. Loadings near zero in $P_{m \times p}$ are closer to zero in $V_{m \times p}$, while high $P_{m \times p}$ loadings are slightly lower in $V_{m \times p}$.

> *Example 17–2.* For comparison, the primary pattern matrix of Example 17–1 is shown in Table 17–4 alongside the reference structure matrix for the 16 foreign conflict variables.

Although the reference factors have been extensively employed by some factor analysts, such as Thurstone and Cattell, the greater complexity of the resulting representation may not warrant the slight improvement in simple structure. Conceptually and geometrically, the interpretation of the primaries is simpler.

One virtue of reference axes may dictate their use for some data, however. If the primary factors are highly correlated, several of the primary pattern loadings may exceed an absolute value of 1.00 by an order of magnitude. Some pattern loadings may be as high as ± 10.00 or ± 20.00. The interpretation of a pattern matrix with a mixture of such loadings is difficult. Fortunately, the *reference structure* matrix then serves as a convenient alternative. Even though the primary pattern loadings are far in excess of an absolute value of 1.00, the reference structure loadings will still not exceed $+1.00$.

17.1.3 CORRELATION MATRIX

In the case of orthogonal factors, the correlations between factors are uniformly zero. Therefore, they are neither given as output of computer programs nor reported along with the results. In oblique rotation, however, the factor correlations are important information and are usually displayed by a correlation matrix. *These correlations are equivalent to the product moment correlations between the factor scores.*

Table 17–5. Primary and Reference Factor Correlations for Sixteen Foreign Conflict Variables

Factors	Primary Factor				Reference Factor			
	1	2	3	4	1	2	3	4
1.	1.00				1.00			
2.	.30	1.00			−.30	1.00		
3.	.09	.02	1.00		−.08	.00	1.00	
4.	.04	−.01	.07	1.00	−.04	.03	−.07	1.00

Example 17–3. The correlation matrix for the primaries of the 16 foreign conflict variables of Example 17–1 is given in the left half of Table 17–5; the correlation matrix for the reference axes of Example 17–2 is given in the right half. The slight difference between reference and primary correlation matrices is due to the slight change in loadings from one coordinate system to the other.

17.1.4 TRANSFORMATION MATRIX

The transformation matrix, $T_{p \times p}$, enables the rotated solution to be computed directly from the preliminary solution. Often the transformation matrix will be given as computer output along with the oblique factor matrices and the factor correlation matrix. $T_{p \times p}$ is not itself interpretable, but it is useful in polishing an analytic oblique rotation or in doing the oblique rotation in stages.

Example 17–4. The transformation matrix for the primaries of the 16 foreign conflict variables given in Example 17–1 is shown in Table 17–6. The transformation matrix for the reference axes differs from that for the primaries, but will not be given here.

Table 17–6. Transformation Matrix of Primary Factors of Sixteen Foreign Conflict Variables

Factors	(1)	(2)	(3)	(4)
1.	.9858	.1503	.0268	.0199
2.	−.1552	−.9885	−.0002	.0159
3.	.0597	.0183	.9992	.0434
4.	.0227	.0003	.0298	.9987

Example 17–5. In an analytic oblique rotation of 15 factors for the 236 variables of Example 9–6, the rotation was done in stages to enable the shift to oblique factors to be charted and to minimize the computer expense involved. At the beginning of each successive stage, the transformation matrix from the previous stage was input to a computer program developed by Carroll (1958). In this way the rotation could begin again where it had left off. Each stage could be monitored, and the rotation could be terminated when no improvement was evident.

17.2 The Oblique Rotation Model

The discussion of the factor models in Chapter 5 assumed, for simplicity, that the factors were orthogonal. For oblique factors, some modifications in the models are required or some distinctions must be made.

When the factors are orthogonal, no distinction is necessary between pattern and structure loadings in the factor models of Eqs. (5–2) or (5–19): Orthogonal pattern and structure loadings are the same. These factors models are still valid for the oblique factors, except that the loadings, α_{jl}, now *refer to primary pattern or reference structure loadings*.

With regard to the fundamental theorems of the factor models [Eqs. (5–14, 21, 27, 42, and 54)], some changes must be made for oblique factors. Since the changes are similar for each model, only component factor analysis will be dealt with in detail. First, we will need additional notation.

Notation 17–4. $\phi_{p \times p}$ = correlation matrix for *primary* oblique factors,

$\psi_{p \times p}$ = correlation matrix for *reference* oblique factors.

Now, the component factor model is

$$Z_{n \times m} = S_{n \times p}P'_{p \times m},\tag{17–1}$$

where $Z_{n \times m}$ = standardized data for n cases and m variables, $S_{n \times p}$ = standardized factor scores for p factors, and $P_{p \times m}$ = primary pattern matrix.

Left-multiply each side of Eq. (17–1) by its transpose and divide by n:

$$\frac{1}{n}Z_{m \times n}Z_{n \times m} = \frac{1}{n}(S_{n \times p}P'_{p \times m})'S_{n \times p}P'_{p \times m},$$

$$= \frac{1}{n}P_{m \times p}S'_{p \times n}S_{n \times p}P'_{p \times m},\tag{17–2}$$

$$= P_{m \times p}\left(\frac{1}{n}S_{p \times n}S_{n \times p}\right)P'_{p \times m}.$$

Since the left side of Eq. (17–2) equals the correlation matrix [Eq. (4–12)] and since the correlation between factor scores on the right side of Eq. (17–2) is given by the factor correlation matrix,

$$\phi_{p \times p} = \frac{1}{n}S'_{p \times n}S_{n \times p},\tag{17–3}$$

then Eq. (17–2) reduces to

$$R_{m \times m} = P_{m \times p}\phi_{p \times p}P'_{p \times m}.\tag{17–4}$$

This is the fundamental theorem [Eq. (5–21)] for component analysis with the restriction of orthogonality relaxed to allow oblique factors.[5]

5. There are a number of mathematical connections between the various oblique primary and reference matrices that might be of interest. The reader is

If the factors are indeed orthogonal, then the factor correlation matrix is an identity matrix and Eq. (17–4) reduces to Eq. (5–21),

$$R_{m \times m} = P_{m \times p} I_{p \times p} P'_{p \times m} = P_{m \times p} P'_{p \times m} = F_{m \times p} F'_{p \times m}. \quad (17\text{–}5)$$

It should be pointed out that oblique factors are still *basis dimensions* (Definition 3–33) of the data. Basis dimensions are required to be *linearly independent* (Definition 3–29) but not necessarily orthogonal.[6]

17.3 Analytic Techniques

Analytic oblique rotation is in the experimental stage. There is a profusion of techniques, each giving a slightly different solution. No one technique stands out as being clearly better, but the range of available techniques can be narrowed, depending on complexity of the data, simplicity of technique, resources available, and the desire to maximize the number of near-zero loadings or the desire for best approximation to an intuitive graphical simple structure solution. Eight different techniques will be discussed here. Some of them, such as promax, have just recently been proposed and are relatively untried. Several, such as quartimin and biquartimin, have had extensive application. Except for target rotation, all techniques to be discussed are attempts to satisfy simple structure criteria (Section 16.2.2). The eight techniques to be considered are oblimax, quartimin, covarimin, biquartimin,[7] binormamin, maxplane, promax, and target rotation.[8]

The profusion of oblique techniques, not to mention their complexity and the fact that no one technique clearly deserves the accolade "best," may deter the researcher from doing an oblique rotation. If a computer is available and programs facilitating different oblique rotations exist, however, several different oblique rotations may be tried on the data. If they all agree on the pattern of loadings, i.e., if the substantive interpretation of the factors is unaltered, *as usually appears to be the case in practice*, then a satisfactory solution has been found. If they disagree, then the solution that is compatible with the researcher's knowledge and purposes will have to be selected. Moreover, any one

referred to Harman (1967, Chapter 13) for an excellent mathematical treatment of their interconnections. See also Cattell (1962b).

6. See, for example, Kemeny *et al.* (1959, pp. 269–70; also Example 8, p. 271).

7. For a mathematical description of the first four techniques with comparative examples, see Harman (1967, Chapter 15).

8. These do not exhaust the available techniques. Currently in the stage of development, for example, is a promising technique involving oblique rotation through orthogonal transformations (Harris and Kaiser, 1964). See also Jennrich and Sampson (1966).

of the techniques can be selected as a preliminary solution to be polished by graphical rotation.

17.3.1 OBLIMAX

Saunders' (1960) development of an analytic orthogonal rotation technique has been generalized to oblique rotation. His technique, called *oblimax*, seeks to rotate the factors so that the number of high and low loadings are increased by decreasing those in the middle range.

Consider a frequency distribution of loadings on a factor in which each loading is included twice—once with its proper sign and once reflected. This produces a symmetrical distribution about a mean of zero. By maximizing the kurtosis (peakedness) of this distribution, Saunders points out, the frequency of low and high loadings can be increased. The kurtosis function, K, to be maximized, is

$$K = \sum_{j=1}^{m} \sum_{l=1}^{p} \alpha_{jl}^4 \Big/ \left(\sum_{j=1}^{m} \sum_{l=1}^{p} \alpha_{jl}^2 \right)^4, \qquad (17\text{--}6)$$

where α_{jl} is the oblique reference structure loading, leaving out the statistical constants that can be disregarded in the maximization.[9]

Oblimax yields an oblique solution very close to an intuitive graphical solution *if the data have a clean simple structure.* In geometric terms, if the variable-points fall into clusters close to each axis, then oblimax will determine a highly satisfactory oblique structure. If, however, the data are highly complex—the variable-points are spread throughout the space without clear breaks—oblimax may be unsatisfactory. The solution to Eq. (17–6) involves the determination of roots (eigenvalues) that can be complex numbers (involves roots of negative numbers) for data without a clear simple structure. In a private communication to Harman, Saunders wrote that the persistence of such complex roots indicates that the data are not appropriate to oblique simple structure (Harman, 1960, p. 319).

17.3.2 QUARTIMIN

This technique, which was developed by Carroll (1953), minimizes the sum of inner products (Definition 3–22) of the reference structure loadings. As discussed in terms of orthogonal rotation (Section 16.4.2.1), when a variable-point increases its loading on one factor and decreases its loading on the others, the sum of the inner product of its loadings

---

9. For computational procedure and program see Pinzka and Saunders (1954). Harman (1967, Section 15.2) gives an excellent treatment of the procedures.

gets smaller. In the minimum case the variable will have zero coefficients on all except one factor, and the sum of inner products will be zero. The quartimin function to be minimized is

$$Q = \sum_{l<q=1}^{p} \sum_{j=1}^{m} \alpha_{jl}^2 \alpha_{jq}^2, \qquad (17\text{--}7)$$

where α_{jl} is the oblique reference structure loading, and l and q are the lth and qth factors.

Computationally, minimizing Q involves iteration toward an eigenvalue-eigenvector solution for each factor, while the other factor loadings are held constant. This solution is computed successively for each factor and, when completed for all the factors, constitutes a cycle. The factors are iterated through as many cycles as are needed to minimize Q within an acceptable range.

The quartimin technique does not embody the difficulty of oblimax. It will give a solution for complex data that are without a clear simple structure. A serious problem, however, is that quartimin will result in oblique factors biased toward high intercorrelations. Correlations of near .50 may not be unusual, and correlations over .70 may occasionally result. The researcher may find these correlations quite acceptable if clear simple structure with many zero coefficients results. However, better simple structure is not always a concomitant of high interfactor correlations.

> *Example 17–6.* Again, the data of Example 17–1 will be employed. Table 17–7 gives the quartimin rotation and the interfactor correlations for the unrotated solution of Table 17–2.

17.3.3 COVARIMIN
Kaiser (1958) sought to extend his varimax criterion to oblique rotation by minimizing

$$C = \sum_{l<q=1}^{p} \left\{ m \sum_{j=1}^{m} \left(\frac{\alpha_{jl}^2}{h_j^2}\right)\left(\frac{\alpha_{jq}^2}{h_j^2}\right) - \left[\sum_{j=1}^{m} \left(\frac{\alpha_{jl}^2}{h_j^2}\right)\right]\left[\sum_{j=1}^{m} \left(\frac{\alpha_{jq}^2}{h_j^2}\right)\right] \right\}, \qquad (17\text{--}8)$$

where $\alpha_{jl} = $ oblique reference structure loading, and l and q are the lth and qth factors.

The difficulty with *covarimin*, as the rotation given by the minimization of C is called, is that it is biased in a direction opposite to quartimin. Covarimin tends to give factors with intercorrelations that are too low. Covarimin factors are usually very close to the orthogonal varimax solution.

Table 17–7. Quartimin Factors of Sixteen Foreign Conflict Variables[a]

	Primary Pattern Matrix			
Variables	S_1	S_2	S_3	S_4
1. Violence	−.17	(1.08)	−.01	.00
2. Planned violence	−.19	(1.09)	−.01	.02
3. Incidence of violence	.49	.18	−.12	(−.62)
4. Military acts	−.17	(1.08)	−.02	.04
5. Days of violence	−.23	(1.04)	.00	.07
6. Negative acts	(.74)	−.10	.03	.29
7. Diplomatic rebuffs	.14	.28	−.18	(.74)
8. Negative communications	(1.02)	−.04	.00	−.05
9. Written communications	(1.15)	−.33	−.14	−.05
10. Oral communications	(.90)	.03	.09	−.04
11. Written and oral communications	.12	(.64)	.16	−.09
12. Unclassified communications	.27	−.03	.41	.12
13. Accusations	(1.08)	−.12	−.06	−.08
14. Protests	(.58)	.07	.14	.02
15. Warnings	(.57)	.31	.14	−.02
16. Antiforeign acts	−.30	.05	(1.01)	−.08
Sums of squares	6.14	5.37	1.34	1.07

	Factor Correlations			
	(1)	(2)	(3)	(4)
1.	1.00			
2.	.59	1.00		
3.	.43	.17	1.00	
4.	.26	.05	.18	1.00

[a] Unrotated factors are given in Table 17–2. Coefficients $\geq |.50|$ shown in parentheses. Beginning with the varimax factors, the solutions took 11 cycles and 990 iterations, achieving a precision level for the criterion of 4.77×10^{-7}.

Example 17–7. Table 17–8 presents the covarimin solution for the 16 foreign conflict variables of Example 17–1. Note how close the covarimin factors are to the orthogonal rotated solution of Table 17–2 and how low the interfactor correlations are in comparison to those for the quartimin solution of Table 17–7.

17.3.4 BIQUARTIMIN

Because the quartimin and covarimin solutions were biased in opposite directions, Carroll (1957) proposed splitting the difference. By combining the criteria Q and C, the virtues of both might be retained while their opposite biases could be compensated. The resulting function to be minimized is

$$B = Q + \frac{C}{m}, \qquad (17\text{–}9)$$

Table 17–8. Covarimin Factors of Sixteen Foreign Conflict Variables[a]

Variables	Primary Pattern Matrix			
	S_1	S_2	S_3	S_4
1. Violence	.22	(.98)	−.01	−.01
2. Planned violence	.21	(.98)	−.01	.00
3. Incidence of violence	.31	.35	−.08	(−.59)
4. Military acts	.22	(.97)	−.02	.02
5. Days of violence	.17	(.92)	.00	.05
6. Negative acts	(.79)	.13	.18	.31
7. Diplomatic rebuffs	.38	.28	−.08	(.72)
8. Negative communications	(.97)	.29	.18	−.01
9. Written communications	(.93)	.05	.05	.00
10. Oral communications	(.93)	.33	.24	.00
11. Written and oral communications	.40	(.66)	.19	−.08
12. Unclassified communications	.46	.07	.46	.13
13. Accusations	(.96)	.24	.11	−.04
14. Protests	(.66)	.25	.24	.05
15. Warnings	(.73)	.48	.25	.00
16. Antiforeign acts	.14	−.01	(.93)	−.08
Sums of squares	6.02	4.94	1.39	1.00

	Factor Correlations			
	(1)	(2)	(3)	(4)
1.	1.00			
2.	−.07	1.00		
3.	−.18	.04	1.00	
4.	−.06	.03	.04	1.00

[a] Unrotated factors are given in Table 17–2. Coefficients $\geq |.50|$ shown in parentheses. Beginning with the varimax factors, the solution took 100 cycles and 1,148 iterations, achieving a precision level of 1.33×10^{-4}.

where Q = quartimin function, C = covarimin function, and m = number of variables. This is called the *biquartimin* solution. Experience with the technique has shown that biquartimin generally gives a simple structure solution that is more satisfactory in terms of interfactor correlations and factor loadings than does either covarimin or quartimin.

Carroll has generalized the biquartimin function to a class of solutions termed *oblimin* that have covarimin and quartimin as subcases. By weighting the functions [Eq. (17–9)] by two parameters β_1 and β_2, he is able to combine Q and C in different combinations:

$$B^* = \beta_1 Q + \frac{\beta_2 C}{n}. \qquad (17\text{–}10)$$

Replacing Q and C with the appropriate functions and putting $\gamma = \beta_2/(\beta_1 + \beta_2)$, Carroll determines the oblimin criterion:

$$B^* = \sum_{1 < q = 1}^{p} \left\{ m \sum_{j=1}^{m} \left(\frac{\alpha_{jl}^2}{h_j^2}\right)\left(\frac{\alpha_{jq}^2}{h_j^2}\right) - \gamma \left[\sum_{j=1}^{m} \left(\frac{\alpha_{jl}^2}{h_j^2}\right)\right]\left[\sum_{j=1}^{m} \left(\frac{\alpha_{jq}^2}{h_j^2}\right)\right] \right\}, \quad (17\text{--}11)$$

where α_{jl} is the oblique reference structure loading, and l and q are the lth and qth factors.

The oblimin class of solutions is entirely dependent on the value of γ. If $\gamma = .5$, the biquartimin solution results. Covarimin can be obtained from $\gamma = 1.0$, and quartimin from $\gamma = 0.0$. Different in-between values of γ allow for any weighted combination of covarimin and quartimin.

> *Example 17–8.* The biquartimin, covarimin, and quartimin solutions for the 16 foreign conflict variables are shown in Table 17–9.

17.3.5 BINORMAMIN

In the oblimin function [Eq. (17–11)], the parameter γ can be set to some value between 0.00 and 1.00 to compensate for the opposite biases of covarimin and biquartimin. The biquartimin solution results from arbitrarily setting $\gamma = .5$. Kaiser and Dickman (1959) offer a more determinant solution to the appropriate balancing value of γ. This solution, called *binormamin*, is the minimization of the function

$$B^{**} = \sum_{1 < q = 1}^{p} \left\{ \frac{\sum_{j=1}^{m} (\alpha_{jl}^2/h_j^2)(\alpha_{jq}^2/h_j^2)}{\left[\sum_{j=1}^{m} (\alpha_{jl}^2/h_j^2)\right]\left[\sum_{j=1}^{m} (\alpha_{jq}^2/h_j^2)\right]} \right\}, \quad (17\text{--}12)$$

where $\alpha_{jl} = $ oblique reference structure loadings, and l and q are the lth and qth factors.

Binormamin appears to be best for data with very clear or very complex simple structure. Often, however, the data are somewhere in between. Then, according to Kaiser and Dickman (1959), the biquartimin solution is better.[10]

17.3.6 MAXPLANE

The oblique techniques previously considered rotate to simple structure through a variance or covariance function of the factor loadings. Cattell and Muerle (1960) have proposed a different approach based on

---

10. Warburton (1963), concluding a discussion of analytic rotation, says that "on the whole" binormamin is best for oblique rotation. For applications of binormamin, see Kaiser and Dickman (1959) and Harman (1967, p. 332).

Table 17–9. Oblique Rotation of Sixteen Foreign Conflict Variables—Primary Pattern Loadings[a]

Variables	Covarimin				Biquartimin				Quartimin			
	S_1	S_2	S_3	S_4	S_1	S_2	S_3	S_4	S_1	S_2	S_3	S_4
1. Violence	.22	(.98)	−.01	−.01	.04	(.98)	−.02	−.01	−.17	(1.08)	−.01	.00
2. Planned violence	.21	(.98)	−.01	.00	.03	(.98)	−.02	.00	−.19	(1.09)	−.01	.02
3. Incidence of violence	.31	.35	−.08	(−.59)	.29	.27	−.10	(−.60)	.49	.18	−.12	(−.62)
4. Military acts	.22	(.97)	−.02	.02	.04	(.97)	−.03	.02	−.17	(1.08)	−.02	.04
5. Days of violence	.17	(.92)	.00	.05	.00	(.92)	−.02	.05	−.23	(1.04)	.00	.07
6. Negative acts	(.79)	.13	.18	.31	(.77)	.00	.04	.27	(.74)	−.10	.03	.29
7. Diplomatic rebuffs	.38	.28	−.08	(.72)	.32	.25	−.16	(.71)	.14	.28	−.18	(.74)
8. Negative communications	(.97)	.29	.18	−.01	(.94)	.12	.01	−.07	(1.02)	−.04	.00	−.05
9. Written communications	(.93)	.05	.05	.00	(.96)	−.13	−.11	−.06	(1.15)	−.33	−.14	−.05
10. Oral communications	(.93)	.33	.24	.00	(.88)	.17	.09	−.05	(.90)	.03	.09	−.04
11. Written and oral communications	.40	(.66)	.19	−.08	.27	(.61)	.14	−.09	.12	(.64)	.16	−.09
12. Unclassified communications	.46	.07	.46	.13	.42	.00	.37	.11	.27	−.03	.41	.12
13. Accusations	(.96)	.24	.11	−.04	(.95)	.06	−.05	−.09	(1.08)	−.12	−.06	−.08
14. Protests	(.66)	.25	.24	.05	(.62)	.14	.13	.01	(.58)	.07	.14	.02
15. Warnings	(.73)	.48	.25	.00	(.64)	.37	.13	−.03	(.57)	.31	.14	−.02
16. Antiforeign acts	.14	−.01	(.93)	−.08	.07	−.01	(.91)	−.08	−.30	.05	(1.01)	−.08
Sums of squares	6.02	4.94	1.39	1.00	5.32	4.45	1.09	.99	6.14	5.37	1.34	1.07

Factor Correlations

	(1)	(2)	(3)	(4)	(1)	(2)	(3)	(4)	(1)	(2)	(3)	(4)
1.	1.00				1.00				1.00			
2.	−.07	1.00			.30	1.00			.59	1.00		
3.	−.17	.04	1.00		.09	.02	1.00		.43	.17	1.00	
4.	−.05	.03	.04	1.00	.04	−.01	.07	1.00	.26	.05	.18	1.00

[a] These results are from Tables 17–3, 7, and 8.

hyperplanes. Rotating a factor to increase the number of high and near-zero loadings is almost equivalent to measuring the hyperplane count of a factor.

The hyperplane of a factor is the "plane" seen edgewise, that is, the plane formed by that factor with the $p - 1$ other factors.

> *Example 17–9.* Consider two factors, S_1 and S_2, defining the two-dimensional surface of a sheet of paper. Imagine a plot of points on this plane. Look edgewise along factor S_1 (along the edge of the paper). All the points will then appear to hover around the S_2 axis. These points are then in the *hyperplane* of S_1.

Usually a hyperplane is defined with regard to a plot of two factors at a time. Variable-points that lie along one or the other axis or at the origin are then considered members of one or the other hyperplane

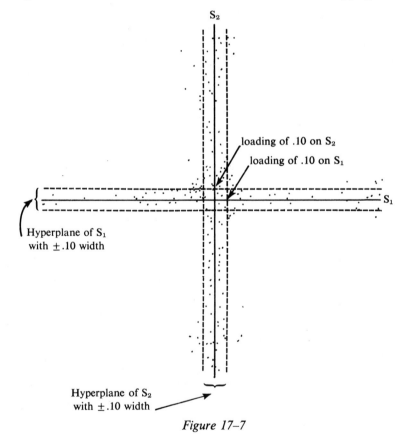

Figure 17–7

and are counted. Because of a certain amount of "noise" in empirical data, exact zero loadings are unlikely. Consequently, variable-points will seldom lie exactly on a plane and thus will not lie exactly along the axis—on the hyperplane—of a factor. Therefore, a deviation from the axis is usually allowed of, say, $\pm.10$, and all points within this range are considered as members of the hyperplane. Figure 17–7 may help clarify this.

Cattell and Muerle's program, called *maxplane*, considers one pair of factors at a time. It rotates one factor with regard to the other through successive angles and counts the number of variables in the hyperplane at a width of $\pm.10$. The best position for each factor that maximizes its hyperplane count is determined. A final determination of positions is at a hyperplane width of plus or minus two standard deviations of a zero coefficient for the data. By successively rotating pairs of factors through a number of cycles, the program iterates to an oblique factor matrix that has the maximum number of near-zero coefficients. Eber (1966b) has revised maxplane to overcome some of the difficulties of Cattell's version.

The maxplane technique appears more efficient on large samples than do other techniques and yields a solution closest to the graphical intuitive results (Warburton, 1963).[11]

17.3.7 PROMAX

Hendrickson and White (1964) have proposed a computationally fast rotation technique. This speed is achieved by first rotating to an orthogonal varimax solution (Section 16.4.2.2) and then relaxing the orthogonality of the factors to better fit simple structure.

From the orthogonally rotated matrix an ideal factor matrix is constructed in which high loadings of varimax are made higher and low loadings smaller. This is done by normalizing the orthogonal matrix by rows and columns and taking the kth power of each loading. The final step is to find the least squares fit to the ideal matrix, using Hurley and Cattell's "Procrustes technique" [Eq. (16–5)]. This best fit is then the oblique solution.

A problem exists in selecting the best kth power to employ. Hendrickson and White experimented with data of known factor structure. For the 24 psychological variables exemplified in Harman (1960,

11. Eber (1966b) compares maxplane results with the graphical and biquartimin rotations of the 24 psychological variables exemplified in Harman (1960, 1967). Biquartimin and maxplane appear very close, with a slightly higher hyperplane count for maxplane.

1967), $k = 4$ was found to give better results than Kaiser and Dickman's (1959) binormamin technique (Section 17.3.5) and "was indeed somewhat cleaner than the subjective visual solution which we regarded as a criterion" (Hendrickson and White, 1964, p. 69). After applying promax to other textbook examples, such as Thurstone's box study, Hendrickson and White conclude that "for the majority of cases, the optimal value for k is 4; however, for the occasional factor analysis where the data is particularly 'cleanly' structured, a lower power seems to provide the best solution" (1964, p. 70).

> *Example 17–10.* Table 17–10 gives the promax solution
> of $k = 2$ and $k = 4$ for the 16 foreign conflict variables.

17.3.8 TARGET ROTATION

Rotating to a hypothesized factor matrix has been discussed in Section 16.2.5. Moreover, the promax technique discussed in the last section uses target rotation, although the target matrix is an idealized simple structure derivation of a varimax solution. In target rotation, the factors may become correlated in fitting the hypothesized matrix. Equation (16–4) will result in oblique factors if such give a best fit to the hypothetical matrix. Two hypotheses are therefore tested simultaneously. One hypothesis concerns the configuration of pattern loadings and the other concerns the correlation between the factors.

Allowing oblique factors in target rotation does not mean that any pattern hypotheses can now be proved. The origin of the space and the configuration of variables in the space are defined by the initial solution and are *invariant of rotation*. Variables cannot be given high *pattern* loadings on the same factor and near-zero loadings elsewhere regardless of how a factor-axis is rotated to fit them. A factor will have uniquely high pattern loadings for variables hypothesized to go together only if the variables are interrelated in the data.

17.3.9 SUMMARY TABLE

A number of oblique techniques have been briefly discussed above. Table 17–11 lists the salient characteristics of each.

Table 17-10. Promax Oblique Factors of Sixteen Foreign Conflict Variables—Primary Pattern Factors

Variables	k = 2				k = 4			
	S_1	S_2	S_3	S_4	S_1	S_2	S_3	S_4
1. Violence	.02	(−.98)	−.02	−.01	−.06	(−1.02)	−.02	−.01
2. Planned violence	.01	(−.99)	−.02	.00	−.07	(−1.02)	−.02	.01
3. Incidence of violence	.27	−.29	−.13	(−.60)	.31	−.25	−.13	(−.60)
4. Military acts	.02	(−.97)	−.03	.02	−.05	(−1.01)	−.03	.02
5. Days of violence	−.01	(−.93)	−.01	.05	−.09	(−.97)	−.01	.06
6. Negative acts	(.78)	.02	.06	.29	(.80)	.08	.02	.28
7. Diplomatic rebuffs	.33	−.21	−.12	(.71)	.29	−.23	−.16	(.71)
8. Negative communications	(.94)	−.11	.01	−.04	(.98)	−.01	−.01	−.05
9. Written communications	(.96)	.14	−.11	−.04	(1.04)	.25	−.14	−.05
10. Oral communications	(.88)	−.16	.09	−.02	(.90)	−.07	.07	−.04
11. Written and oral communications	.26	(−.62)	.14	−.08	.21	(−.61)	.14	−.09
12. Unclassified communications	.43	.00	.38	.14	.41	.04	.37	.12
13. Accusations	(.95)	−.05	−.05	−.07	(1.00)	.05	−.07	−.08
14. Protests	(.62)	−.14	.14	.03	(.62)	−.08	.12	.02
15. Warnings	(.64)	−.37	.13	−.01	(.63)	−.31	.11	−.02
16. Antiforeign acts	.09	−.01	(.91)	−.04	−.01	.01	(.92)	−.06
Sums of squares	5.33	4.48	1.09	.99	5.68	4.71	1.10	.99

Factor Correlations

	(1)	(2)	(3)	(4)	(1)	(2)	(3)	(4)
1.	1.00				1.00			
2.	−.33	1.00			−.48	1.00		
3.	.05	.02	1.00		.19	−.06	1.00	
4.	.01	−.03	−.03	1.00	.06	.00	.04	1.00

Table 17–11. Summary of Oblique Rotation Techniques[a]

Technique	Procedure	Fit to Intuitive Graphical Solution	Speed	Comments
Oblimax	Maximizes kurtosis of doubled distributions of loadings on a factor.	Very close for data with clean simple structure.	Moderate	Complex data may not yield a solution because of negative roots.
Oblimin	A weighted combination of quartimin and covarimin determined by a parameter γ.			
Quartimin	$\gamma = 0.0$; minimizes sum of inner products of squared factor pattern loadings.	Close	Slow	Biased toward high interfactor correlations; may give better hyperplane count than covarimin or biquartimin.
Covarimin	$\gamma = 1.0$; minimizes covariances of squared factor pattern loadings.	Close	Slow	Biased toward low interfactor correlations; solution is close to varimax results.
Biquartimin	$\gamma = .5$; equal combination of quartimin and covarimin.	Very close	Slow	Compensates for the opposite biases of quartimin and covarimin; best for moderately complex data.
Binormamin	Minimizes the ratio of covariances of squared factor pattern loadings to their inner products.	Very close	Slow	Appears better than biquartimin for very simple or complex data.
Maxplane	Maximizes the hyperplane count of variables.	Best	Fast	Procedures are closest to those of visual graphical rotation.
Promax	Target rotation to ideal matrix determined by kth power of doubly normalized varimax loadings.	Very close	Fast	Value of k depends on data complexity; results appear to differ little from binormamin.
Target	Best least squares fit with hypothesized matrix.	Very close	Fast	

[a] Considerable mathematical and empirical comparison of these techniques is needed before definitive evaluations are possible. Comments made here are aimed at helping the reader to select rotations with some idea as to the alternatives.

18. Higher-Order Factors

Very rarely have second- or third-order factors been computed outside the field of psychology. A higher order presents little new in methodology, however. The procedure involves factoring the correlations of the oblique factors and rotating the results, as was done for the original variable correlation matrix. The higher-order design will be discussed in more detail in Section 18.2, below, after we have considered the characteristics of the higher-order space in Section 18.1.

As part of the research design, computing higher-order factors is not a discrete step in the application of a factor analysis. Rather, it involves looping back through previous steps and entails nearly the whole factor analysis research design. This is brought out in Fig. 18–1.

18.1 Higher-Order Factors

Second-order factors are defined by a factor analysis of the correlations between the oblique factors of the data.[1] The factors derived from the

1. Excellent (and perhaps the best) discussions of the nature and interpretation of second-order factors will be found in Thurstone (1947, Chapter 18) and in

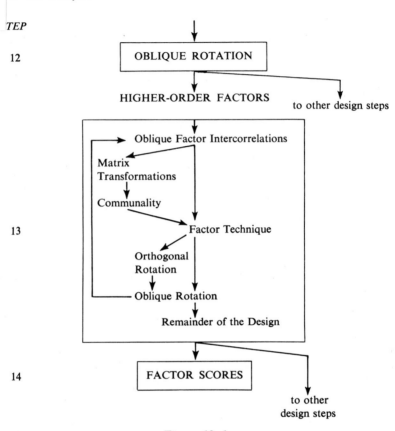

Figure 18–1

data are termed *first-order* factors. The relationship between the data and factor orders might be laid out as a hierarchy of factors (or orders), as shown in Fig. 18–2.[2] The lines connecting the orders index moderate or high loadings. Thus, the lines connecting the variables and first-order factors show what variables have at least moderate loadings on the first-order factors; lines connecting the first- and second-order factors indicate what first-order factors have at least moderate loadings on the second-order factors.

Cattell (1965b), who discusses the scientific and philosophical implications of higher-order factors. Cattell (1957, Appendix 12) summarizes the findings on second-order personality factors.

2. Because it produces such a hierarchy of factors, higher-order factor analysis has been suggested as a good approach to simplifying diversity. See, for example, Warburton (1963) and Schmid and Leiman (1957).

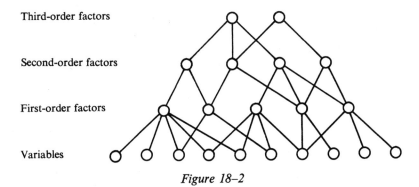

Third-order factors

Second-order factors

First-order factors

Variables

Figure 18–2

Example 18–1. A second-order component factor analysis of the oblique primary factors of 236 cross-national variables (Example 9–7) is shown in Table 18–1. Table 18–2 presents the correlations between the first-order and the second-order primary factors.

Example 18–2. The correlations between the primary factors of the 16 foreign conflict variables of Example 17–1 are given in Table 17–5. The second-order orthogonal factors are shown in Table 18–3.

In some ways, the second-order factors appear more substantively interesting than do those of the first order. Actually, many social science theories seem to involve a mental—an intuitive—higher-order factor analysis. The first-order factors define the basic dimensions, concepts, or categories within a substantive domain. They delineate functional interrelationships among the varied phenomena. Social theories, however, are interested in such dimensions mainly as empirical concepts to interrelate in a global description of a domain. A social theory, for example, may relate economic development to the characteristics of a political system or domestic conflict. In factor analysis terms, *there is a second-order social factor tying together these three factor-dimensions.* The social theory of Karl Marx that made the economic system basic to social institutions is a second-order factor theory. An economic second-order factor is presumed to encompass first-order social and political dimensions. A general social theory, such as that of Marx, might be better tested in the second- (or third-) order domain.

Conceptually, the higher-order factor analysis and *simple structure rotation* delineates the comprehensive clustering of the oblique factors,

Table 18–1. Second-Order Factors of 236 Cross-National Variables[a]

First-Order Factors[b]	Unrotated[c]					h^2	Primary Oblique Pattern Matrix[d]				
	S_1	S_2	S_3	S_4	S_5		S_1	S_2	S_3	S_4	S_5
1. Economic development	(−.57)	−.10	.09	.18	.22	.42	.07	−.17	−.23	(.50)	.13
2. Size (power bases)	(.57)	.18	.03	−.24	−.27	.49	−.06	.19	.15	(−.61)	−.03
3. Political orientation	.32	.28	−.04	.42	−.06	.36	.22	(.53)	.12	.01	−.08
4. Foreign conflict	−.03	−.13	−.21	(.52)	(.56)	.65	.06	.14	.44	(.75)	−.01
5. Domestic conflict	(−.58)	−.11	.29	.01	−.26	.50	−.05	−.11	(−.65)	.09	.05
6. Catholic culture	(.59)	.09	.08	.15	.32	.48	−.10	.33	(.54)	.00	.21
7. Density	.26	.05	(.52)	.41	−.19	.55	−.20	(.66)	−.23	−.06	.17
8. Oriental culture	.43	−.33	−.13	−.32	.37	.55	−.39	−.27	(.62)	−.03	.05
9. High foreign student ratio[e]	.27	.45	.18	−.33	.01	.42	.19	.01	.10	(−.47)	.37
10. Seaport dependency	−.49	−.08	−.09	−.44	.18	.47	.05	(−.65)	−.09	.08	.13
11. Diversity	−.27	.13	(.67)	.03	.12	.56	−.08	.11	−.36	.08	(.60)
12. Equality	.02	.44	.34	−.27	.47	.60	.20	−.13	.22	−.05	(.73)
13. Traders	−.31	(.62)	−.26	.00	.10	.56	(.73)	−.13	−.03	.05	.11
14. Sufficiency	.23	(−.63)	.10	−.12	−.06	.47	(−.66)	−.07	.09	−.03	−.17
15. Multiple party system[e]	−.12	.32	(−.50)	.10	−.23	.43	(.52)	−.01	−.05	−.05	−.39
Per cent of total variance	14.9	10.5	9.2	8.1	7.4	50.2					
Sums of squares							1.59	1.47	1.65	1.45	1.33

a Loadings and coefficients ≥ |.50| shown in parentheses.
b From Rummel (1969).
c Principal axes technique and component factor analysis model. Correlation matrix of first-order factors is given in Table 18-2. Factoring stopped when eigenvalues fell below 1.00.
d Biquartimin solution at 20 cycles and 876 iterations for a final precision level of 1.36 × 10⁻⁴.
e These factors were left unnamed in Rummel (1969); they are here labeled by their highest loading variable.

Table 18–2. First- and Second-Order Factor Correlations[a]

First-Order Factor Correlations

Factors	(1)	(2)	(3)	(4)	(5)	(6)	(7)	(8)	(9)	(10)	(11)	(12)	(13)	(14)	(15)
1.	1.00														
2.	−.33	1.00													
3.	−.12	.11	1.00												
4.	.05	−.12	.05	1.00											
5.	.23	−.23	−.12	−.07	1.00										
6.	−.17	.17	.12	.06	−.25	1.00									
7.	−.07	.10	.09	−.02	−.03	.15	1.00								
8.	−.12	.11	−.01	−.01	−.20	.23	−.06	1.00							
9.	−.12	.15	.08	−.14	−.09	.13	.02	.03	1.00						
10.	.13	−.15	−.18	−.00	.17	.24	−.19	−.03	−.08	1.00					
11.	.13	−.09	−.06	−.05	.20	−.04	.15	−.13	.01	.08	1.00				
12.	.01	.05	.02	−.04	−.06	.06	.03	−.01	.15	.05	.17	1.00			
13.	.08	−.08	.01	.02	.03	−.09	−.10	−.18	.08	.10	.01	.13	1.00		
14.	−.05	.03	−.07	−.01	−.06	.02	.06	.18	−.08	−.03	−.06	−.11	−.28	1.00	
15.	.02	−.03	.01	−.04	−.05	−.03	−.06	−.08	−.04	.02	−.10	−.05	.21	−.12	1.00

Second-Order Factor Correlations

	(1)	(2)	(3)	(4)	(5)
1.	1.00				
2.	−.01	1.00			
3.	.04	.12	1.00		
4.	−.02	−.04	−.20	1.00	
5.	−.01	.05	−.08	.01	1.00

[a] Correlations are for the oblique primaries.

Table 18–3. Second-Order Factors of Sixteen Foreign Conflict Variables[a]

First-Order Factors[b]	Unrotated[c]			Orthogonally Rotated[d]	
	F_1	F_2	h^2	F_1	F_2
1. Negative communication·	(.80)	−.08	.65	(.79)	.14
2. Military violence	(.76)	−.31	.67	(.81)	−.08
3. Antiforeign behavior	.30	(.64)	.50	.11	(.70)
4. Negative sanctions	.14	(.75)	.57	−.07	(.75)
Per cent of total variance	33.2	26.6	59.8	32.3	27.5

a Loadings ≥ |.50| shown in parentheses.
b From Table 17–3.
c Principal axes technique and component factor analysis model. The factor correlation matrix is given in Table 17–1. Factoring stopped when the eigenvalues fell below 1.00.
d Varimax rotation.

which themselves represent clusters of variables,[3] as shown in Fig. 18–3. This characteristic of second-order analysis makes it especially useful in Q-factor analysis (Definition 8–2). Beginning with the first-order factors, the analysis can be carried to the third and fourth orders to define increasingly comprehensive groups of cases.

> *Example 18–3.* A Q-factor analysis of roll call votes in the UN can reveal various voting blocs. A higher-order analysis will show the larger grouping of these blocs, which may be into rich and poor or Western and Eastern nation bloc clusters.

18.2 A Typology of Higher Orders

Raymond Cattell (1965b) has presented a clear discussion of the nature and interpretation of higher-order factors, and I will draw on him for much of the content of this section. Figure 18–2 above has shown a hierarchy of factor orders. Four such hierarchies may be identified:

One is the *monarchical hierarchy* in which the first-order factors are nonoverlapping group factors, and the second order consists of one overarching factor tying the group factors together. Figure 18–4 displays this type.

A second type is the *nonoverlapping hierarchy*. This is a realization of Spearman's two-factor theory (Section 14.2.1) at the second order

3. Cattell (1965b) develops equations relating data and higher-order results. His formulation also enables the determination of the loadings of the original variables on the higher-order factors. See also Schmid and Leiman (1957).

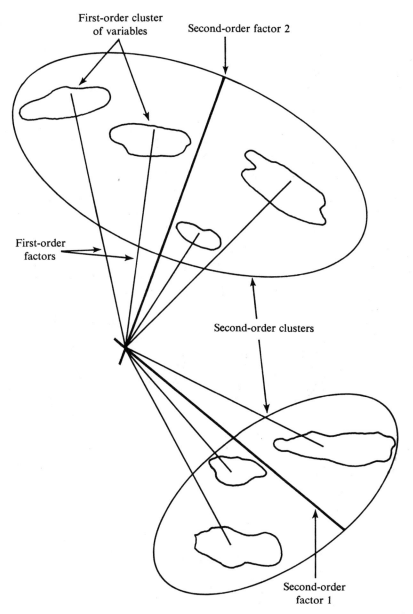

Figure 18–3

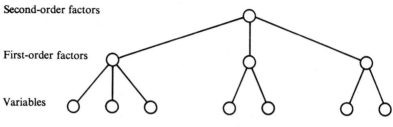

Second-order factors

First-order factors

Variables

Figure 18–4

and is shown in Fig. 18–5. The first order may be composed of over-lapping group factors (usually a result of the simple structure rotation of principal axes or centroids), while the second order consists of one general factor (like Spearman's intelligence factor) and specifics.

The third type of hierarchy is that already presented in Fig. 18–2. This is called a *tapering hierarchy*.

The fourth type is a *pyramid hierarchy* and has a visual representation similar to that of the tapering hierarchy. The difference between these two types lies in the reality of their representation. The tapering hierarchy may be an empirical artifact not existing in reality, due to the factoring procedure which may have necessarily reduced the number of factors at each level.

> *Example 18–4.* Consider a common factor analysis of 70 variables. Since small residual factors will be ignored, the number of factors retained for interpretation may be considerably less than 70, say about 20. At the second order, residual factors may again be ignored, and only about 5 to 10 factors may be extracted. The retention of only meaningful or "significant" factors, therefore, can cause successively large reductions in factor number as one moves up the factor orders.

Second-order factors

First-order factors

Variables

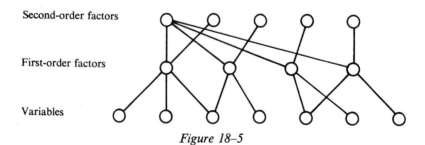

Figure 18–5

A tapering hierarchy may only be a portion of a nonhierarchical structure of factors operating in a domain. The particular portion defined is a function of the number and catholicity of the variables analyzed. The unbroken lines in Fig. 18–6 show the variables of analysis and the factor orders that may be delineated. The broken lines show other factors in the domain whose existence is untapped by virtue of the variables selected. As illustrated in the figure, the number of first-order factors in a domain may be more than the number of variables analyzed. Since the number of variables analyzed is an upper limit on the number of factors that can be delineated, it is unwise to assume that the factors of a particular study encompass all the factors existing in a domain. This caveat is embodied in the idea of a tapering hierarchy as a representation of reality specific to the method of analysis used.

The pyramidal hierarchy, however, *is* a representation of reality. By virtue of theory, multimethod validation, and extensive replication across different samples of data,[4] the investigator may have reason to believe that the hierarchical factor order of Fig. 18–2 does reflect reality. That is, factors other than those defined do not exist in the domain. The reality of a pyramidal versus a tapering hierarchy may be suggested by the addition of more variables to a study. As additional and diverse variables are added without altering the number and interpretation of the higher-order factors, the existence of a pyramidal hierarchy is rendered increasingly likely.

The tapering hierarchy probably exists in most social science data,

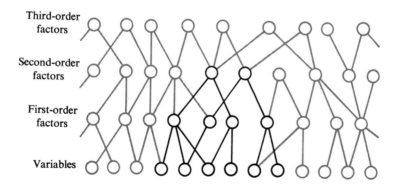

Figure 18–6

4. Cattell (1965b and 1957, Appendix 12) discusses the convergence of research on second- and third-order personality factors. It is of particular interest to the layman that replications at the third-order have agreed on factors resembling the *id*, *ego*, and *superego*.

although for particular domains other hierarchies may be more suitable. Some social theories, it seems, assume some definite hierarchy. Marxists, for example, imply a monarchical hierarchy with one economic-system second-order factor in operation. Voting behaviorists assume a non-overlapping hierarchy of one social-background second-order factor and second-order specifics associated with each major voting factor. The technique of target rotation (Section 16.4.2.3) at the higher order makes it possible to test such theories explicitly.[5]

5. Cattell (1965b, p. 238, Fig. 6) presents a classification of patterns of hierarchical relations and causation that may be useful for explicating a theory or describing and conceptualizing higher-order results.

19. Factor Scores

Research procedures thus far have been concerned with defining the factor loading matrix. When a satisfactory set of loadings has been determined, whether unrotated or rotated to orthogonal or oblique solutions, then the factor scores can be found.

The first section of this chapter will consider the geometry of factor scores, and the following section will classify four approaches to finding such factor scores when the loadings are known. The final section will discuss the determinacy of factor scores. The alternatives involved in the factor score research design step are shown in Fig. 19–1.

19.1 Geometry of Factor Scores

A factor score matrix is given in Table 6–8. Each row of the factor score matrix gives the scores of a case on the p factors delineated by the factor matrix $F_{m \times p}$.[1] These rows are vectors describing the location of

---

1. We have defined five different factor loading matrices: $F_{m \times p}$ for the unrotated and rotated orthogonal factors, and two different pattern and structure matrices for primary and reference axes. Unless otherwise indicated, $F_{m \times p}$ will henceforth be used to refer to any of these five loading matrices.

STEP

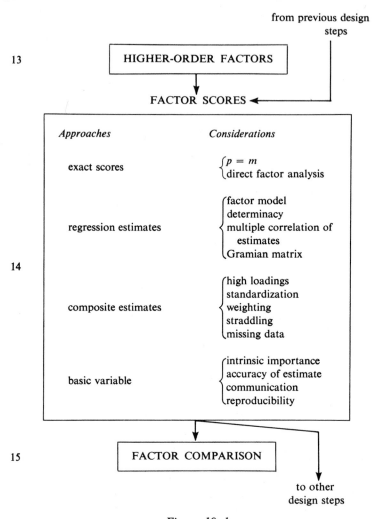

from previous design
steps

13   HIGHER-ORDER FACTORS

FACTOR SCORES

Approaches	*Considerations*
exact scores	$\begin{cases} p = m \\ \text{direct factor analysis} \end{cases}$
regression estimates	$\begin{cases} \text{factor model} \\ \quad \text{determinacy} \\ \text{multiple correlation of} \\ \quad \text{estimates} \\ \text{Gramian matrix} \end{cases}$
composite estimates	$\begin{cases} \text{high loadings} \\ \text{standardization} \\ \text{weighting} \\ \text{straddling} \\ \text{missing data} \end{cases}$
basic variable	$\begin{cases} \text{intrinsic importance} \\ \text{accuracy of estimate} \\ \text{communication} \\ \text{reproducibility} \end{cases}$

14

15   FACTOR COMPARISON

to other
design steps

Figure 19–1

each case in the space of the factors, as shown in Figs. 6–2 and 6–3. The scores give the projections of a case on the factors.

> *Example 19–1.*   Figure 6–4 of Chapter 6 shows the vector configuration of selected nations on the three dimensions of 10 political characteristics. Table 6–9 displays the factor scores.

The factor model describes the linear relationship between a set of variables and a set of orthogonal or oblique factors, as shown in Eq. (5–19) for the component analysis model and in Eq. (5–2) for the common factor analysis model. The component analysis model is reproduced here for convenience:

$$X_j = \alpha_{j1}S_2 + \alpha_{j2}S_2 + \cdots + \alpha_{jl}S_l + \cdots + \alpha_{jp}S_p. \qquad (19\text{–}1)$$

The factor matrix $F_{m \times p}$ contains the loadings α_{jl}, which measure the statistical dependence of the data X_j on the factors S_l. *The elements of the factors* S_l *are the factor scores.*[2]

> *Example 19–2.* Let there be three cases, *a*, *b*, and *c*, with data x_{aj}, x_{bj}, and x_{cj} on variable X_j. Let the factor loadings of X_j on two factors, S_1 and S_2, be α_{j1} and α_{j2}. Also let the factor scores for the three cases on S_1 be s_{a1}, s_{b1}, and s_{c1}, and on S_2 let them be s_{a2}, s_{b2}, and s_{c2}. Then the factor model for component analysis is

$$
\begin{array}{cccc}
X_j & S_1 & S_2 \\
\begin{bmatrix} x_{aj} \\ x_{bj} \\ x_{cj} \end{bmatrix} = \alpha_{j1} \begin{bmatrix} s_{a1} \\ s_{b1} \\ s_{c1} \end{bmatrix} + \alpha_{j2} \begin{bmatrix} s_{a2} \\ s_{b2} \\ s_{c2} \end{bmatrix}
\end{array}
$$

The identification of the loadings showing which factors are related to what variables may be the goal of the factor analysis. For this the factor loading matrix is sufficient. It should be clear, however, that when the correlation between factors, the dimensions of the factor space, or the relationship between variables and factors are considered, it is the vectors of factor scores, S_l, that are involved. The factor loadings measure only the dependence of variables on factor scores.

19.2 Approaches to Factor Scores

A number of techniques have been developed to compute or estimate factor scores.[3] Many of them, such as grouping procedures to estimate factor scores (Harman, 1967, Section 16.6), are aimed at reducing the labor involved in the computations. With the greater availability of

2. The reader may wish to review the discussion in Section 6.5.

3. A good discussion of various technical approaches to factor scores is given by Harman (1967, Chapter 16). He is also a good source for the literature involved. For an empirical comparison of different approaches to factor scores, see Horn (1965a).

computers, however, these labor-saving techniques have grown increasingly unnecessary. Moreover, where computers are not available, the composite estimates of Section 19.2.3 may be quite satisfactory.

Three approaches to factor scores will be focused on here. The first, *exact scores*, gives the scores as linear combinations of the variables and is useful for the component analysis model. The second approach is *regression estimates* and is most applicable in common factor analysis. The *composite estimates* approach involves selecting a small group of variables to represent the factor and summing them together to form the estimated scores. A final approach to be considered is selecting a *basic variable* to represent a factor.

19.2.1 EXACT FACTOR SCORES

If component analysis is applied to a data matrix with rank (Definition 4–21) equal to the number of variables, then the factor scores can be obtained directly from the component model. From Section 5.1, the model is

$$A_{n \times m} = S_{n \times p} F'_{p \times m}, \qquad (19\text{--}2)$$

where $A_{n \times m}$ = data matrix; $F_{m \times p}$ = any orthogonal, oblique primary structure, or reference pattern loading matrix; and $S_{n \times p}$ = factor score matrix. If all factors are extracted, then $p = m$ since the rank of the data matrix is m. This means that $F'_{p \times m}$ is square and has an inverse. Therefore, by multiplying both sides of Eq. (19–2) by $(F'_{p \times m})^{-1}$, we get

$$A_{n \times m}(F'_{p \times m})^{-1} = S_{n \times p}, \qquad (19\text{--}3)$$

where $m = p$. This equation gives an exact and unique solution to the desired factor score matrix. However, for the solution to be possible, the number of factors must equal the number of variables.

If the data matrix is of rank less than m (as when $n < m$, for example) or, as is most often the case, when you decide to extract only factors that are considered nontrivial in some sense (say those over an eigenvalue of one), then $p < m$. For this situation also, an exact solution exists. Starting with the component model of Eq. (19–2),

$$
\begin{aligned}
A_{n \times m} &= S_{n \times p} F'_{p \times m}, \\
A_{n \times m} F_{m \times p} &= S_{n \times p} F'_{p \times m} F_{m \times p}, \\
A_{n \times m} F_{m \times p}(F'_{p \times m} F_{m \times p}) &= S_{n \times p},
\end{aligned}
\qquad (19\text{--}4)
$$

where $p < m$.

If $F_{m \times p}$ is the unrotated matrix, then

$$F_{p \times m} F_{m \times p} = \lambda_{p \times p},$$

the matrix of eigenvalues.

Depending on whether the number of factors is less than or equal to the number of variables in component factor analysis, we can employ Eq. (19–3) or (19–4). Variants of these formulas can be derived, enabling us to compute scores from the transformation or correlation matrices—for which the reader is referred to Kaiser (1962).

19.2.2 REGRESSION ESTIMATES

While an exact solution to the factor scores for component analysis can be computed, this is not generally possible for common factor analysis. This is because the matrix of uniqueness, $U_{m \times m}$, is unknown and there are two sets of factor scores, $S_{n \times p}$ and $S^*_{n \times m}$, to solve for in the common factor model:

$$A_{n \times m} = S_{n \times p}F'_{p \times m} + S^*_{n \times m}U_{m \times m}.$$

For this model, regression methods (Definition 3–11) can be employed to compute an $S_{n \times p}$ that is a least squares fit to the data. The resulting estimates, $\hat{S}_{n \times p}$, will vary from the true common factor scores, $S_{n \times p}$, depending on the information in $F_{m \times p}$ and the statistical dependence of $\hat{S}_{n \times p}$ on $Z_{n \times m}$. These issues will be discussed in more detail after the regression equations are developed.

From Eqs. (4–13) and (4–14), the regression equation for estimating a matrix of common factor scores from the data is

$$\hat{S}_{n \times p} = A_{n \times m}B_{m \times p}, \tag{19–5}$$

where $\hat{S}_{n \times p}$ = regression estimates of n common factor scores on each of p common factors, and $B_{m \times p}$ = p columns of m regression coefficients, where the lth column gives the m regression coefficients for estimating the n common factor scores on the lth common factor. Since it is a correlation matrix of the m variables that is most often factored, we can restrict our discussion to the standardized data matrix $Z_{n \times m}$, where $R_{m \times m} = (1/n)(Z'_{m \times n}Z_{n \times m})$ from Eq. (4–12). Then Eq. (19–5) becomes

$$\hat{S}_{n \times p} = Z_{n \times m}\beta_{m \times p}, \tag{19–6}$$

where $\beta_{m \times p}$ = p columns of m standardized regression coefficients.

Multiply both sides of Eq. (19–6) by the transpose of $Z_{n \times m}$ and divide through by n:

$$\frac{1}{n}Z'_{m \times n}\hat{S}_{n \times p} = \frac{1}{n}Z'_{m \times n}Z_{n \times m}\beta_{m \times p}. \tag{19–7}$$

By Eq. (4–12), we may substitute on the right the correlation matrix,

$$\frac{1}{n}Z'_{m \times n}\hat{S}_{n \times p} = R_{m \times m}\beta_{m \times p}. \tag{19–8}$$

Now, the product on the left of the above equation is an $m \times p$ correlation matrix of variables with common factors. But these correlations are also given by $F_{m \times p}$, the orthogonal factor matrix, or oblique primary *structure*, or reference *pattern* matrix. Therefore, we can substitute $F_{m \times p}$ on the left:

$$F_{m \times p} = R_{m \times m}\beta_{m \times p}, \tag{19–9}$$

where $F_{m \times p}$ is an orthogonal, primary structure, or reference pattern matrix. If $R_{m \times m}$ is singular, as with most empirical data,

$$R_{m \times m}^{-1}F_{m \times p} = \beta_{m \times p}. \tag{19–10}$$

Replacing $\beta_{m \times p}$ in Eq. (19–6) by Eq. (19–10),

$$\hat{S}_{n \times p} = Z_{n \times m}R_{m \times m}^{-1}F_{m \times p}. \tag{19–11}$$

The above equation gives the regression estimates of the common factor scores in terms of the standardized data matrix, correlation matrix, and factor loadings.

The development of Eq. (19–11) assumed that we were dealing with orthogonal factor loadings or with those oblique loadings that are equivalent to correlation coefficients (see Table 6–6). If we wish to employ primary pattern loadings, $P_{m \times p}$, or reference structure loadings, $V_{m \times p}$, then the factor correlation matrix is also involved:

$$\hat{S}_{n \times p} = Z_{n \times m}R_{m \times m}^{-1}P_{m \times p}\Phi_{p \times p}, \tag{19–12}$$

and

$$\hat{S}_{n \times p} = Z_{n \times m}R_{m \times m}^{-1}V_{m \times p}\Psi_{p \times p}, \tag{19–13}$$

where $\Phi_{p \times p}$ and $\Psi_{p \times p}$ are the respective factor correlation matrices.

The common factor score regression estimates[4] make use of all the information contained in the standardized data and the factor loadings. They are therefore better estimates of the true common factor scores than the composite and basic variable estimates to be discussed below. Nevertheless, in common factor analysis (with non-unity communality approximations) *the regression estimates may depart considerably from the true scores*. A measure of the deviation of the estimates, $\hat{S}_{n \times p}$, from the true scores, $S_{n \times p}$, is the coefficient of correlation between each factor pair $\hat{S}_l$ and S_l.

Harman (1967, p. 352) shows that the correlation between estimated and true scores is equal to the multiple correlation (Definition 3–12)

4. Kaiser (1962) develops a set of computing equations for the case of the component factor analysis model. For computing the factor scores for image analysis, see Horst (1965, Section 20.7). Harris (1962) has shown that *scaled* component, common, and image factor analyses (Section 5.6) have the same (or simply related) factor scores.

of the estimated scores with the m variables of the data matrix. He then shows that *this is equal to the standard deviation of the estimated common factor scores.* Thus,

$$r_{\tilde{l}l} = r_l = \sigma_l, \qquad (19\text{-}14)$$

where $r_{\tilde{l}l}$ = correlation between regression estimates and true common factor scores for factor S_l; r_l = multiple correlation coefficient between the regression estimates of common factor S_l and the m variables of the raw data; and σ_l = standard deviation of regression estimates of common factor S_l.

This equation is important. It means that the accuracy of the common factor score estimates of a study can be determined just by computing their standard deviations. Moreover, as discussed below in Section 19.3, r_l measures the *uniqueness* of the estimates. It will always equal 1.00 in component factor analysis or in common factor analysis with communalities estimated by unities.

If the regression coefficients, $\beta_{m \times p}$, are available, the value of r_l may also be determined from

$$r_l^2 = \beta_{l1}\alpha_{1l} + \beta_{l2}\alpha_{2l} + \cdots + \beta_{lj}\alpha_{jl} + \cdots + \beta_{lm}\alpha_{ml}, \qquad (19\text{-}15)$$

where β_{lj} = regression coefficients for m variables, used to estimate the common factor scores for factor S_l, and α_{jl} = factor *structure* loadings for m variables on common factor S_l.

By taking the products of the loadings and factor score regression weights of the variables and summing, we can determine the squared multiple correlation of estimates with data and thus, by Eq. (19–14), determine the accuracy of estimate. An additional payoff of Eq. (9–15) is that any of the products, $\beta_{lj}\alpha_{jl}$, of regression weight and loading gives the statistical dependence of the factor score estimates on the variable X_j (Harman, 1967, p. 353). This cannot be determined from the loadings of X_j alone, since the variable contributes to a factor both in terms of its *direct* individual correlation with a factor and through its *indirect* correlation with other variables loaded on the factor. The product terms of Eq. (9–15) measure both the direct and indirect contributions of a variable to the common factor and are thus of great substantive interest in their own right.

> *Example 19–3.* The regression coefficients for estimating the factor scores of the first orthogonally rotated factor on 10 political variables (Example 16–3) are
>
> $$s_{i1} = .158Z_{i1} + .098Z_{i2} + .220Z_{i3} + .097Z_{i4} - .018Z_{i5}$$
>
> $$- .183Z_{i6} + .200Z_{i7} + .125Z_{i8} + .170Z_{i9} - .570Z_{i10},$$

where s_{il} is the factor score of the ith nation on factor S_l, and $Z_{i1}, Z_{i2}, \ldots, Z_{i10}$ are the standardized data of the ith nation on variables $X_1, X_2, \ldots, X_{10}$. From Eq. (19–15), the loadings given in Table 16–3, and the above regression coefficients, the multiple correlation squared of the S_1 estimates is computed to be 1.00. By virtue of the discussion in Section 19.3, below, $r_1^2 = 1.00$ implies that the estimates on factor 1 are unique for each nation. The contribution each variable makes toward the factor scores on S_1 can be determined also from Eq. (19–15) by taking the product of the loadings and regression coefficients. For orthogonal factor 1 of the 10 political variables:

Variable X_j	Factor 1 α_{j1}	Joint Product $\alpha_{j1}\beta_{1j}$
1	−.11	−.02
2	.61	.06
3	.78	.17
4	.63	.06
5	.49	−.01
6	.08	−.01
7	.72	.14
8	.68	.09
9	−.11	−.02
10	−.95	.54
		Sum = 1.00

It can be seen from the joint product that variable 10 is contributing far more variance to the factor than is evident from the loadings alone.

The use of Eqs. (19–11-13) does not require unities in the principal diagonal of the correlation matrix that was factored. Various communality estimates may be employed to determine the *common* factors. However, the $R_{m \times m}$ matrix employed to compute factor scores must have unities in the diagonal, even though the correlation matrix that was factored had non-unity communality estimates. If such estimates are used, however, a crucial problem may arise.

Communality estimates, such as the squared multiple correlation coefficient (Section 13.2.3), may result in non-Gramian matrices (Definition 4–16). This implies that some negative eigenvalues will be found and that the factor loadings based on positive eigenvalues will be inflated (Section 10.3.1.1). The factor score estimates computed from such loadings by Eqs. (19–11-13) will therefore be *deflated*. Accordingly, the standard deviation of the common factor score estimates will *underestimate* the accuracy of the regression estimates.[5]

If a computer program does not explicitly identify negative eigenvalues, their existence can still be determined. First, sum all the eigenvalues. Then compare this sum with the trace (Definition 4–20) of the correlation matrix. If the sum of the eigenvalues is greater than the trace, the correlation matrix is non-Gramian, and we have some negative eigenvalues.

19.2.3 COMPOSITE ESTIMATES

An approach highly recommended by Cattell (1957, pp. 287–96)[6] and often employed involves selecting a group of variables to represent a factor and summing their values for each case. This sum is then the factor score estimate. A number of considerations are involved:

1. Variables with high loadings on the factor and near-zero loadings elsewhere should be selected, since their variance is almost purely associated with the factor.

2. Variables that straddle the factor in space should be selected, insofar as possible. Straddling, or being on the various sides of the factor, is indicated by each variable selected having some loadings on the other factors that are different in sign from the other selected variables.

3. If the means and standard deviations of the selected variables for a factor differ, the selected variables should be standardized (Definition 3–4). Otherwise, variables with larger means and standard deviations will have greater weight in determining the factor estimates.

4. We may wish to use a variable's factor loading to weight the variable's contribution to the factor estimate. For orthogonal factors, the square of the loading is a measure of the variance of the variable directly associated with the factor and is thus a good weighting coefficient.

5. I discovered this after many days of testing out a factor analysis computer program to determine why regression estimates with an r_i of 1.00 (based on an independent regression program) had a standard deviation of .64. It seemed that either the theory or the program was wrong, but much effort indicated that both were right. The correlation matrix (a four-variable test case) had SMC communality estimates and was non-Gramian with two large negative eigenvalues. This inflated the factor loadings sufficiently to reduce the size of the factor score estimates by over a half. I am indebted to Mrs. Bette Bockelman for her invaluable aid in these tests.

6. The reader interested in composite estimates will find the Cattell reference profitable reading, especially in regard to estimating factor scores on oblique factors. Cattell also presents formulas for computing the number of variables to employ in the summation estimate

5. Often, we will be forced to employ composite estimates because the data contain missing values. In computing the estimates we can standardize the selected variables and sum them for the available data on each case. Dividing the resulting estimate for each case by the number of data involved in the estimate for the case will adjust the estimates for missing data.

6. Although missing data exist, and the regression estimates are thus incalculable, the $\beta_{m \times p}$ matrix of regression coefficients can still be calculated by Eq. (19–10) from $F_{m \times p}$ and $R_{m \times m}$, if $R_{m \times m}$ is non-singular. If $\beta_{m \times p}$ is computed, the product terms between the regression coefficients and factor loadings in Eq. (19–15) can be used to select the best variables for the composite estimate. These product terms are better guides for selecting variables to estimate a factor than the squared factor loading, since the former measures the direct and in-direct variance contributions to a factor, while the loading squared measures only the direct contribution.

19.2.4 BASIC VARIABLE ESTIMATES

In many substantive domains, the individual variables employed in an analysis may be of great interest. Some of the variables may have long histories of research on their characteristics, as with a war variable, or even cover subfields within academic departments, as with an international trade variable. The application of factor analysis to domains containing such variables has posed a dilemma that has not, in general, been faced by psychologists: Should the researcher compute exact factor scores or estimates for relatively unknown factors that are only arithmetical combinations of the variables, or should he take a well-known variable as representative of the factor even though the variable gives a comparatively poor estimate?

A well-known variable selected to estimate factor scores may be called a *basic variable* (or basic measure, or basic indicator), since it is fundamental in representing a component of variance in the data (for an unrotated factor), or a cluster of interrelated variables (for simple structure rotation), *and* in being of great intrinsic interest in its own right.[7] Three arguments for and against the use of basic variable estimates may be noted. In favor of basic variables it can be pointed out that:

1. The basic variable is well known and many research articles and books may have investigated its characteristics. It is therefore a better research strategy to select one basic variable to represent a factor than to combine a number of such variables into a composite or

---

7. On the use of a basic variable, see Bechtoldt (1962, p. 332).

regression estimate. Such factor score estimates usually have little, if any, history of research and study, and these estimates may be specific to the peculiarities of the study itself.

2. Data on the basic variable are usually available, as with gross national product or population, and thus can be easily collected by other researchers. To reproduce the factor score regression estimates, however, requires first reproducing the whole data matrix employed in the study. To reproduce the composite score estimates requires data collection on the group of variables selected and combining these variables in the appropriate manner. Basic variable estimates are good research currency in that they can easily be used by others to represent the same factor scores. The exact scores or regression or summation estimates of them are difficult to reproduce and thus may remain largely specific to one study.

3. Basic variables usually communicate more meaning than other estimates. To make a known variable a central representation of a factor can make the factor more understandable and useful to the interested scientific and policy community.

Against the use of basic variables we may note the following points:

1. At their best, basic variables are usually poor estimates of the factor. A high loading of .80 or .90 for a basic variable means that for the orthogonal factors the inaccuracy of estimate will be 36 or 19 per cent, respectively.[8] In studies in which factor scores will be employed, as for computing distances (Chapter 22), the use of basic variables may introduce enough inaccurate variance to produce misleading results.

2. Associating a factor with a basic variable may mislead others and perhaps the researcher himself as to the meaning of the factor. The factor is certainly in part the basic variable, but it is something also related to the other variables involved. This "something more" may be significant in a domain but may be lost sight of, as the empirical characteristics of a basic variable dominate the abstract interpretation of a factor.

3. The relationship of a basic variable to other variables may change in time, while the factor may not. The same cluster of inter-relationships may have persistence in time, but a particular variable may change its relationship to the cluster.

Whether a researcher decides in favor of basic variables is really a matter of research taste and strategy. However, the arithmetic clearly favors (in decreasing order of accuracy) regression estimates, summation estimates, and, lastly, basic variables.

8. These per cents are 1 minus loading squared times 100.

19.3 Determinacy of Factor Scores

Determinacy refers to the uniqueness of the factor scores for a given set of data and a given factor matrix. Can other sets of factor scores be found for the same data and factors? If so, what is the relationship between the different sets?

In the case of exact factor scores for the component model, the answer is clear: Factor scores derived by Eq. (19–3) or (19–4) are unique for a given factor matrix. The case of summation estimates or basic variable estimates is also clear: They are not unique for a given matrix. For summation estimates, the selection of variables and their weighting is a matter of the researcher's judgment, as is the selection of the basic variable.

For regression estimates of scores *in the component model*, the estimates are unique (Heerman, 1964, p. 380). The estimates are also unique when *unities* are employed as communality approximations (Section 13.2.3) *in the common factor analysis model*. However, when non-unity communality approximations are employed in common factor analysis, such as the squared multiple coefficient (Section 13.2.3), the situation is less clear-cut. In an important article, Louis Guttman (1955) investigated this question. For the derivations the reader is referred to Guttman;[9] the pertinent conclusions will be presented here.

To state the question explicitly, do common factor score regression estimates uniquely exist for given correlation and *common* factor loading matrices? Let $\hat{S}_{n \times p}$ be the matrix of common factor score regression estimates. Then, is there only one possible $\hat{S}_{n \times p}$, or do a number of such matrices exist? Guttman's answer is that *distinctly different common factor score matrices can exist for the same data, correlation, and common factor loading matrices.*

An immediate question then is: How different are various possible $\hat{S}_{n \times p}$, and under what conditions is there a unique estimated common factor score matrix? Both parts of this question can be answered by focusing on the *maximally* different possible score estimates for the same data.

Let $\hat{S}_{n \times p}^q$ define the alternative set of common factor scores for the data that are *maximally* different from the factor score regression estimates, $\hat{S}_{n \times p}$, that have been determined. Let the *maximum difference* be further defined as the *smallest* possible correlation between the common factor scores for each factor $\hat{S}_l^q$ of $\hat{S}_{n \times p}^q$ and the corresponding factor $\hat{S}_l$ of $\hat{S}_{n \times p}$. Then, when the smallest correlations between all

9. For the geometry of Guttman's algebraic derivations, see Heerman (1964).

the factor estimates of $\hat{S}^q_{n \times p}$ and $\hat{S}_{n \times p}$ are all 1.00, $\hat{S}_{n \times p}$ is a unique solution.[10]

The essence of Guttman's finding is that the minimum correlations between alternative common factor score matrices is dependent on the multiple correlation of the regression estimates on the original data. Only if this multiple correlation is 1.00 will the minimum correlation between alternative factor scores be 1.00.

We have already discussed in Section 19.2.2 the multiple correlation, r_l, of the estimates of factor $\hat{S}_l$ on the original data [see especially Eq. (19–14)]. Let r_{min} stand for the minimum correlation between alternative common factor score matrices $\hat{S}^q_{n \times p}$ and $\hat{S}_{n \times p}$. Then, the equation for measuring the uniqueness of $\hat{S}_{n \times p}$ is

$$r^l_{min} = 2r^2_l - 1, \tag{19–16}$$

where r_l is the multiple correlation of factor score estimates $\hat{S}_l$ on m variables of the data matrix, and r^l_{min} is the minimum correlation possible between factor estimates of alternative factor scores $\hat{S}^q_l$ and $\hat{S}_l$.

Equation (19–16) enables the relationship between r_l and r^l_{min} values to be tabulated. The following table allows a comparison of the two for selected values of r_l:[11]

r_l	.00	.20	.40	.60	.80	.90	.95	.98	.99	1.00
r^l_{min}	−1.00	−.92	−.68	−.28	.28	.62	.81	.92	.96	1.00

The above table shows that the multiple correlation of a set of common factor regression estimates has to be very high in order to be unique, within even a moderate correlation. A multiple correlation of .80 means the common factor estimates are correlated only .28 with a maximally different possible set of scores. Only when the multiple correlation closely approaches 1.00 do the maximally different scores closely approach the computed regression estimates.

The importance of computing r_l for common factor scores is highlighted by this section. This coefficient will indicate to the researcher the confidence he can place in his common factor score estimates and in their subsequent use. If factor scores or their derivatives, such as distances, are the primary object of an investigation, particular attention should be paid to this indeterminacy of the common factor analysis model. Component factor analysis may then seem the most desirable model to employ.

10. As far as the correlation coefficient is concerned, the uniqueness is only within a linear transformation. Guttman's proof is stronger than this, however, and implies that when the correlation between maximally different solutions is 1.00, the solutions are identical.

11. Guttman (1955, p. 74) has a similar table.

Part Five · The Results

20. Factor Comparison

To build a science requires that findings be sufficiently explicit to make possible evaluation, replication, and comparison with other studies. Each study in its own right may contribute a bit of knowledge —a datum—to building a science. But these data output of different studies must be integrated into general propositions and given meaning in terms of a theoretical framework. This requires that comparison between findings be possible so that the replicable substantive patterns can be identified, and the unique, research-design-specific results can be discarded.

In the discussion of various research procedures and criteria, the possibility of comparison has been stressed. This stems from a conviction that no theoretical-empirical study can by itself contribute to a science. It must be replicated and compared if its findings are to find a proper theoretical niche, and the researcher interested in contributing to building a science—to converging on natural or social laws—should try to construct a research design that will maximize the ability of himself or others to make this comparison.

Factor comparison procedures involve a number of alternatives.

STEP

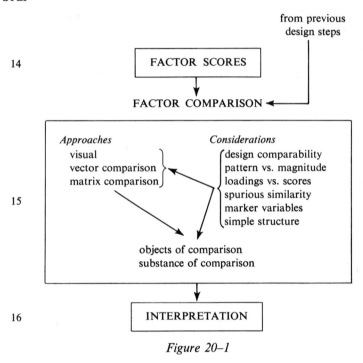

Figure 20–1

These will be discussed in Section 20.2. First, however, the objects of comparison and the considerations related to the selection of the appropriate procedure will be outlined. The content of this research design step is presented in Figure 20–1.

20.1 Considerations

Before discussing the relevant considerations, it may be useful to define the various objects of comparison. Subsequently, the alternatives in the factor design most relevant to the comparison will be discussed, and some attention will be devoted to those elements to be considered in contemplating or making a comparison.

20.1.1 OBJECT OF COMPARISON

Five types of matrices may result from a factor analysis. Not all may be output from a particular study, but each type gives different information about the data and may therefore be the object of comparison. Since all these matrices have been discussed elsewhere, little need be done here except to list them with brief comment where necessary.

1. *Correlation inverse.* If a correlation matrix is factored, then the *inverse* of the correlation matrix is a matrix for comparison. The reciprocal of the diagonal of the inverse is proportional to the squared multiple correlation of each variable with the $(m - 1)$ others [Eq. (4–17) and Notation 4–11]. Moreover, the off-diagonal elements of the inverse are proportional to the partial correlation coefficients between each pair of variables holding the other $(m - 2)$ variables constant [Eq. (4–18)]. A basic assumption of common factor analysis is that the off-diagonal elements of the inverse tend to zero (see Sections 5.2 and 5.4), and, by comparing the inverse, studies can be contrasted as to their satisfaction of this assumption.

2. *Factor loading matrices.* These are the matrices that give the loadings of variables on factors. There are two major types of matrices, the initial or *unrotated factor matrix* and the simple structure or *rotated factor matrix*. The unrotated matrix defines the patterns of variance in the data; the rotated matrix identifies the clusters of intercorrelation among the variables. Among the rotated matrices, comparison may be of the *orthogonal* or the *oblique* factor matrices. For the oblique, one of two alternative coordinate systems may be selected. One is the system of *primary* factors and the other the system of *reference* axes, which are orthogonal to the primaries. Within each oblique system there is a *pattern* and a *structure* matrix. The primary pattern and reference structure defines the clusters of intercorrelation; the primary structure and reference pattern define the correlation of variables with factors. Figure 20–2 brings out the relationship between these various matrices. The six factor loading matrices that may be selected for comparison are circled.

3. *Factor correlation and higher-order matrices.* Comparison of the correlation matrix for the oblique factors with those of other studies measures the consistency or shift in interfactor relationships between studies. If higher-order factor analysis is done of this correlation matrix, the higher-order factor matrices that describe the components of variation in the correlations may be the objects of comparison.

4. *Factor regression matrix.* The regression coefficients of factors on variables (Section 19.2.2) describe the direct and indirect contribution that each variable makes toward defining the factors. It thus highlights the relationship of variables to factors and is therefore an important matrix for comparison.

5. *Factor score matrix.* If the cases as well as variables are of interest, factor scores also may be compared between studies. Instead of com-

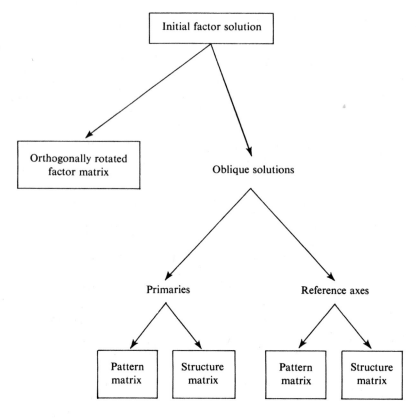

Figure 20–2

paring the scores directly, the researcher may choose to compare the distance matrices or the grouping of cases on their distances (Section 22.1).

20.1.2 SUBSTANCE OF COMPARISON
Comparison may involve several aspects of the factor results. While one aspect, such as the loadings, may predominate in the comparison, a full assessment of the similarity of two studies should involve other considerations as well.

1. *Configuration.* The configuration of variables refers to their pattern and magnitude of loadings. In discussing factor comparison, it is usually the configuration that is of concern. Most of the comments made in subsequent subsections will relate to the comparison of configurations, as will the discussion of the approaches to comparison in Section 20.2, below.

2. *Complexity.* Although implicitly involved in the comparison of configurations, the relative complexity of variables and factors may be explicitly noted. Does a variable highly loaded in one study spread across the factors in another? Does a specific factor in one study shift to a common factor in another? Shifts in complexity are clues to the underlying differences in the data. They provoke "why" questions, answers to which may explain some of the differences between studies.

3. *Variance.* The total variance of the factors measures the relative importance of the factors in accounting for the relationships in the data. In the rotated solution, this variance is dependent on the number of variables involved in the cluster identified by the factor, and may be expected to change as different combinations of variables are included in separate studies. If, however, a particular factor extracts considerable variance consistently across studies, this is valuable information. It increases our confidence in the reliability of the factor and suggests that the importance of the factor is not peculiar to a study, but rather is inherent in the substantive domain being investigated.

4. *Number of factors.* The number of factors of the different studies can be compared. This will measure the degree to which the studies are converging on the dimensionality of the domain. Moreover, such comparisons can be helpful in assessing the best number of factors to rotate in future designs.

5. *Communality.* The communality measures the variance of a variable accounted for by the factors. A comparison of the communalities between studies (assuming similar communality estimates if the common factor model is involved) helps distinguish variables that are consistently interrelated and those that are consistently unique. The latter may result from poor measurement characteristics, poor data, or causal influences exogenous to the domain under investigation. The identification of these consistently unique variables encourages such questions and may provoke research to answer them.

20.1.3 DESIGN COMPARABILITY

In order for matrices to be compared, it is essential that the procedures employed in the different studies be as similar as possible. It may be useful to note those aspects of a research design that are especially relevant to a factor comparison.

Throughout this book variables and cases have been distinguished from each other. The columns of a data matrix identify the variables; the cases are identified by the rows. This distinction applies to any slice of the data box (Section 8.3), such data slices as characteristics by entities or entities by occasions. Continuing this distinction, four possible situations of comparison may be noted: (1) Several of the variables and cases of both studies are the same; (2) several of the variables are the same, but cases differ; (3) several cases are the same, but variables differ; (4) neither variables nor cases are the same.

The last situation does not allow for comparison to be made between studies unless some kinds of linkages are established apart from the factor analysis. For the first situation the comparisons may be done on the factor loading matrix or the factor score regression matrix. These will determine to what extent the relationships between the variables are consistent between the studies. Since the same cases were used, the factor score or distance matrices may be used.

For the second situation, in which several variables are similar but cases differ, comparison is restricted to the factor loading matrices or factor score regression matrix. In the third situation, only the factor scores may be compared.

In addition to the similarities or differences of variables and cases, consideration must be given to the *measurement* of the variables and their *transformations*. Differences in measurement (Section 9.1.3) of the same variables, say between dichotomized and interval-scale measurement, can cause small differences in the factor loadings and scores. Even more important are the distributional transformations applied (Chapter 11). For the *same* data, real differences in the number of factors and loadings have been found between a factor analysis of raw data and one of transformed data.[1] For some of the factors, these differences would be sufficient to reject a hypothesis of similarity, even though the same original data are involved. When comparing studies, therefore, it is important, if possible, to avoid comparing raw data results with results based on transformed data.

This does not mean that the data in both studies should have similar transformations. The transformations may vary as long as the criteria for transformation are the same, that is, the studies being compared should both be transformed, for instance, to increase the normality of the distributions and reduce the influence of extreme values. Comparison will then be of studies that have similarly controlled the data to maximize the generality of the findings to the cases.

Although distributional transformations can vary between studies, *matrix transformations* may not. Compared studies should have data matrices similarly normalized or standardized, and the same correlation coefficients (Section 12.3) should have been applied to both. The choice of correlation coefficient, as between product moment and phi coefficients, for example, can lead to slight differences in the major

1. For an empirical example of this, see Rummel (1967, Fig. 8).

factors and to different minor factors altogether. Such artifactual differences will influence the comparison in a way we may want to avoid.

The *choice of factor model* can also cause artifactual differences between studies. For the same data, some astounding factor differences can be seen for component analysis versus common factor analysis. For the latter, the number of factors can be sharply reduced (influencing therefore the rotated loadings) and the configuration of loadings can be altered.

In the computation of factor loadings, the *factoring technique* may introduce artifactual differences that can be avoided. The centroid and principal axes techniques give results with loadings that are not very different, but the multiple-group, diagonal, two-factor, and bifactor techniques involve different factor loading configurations. The *number-of-factors criterion* should also be similar between studies. It was pointed out in Section 15.1 that the number of factors extracted can influence and considerably alter the loadings on the rotated factors.

Orthogonally and oblique rotated factors ordinarily should not be compared,[2] nor in the oblique case should pattern matrices be compared against structure matrices. However, if a pattern comparison coefficient is being employed (Section 20.2.3, below), the structure (or pattern) reference axes of one study may be compared with the pattern (or structure) primaries of the other. This is because of the relationship between the two alternative coordinate systems summarized in Table 6–6. If different *analytic oblique rotation techniques* are used, small differences between studies may be created in the loadings and factor correlations (and thus in higher-order factors).

If factor scores are compared, a number of procedural differences between studies are relevant. The *mode of estimating* scores should be the same. For regression estimates in common factor analysis we should be wary of comparing unstandardized scores with standardized scores if we are interested in magnitude (and not solely pattern) differences. In the case of composite estimates, the *weighting of the variables* involved in the composite should be comparable. Whether both studies standardize the variables prior to summation is important to note in evaluating any differences that may appear.

Procedures can also influence a comparison of distances (Chapter 22). The *number of factors* involved in the computation of the distances

2. If the matrix comparison method discussed in Section 20.2.3, below, is employed, then an orthogonal solution *can be* compared with an oblique rotation since the technique rotates the orthogonal results of one study to those oblique factors having the best fit to the oblique factors of the second study.

can create differences. Moreover, the *weighting of factors* can change the distances considerably. The problem of standardization is again involved. Before computing distances in the two studies being compared, the factor score estimates (which may be composite scores of basic variables) should be similarly standardized or unstandardized to avoid differential weighting by variance.

20.1.4 PATTERN VERSUS MAGNITUDE

A serious question about comparison is whether the interest is in the similarity of loading (or score) patterns between factors or in the pattern-magnitude similarity. The difference between pattern and pattern-magnitude similarity has been discussed with regard to correlation coefficients (Section 12.3.3). The distinctions made then are also relevant for comparing factors. If the concern is whether two factors have the same pattern of high and low loadings for the same variables or cases, then some pattern coefficient like the product moment correlation coefficient or rank correlation coefficient is desirable. However, the concern may be whether two factors have both pattern and magnitude similarity. Then, as discussed below in Section 20.2.3, the root mean square, coefficient of congruence, or intraclass coefficient may be employed.

Whether pattern or pattern-magnitude similarity is of interest depends on the purpose of the comparison. With a comparison of studies on different data for different samples, data error and specific variance may differentially attenuate the factor loadings. If such be the case, requiring magnitude as well as pattern similarity of loadings may be too stringent. We may want to compare, however, selected subsamples on the same data to determine the factor shift from one subsample to the other. A precise measure of such a shift may be desired, and the pattern-magnitude coefficients will be appropriate.

When simple structure solutions are being compared, error and specific variance unique to the studies may not warrant precise pattern or pattern-magnitude measures. Interest may lie in gauging the existence of similarly high and near-zero loadings, while the intermediacy loadings that contribute little to identifying simple structure are ignored. Cattell's *salience* index, discussed below, is especially useful for this type of comparison.

20.1.5 LOADINGS VERSUS SCORES

For studies with similar variables and dissimilar cases, only the variable loadings can be compared. For other studies, similarity of cases and dissimilarity of variables will enable comparison of factor scores only.

Occasionally, similarity in cases and variables between studies facilitates comparing either loadings or scores. It is pertinent to ask, therefore, to what extent similarity of scores implies similarity of factor loadings and vice versa. This question involves the *sufficiency* and *necessity* of loading and score similarity. If we know $F_{m \times p}$, is $S_{n \times p}$ unique? Alternatively, if we know $S_{n \times p}$, is $F_{m \times p}$ unique?

The answer is no. Perhaps the reason for this can be seen in terms of a correlation coefficient. A correlation coefficient between variables X_j and X_k does not uniquely define the values of the cases on the two variables. The values of cases on two variables can be altered in an infinite number of ways without changing the correlation between the variables. For this reason, it is incorrect to consider identity in correlation between data from two periods as implying that the values for the cases are similarly constant—what is constant is the direction and degree of *relationship* for all the data and not the individual values. Likewise, the factor scores for these cases may not be the same for identical factor loading matrices. Similarity of factor scores between studies does not imply similarity of factor loadings. Moreover, similarity of factor loadings between studies does not imply similarity of factor scores.[3]

20.1.6 SPURIOUS SIMILARITY

Cattell (1962b, pp. 669–71) has pointed out the possibility of two different factors appearing similar in a comparison. This may result from comparing studies in which only a subset of variables are similar. The necessary elimination of dissimilar variables from the factor matrices being compared may also remove the high loaders that delineate some of the factors. It is the high loaders, however, that bear the major weight of defining similarity and difference between factors; their exclusion forces the comparison to rest on the middle-range loadings, and these may be the same for dissimilar factors.

> *Example 20–1.* Consider the one-factor matrices for studies A and B, presented in Table 20–1. The two factors are obviously different (although correlated to a certain degree), and this difference is based mainly on the first three variables, whose high loadings for

3. In comparing studies on *common* factor scores, regression estimates can be especially hazardous if the multiple correlation of scores with data is unknown (Section 19.2.2). For multiple correlations less than near unity, say below .8, alternative sets of *nearly uncorrelated factor scores* are possible for the same factor matrices and data. In other words, if the multiple correlation is low, the common factors *and* data of two studies may be identical but their scores may be uncorrelated.

S_A are blocked in the table. Assume that the low loadings on S_B of the first three variables are *what would
be found had these three variables also been included in
study B*. Now, if the first three variables are actually
included in study A, *but not in study B*, the factor comparison must be limited to variables 4–10. Note that for
these variables the middle-range loadings, shown in
parentheses, are nearly the same. A comparison of S_A
and S_B for variables 4–10, therefore, will conclude that
the factors are similar, when indeed they define different
dimensions.

Table 20–1. One-Factor Matrices

Variables	S_A	S_B
1	.98	.00
2	.86	−.17
3	.92	−.43
4	(.70)	(.43)
5	.06	.08
6	.05	−.02
7	(.52)	(.68)
8	.01	.02
9	−.04	.01
10	(−.63)	(−.62)

One way to guard against such spurious similarity is to include in the
comparison only factors with very high loadings on those variables
that are similar between the studies. In selecting high loadings, we may
be guided by the communality of the variables. If a variable has a .71
loading on one orthogonal factor, then its loading on any one other
factor in the same matrix cannot exceed .70, since the sum of the squares
of the loadings for a variable are less than or equal to 1.00 [Eq. (5–17)].[4]
Therefore, if the loadings for a variable on an orthogonal factor are
above, say, .85 or .90, its loadings on other factors must be low. The
variable will thus uniquely define the factor in comparisons with other
studies.

The comments made on spurious similarity hold equally for spurious
dissimilarity. The middle-range loading variables may differ between
two factors, while the high loading variables define the factors as being

4. This holds only when a Gramian matrix is factored, i.e., when no eigenvalues
are negative (Section 10.3.1.1).

alike. The exclusion from the comparison of these high loading variables will throw the weight of comparison onto the dissimilar middle-range loadings and lead to a conclusion that the factors are quite different.

20.1.7 MARKER VARIABLES

We can anticipate doing factor comparisons by including in the data matrix *marker variables* (Section 9.1.2.7) from other studies. If these variables are selected because of high loadings unique to individual factors in the other studies, then when the results are compared with the factors of these studies, there will be little danger of spurious similarity or dissimilarity. Moreover, planning ahead by selecting marker variables avoids the possibility of not being able to compare substantively important factors from other studies because variables defining them were not included in the analysis.

20.1.8 SIMPLE STRUCTURE

The invariance property of simple structure rotation has been discussed (Section 16.2.4). This characteristic allows for factor comparison to be done on subsets of similar variables. The simple structure criteria identify a cluster of variables in a study regardless of the number of other variables involved and their intercorrelations. If (1) variables defining the same cluster are included in different studies, if (2) the same relationships between the variables exist, and if (3) simple structure rotation is done, then the same factors should be found and identified in the comparison. Although this usually appears to be the case, there may be instances when simple structure rotation is not sufficient to identify similar clusters. Three such instances follow:

1. One study may be a small variable study involving 10 variables, and the other study may be large and involve about 60 variables. Small clusters identified in the smaller study are merged or shown to be part of clusters of different variables in the much larger study.

2. Error and specific variances in the different studies can muddy the final simple structure solution.

3. One study may not have rotated enough factors to properly identify the simple structure for the factors being compared.

These difficulties point up the problem of a one-to-one comparison of factors from different studies on subsets of similar variables. The same factors may exist, but the independent simple structure rotations in the two studies may create "noise" in the comparison. The matrix comparison method of Section 20.2.4, below, is designed specifically for this kind of problem. Rather than let the independent rotations stand as they are, the method takes the solution of one study and rotates the factors into the space of the other so that the two sets of factors have the best linear fit. It is then that comparison is made.[5]

20.2 Approaches

20.2.1 VISUAL COMPARISON

This approach to factor comparison involves the visual matching and assessment of the results from various studies. The experienced researcher can simultaneously relate a number of aspects. He can compare the configuration, communalities, and complexities of the variables and factors and get an overall impression of their agreement. Moreover, he can look for subtle differences of peculiar meaning in his domain, not measurable by the comparison techniques discussed below. There is no replacement for the experienced researcher in this regard. The specialist with a "feel" for his data and a knowledge of his domain will probably do preliminary comparisons by observation. Mathematical techniques of comparison may then be relied on to augment his judgment or to handle large studies not easily compared visually.

20.2.2 VECTOR COMPARISON

The techniques available for comparison can be divided into those that compare several pairs of factors at a time and those that compare the whole factor matrix. This latter approach will be discussed in the next section. The vector comparison approach takes the factors in the different studies as they are. No attempt is made to compensate for their peculiar errors, specific variances, and effects of dissimilar variables. Factors are compared in pairs and their similarity measured by one of the techniques to be discussed.

If the researcher is interested in comparing only the *pattern* of loadings (or factor scores) between factors, then the product moment correlation coefficient appears to be the best measure to use (Definition 3–6).

If we are interested in comparing pattern-magnitude (Section 12.3.3.) similarity of factor loadings (or factor scores), several techniques have

---

5. Meredith (1964a) mathematically investigates the conditions of factor invariance for samples (entities) derived from the same population. His study (p. 184) "suggests that before matching is carried out the orthogonal factor structure matrices should first be rotated to best fitting 'proportional profiles' . . . (or 'similarity' . . .) and the matching performed subsequently. If, prior to matching, an oblique rotation (e.g., simple structure) is carried out, the matching must be done in terms of factor pattern matrices rather than factor structure matrices."

been suggested. One is the *root mean square coefficient* (Harman, 1967, p. 269). Let the coefficient be denoted by μ, then

$$\mu_{lq} = \left[\sum_{j=1}^{m} \frac{(\alpha_{jl} - \alpha_{jq})^2}{m} \right]^{1/2}, \tag{20–1}$$

where α_{jl} = loading of variable X_j on factor S_l of one study, α_{jq} = loading of variable X_j on factor S_q of another study, and m = the number of variables common to both studies. Summation, as can be seen, is over the m common variables, and the comparison is between factors l and q. The root mean square is proportional to the Euclidean distance between the factors. The factors l and q are treated as vectors in the space whose common coordinates are the m variables. The root mean square coefficient then measures the distance between the two factors within a proportionality constant $1/m^{1/2}$. If the distance is zero, the two factors are similar in magnitude and direction. As μ departs from zero, the two factors are less alike.

To see the relationship between the Euclidean distance and μ, consider the distance equation (Definition 3–26, Notation 3–18) for d_{lq}, the distance between factors l and q. This is:

$$d_{lq} = \left[\sum_{j=1}^{m} (\alpha_{jl} - \alpha_{jq})^2 \right]^{1/2} = \frac{m^{1/2}}{m^{1/2}} \left[\sum_{j=1}^{m} (\alpha_{jl} - \alpha_{jq})^2 \right]^{1/2}$$

$$= m^{1/2} \left[\sum_{j=1}^{m} \frac{(\alpha_{jl} - \alpha_{jq})^2}{m} \right]^{1/2} = m^{1/2} \mu_{lq}, \tag{20–2}$$

where d_{lq} is the distance between factors l and q in the space of m orthogonal variables. Therefore,

$$\frac{d_{lq}}{m^{1/2}} = \mu_{lq}. \tag{20–3}$$

The root mean square coefficient measures *any* deviation between the two factors and thus imposes very stringent similarity requirements on a comparison.

Another and less stringent coefficient for comparing factors (or factor scores) is the *coefficient of congruence* (Harman, 1967, pp. 269–70). It is more like the correlation coefficient in that it ranges from −1.00 (for perfect negative similarity) through zero (for complete dissimilarity) to 1.00 (for perfect similarity). The coefficient differs from the correlation in not equating means—in not standardizing the data. It therefore measures not only pattern similarity, like the correlation coefficient, but an aspect of magnitude similarity as well.

Let δ stand for the coefficient of congruence. Then its computation is

$$
\delta_{lq} = \frac{\sum\limits_{j=1}^{m} \alpha_{jl}\alpha_{jq}}{\left[\left(\sum\limits_{j=1}^{m} \alpha_{jl}^2\right)\left(\sum\limits_{j=1}^{m} \alpha_{jq}^2\right)\right]^{1/2}}. \tag{20-4}
$$

While geometrically the root mean square is proportional to the distance between factors, the coefficient of congruence is the *cosine* of the angle between the factors in the space of m orthogonal variables.[6] With μ_{lq} and δ_{lq}, we have two quite geometrically important and meaningful ways of comparing factors.[7] The δ_{lq} coefficient is less demanding than μ_{lq}, since the denominator of Eq. (20-4) normalizes (Definition 3–25) the factors prior to comparison.

Another coefficient that varies between −1.00 and +1.00 is the intraclass correlation coefficient. When applied to factor loadings, the coefficient is roughly a ratio of the difference of within- and between-factor loading variation to the total variation of loadings on the factors. It is described more fully in Section 12.3.3.

Often one may not wish to *precisely* measure pattern or magnitude. All the coefficients so far considered are metric in that they make use of all the numerical information in the loadings when making the comparison. For some studies, however, extraneous influences and different design procedures may not allow for such precision. Only the contingency of high and low loadings can be compared. One approach is to group the loadings on each factor (e.g., into ranges of 0.00 to .29, .30 to .49, and .50 to 1.00) and array the results in a contingency table, where the columns refer to the ranges for a specific factor of one study, and the rows are for the same ranges of a factor of the second study. If the comparison is perfect, nonzero frequencies would appear only in the principal diagonal of the table.

At the lowest level of measurement, another approach is to divide the factor results into high and low loadings, for which the traditional social science fourfold table may be used. For such contingency tables, the comparison may be measured by the chi-square or phi coefficient (Section 12.3.2).

6. Compare Eq. (20–8) with Definition 3–27 for the cosine of an angle between vectors. In addition to the literature on factor comparison to be cited below, we might also note Cattell (1965c), Barlow and Burt (1954), Henrysson (1957, Chapter 7), Horn and Little (1966), Levin (1966), Meredith (1964b), and Webster (1952).

7. Jöreskog (1963, pp. 128–29) feels that the root mean square is a more discriminating measure of factor difference than the coefficient of congruence.

Cattell and Baggaley (1960) have developed a *salience* coefficient for the comparison of factor loadings arranged in contingency tables.[8] The coefficient takes into account the number of coincident high loadings relative to the number of variables common to both studies. A probability is then obtained of finding such a matching by chance. The reader is referred to Cattell and Baggaley (1960) or Cattell (1957, pp. 821–28) for the computation of the coefficient.[9] Cattell (1957, p. 824) has tabulated values of the salience coefficient for various numbers of contingent loadings and numbers of common variables.

20.2.3 MATRIX COMPARISON

The difficulty with the vector comparison approach is that the factors are compared as given. Exogenous influences may affect the independent rotations of two studies and confound the comparisons. Accordingly, we may desire to first rotate the factors of one study to a least squares fit (Definition 3–8) with those of another and then compare. This minimizes extraneous elements from influencing the comparison and assures that the comparisons are done of factors with the closest possible congruence.

Ahmavaara (1954a, 1954b)[10] discusses a technique for making this kind of comparison, which he calls *transformation analysis.* First, a transformation matrix is determined that will rotate the factors of one study to a least squares fit to factors of another, i.e., that will define the maximum congruence between the two sets of factors. The elements of

8. With regard to factor comparison, Cattell (1962b, p. 672) discusses a pattern coefficient he developed, the intraclass, the coefficient of congruence, and the salience coefficient. His preference (1962b, p. 692) is for the salience coefficient.

9. For a comparison of results using the product moment and the salience coefficient, see Cattell (1957, pp. 821–28).

10. Ahmavaara (1954a, 1954b) gives the complete development of the technique. Part I of Ahmavaara and Markkanen (1958) presents a more abbreviated version with comments that may be helpful for purposes of orientation. Part II analyzes the sociological difference between Finnish alcoholic drinkers and nondrinkers by applying the comparison method. The mathematics underlying the approach are given in Ahmavaara (1954a, 1954b). See also Meredith (1964a). A far more extensive application is given in Ahmavaara (1957), in which 26 psychological studies are compared by transformation analysis. Especially useful is the manner in which Ahmavaara summarizes the various comparisons (Chapter 8). Transformation analysis has been used by Rummel (1965a) to compare a dozen studies on domestic conflict, by Rummel (1969) to compare several cross-national data studies, and by Russett (1967a) for a similar purpose. Horst (1965, Chapter 24) develops a similar technique for transforming one set of factors to maximum congruence with another to facilitate comparison. Harman (1967, Section 12.2) discusses a similar method but does not generalize it for purposes of comparing factors of different studies.

this transformation matrix, normalized, measure the relationship between the factors of both studies in the same space. This approach is the same as target rotation (Section 16.4.2.3). In this case, however, the target matrix, rather than being a hypothetical matrix, is composed of the factors of the study against which the findings are to be compared.

Transformation analysis enables several aspects of the results to be compared. Not only is a matrix—the transformation matrix—giving the relationships between factors determined, but, by using this matrix in conjunction with the factor matrices and a knowledge of the correlations between factors, the following can also be determined:

1. The overall fit of one set of factors to the vector space of the other set can be measured.

2. The variables most accounting for the similarity or dissimilarity of factors can be defined.

3. The shift in factor correlations between studies can be compared.

4. The factors that most change their meaning or interpretation between two studies can be delineated.

Before giving the equations describing the technique it may be helpful to lay out the notation involved.

Notation 20–1. $F^1_{m \times p}$ = factor matrix of p factors to be rotated to a least squares fit with the factors of a second study.

$F^2_{m \times q}$ = factor matrix of q factors of the second study.

$L_{p \times q}$ = *comparison matrix:* transformation matrix for rotating $F^1_{m \times p}$ to a best fit with $F^2_{m \times q}$.

$L^n_{p \times q}$ = $L_{p \times q}$ normalized by rows; elements are now the cosine between factors of $F^1_{m \times p}$ and $F^2_{m \times q}$.

$C_{m \times q}$ = *comparison matrix:* $F^1_{m \times p}$ transformed to a best fit with $F^2_{m \times q}$.

$D_{m \times q}$ = *difference matrix:* shows which variables and factors account most (or least) for the comparison between studies.

$D^*_{m \times q}$ = *rotated difference matrix:* shows which loadings and factors of $F^1_{m \times p}$ are most different in interpretation from those of $F^2_{m \times q}$ after transformation.

$R_{q \times q}^2$ = correlations between factors of $F_{m \times q}^2$.

$Q_{q \times q}$ = correlations between factors of $F_{m \times p}^1$ after transformation of $F_{m \times p}^1$ to a best fit with $F_{m \times q}^2$.

$M_{q \times q}$ = *differentiation matrix:* the difference in factor correlations between $F_{m \times p}^1$ and $F_{m \times q}^2$.

Analogous to the development of the equations for target rotation [Eqs. (16–4) through (16–7)], where the hypothetical matrix $H_{m \times p}$ is equivalent to our matrix of the second study $F_{m \times q}^2$, we can derive a transformation matrix $L_{p \times q}$:

$$L_{p \times q} = (F_{p \times m}^{1\prime} F_{m \times p}^1)^{-1} F_{p \times m}^{1\prime} F_{m \times q}^2. \tag{20–5}$$

The matrix $L_{p \times q}$ then gives the transformation matrix for the least squares fit (rotation) of the first study to the second. The elements of $L_{p \times q}$ can be read as *regression coefficients*, giving the best prediction of each factor of $F_{m \times q}^2$ (columns of $L_{p \times q}$) in terms of the factors of $F_{m \times p}^1$ (rows of $L_{p \times q}$).[11]

By normalizing $L_{p \times q}$ by rows, $L_{p \times q}$ is scaled to a matrix $L_{p \times q}^n$ that gives the cosines between the factors of $F_{m \times p}^1$ (rows of $L_{p \times q}^n$) and $F_{m \times q}^2$ (columns of $L_{p \times q}^n$) if the factors of $F_{m \times p}^1$ are orthogonal.[12] These cosines are similar to the coefficient of congruence of the last section, except that they are now measuring the similarity between factors that are not independently rotated. The elements of $L_{p \times q}^n$ can also be read as the *loadings* of the factors of the first study on the factors of the second.

> *Example 20–2.* In Table 13–2 (h_j^2 estimate = 1.00) are presented three orthogonally rotated factors of 10 domestic conflict variables. This is a replication of a similar analysis on 1955–57 data for nine variables (Rummel, 1963). Let the earlier 1955–57 results be those of the first study, $F_{m \times p}^1$, and the 1962–63 data results be $F_{m \times q}^2$. Both studies found three factors, and in each they were named *turmoil, revolution,* and *subversion.* Seven of the variables involved in both studies were similarly defined: guerrilla warfare,

11. The geometric picture of such a transformation is nicely illustrated in Figs. 1 and 2 of Ahmavaara (1954b, pp. 48–49).

12. If oblique factors are being compared, $L_{p \times q}^n$ can be adjusted so that the elements are cosines between the oblique factors of both studies. See Ahmavaara (1954b, pp. 57–59).

major government crises, purges, riots, revolutions, anti-government demonstrations, and number killed. These seven variables, therefore, are the only ones to be involved in the comparison. The $L_{p \times q}$ transformation matrix is shown in the first part of Table 20–2; the $L_{p \times q}^{n}$ transformation matrix is given in the second part. From the latter, we can see that *turmoil* is similarly delineated in both

Table 20–2. Transformation Comparison of 1955–57 against 1962–63 Domestic Conflict Factors

1955–57 Factors	1962–63 Factors		
	Subversion	Revolution	Turmoil
$L_{p \times q}$ Transformation Matrix			
Subversion	.93	−.47	−.07
Revolution	.15	.83	−.06
Turmoil	−.07	.04	.92
$L_{p \times q}^{n}$ Normalized Transformation Matrix			
Subversion	.89	−.45	−.06
Revolution	.18	.98	−.07
Turmoil	−.07	.05	1.00

studies. The *revolution* factor of the first study has a small congruence (.18) with *subversion* and is mainly (.98) identified with the *revolution* factor of the second study. While *subversion* of the first study also has a high congruence (.89) with that factor called *subversion* in the second study, there is also a moderate (−.45) negative similarity with *revolution*. The *turmoil* factor is identical in both studies.

One possible difficulty in employing this matrix comparison technique is that the comparison is asymmetrical. Reversing which of the two studies is to be $F_{m \times p}^{1}$ will not generally yield the same comparison matrix. That is, the comparison is asymmetrical.[13] Now, in maximizing the linear fit of $F_{m \times q}^{2}$ to $F_{m \times p}^{1}$, we are determining the best linear estimate of $F_{m \times q}^{2}$ from $F_{m \times p}^{1}$. We are trying to define the best linear prediction of the factors of the second study from those of the first. In this sense, which study should logically be the prior study, $F_{m \times p}^{1}$, may be easy to decide for many designs. If there are two studies on the same variables and cases for different periods, for example, then we will probably

13. This is similar to the situation in regression analysis in which the regression coefficient for X_1 regressed on X_2 is not the same as X_2 regressed on X_1.

want to "predict" from the earlier period. Or, to consider another example, if we want to compare results with a number of other studies, then we may make our results, $F^1_{m \times p}$, measure how well we could estimate the results of each of the other studies from a knowledge of our own.

In some cases, however, there may not be any logical reason for one study being prior to another in the comparison. Then we can use canonical analysis to determine the linear fit between both studies. Canonical analysis has already been touched on in the introduction to Section 5.5. This method will determine a transformation matrix for each study that will maximize the canonical correlations between linear combinations of the factors of each study. These correlations squared then measure the variance in common between these transformed factors. Although canonical analysis as a mode of comparison is not highlighted here, it nonetheless appears to be the best method of comparing matrices when the comparison is symmetrical, i.e., when neither study is logically prior to the other.

Returning to our consideration of transformation analysis, once we have selected which study is $F^1_{m \times p}$, two sources of error may enter the determination of $L_{p \times q}$. There may be computational error, or the transformation of $F^1_{m \times p}$ to a best fit with $F^2_{m \times q}$ may not be linear. A comparison matrix $C_{m \times q}$ can be computed to investigate both possibilities. After $L_{p \times q}$ is determined,

$$C_{m \times q} = F^1_{m \times p} L_{p \times q}. \qquad (20\text{–}6)$$

The comparison matrix $C_{m \times q}$ can then be compared with matrix $F^2_{m \times q}$ either by plotting all corresponding elements on $C_{m \times q}$ (ordinate) and $F^2_{m \times q}$ (abscissa) or by computing one correlation coefficient between the corresponding elements. The closer the plot to a linear regression line at a 45° angle, or the closer the correlation to unity, the closer to linearity is the transformation.

In addition to measuring linearity and error, $C_{m \times q}$ indicates the configurational invariance between transformed $F^1_{m \times p}$ and $F^2_{m \times q}$. A correlation coefficient, such as the intraclass [Eq. (12–6)], calculated between the elements of $C_{m \times q}$ and $F^2_{m \times q}$, then describes with one value the degree to which the overall findings of one study correspond to those of another.

> *Example 20–3.* For the transformation of Example 20–2, the $C_{m \times q}$ matrix is given in Table 20–3. In order to check the linearity and error of transformation, and to compare the best-fitting configuration of both studies, the intraclass correlation between the elements of $C_{m \times q}$ and those

of $F^2_{m \times q}$ was computed. It is .87, which indicates a fairly high degree of correspondence between the patterns of conflict in 1955–57 and in 1962–63.

Table 20–3. Domestic Conflict Factor Comparison Matrix $C_{m \times q}$

Variables	Subversion	Revolution	Turmoil
1. Guerrilla war	.88	−.19	−.11
2. Major government crises	−.04	.22	.54
3. Purges	.12	.59	.25
4. Riots	.08	.25	.70
5. Revolutions	.24	.65	.03
6. Antigovernment demonstrations	.15	.09	.76
7. Killed	.49	.44	.14

The computation of the matrix $C_{m \times q}$ also enables us to determine the *difference matrix $D_{m \times q}$*:

$$D_{m \times q} = C_{m \times q} - F^2_{m \times q}. \qquad (20\text{–}7)$$

The elements of $D_{m \times q}$ indicate the magnitude of deviation of the loadings of the variables between transformed $F^1_{m \times p}$ and $F^2_{m \times q}$. By squaring and summing these deviations by row for each variable, an overall *index of deviation, d,* for each variable can be given. This measures the factor loading similarity of a variable from one study to the next. The index is zero if a variable has identical loadings in both studies.

> *Example 20–4.* The $D_{m \times q}$ matrix for $F^1_{m \times p}$ and $F^2_{m \times q}$ of the previous examples is given in Table 20–4. By looking at the *d* coefficient in the table one can see which variables changed in relationships from F'_1 to F_2. "Killed" had the biggest shift between the two studies.

Table 20–4. Difference Matrix ($D_{m \times q}$) for Transformed Comparison of 1955–57 and 1962–63 Domestic Conflict Factors

Variables	Subversion	Revolution	Turmoil	d^{a}
1. Guerrilla war	.05	−.19	.06	.04
2. Major government crises	.02	−.29	.14	.10
3. Purges	−.07	−.22	.19	.09
4. Riots	−.13	.12	−.14	.05
5. Revolutions	.26	−.05	−.11	.09
6. Antigovernment demonstrations	.18	.08	−.01	.04
7. Killed	−.24	.35	−.05	.18

a Sum of squares of row elements.

The matrix $D_{m \times q}$ can now be rotated using $L_{p \times q}$ to determine what specific loadings and which of the factors alter their meaning and interpretation the most between studies. The rotated difference matrix $D^*_{m \times q}$ is

$$D^*_{m \times q} = D_{m \times q} L^{-1}_{p \times q}, \qquad (20\text{–}8)$$

where $p = q$.

For these and the following computations, both studies must have the same number of factors. The factor columns of $D^*_{m \times q}$ can be summed to measure whether the factor changes from $F^1_{m \times p}$ to $F^2_{m \times q}$ are in a positive (higher loading) or negative (lower loading) direction. Negative sums indicate positive factor shifts. Moreover, the column elements can be squared and summed to index the magnitude of the shift.

> *Example 20–5.* The rotated difference matrix for the domestic conflict studies is shown in Table 20–5. The sum of squares shows that the *subversion* and the *revolution*

Table 20–5. *Rotated Difference Matrix* $(D^*_{m \times q})$ *for Transformation Comparison of 1955–57 and 1962–63 Domestic Conflict Factors*

Variables	Subversion	Revolution	Turmoil
1. Guerrilla war	.09	−.15	.05
2. Major government crises	.08	−.27	.13
3. Purges	−.02	−.24	.17
4. Riots	−.17	.05	−.15
5. Revolutions	.27	.08	−.09
6. Antigovernment demonstrations	.17	.16	.01
7. Killed	−.32	.21	−.06
Sum	.11	−.16	.07
Sum of squares	.25	.23	.08

> factors changed their meaning most between the studies. The sums indicate that the *revolution* factor of the second study was defined by higher loadings, whereas the *subversion* factor loadings had lower magnitudes. In terms of the variable loadings, the number killed can be seen to have changed its relationship to the *revolution* and *subversion* factors between the studies.

It may be desirable to compare the factor correlations between two studies. First, however, we must again compute the best fit of $F^1_{m \times p}$ to $F^2_{m \times q}$. Then, we compute the correlations between the transformed factors of $F^2_{m \times p}$ and compare them with those of $F^1_{m \times q}$. If $Q_{q \times q}$ is the correlation matrix for the factors of $F^1_{m \times p}$ with the best fit to $F^2_{m \times q}$,

$$Q_{q \times q} = L^n_{q \times q} L^{n'}_{p \times q}. \tag{20-9}$$

If $R^2_{m \times q}$ is the correlation matrix of the factors of $F^2_{m \times q}$, then a *differentiation matrix* $M_{q \times q}$ can be computed:

$$M_{q \times q} = Q_{q \times q} - R^2_{q \times q}. \tag{20-10}$$

The elements of the matrix $M_{q \times q}$ will indicate whether the factors of transformed $F^1_{m \times p}$ are more or less correlated than $F^2_{m \times q}$. Moreover, by computing a sum of all the elements in the matrix we can determine a *differentiation index* that will measure the direction and magnitude of the overall shift in correlations. If positive, it indicates that the factors of $F^2_{m \times q}$ are more differentiated (less correlated) than those of $F^1_{m \times p}$. If negative, the reverse is true. By summing the squares of all the elements of $M_{q \times q}$, the magnitude of total change in correlations can be discerned.

> *Example 20–6.* The rotated domestic conflict factor matrices of $F^1_{m \times p}$ and $F^2_{m \times q}$ used in the previous examples are orthogonal. Therefore $R^2_{q \times q}$ is an identity matrix. When $F^1_{m \times p}$ is transformed to the space of $F^2_{m \times q}$, however, the factors of $F^1_{m \times p}$ become oblique. This is shown by the $Q_{q \times q}$ matrix given in the first half of Table 20–6; the second part of the table gives the $M_{q \times q}$ matrix. Since

Table 20–6. *Factor Correlations of Transformed* $F^1_{m \times p}$

	(1)	(2)	(3)
		$Q_{q \times q}$ *Matrix*	
1. Subversion	1.00	−.28	−.15
2. Revolution	−.28	1.00	−.03
3. Turmoil	−.15	−.03	1.00
		$M_{q \times q}$ *Matrix*	
1. Subversion	.00	−.28	−.15
2. Revolution	−.28	.00	−.03
3. Turmoil	−.15	−.03	.00
Sum	−.42	−.31	−.18
Sum of squares	.02	.08	.10
Differentiation index (total sum) = −.92			
Total sum of squares = .20			

$R_{q \times q}$ is identity, the only change between $M_{q \times q}$ and $Q_{q \times q}$ is in the diagonals. The sums and differentiation index given for $M_{q \times q}$ show that the shift in correlation of the $F^1_{m \times q}$ factors was uniformly in the negative direction.

Factor comparison through *transformation analysis* yields a number of interesting matrices comparing various aspects of two studies. If this approach is also to be used for hypothesis testing in target rotation, where $F^2_{m \times q}$ is the target or hypothetical matrices, *then the matrices* $L^n_{p \times q}$, $C_{m \times q}$, $D_{m \times q}$, $D^*_{m \times q}$, *and* $M_{q \times q}$ *are also very useful for explicitly delineating the fit between data and hypothesis.*

Transformation analysis can also be employed in causal analysis. If a condition is believed to be causally related to a number of variables, two factor analyses can be done. One factor analysis, $F^1_{m \times p}$, would be on those cases not manifesting the causal condition for the variables. The second analysis, $F^2_{m \times q}$, would be of the same variables, but now with *cases* also included that manifest the causal condition. A comparison of $F^1_{m \times p}$ to $F^2_{m \times q}$ could then be done, and the matrices $C_{m \times q}$, $D_{m \times q}$, $D^*_{m \times q}$, and $M_{q \times q}$ would pinpoint the effect of the causal condition on the variables. An alternative approach is to divide the data by subgroups, say for sociological variables into racial, income, and educational groups, and to determine, through factoring each group separately and comparing the results, the change in sociological variables as one shifts from group to group.[14]

14. This is the approach used by Markkanen (Ahmavaara and Markkanen, 1958, Part II). This study is a model for applying transformation analysis and should be read by all those who are seriously interested in this approach.

21. Interpretation

Although this phase of the factor analysis research design has no data preparation or computational function, it may be one of the most important steps of the factoring process. Results have to be interpreted, meaning has to be given to the factor structure, labels have to be given to the factors, and the findings have to be given a visual representation as an aid to our understanding and communicating them.

These considerations will be discussed in two sections. The first will present the symbolic, causal, and descriptive approaches to factor naming and the criteria and conditions relevant to interpretation. The second section will present several ways in which factors may be visually represented. The content of the interpretation step is displayed in Fig. 21–1.

21.1 Naming Factors

The perspective the researcher has on his factor results colors their interpretation. Basically, three perspectives may be identified.[1] One

1. For additional reading, see Cattell (1957, pp. 296 ff.; 1952a, pp. 337–40).

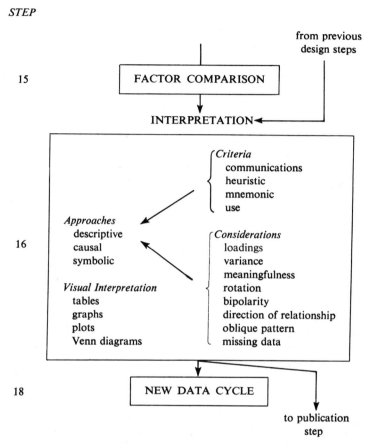

STEP

15

16

18

Figure 21-1

perspective considers the factors as *descriptive* of the interrelationships in the data. The factor structure is then a typology, and the factors are classifications to which descriptive names have been assigned. The second perspective is a *causal* approach, in which the factors are looked at as underlying causes of the interrelationships delineated and are causally labeled. The third perspective is *symbolic*, that is, the factors represent new concepts or variables that are designated by algebraic symbols only.

The criteria relevant to the causal, descriptive, and symbolic naming of factors will be discussed first, followed by a consideration of the approaches to naming factors.

21.1.1 CRITERIA

One of the most important reasons for naming a factor is to *communicate* to others. The name should capsulize the substantive nature of the factor and enable others to grasp its meaning. When mentioned in abstracts or footnotes, the factor names should lead other researchers, who might be interested in the substantive domain or in particular substantive results, to that particular study. With the number of factor analyses multiplying, the researcher interested in factor comparisons may not be able to investigate the particulars of every factor analysis. Factor names that communicate the essence of the results are important in enabling the rapid identification of similar factors across studies.

One difficulty of substantive labels is that they contain *surplus meaning*. Connotations irrelevant to a factor may become mixed with the substance of a factor and confuse communication. This source of confusion appears almost inevitably in the social sciences, where much of the substantive vocabulary is in the vernacular (e.g., size, economic development, conservatism, turmoil, cold war, totalitarianism) and accordingly will have diverse implications.

A second difficulty of substantive labels is that the factor may be *reified*. It may become the embodiment of the label. All the qualities of the label attached to a factor may be transferred to that factor, and then a study may be criticized if the factor does not manifest all these properties.[2] Moreover, the researcher himself may in time confuse the label with the factor and assume the factor has qualities transcending its loadings.

A factor name can also serve a *heuristic* function. The name can be theoretically suggestive or invoke hypotheses for future testing. Moreover, it can relate to the major theoretical consensus of the field, stimulate wide interest, and promote additional experimentation. A name that is suggestive and stimulating, rather than apt but dry, will aid the communication of the studies' results and help to further their utilization, testing, and replication.

> *Example 21-1.* The 236-variable factor analysis described in Examples 9–6 and 9–7 delineated a dimension involving

2. In a draft of a paper, I named a factor "cooperation" because it involved a number of nonconflict international transactions and communications of nations, such as mail, international organizations, trade, embassies, and foreign aid. Another orthogonal factor involved almost entirely the diverse conflict behavior of nations and was labeled "conflict." A reader for a journal to which the paper was submitted rejected the paper in part because it is "fairly well known" that cooperation and conflict are not independent. Perhaps as a commentary on the vagaries of professional judgment, a second reader pointed out that the results of the study presented nothing "new."

such variables as population, area, national income, resources, military personnel, and political centralization. The dimension could be named "size," a straightforward descriptive label of what the factor involves. An alternative label, "power bases," implies that most of the alleged elements of the political power capability of a nation are highly loaded on the factor. This alternative label is far more suggestive and would surely stimulate more research interest among students of international relations than "size."

Another criterion for naming a factor is *mnemonic*. How well a possible label lends itself to recall is an important consideration. A one- or two-word name is much better in this regard than a four- or five-word title, although perhaps slightly less descriptive. Factors that are easily remembered can be drawn on in teaching, in thinking through research designs, or in weighing the implications of results. A large measure of scientific research is mental. Developing a theory or set of hypotheses, drafting a design, and relating the results and initial theory are basic ingredients of research. As with the color codes among airplane instruments that make identification easier and confusion less likely, factor names facilitate analysis if they are clear and simple tags for the concepts involved.

A final criterion of factor naming to be mentioned here is future *use*. The purpose of the research and the subsequent use of the factors should govern the labeling. If the factor study is classificatory, for example, factor names will be selected that are descriptive of the loadings. If the substantive content of the factors is unimportant, however, as in a study that may only want to develop orthogonal components for the regression test of some social theory, then the factors may be conveniently tagged A, B, C, etc.

21.1.2 APPROACHES

The choice of factor names should be related to the basic purpose of the factor analysis. If the goal is to describe or simplify the complex interrelationships in the data, a descriptive factor label can be applied. The *descriptive approach* to factor naming involves selecting a label that best reflects the substance of the variables loaded highly *and near-zero* on a factor. The factors are classificatory and names to define each category are sought.

Example 21–2. Consider the four orthogonally rotated factors of the 16 foreign conflict variables given in Table

17–2. Descriptively, the factors may be named *military violence, negative communications, negative sanctions,* and *antiforeign behavior.* Nothing beyond the actual loadings of the variables is implied by these labels.

Rather than description, the purpose of the analysis may be to identify causal relationships. Patterns of empirical relationship are assumed to *reflect* a common underlying influence, and the existence of a highly intercorrelated cluster of variables implies a common "factor."[3] The factor analysis is believed to delineate causal nexus; the *causal approach* to factor interpretation is to impute substantive form to the underlying and unknown causes.

Example 21–3. Consider again the orthogonally rotated factors of the 16 foreign conflict variables. The second factor (negative communication) may be causally labeled *deterrence.* This assumes that each nation is concerned with deterring others from actions detrimental to its national interests and in so doing will communicate warnings and threats and make diplomatic protests. Moreover, it is assumed, deterrence will involve accusations and perhaps denunciations as a nation communicates the importance of the national interests involved and its perception of the situation. Deterrence may thus be the factor influencing the clustering of these negative communications, since various kinds of negative communications will be made when a *deterrence situation* exists between two nations.

The fourth factor (antiforeign behavior) may be causally labeled "hostility." This involves the interpretation of attacks on embassies, of antiforeign riots and demonstrations, etc., as the result of hostility by part of the population of one nation against another nation.

The third approach to factor naming is *symbolic.* The factors are labeled by symbols, such as *A, B,* and *C,* or F_1, F_2, and F_3. This approach avoids the possibility of confusing the label and the factor or of transferring to a factor surplus meaning in the label. But the symbolic tags may communicate almost nothing to others, or even to oneself eventually. In some fields the use of symbols for factors has gained little

3. Early applications of factor analysis were made mainly to identify these underlying "factors." See Burt's illuminating history of multivariate analysis (1966).

acceptance so far; in such cases it may be wise to avoid symbols altogether. If symbolic labels are completely avoided in a newly developing field, however, such symbols will never come into use. Once accepted, a symbolic label has great utility. It is a handy label that can be employed directly in equations or models without having to establish intermediary definitions.

21.1.3 CONSIDERATIONS

There are a number of considerations involved in descriptively or causally naming factors.

1. Those variables with zero or near-zero loadings are unrelated to the factor. In interpreting a factor these unrelated variables should also be taken into consideration. The name should reflect *what is* as well as *what is not* involved in a factor.

2. The loading squared gives the variance of a variable explained by an *orthogonal* factor. Squaring the loadings on a factor helps determine the relative weight the variables should have in interpreting a factor.

3. Some of the smaller factors may be strange—difficult to interpret. For empirical data, these may be the result of random error. Possibly unique to the peculiarities of the sample, these small factors may be left uninterpreted. Replication over a number of studies can establish their reliability or unreliability.[4]

4. A test of significance[5] can be applied to factor loadings to determine at what magnitude loadings are not a chance deviation (say, at $P \leq .05$) from zero. The standard errors of factor loadings for differing sample sizes and average correlation between the variables are tabulated by Harman (1967, p. 435, Table B[6]).

5. Unrotated factors define the major patterns of variation in the data and not necessarily the major clusters of interrelationships (simple structure rotation does this). The first unrotated factor establishes the most general pattern of covariation. For physiological characteristics

4. "Incidental factors are almost certainly present in every study. Hence the investigator should feel free to leave without interpretation those primary factors which do not lend themselves to rather clear scientific interpretation. Even then the interpretation should, at first, be in the nature of a hypothesis to be sustained, if possible, by subsequent factorial studies" (Thurstone, 1947, p. 437).

5. Some of the major literature on significance tests in factor analysis include Bartlett (1950, 1951), Henrysson (1950), Jöreskog (1963), Lawley and Swanson (1954), and Rao (1955).

6. Harman (1967) discusses this table on p. 433.

of the human body, for example, it is *size*[7] (rotation shows size to be composed of two distinct dimensions—*height* and *girth*). For the 16 foreign conflict variables (see Table 17–2), for example, the general dimension of variance is *official conflict behavior* (rotation shows this to be composed of the dimensions *military violence, negative communications,* and *negative sanctions*).

6. The naming of the factors with high positive and high negative loadings should reflect this bipolarity. One term may be appropriate, as is "temperature" for a hot-cold bipolar factor, or "economic development" for a factor with high positive loading for GNP per capita and high negative loading for ratio of agricultural workers to the work force. For many bipolar factors, however, a suitable name incorporating both poles may not exist. Each pole then may be interpreted separately and the factor named by its opposite, e.g., hot versus cold, industrialized economies versus agricultural economies, height versus girth, or military violence versus negative communications.

7. Some factors that are difficult to name can be better interpreted by reversing the sign of some of the loadings. Reversing the sign for a variable has the effect of reversing the scaling.

> *Example 21–4.* In the following list, variables on the left are named in terms of their original scaling. Changing the sign of their loading reverses their scaling as indicated.

Original Variable	Sign of Loading Changed	New Variable
censorship	→	noncensorship
agricultural product/GNP	→	nonagricultural product/GNP
geographic distance	→	geographic propinquity
defense budget/budget	→	nondefense budget/budget
% socialist party votes	→	% nonsocialist party votes

8. Attaching adjectives to the variables to describe the direction of relationship with the factors aids in interpretation.[8]

> *Example 21–5.* The following selected loadings are taken from the *orthogonal economic development* factor of the 236-variable study described in Examples 9–6 and 9–7. Appropriate adjectives modify the variables.

---

7. See Harman's various analyses of eight physiological variables. These analyses are referenced in the index to his earlier edition (1960).
8. This approach has been used by Cattell (1949a).

Variable	*Factor*
Low ratio of agricultural population to population	−.92
High ratio of book titles to population	.67
High ratio of telephones to population	.95
Low birthrate	−.64
Low average temperature	−.68
High GNP per capita	.91
Many treaties	.52

9. For oblique factors, the *primary pattern* or *reference structure* matrices (Section 17.1) are best for interpretation. They display the saturation of the variables with the factors, whereas the loadings of primary structure and reference pattern matrices give the correlations of the variables with the factors and are influenced by the interactions (correlations) between the factors.[9]

10. If the factor analysis was done on a matrix with missing data, then some of the loadings will be inflated (Section 10.3.1.1). Variables with loadings excessively inflated will be indicated by communalities far in excess of unity. These variables will play a greater role in the interpretation of factors than warranted unless their loadings are normalized (Definition 3–25) for the variable.

> *Example 21–6.* As a result of missing data let the loadings of a variable across 10 factors be very high, with the sum of the squared loadings adding to a communality of 2.36. Before interpretation this variable can be squeezed back into the factor space and given a communality of 1.00 by dividing each of its loadings by the square root of 2.36.

11. For higher-order analyses, the lower-order *factors* loaded on higher-order ones give a better basis of interpretation than transforming back to the original variables (Cattell, 1965b, pp. 260–61).

21.2 Visual Interpretation

An important aspect of interpreting and communicating factor results is the visual presentation. A good display can bring out the salient features of the interpretation and aid in making the relationships clear. Relevant to factor analysis, four kinds of displays can be distinguished: *tables, graphs, plots,* and *Venn diagrams.*

9. For a more thorough and technical discussion of interpreting oblique matrices, see Cattell (1962b) and White (1966).

21.2.1 TABLES

One way of representing factor results is through a table giving the loadings by *original variable order*. This is the approach used throughout this book. The order of the variables (in terms of their numbering) established during the operationalization stage of the analysis is maintained when laying out the factor matrix.

Another approach, used for example by Russett (1967a, 1967b), is to reorder the variables by size of high loading. This *loading order* approach better displays the factor saturation than the variable order table that is traditional in the literature.

> *Example 21-7.* Table 21-1 gives the loading order of the variables presented by variable order in Table 17-2.

Table 21-1. Loading Order of Sixteen Foreign Conflict Variables on Orthogonal Factors[a]

| Variables | Orthogonally Rotated Factors | | | |
	S_1	S_2	S_3	S_4
8. Negative communications	(.95)	−.27	.07	−.04
13. Accusations	(.94)	−.21	.01	−.07
9. Written negative communications	(.92)	−.02	−.06	−.04
10. Oral negative communications	(.89)	−.30	.14	−.03
6. Negative acts	(.77)	−.12	.09	.29
15. Warnings	(.69)	−.46	.17	−.01
14. Representations—protests	(.63)	−.24	.17	.03
1. Violent acts	.19	(−.97)	.00	−.01
2. Planned violence	.18	(−.97)	.00	.00
4. Military acts or clashes	.19	(−.97)	−.01	.02
5. Days of violence	.14	(−.91)	.00	.05
11. Written or oral negative communications	.36	(−.65)	.17	−.08
16. Antiforeign demonstrations	.09	.00	(.91)	−.05
7. Diplomatic rebuffs	.36	−.28	−.11	(.71)
3. Incidence of violence	.31	−.33	−.11	(−.60)
12. Unclassified communications	.43	−.07	.40	.13

[a] From Table 17-2.

For a small number of variables there may be little gain in clarity by using the loading order table, but for large variable matrices the loading order presentation may be a distinct help. Even greater clarity can be gained by removing the structure of the table and the low loadings.

Table 21–2. Highest Loadings of Sixteen Foreign Conflict Variables on Orthogonal Factors[a]

Variables	Orthogonally Rotated Factors			
	S_1	S_2	S_3	S_4
8. Negative communications	.95			
13. Accusations	.94			
9. Written negative communications	.92			
10. Oral negative communications	.89			
6. Negative acts	.77			
15. Warnings	.69			
14. Representations—protests	.63			
1. Violent acts		−.97		
2. Planned violence		−.97		
4. Military acts or clashes		−.97		
5. Days of violence		−.91		
11. Written or oral negative communications		−.65		
16. Antiforeign demonstrations			.91	
7. Diplomatic rebuffs				.71
3. Incidence of violence				−.60
12. Unclassified communications				

[a] From Table 17–2.

> *Example 21–8.* The low loadings of Table 21–1 are removed as shown in Table 21–2.

By shifting from displaying numerical loadings to representing loading ranges by circles or squares, the contrast in loadings can be made more graphic.

> *Example 21–9.* The loadings of Table 21–1 are shown as different sized circles in Table 21–3.

21.2.2 GRAPHS

As an adjunct to the factor matrix, the loadings on the individual factors may be presented in bar graphs.[10] Each factor is a graph with the loading magnitudes given by a vertical bar.

> *Example 21–10.* The first and second factors of the 16 foreign conflict variables given in Table 17–2 are shown in bar graphs in Fig. 21–2.

10. For an applied example of this approach, see Ahmavaara and Markkanen (1958, Part II).

Table 21–3

Loadings of Sixteen Foreign Conflict Variables on Orthogonal Factors[a]

Variables[b]	S_1	S_2[c]	S_3	S_4
	Orthogonally Rotated Factors			
8.	●			
13.	●c			
9.	●			
10.	●			
6.	●			
15.	•			
14.	•			
1.		●		
2.		●		
4.		●		
5.		●		
11.		•		
16.			●	
7.				●
3.				•
12.				

● ≥ .86 ⎫
● ≥ .71 ⎬ absolute loadings
• ≥ .50 ⎭

[a] From Table 17–2.
[b] Numbers refer to variables listed in Table 21–1.
[c] All signs reversed.

Another form of graph can be used to display the relative contributions of each factor to the total variance. This is the pie graph often employed in national budget displays.[11] Since the factor contribution to total variance is dependent on the sample of variables, the researcher may be wary of using pie graphs except when the variables exhaust the population (as in a factor analysis of a transaction matrix of all nations, where the nations are the variables).

11. This type of graph has been used for factor results by Wood (1961).

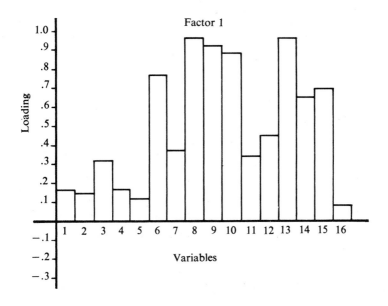

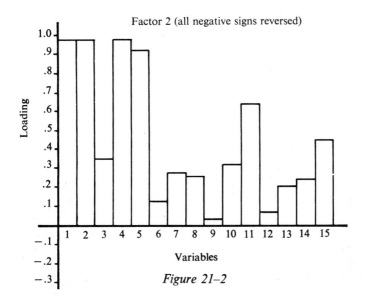

Figure 21–2

Example 21–11. A pie graph of the variance contribution of the factors of the 16 foreign conflict variables given in Table 17–2 is shown in Fig. 21–3.

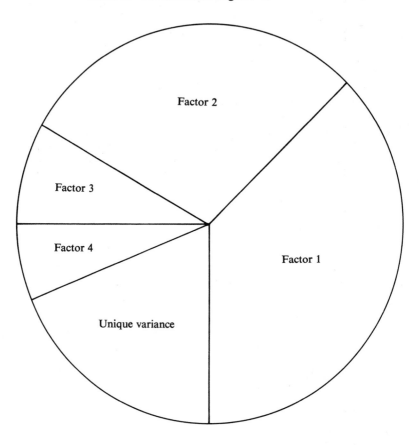

Figure 21–3

21.2.3 PLOTS

Two kinds of plots that may be helpful in displaying the factor results are *point* and *vector* plots. The point plot simply locates the position of a variable in the space of the factors by a point. This type of plot is familiar from analytic geometry or statistics. A point plot is also very useful for factor scores and shows the relative location of the cases on the dimensions, as shown, for example, in Fig. 6–3. A point plot is limited by the number of dimensions that can be clearly laid out in a plane. For more than three dimensions, a selection of the most interesting two or three dimensions must be made for the plot, or several different plots of factor pairs or triads can be made.

If there are no bipolar factors, *isoplanes* can be added to the point plots. Drawn to distinguish loading magnitudes, isoplanes nicely display the variable clusters and complexity. Moreover, although plotted in two or three dimensions, the isoplane lines can be drawn around variables loaded on additional factors. A variation is achieved by removing the axes from the figure and letting the isoplanes stand alone.

> *Example 21–12.* In Fig. 21–4, the 16 foreign conflict variables are plotted in the space of the first two ortho- gonal factors. Isoplanes identify all four factors. As

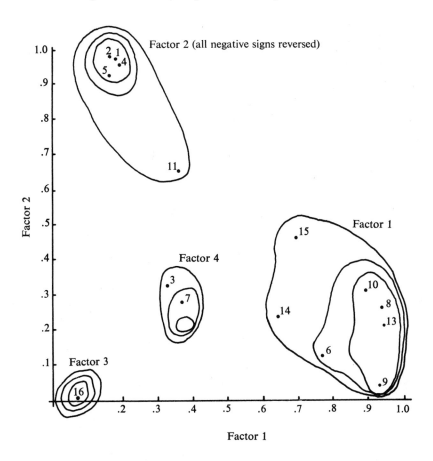

Figure 21–4

measured by the squared loadings, the inner isoplane is
drawn around variables with 75 per cent or more of their
variance accounted for by the factor. The second isoplane
includes variables with 50–75 per cent, and the outer
isoplane incorporates those with 25–49 per cent.[12] The
factor axes may be removed for greater clarity as shown in
Fig. 21–5. When axes are removed, the factors defining the
space (factors 1 and 2 in the figure) must still be indicated.

As an alternative to a point plot, variables can be plotted as vectors.
This is most in accord with the geometric representation of the factor
model given here. Vector plots clearly display the direction of the

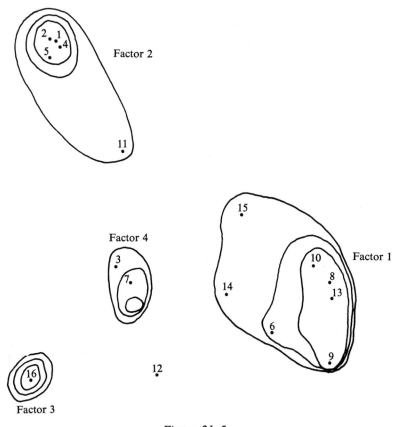

Figure 21–5

12. The plot suggests that factors 1 and 2 would better represent the clusters if
they were given an oblique rotation toward each other. That this is indeed the case
is shown by the oblique solution in Table 17–3 and the correlation of .30 in the
left half of Table 17–5 between oblique factors 1 and 2.

variables in the factor space and the degree to which the variables are explained (h_j = length of vector) by the factors. This approach is also very useful for plotting the factor scores.

> *Example 21–13.* Figure 21–6 displays the vector plot of the 16 foreign conflict variables of Table 17–2. A vector plot can also be made of factor scores, as shown in Fig. 21–7. Only those dyads with the largest factor scores on the two dimensions of Fig. 21–6 are shown.

21.2.4 VENN DIAGRAMS

By defining a circle or oval as being the total variance of a variable or factor, the saturation and complexity of the variables can be displayed by overlapping Venn diagrams. This approach is most useful for small variable studies.

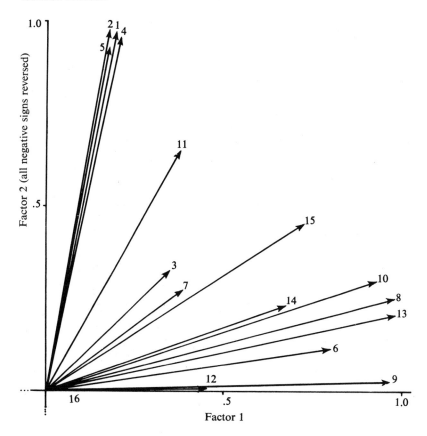

Figure 21–6

Example 21–14. Figure 21–8 diagrams the factors of the 16 foreign conflict variables. The overlap portions of the ovals are in proportion to the variance of a variable accounted for by the factor. Variables with less than 25 per cent variance in common with a factor are not shown.

Rather than overlap the ovals, factors can be connected to variables by linkage lines. The strength of the relationship can be indicated by the width of the lines. This approach is especially clear for higher-order analyses, as shown in Fig. 18–2.

Example 21–15. The linkages of variables and ortho-gonally rotated factors of Table 17–2 are shown in Fig. 21–9.

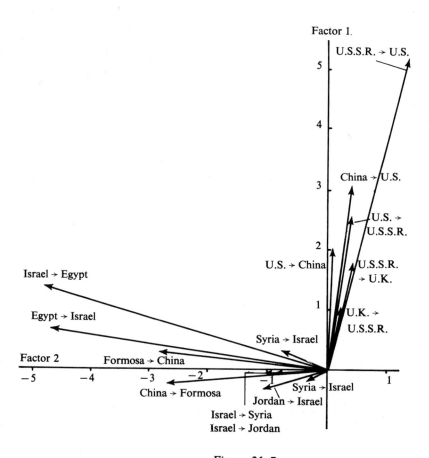

Figure 21–7

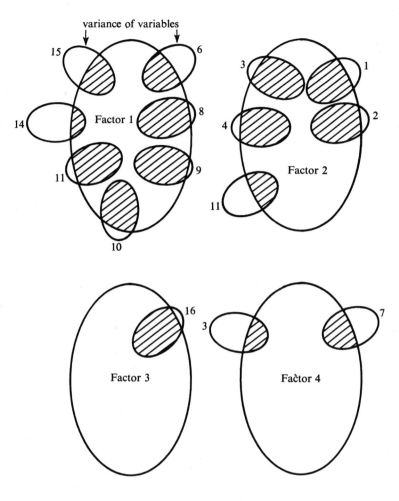

Figure 21–8

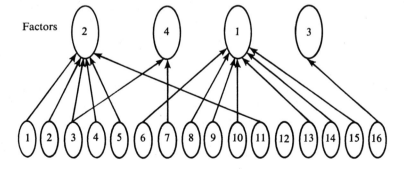

Figure 21–9

22. Distances

Factor analysis has been most often applied to *samples* of individuals to derive general factors of performance, ability, achievement, personality, attitudes, and so on. The individuals involved in such studies were not of intrinsic interest except in the variance they contributed to defining the factors.

Lately, however, factor analysis is being increasingly applied to samples that *are* of inherent interest. Analyses of Senate voting, judicial attitudes, UN voting, national socioeconomic variables and characteristics of cities, to name just a few current interests, are being done (see Chapter 24). Each case involved in these studies, such as the United Kingdom, Supreme Court Justice Black, or Chicago, may itself be of great substantive interest and a frequent focus of research. It was to be expected that with the analyses of such samples, therefore, a greater interest would grow in their factor scores (Chapter 19).

Once factor scores are determined, an interesting question can be asked of the cases: "What are the distances between cases in the factor space?" In other words, how dissimilar are the cases from each other? If the interest is in a particular pair of cases, g and i, such as the U.S.

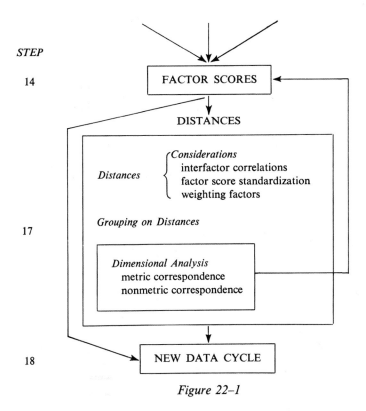

STEP

14

17

18

Figure 22-1

and U.S.S.R., Chicago and Munich, or Senators Thurmond and Smith, then the question can be made specific: What is the distance between cases *g* and *i* in factor space?

Although previous texts on factor analysis have not dealt with this question, the increasing usefulness and importance of the distance notion and the close relationship of mathematical distances to the factor model warrants consideration here. The first section will discuss the geometry and computing considerations of distances in *p*-dimensional space and will be followed by a section on the grouping of cases according to their distances. The final section of this chapter will deal with *dimensional analysis*—the determination of the dimensions defining the space containing the distances when only the distances are known.

The distance mode of the factor analysis research design is shown in Fig. 22-1. Dimensional analysis has an arrow leading back to factor scores to indicate that the factor scores result from dimensional analysis and not the other way round.

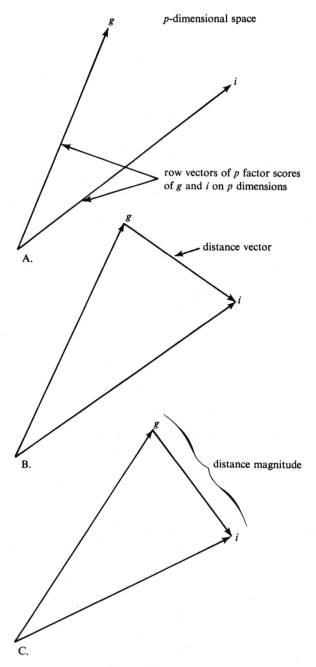

Figure 22–2

22.1 Distances in *p*-Dimensional Space

22.1.1 GEOMETRY

As discussed in Section 19.1, a factor score locates a case as a point in the space defined by the factors. The factor scores describe, geometrically, a vector representing the location and magnitude of a case in *p*-dimensional space. This is shown in Fig. 6–4, for example.

Let a line be drawn between the *p*-dimensional vector points of any two cases, *g* and *i*, as in Fig. 22–2A. This line can also be treated as a vector, in this case a *distance vector* (Definition 3–21), as shown in Fig. 22–2B. Now, as indicated in Fig. 22–2C, the *magnitude* or length (Definition 3–25) of the distance vector is a precise measure of the Euclidean distance between cases *g* and *i*. *By computing the magnitudes of the distance vectors between cases of interest, the researcher can compare his cases in terms of their similarity to each other on the p factors.*[1]

> *Example 22–1.* Consider the following hypothetical factor scores of the U.S., U.S.S.R., and U.K. on factor-dimensions of economic development, size, and density.
>
> | | Economic Development | Size | Density |
> |---|---|---|---|
> | U.S. | 2.0 | 1.5 | .6 |
> | U.S.S.R. | 1.0 | 2.0 | .9 |
> | U.K. | 1.4 | .5 | 2.0 |
>
> These nations can be plotted as vectors in the space of the three dimensions as shown in Fig. 22–3A. For clarity, Fig. 22–3B gives the point representation of each nation's location and the distance vectors between them. The relative lengths of the distance vectors shows the U.S. and U.S.S.R. to be closer to each other in the space of economic development, size, and density than are the U.S. and U.K. or the U.S.S.R. and U.K.

Distances provide a powerful tool for comparing cases.[2] The *variance* of the variables that were factor-analyzed is embodied in the resulting

1. Harman (1967, Section 4.8) treats of the geometric representation of distance. A less technical discussion is given by Torgerson (1958, pp. 251–54). A geometric consideration of distance can be found in most linear or vector algebra texts, such as Paige and Swift (1961).

2. For an applied example, see Osgood *et al.* (1957), who measure distances between concepts in the space of their dimensions and develop a physical model of these distances, applying the distance notion directly to data. For other applied examples, see Berry (1961a, 1965a), Ray and Berry (1965), Russett (1967a, 1967b), and Rummel (1965b).

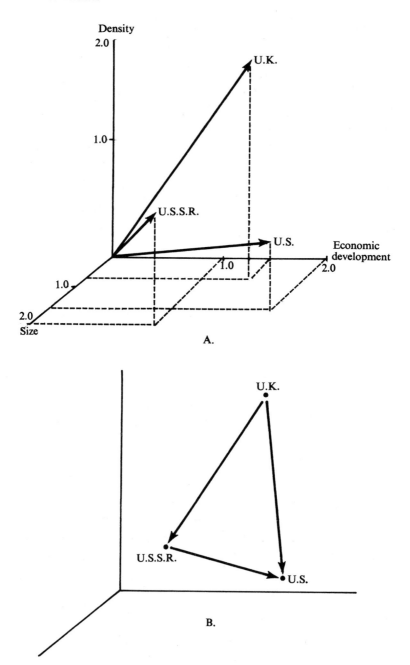

Figure 22–3

factors and reflected in the distances between cases. Therefore, comparing cases on their distances is in effect comparing the cases on the original variables *except that the artificial weighting of correlated variables is removed.*

> *Example 22–2.* Consider eight intercorrelated economic variables and two additional uncorrelated variables, one social and one political. A comparison of cases across these variables would be highly weighted by the economic variables. A component analysis (Section 5.3) would reduce the variation among these 10 variables to three statistically independent dimensions—economic, social, and political—that then could *equally* enter into computing distances between cases.

22.1.2 COMPUTING DISTANCES

We have already established the notation (3–18) for the distance *magnitude* as d. Subscripts g and i will be used to indicate that the distance is measured between (factor score) vectors g and i.

> *Notation 22–1.* $\vec{d}_{gi}$ = distance vector between (factor score) vectors g and i.

By Definition 3–21, the distance vector between factor score vectors for cases g and i is computed by subtracting one from the other:

$$\vec{d}_{gi} = S_i - S_g, \qquad (22\text{–}1)$$

where S_i and S_g are vectors of factor scores on p dimensions for cases i and g, respectively. More explicitly, but less concisely, the equation can be given as

$$
\begin{array}{cccc}
\vec{d}_{gi} & S_i & S_g & S_i - S_g \\[4pt]
\begin{bmatrix} d_{gi1} \\ d_{gi2} \\ \vdots \\ d_{gip} \end{bmatrix}
& = \begin{bmatrix} s_{i1} \\ s_{i2} \\ \vdots \\ s_{ip} \end{bmatrix}
& - \begin{bmatrix} s_{g1} \\ s_{g2} \\ \vdots \\ s_{gp} \end{bmatrix}
& = \begin{bmatrix} s_{i1} - s_{g1} \\ s_{i2} - s_{g2} \\ \vdots \\ s_{ip} - s_{gp} \end{bmatrix} \\[6pt]
\uparrow & \uparrow & \uparrow & \uparrow \\
& \text{factor scores} & \text{factor scores} & \\
& \text{of case } i & \text{of case } g &
\end{array}
$$

distance
vector

The length or *magnitude* of the distance vector is then the square root of the inner product of the distance vector with itself. From Notation 3–17 and Definition 3–26,

$$d_{gi} = |\vec{d}_{gi}| = |S_i - S_g| = \left[\sum_{l=1}^{p} (s_{il} - s_{gl})^2\right]^{1/2}$$

(22–2)

$$= [(s_{i1} - s_{g1})^2 + (s_{i2} - s_{g2})^2 + \cdots + (s_{ip} - s_{gp})^2]^{1/2}.$$

Example 22–3. Let there be cases a and b with factor scores s_{a1}, s_{a2} and s_{b1}, s_{b2} on two factor-dimensions. The distance vector $\vec{d}_{ab}$ is

$$\begin{bmatrix} s_{b1} - s_{a1} \\ s_{b2} - s_{a2} \end{bmatrix}$$

and is shown in Fig. 22–4A, along with the factor score vectors for cases a and b. The length of the distance vector is

$$d_{ab} = [(s_{b1} - s_{a1})^2 + (s_{b2} - s_{a2})^2]^{1/2}.$$

Let $A = (s_{b2} - s_{a2})$, $B = (s_{b1} - s_{a1})$, and $C = d_{ab}$. Then, as shown in Fig. 22–4B, $C = (A^2 + B^2)^{1/2}$. This is the well-known Pythagorean theorem for two dimensions. For $p > 2$, the formula

$$d_{gi} = \left[\sum_{l=1}^{p} (s_{il} - s_{gl})^2\right]^{1/2}$$

is a straightforward extension of the theorem.

Example 22–4. In Table 17–2 are shown the factors of 16 foreign conflict variables. The distances between 6 selected nation dyads in the four-dimensional factor space are given in Table 22–1.

Example 22–5. The distances between 6 selected nations in the space of 14 dimensions of the 236 cross-national variables of Example 9–7 are shown in Table 22–2. Also shown are the means and standard deviations of the distances of each nation from the 81 others. Moreover, the mean for the matrix and the standard deviation of nations means in the full 82 by 82 nation-distance matrix are also given. These statistics enable the relative distance values in Table 22–2 to be assessed.

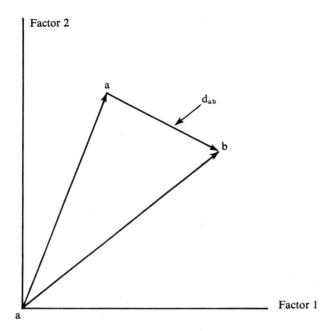

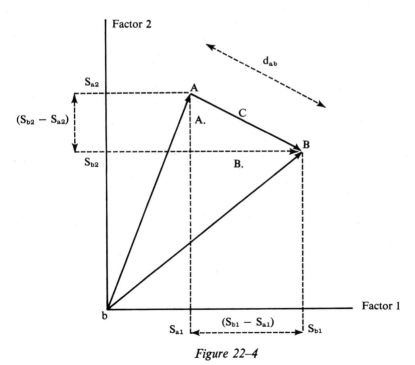

Figure 22–4

Table 22-1. Distance between Selected Dyads in the Factor Space of Sixteen Foreign Conflict Variables[a]

Dyad[b]	U.S. → U.S.S.R.	U.S. → China	U.S.S.R. → U.S.	U.S.S.R. → U.K.	Egypt → Israel	Israel → Egypt
U.S. → U.S.S.R.	.00					
U.S. → China	4.22	.00				
U.S.S.R. → U.S.	6.08	4.39	.00			
U.S.S.R. → U.K.	4.65	.60	4.52	.00		
Egypt → Israel	6.94	5.36	8.60	5.66	.00	
Israel → Egypt	7.22	5.25	8.08	5.55	1.27	.00

[a] Distances computed on unweighted, standardized factor scores. Average distance for 75 dyads is 2.33.
[b] The conflict data were collected in terms of the behavior of one nation toward another, A → B.

Table 22-2. Distance between Selected Nations in the Factor Space of 236 Cross-National Variables[a]

Nation	U.S.	U.S.S.R.	China	U.K.	France	Mexico	Mean[b]	Standard Deviation[b]
U.S.	.00						13.87	1.80
U.S.S.R.	10.82	.00					7.95	1.36
China	13.43	6.06	.00				5.11	1.68
U.K.	10.38	6.89	6.44	.00			6.03	1.29
France	12.24	7.78	4.94	4.74	.00		4.91	1.58
Mexico	13.95	7.98	4.90	5.73	3.50	.00	3.98	1.99

Matrix mean = 5.139.   Standard deviation of nation means = 1.44.

[a] Distances computed on unweighted, standardized basic variable factor score estimates.
[b] For the full 82 by 82 nation distance matrix, see Rummel (1969). These means and standard deviations are for the distance of each nation from the 81 other nations. Thus, for example, the U.S. has a mean distance of 13.87 from 81 nations.

Equation (22–2) assumes that the dimensions are orthogonal. *These distances are invariant of rotation.* They will be the same whether computed on *p*-unrotated or *p*-rotated orthogonal factors. Although the distances are also invariant of oblique factors, the correlations between the factors have to be included in the computation. For oblique factors,

$$d_{gi} = \left[\sum_{m=1}^{p} \sum_{l=1}^{p} (s_{im} - s_{gm})(s_{il} - s_{gl})r_{lm} \right]^{1/2}, \qquad (22\text{–}3)$$

where r_{lm} is the correlation between factors l and m. If the factor correlations are all zero, then Eq. (22–3) reduces to Eq. (22–2), the orthogonal case.

Because the factor scores may have unequal standard deviations (especially in the case of composite or basic variable estimates), *it should be a practice to standardize the factor scores prior to computing distances.* Otherwise, factors that have scores with larger variance will have greater influence on the distance values.

However, it may not be desirable to give each factor the same weight. We may want factors of greater "importance"—determined either from the per cent of total variance accounted for by a factor or from some external criterion—to have a greater influence on the resulting distances. To accommodate different weights, Eq. (22–2) can be written:

$$d_{gi} = \left[\sum_{l=1}^{p} (s_{il} - s_{gl})^2 w_l \right]^{1/2}, \qquad (22\text{–}4)$$

where w_l = weight of factor S_l. If the factors are to be weighted equally, $w_l = 1.0$ for all factors, and Eq. (22–4) reduces to Eq. (22–2). For the oblique factor space, weights can be included in Eq. (22–3), viz,

$$d_{gi} = \left[\sum_{m=1}^{p} \sum_{l=1}^{p} (s_{im} - s_{gm})(s_{il} - s_{gl})r_{lm}w_l w_m \right]^{1/2}, \qquad (22\text{–}5)$$

where w_l and w_m are weights for factors S_l and S_m.

The Euclidean distance function of Eq. (22–2) is only one of a variety of possible distance models. A set of such functions can be defined for orthogonal dimensions by

$$d_{gi} = \left[\sum_{l=1}^{p} |s_{il} - s_{gl}|^{\theta} \right]^{1/\theta}, \qquad (22\text{–}6)$$

where $|s_{il} - s_{gl}|$ is the absolute value of $s_{il} - s_{gl}$. When the exponent θ equals 2, we have the Euclidean distance or straight line distance between two points. If θ equals 1, the "city block" distance model results.

> *Example 22-6.* A point-to-point straight line distance is appropriate in a desert. In order to get from one point to another in a city, however, we usually go in right-angle patterns around the city blocks. The "city block" model measures this kind of distance, since it is the sum of the absolute difference (the length of each block) in factor scores.

For some data, $\theta = 1$ may be the most appropriate distance model[3] or some value between 1 and 2 may be applicable. It should be pointed out, however, that for $\theta = 2$ the distances are invariant of rotation but for $\theta \neq 2$ the d_{gi} can vary with the position of the factor axes (Kruskal, 1964a, p. 23).

22.2 Grouping on Distances

With the calculation of a distance matrix for cases, we may wish to group cases on their distances. The question is: What cases cluster close together in p-dimensional space? The answer to this question can be approached in a number of ways. Since the distances are proportional to correlations between factor scores [Eq. (3–8)], the distance matrix can be treated like a correlation matrix. Cluster analysis or linkage analysis (Section 8.2.1), or step-wise grouping procedures may be used on such matrices.[4] One possible procedure will be elaborated here.[5]

Cases similarly situated in space at zero distance from each other will have the same distances from other cases. As the distance between two cases departs from zero, the similarity between their distances from all other cases becomes less. Accordingly, a measure of the nearness of two cases is the statistical dependence of their distances from other cases, as given in the columns (or rows, since a distance matrix is symmetrical) of the distance matrix. Clusters of interdependent columns of distances—that is, clusters of cases in terms of their distances—can be determined in the same way that clusters of variables in terms of their columns of correlations in the correlation matrix are defined.

3. For applications, see Householder and Landahl (1945), Coombs (1964, pp. 202–6, Chapter 20), and Attneave (1950).

4. See, for example, Stone (1960).

5. For applications of the approach to be discussed, see Russett (1967a, 1967b) and Rummel (1967a).

The problem is to find the smallest number of orthogonal dimensions that describe the interdependencies among the columns of distances and to rotate these dimensions so that each will delineate a cluster of cases. Each cluster will then be a distinct group of cases that are close together in space in terms of their distances from other cases. This is a factor analysis problem.

The computational procedures are simple if a factor analysis program is available that will allow a correlation matrix to be input. First, scale the distances so that they will be analogous to correlations:

$$d_{gi}^s = 1 - \frac{d_{gi}}{d_{max}}, \tag{22-7}$$

where d_{gi}^s = scaled distance, and d_{max} = largest distance in the distance matrix. The scaled distances will vary between zero and unity; zero will equal the furthest distance between two cases and unity the closest.[6]

Next, input the scaled distance matrix to a factor analysis program *as though it were a correlation matrix* and factor it. The resulting factors may be rotated to simple structure to determine the clusters. The same considerations with regard to factor model, communality, factor technique number of factors, and type of rotation can apply to the distance matrix.

Since cases that are close in space are near unity on their scaled distances, high case loadings on the same factor mean the cases group

6. The discussion in Example 12-2 is relevant here. I have investigated the alternative scaling,

$$d_{gi}^s \leq \frac{d_{gi} - \bar{d}}{\Delta},$$

where $\bar{d}$ = mean distance of distance matrix,
   $\Delta = (d_{max} - \bar{d})$ if $(d_{max} - \bar{d}) \geq (\bar{d} - d_{min})$,
   $\Delta = (\bar{d} - d_{min})$ if $(d_{max} - \bar{d}) < (\bar{d} - d_{min})$,
   d_{max} = largest distance in matrix, and
   d_{min} = smallest distance in matrix.
This scaling places the scaled zero distances at the average and allows high negative or high positive scaled distances to exist. In effect, the factor analysis of this matrix will delineate the *bipolar* groups of cases. An application of this to distances of nations in the space of seven dimensions (weighted by proportion of total variance) of 1955 UN voting (Rummel, 1965b) brought out eight groups, one of which was bipolar: Brazil, Canada, Colombia, France, Nicaragua, Panama, United Kingdom, Union of South Africa, and the United States versus Egypt, India, Saudi Arabia, Syria, Yemen, Yugoslavia, Czechoslovakia, Mexico, Poland, and the U.S.S.R. Bipolar groups can also be found by factoring the product moment correlation or the intraclass correlation of the cases on their distances. The intraclass is the best for this purpose, but neither approach seems to make as fine a distinction among groups as does the factor analysis of the distances scaled according to Eq. (22-7).

Table 22–3. Similarity Grouping of Directed Dyads[a] on Raw Data Dimensions of Foreign Conflict[b]

I	II	III	IV	V
.93 N. Korea–U.S.	.85 Greece–U.S.S.R.	.83 Japan–U.S.	.89 Egypt–Israel	.83 U.S.S.R.–U.S.
.93 Italy–Egypt	.84 Yugoslavia–U.S.S.R.	.83 India–Portugal	.88 Israel–Egypt	.71 China–U.S.
.93 Yemen–U.K.	.84 W. Germany–U.S.S.R.	.78 S. Korea–U.S.	.69 Formosa–China	.50 U.S.–China
.93 China–S. Korea	.83 U.S.S.R.–E. Germany	.76 S. Vietnam–U.S.	.64 China–Formosa	.43 U.S.–U.S.S.R.
.93 Yugoslavia–Italy	.82 Burma–U.S.	.74 Greece–U.K.		
.93 Czech.–W. Ger.	.83 Japan–China	.70 Jordan–France		
.93 U.K.–S. Arabia	.83 Iraq–Egypt	.63 S. Korea–Japan		
.93 Argentina–Brazil	.82 W. Ger.–E. Ger.	.62 Afghanistan–Pakistan		
.93 Guatemala–El Salvador	.81 Argentina–U.K.	.59 U.S.–U.S.S.R.		
.93 Italy–Yugoslavia	.81 U.S.–Czechoslovakia	.55 Pakistan–Afghanistan		
.93 El Salvador–Guatemala	.81 Italy–U.K.	.52 Pakistan–India		
.93 Laos–N. Vietnam	.81 U.S.–Japan			
.93 Israel–Lebanon	.81 Egypt–Turkey			
.93 India–Pakistan	.81 U.K.–N. Vietnam			
.93 Nicar.–Hond.	.81 Yugoslavia–Rumania			
.93 Hond.–Nicar.	.81 Pakistan–China			
.93 U.K.–Yemen	.81 Chile–U.K.			
.93 Egypt–Italy	.80 N. Vietnam–U.S.			
.93 U.S.–N. Korea	.80 Egypt–Iraq			
.92 Formosa–U.S.S.R.	.72 U.S.S.R.–W. Germany			
.92 Burma–Formosa	.71 France–U.S.S.R.			
.92 Formosa–Burma	.61 N. Vietnam–S. Vietnam			
.92 E. Ger.–Czech.	.56 U.K.–U.S.			
.92 N. Vietnam–Laos	.52 U.S.S.R.–U.K.			
.92 Burma–Thailand				

I	
.92 Thailand–Burma	E. Germany–W. Germany
.91 Lebanon–Israel	Jordan–Turkey
.90 Bulgaria–Israel	Jordan–U.S.
.27 Israel–Bulgaria	U.S.–Poland
.89 Egypt–U.K.	
.84 S. Korea–China	
.81 N. Korea–S. Korea	
.81 Syria–Turkey	
.81 U.K.–Egypt	
.80 S. Korea–N. Korea	
.79 Costa Rica–Nicaragua	
.77 Israel–Syria	
.73 Israel–Jordan	
.68 Nicaragua–Costa Rica	
.59 Jordan–Israel	
.54 Pakistan–India	
.52 Syria–Israel	

[a] The first nation is the actor and the second is the object.

[b] These groups are the biquartimin oblique rotated primary pattern factors of the distances between dyads in the space of the raw data dimensions of foreign conflict. Only the 75 dyads high on conflict along any one of the violence, negative communication, negative sanctions, or antiforeign behavior factors are included. "High" equals a score on a factor of more than 1.5 standard deviations. The loadings give the degree of "containment" of a dyad by a group. With the exception of Group V, only loadings ≥ .50 are shown.

together in their distances; the size of the loading can measure the degree of group membership. A low communality (h^2) for a case will mean that the case is fairly isolated in space, that is, that the case is distinctly different on the original data that were analyzed. The sum of squared loadings of each factor will measure the size of each group, and the total sum of squared loadings for all factors will measure the overall cohesion of the cases.[7]

> *Example 22–7.* A distance matrix was calculated between all dyads having at least one high factor score on the 16-variable foreign conflict factors (Table 17–2). Unweighted factor scores were used. The distance matrix was scaled by Eq. (22–7) and input (as though a correlation matrix) to a principal axes factor analysis program; a component factor analysis was computed. The resulting factors were rotated to an oblique biquartimin solution. Six linear independent (oblique) groups were defined, as shown in Table 22–3. To determine whether the groups had an underlying substantive communality, their factor scores were checked. The group characteristics are given in Table 22–4.

Table 22–4. Description of Group Characteristics

		Dimensions			
Central Dyad	Group	Military Violence	Negative Communica- tions	Negative Sanctions	Antiforeign Behavior
N. Korea–U.S.	I	Some	Some	None	None
Greece–U.S.S.R.	II	None	None–some	Some–many	None
Japan–U.S.	III	None	None–many	None–some	Some–much
Egypt–Israel	IV	Much	Many	Some–many	None–some
U.S.S.R.–U.S.	V	None–some	Many	Many	None–much
	VI [a]	None	Some	None–some	None

[a] This group is not shown. It is composed of 258 dyads whose conflict behavior was not significant along any one of the dimensions.

I have used this approach to grouping cases on distances on such diverse data as distances between nations on UN voting dimensions, on political system characteristics, on conflict behavior (Rummel,

7. For some data I have found it convenient to include in the distance matrix a *marker case*: one that has a desired pattern of factor scores, such as all zeros. In foreign conflict studies, for example, I have included an all-zero case among the distances to locate the "peace" dyad in space. Then, the relative loading of this dyad on the resulting dimensions of the distance matrix aids in interpreting the different groupings found.

1967a), and on the dimensions of 236 variables discussed in Example 9–7 (Rummel, 1967a). The resulting groups were always meaningful in containing nations that were indeed near each other in factor space. The results of the political system characteristics can be given here.

> *Example 22–8.* The factor scores (Table 6–9) of 82 nations on 3 orthogonal dimensions of 10 political characteristics (Table 6–4) were used to determine the *political distances* between nations. These were calculated by Eq. (22–2) on unweighted factor scores, scaled by Eq. (22–7), input to a principal axes program, and factored using the component analysis model. The resulting factors were orthogonally rotated. As shown in Table 22–5, four groups emerged: Communist systems, monarchies, Western-type democracies, and dictatorships.

In following the above grouping approach, the distance matrix is considered a data matrix of meaningful magnitudes, and it is desired to find the components or common factors of variation in them, as for a factor analysis of any correlation matrix. *Confusion can result from this procedure, however, unless it is clear that the research question does not involve the dimensions of the space containing the distance vectors.* If the concern is with the space containing the distance *vectors*, that is, the dimensions of these distance *vectors*, then the procedures of the next section are called for. These procedures will determine the very dimensions that were used to generate the distances in the first place and thus will add no new information if these dimensions are already known. If the researcher wants to look at the columns of the distance matrix, however, *where the elements are distance magnitudes and not distance vectors*, and ask "What are the clustering of interrelationships of the columns of distance *magnitudes*?" then this is a simple structure factor analysis question that can be answered by factor analysis. The resulting factors describe this clustering of cases and the number of orthogonal factors indicate the number of such clusters or groups. These factors will in general be different from the dimensions underlying the distance vectors.[8]

8. Confusion on this point may have misled more than one researcher. Ekman, for example, had a matrix of data which he could assume measured the distance between subjects on emotion (1955) or color vision (1954). His implicit question was: "What are the dimensions of the space containing the distance vectors with these lengths?" His technique, however, was the procedure outlined in this section and led to dimensions of interrelationship of the subjects on the magnitude of their distances—an unrelated answer. The proper technique would have been the dimensional analysis of Section 23.3.2, below.

Table 22–5. Similarity Grouping of Nations on Factor Dimensions of Ten Political Variables [a]

I	II	III	IV
	75–100 Per Cent Variation in Common		
Australia	Republic of China	Albania	Afghanistan
Austria	Cuba	Bulgaria	Ethiopia
Belgium	El Salvador	China	Iran
Canada	Guatemala	Czechoslovakia	Jordan
Costa Rica	Haiti	East Germany	Nepal
Denmark	Iraq	Hungary	Saudi Arabia
Finland	South Korea	North Korea	
West Germany	Nicaragua	Outer Mongolia	
Greece	Pakistan	U.S.S.R.	
India	Paraguay	Yugoslavia	
Irish Republic	Peru	Rumania	
Israel	Syria		
Italy	Thailand		
Japan			
Netherlands			
New Zealand			
Norway			
Philippines			
Sweden			
Switzerland			
United Kingdom			
United States			
Uruguay			
	50–74 Per Cent Variation in Common		
Colombia	Argentina		Cambodia
Bolivia	Brazil		Yemen
Ceylon	Burma		
Chile	Honduras		
Dominican Republic	Panama		
France	Spain		
Mexico			
	25–49 Per Cent Variation in Common		
Lebanon	Ecuador		Libya
Libya	Egypt		
Union of South Africa	Lebanon		
Venezuela	Liberia		
	Portugal		
	Turkey		

[a] Dimensions are given in Table 6–4 and factor scores in Table 6–9. Groups are orthogonally varimax factors of the scaled distance matrix. Variations in common have been determined by the square of the factor loadings for each nation.

An important consideration in factoring a scaled distance matrix to determine the similarity grouping of cases is the *number* of such groups that may be defined. Practical experience with the factoring of large-order scaled distance matrices (around 80×80), calculated on factor dimensions ranging from 1 to 14, has shown that $2p$ factors will account

Table 22–6. Number of Factors Obtained from a Factor Analysis of Scaled Distance Matrices

Number (p) of Factors Used in Computing Distances[a]	Order of Distance Matrix	Number of Resulting Factors and Trace Accounted for[b]	Trace Accounted for by 2p Factors (per cent)
1	82×82	3 (96.0%)	95.6
1	82×82	5 (94.0%)	86.2
2	69×69	4 (92.0%)	92.0
4	75×75	5 (91.8%)	94.0
4	99×99	10 (91.3%)	88.8
4	41×41	5 (82.9%)	87.4
5	69×69	6 (92.7%)	95.1
7	56×56	7 (91.4%)	96.1
7	56×56	6 (84.6%)	87.4

a Unweighted dimensions.
b These are the number of factors with eigenvalues greater than unity for a component analysis of the distance matrix. Trace accounted for equals the trace of the scaled distance matrix (which equals the number of cases) divided by the sum of the eigenvalues extracted.

for almost all the trace of the scaled distance matrix. Table 22–6 shows the results of several analyses (computations were all in single precision arithmetic). All percentages of the trace at $2p$ are within 86 per cent, and most are over 90 per cent.

22.3 Dimensional Analysis

Eventually, as the methodological problems are clarified and worked out and as the connection to factor analysis is more thoroughly explored, what is only a section here may become a considerable portion of some future factor analysis text. *For what integral calculus is to differential calculus, dimensional analysis is to factor analysis.* Differential calculus is concerned with differentiating a function—determining the derivative dy/dx (rate of change of a variable y with respect to a variable x at a given value of x). Integral calculus reverses the process and asks: Given the derivative dy/dx, what was the original function differentiated?

The case is similar with *dimensional analysis.*[9] Factor analysis is a process: data → factors (dimensions) → factor scores → distances between cases. Dimensional analysis, however, is a reverse process: distances between cases → factor scores. *In dimensional analysis, the distances are given. The underlying dimensions of the distance vectors with these lengths are unknown.* In dimensional analysis we try to work backward along the factor design. The research question is therefore: What are the original dimensions of the *distance vectors* with given lengths?

> *Example 22–9.* Consider a trade matrix whose elements are the total trade between row and column nations. These trade elements may be considered as measuring the distances between nations in transactions, cooperation, or some other relevant concept. We may ask of this data: "What are the minimum underlying transaction dimensions that would produce distance vectors with *lengths* represented by the trade data?"

Note the difference between this question and that of the previous section, where the concern was with using factor analysis to group cases on the basis of their distances. To be clear as to the difference, both questions will again be given.

GROUPING ON DISTANCES: What are the dimensions defining the clustering of groups of cases in terms of the *interrelationship of their distances* from each other?

DIMENSIONAL ANALYSIS: What are the *original dimensions of the distance vectors whose lengths are those given*?

The procedures for dimensional analysis depend on whether the data are assumed to correspond metrically to the distances or not. These two cases will be discussed in separate sections.[10]

9. In the literature, dimensional analysis often goes under the label of multidimensional scaling, multidimensional analysis, similarity analysis, distance analysis, or multidimensional unfolding.

10. An excellent discussion of various approaches to dimensional analysis and distance models is Chapter 11 of Torgerson (1958). A matrix of distances is often called a dissimilarities matrix, or dissimilarities data. For a number of approaches to such data, see Coombs (1964). Coombs's whole book is very relevant to the notion of distances and well worth reading for modes of generating and analyzing data. His theory of data is that individuals and stimuli are points (vectors) in a psychological space. The preference an individual shows for stimuli means that the stimuli-individual points are closer than other stimuli. There is then a distance between all points in this space, and this distance can be related

22.3.1 METRIC CORRESPONDENCE

If we assume that our data are *equivalent* to distances on an interval scale in Euclidean space and are without error, then the dimensional analysis question has an unambiguous answer. The data may be represented by any numbers measured on any scale whatsoever (with the provision that the data for any given data matrix are measured on the same scale and in the same units). The basic assumption is that there is a one-to-one correspondence between the data and the Euclidean distances in the space whose dimensions are desired.

In a remarkably brief article, Young and Householder (1938) offered a mathematical solution to the dimensional problem for such data.[11] To present their solution, however, we will need the following notation.

> *Notation 22–2.* $D_{n \times n}$ = a case by case symmetrical data matrix (e.g., a trade matrix), where $i = 1, 2, \ldots, g, \ldots, n$.
>
> d_{gi}^* = an element of $D_{n \times n}$ that can be assumed to measure some kind of distance between cases g and i; the larger the d_{gi}, the greater the distance.

We have previously defined d_{gi} as the *length* of a distance vector $\vec{d_{gi}}$ (Notations 3–18, 22–1).

The n cases of $D_{n \times n}$ are points in the space of the desired dimensions, and the d_{gi}^* represent the length, d_{gi}, of the distance vectors between cases g and i. In order to determine these dimensions, an *origin* of the space must be defined. Since any one of the n cases can be taken as the origin, let the origin be at the nth case. The p orthogonal dimensions of the space are defined by the matrix $S_{(n-1) \times p}$ that gives the scores of $(n - 1)$ cases[12] on orthogonal dimensions $S_1, S_2, \ldots, S_l, \ldots, S_p$.

Now, from Eq. (22–1), the distance *vector*, between any two cases, g and i, in the space of $S_{(n-1) \times p}$ is

$$\vec{d_{gi}} = S_i - S_g,$$

where S_i and S_g are the ith and gth row vectors of $S_{(n-1) \times p}$.

---

to individual-stimulus psychological behavior. See also Coombs and Kao (1960) and Ross and Cliff (1964). For a comparison of various dimensional approaches, see Shepard (1962, 1963, 1964, 1965).

11. For a more elementary presentation than that given by Householder and Young, see Torgerson (1958, pp. 254–56).

12. The one case placed at the origin will have zero values on all the dimensions. Therefore, only the $(n - 1)$ other cases need have their scores determined.

From Eq. (22–2), the above equality, and Notation 3–15 for the inner product of vectors, the square of the *length* of the distance vector is then

$$
\begin{aligned}
d_{gi}^2 = (\vec{d}_{gi}, \vec{d}_{gi}) &= (S_i - S_g, S_i - S_g) \\
&= (S_i, S_i) + (S_g, S_g) - 2(S_g, S_i) \\
&= d_{ng}^2 + d_{ni}^2 - 2(S_g, S_i),
\end{aligned}
\tag{22–8}
$$

where d_{ng} and d_{ni} are the lengths of the distance vector from the origin n to the points g and i, respectively.

Let the inner product of the factor score vectors, S_g and S_i, be b_{gi}:

$$
b_{gi} = (S_g, S_i).
$$

Then, from Eq. (22–8),

$$
b_{gi} = (S_g, S_i) = \tfrac{1}{2}(d_{ng}^2 + d_{ni}^2 - d_{gi}^2).
\tag{22–9}
$$

Before continuing, some additional notation must be made explicit.

> *Notation 22–3.* $B_{(n-1) \times (n-1)}$ = a symmetrical matrix of inner products b_{gi}.
> $$ b_{gi} = (S_g, S_i). $$

Since $b_{gi} = (S_g, S_i)$,

$$
B_{(n-1) \times (n-1)} = S_{(n-1) \times p} S'_{p \times (n-1)}.
\tag{22–10}
$$

We began our discussion with the assumption that the data matrix $D_{n \times n}$ contained elements d_{gi}^* that have a one-to-one correspondence to distances in Euclidean space. Therefore,

$$
d_{gi}^* = d_{gi},
$$

and d_{gi} may be replaced by d_{gi}^* in Eqs. (22–8) and (22–9). The underlying dimensions, $S_{(n-1) \times p}$, can now be easily determined. Input $B_{(n-1) \times (n-1)}$, *as though correlations*, to a factor analysis (principal axes) computing program. The resulting factor dimensions will be $S_{(n-1) \times p}$ within a linear transformation (rotation).

In sum, the procedure is to take the distance-like data matrix with elements d_{gi}^* and select one case as the origin. Compute the matrix $B_{(n-1) \times (n-1)}$ from Eq. (22–9) and input $B_{(n-1) \times (n-1)}$ as though a correlation matrix to a factor analysis program and rotate. The resulting dimensions (factor scores within a scaling constant) give the minimum dimensions of the distance vectors. We have thus worked backwards from known d_{gi}^* to the unknown s_{gl} and s_{il} of Eq. (22–2).

Besides the initial assumption of a one-to-one correspondence between data and distances in Euclidean space, it is assumed that

$B_{(n-1)\times(n-1)}$ is *positive semidefinite* (Definition 4–15). This means that the determinant of $B_{(n-1)\times(n-1)}$ is greater than or equal to zero.[13] Operationally, this assumption can be tested in the factoring or the matrix. If any *negative* eigenvalues exist, then the assumption is violated. If no negative eigenvalues exist, the distances d_{gi}^* can be located in a real, Euclidean space.

Different cases can be taken as the origin of the space. For any set of n cases, therefore, there are n different matrices $B_{(n-1)\times(n-1)}$. The dimensions $S_{(n-1)\times p}$ of each $B_{(n-1)\times(n-1)}$ with different origins are linearly related by a rotation and translation, as long as the data, d_{gi}^*, *can be assumed error free*. If some error in correspondence between the d_{gi}^* and the real distances, d_{gi}, exists, the dimensions of each $B_{(n-1)\times(n-1)}$ formed by taking a different origin will linearly differ by the amount of error.

Since empirical data will usually contain such error, we are faced with selecting among n different $B_{(n-1)\times(n-1)}$ matrices, each of which will give a different solution to the desired dimensions. Torgerson (1958, pp. 256–58) has offered a practical solution. The *centroid* of the d_{gi}^* can be considered more reliable than any point taken individually, since in computing the centroid random errors can cancel out. Moreover, by placing the origin at the centroid of the cases, all n cases can be included in the analysis.

Let $\hat{b}_{gi}$ and $\hat{B}_{n\times n}$ be the values of b_{gi} and $B_{n\times n}$, with the origin of the space at the centroid of the n cases. Then,

$$\hat{b}_{gi} = \tfrac{1}{2}\left(\frac{1}{n}\sum_{g=1}^{n} d_{gi}^2 + \frac{1}{n}\sum_{i=1}^{n} d_{gi}^2 - \frac{1}{n^2}\sum_{g=1}^{n}\sum_{i=1}^{n} d_{gi}^2 - d_{gi}^2\right). \quad (22\text{–}11)$$

The same assumption of positive semidefiniteness applies also in the case of $\hat{B}_{n\times n}$.

22.3.2 NONMETRIC CORRESPONDENCE

Often, we may have distance-like data that do not strictly correspond to distances. The data may have no more than a *rank order* correspondence to Euclidean distances.[14]

> *Example 22–10.* Each of n senators may be ranked with regard to the $(n-1)$ others in terms of attitudinal similarity. The resulting matrix may be assumed to have

---

13. For $n-3$, this is the triangular inequality law: The side of a triangle is less than or equal to the sum of the other two sides (Householder and Young, 1938, p. 21).

14. A number of techniques for generating such similarity data are given by Torgerson (1958, pp. 259–80).

only a rank order relationship to real attitudinal distances between senators on underlying dimensions of attitudes. This means that the real rank of senators on the underlying attitudinal distances would be the same as their empirical or assigned rank. The interval between ranks, however, may not be the same as the interval between the underlying attitudinal distances. This may be seen in the hypothetical data on a senator presented in Table 22–7.

Table 22–7. Hypothetical Data on a Senator

Compared with Senators	Assigned Ranking in Similarity	Real Attitudinal Distances
Dodd	24	4.8
Smith	23	3.2
Fong	22	3.1
⋮	⋮	⋮
Long	1	0.5

A number of techniques have been developed (Torgerson, 1958, Chapter 11; Coombs, 1964, Part 5) for determining the underlying dimensionality of distances with rank order correspondence to such data. That which seems most elegant mathematically has been proposed by Shepard (1962) and made mathematically rigorous by Kruskal (1964a, 1964b).[15] The Shepard-Kruskal solution has apparently put dimensional analysis of this data on a par with the mathematical solution of the last section. The Shepard-Kruskal and Householder-Young solutions together place dimensional analysis on a level with factor analysis. They theoretically now allow us to work toward distances or back from distances to dimensions with equal facility.

For the computing procedures, the reader is referred to Kruskal (1964a, 1964b). The approach involves finding a set of real distances that will have a monotonic relationship to the data, d_{gi}^*. Shepard found that this requirement is sufficient to determine the dimensions of the space, using rank order data. The primary notion is that the latent information in the ranked data is sufficient, for a reasonable n, to uniquely specify for practical purposes the dimensions of the real

15. See also Shepard (1963, 1964, 1965). His anticipation of the technique can be seen in his earlier studies (1957, 1958a, 1958b). Others (Lingoes, 1963, 1966a, 1966b; Guttman, 1967) are working along similar lines, and great progress in this area can be anticipated.

distances monotonically related to the original data. Beyond an assumption of monotonicity, the data are not assumed to be related to the real distances by some formula or to have a specific distribution.

The task is essentially one of finding the least squares fit of the data to a set of real distances. Once this fit is found, the dimensions can be determined. An interesting finding in the development of this technique is that a matrix of ordinal data can contain enough constraints to enable us to find a smaller and practically unique matrix of ratio measurements (real distances, dimensions) on the cases. The ability to scale "soft" data into ratio measurements *opens the door to the entrance of calculus into many substantive domains.*[16]

16. At the minimum, calculus requires a meaningful interval measurement.

23. Publication

Publication is the final step of the factor analysis research design. It is the culmination of the research process—the display of its fruits to the interested public.

The inclusion of a publication step in the analysis process, however, should not imply that the investigator makes one run through the design and publishes the results, although this has occasionally been the practice. The data may be rerun dozens of times, altering such choices as factor model, matrix transformations, communality estimate, type of rotation, and so on. This possibility is indicated by step 18, the new data cycle, of the design (see Fig. 7–1).

By rerunning the data and altering the design decisions, the investigator can develop a feel for the patterns in his data—get to know his data—and gain an awareness of the alternative results possible with regard to the final solution or set of solutions he publishes. Like the chemist trying out various combinations of chemicals to determine the precise nature of a compound, so too should the factor analyst experiment on his data with various combinations of correlation coefficients, factor cutoffs, communality options, and the like.

Publication is not the golden ball on top of the flagpole; rather, it is more like the top of an iceberg. Much of what is done will not be seen by the reader, although what is below the surface is indeed necessary to support what is above.

Several considerations should be weighed in the writing of the research report and the presentation of the results. These will be discussed

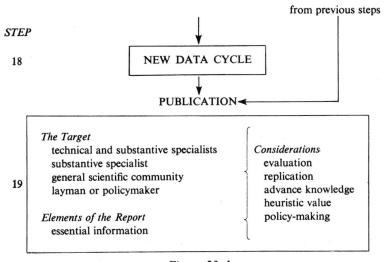

Figure 23–1

in the following section. The vehicle and target of the publication will be considered in the second section, and the final section will discuss the elements of the report and present a checklist of essential information to be included in it. The contents of the publication step are shown in Fig. 23–1.

23.1 Considerations

Publication is in effect a bid for nomination of the research results for entry into the corpus of science. This corpus contains the laws and substantive propositions in which science has confidence and which serve as the foundation for continual scientific exploration along the periphery of the unknown. Propositions are only conditionally accepted into this corpus, however, and may be ejected at any time that contradictions are found with other propositions in which science has more confidence.

Before research results can be nominated, they must be *evaluated.* Evaluation is the weighing by the interested scientific community of the adequacy of the data and of research design that links research question to findings. In order for this evaluation to be made it is crucial that sufficient information about the design be included. This is one of the major considerations in preparing a report.

If the design and findings are favorably evaluated, they stand in nomination for membership in the corpus of science. The crucial step between initial evaluation of the results and membership is *replication.* The results must be tested on different data samples, the research design repeated, and alternative designs experimented with. To replicate, however, requires sufficient information about the data and design to reproduce the study. To communicate such information is a primary task of the report. Enough information must be included or filed elsewhere in public archives to enable the reproduction of the study without the necessity of personal contact with the investigator. This is to ensure that a study is always replicable regardless of the decades or generations that may pass.

Evaluation and replication are the most important factors governing a report's content and controlling its contribution to knowledge. Other considerations, however, should not be forgotten. The *heuristic value* of the design and findings are significant in domains that have not had the benefit of much multivariate research or the particular design of the study (say, P-factor analysis). The design may then stimulate emulation and may perhaps serve as a model for other investigators. If the heuristic value of a report is to be realized, however, it has to be clearly written. The report may be technically perfect, but unless it communicates beyond the small group that is literate in the report's methodology, it may stimulate little research and thought outside that inner circle.

Another consideration that is gaining in importance as government becomes aware of social science is political *policy-making.* Often a study will be classified as basic science and have no link to policy concerns. In social research, however, there is considerable overlap between the interest of the social scientist and government policy. Results of analyzing such data as criminal statistics, conflict behavior, cross-national characteristics, riots, legislative voting, public opinion, and international behavior may be considered basic science research but are also of considerable policy relevance. Accordingly, the researcher may first wish to meet the evaluation, replication, and heuristic requirements by writing a formal report *and then later spinning off less technical reports that can be understood and utilized by the policy-making community.*

The audience to which a report is directed should be considered carefully before a report is written. The audience will have a bearing on the style of writing, the organization of the report, and the technical elements that are included. One audience is the small number of scientists *technically competent* to evaluate and replicate the study. This will be the major audience for the research if it is to gain any long-run scientific status. A second audience consists of *substantive specialists* with some conceptual understanding (but not competence) in the techniques involved. This audience will also be of concern to the researcher if the results are to have wider currency and stimulate interest and research.

A third audience is the *general scientific community.* This audience comprises scientists working in other fields who may have an interest in the results and implications of a design. Adequately communicating with them keeps the lines of contact between the disciplines open and aids the search for analogies. A method, a model, or a set of results from one field may be of great aid in another. A problem long intractable in, say, biology may have a research solution suggested by the design of a study on, say, juvenile delinquency. The final audience is composed of the *layman*—the nonscientist and/or policy-maker. Technical details are unimportant for him. He is interested in the relevance of the findings to his interests and in the meaning of it all.

Which of these audiences a report reaches depends on the publication vehicle used. A book, of course, will allow the greatest latitude for visual displays and for technical and substantive elaboration. If the material is directed to laymen and specialists, appendices can be used to present the technical details, while the text is reserved for substantive elaboration and discussion.[1]

Unlike books, papers or journal articles allow little room for simultaneously meeting the communication requirements of diverse audiences. A decision usually must be made as to the major audience of concern, and the report must then be tailored to the demands of that audience. For the technical specialist, the article will be short on discussion and long on factor tables and methodology. For the substantive specialists, the substantive findings and implications will be elaborated, with the factor tables and some methodology serving as a background. For the general scientist, the factor tables may be omitted and some methodology may be consigned to footnotes.

1. An excellent example of this approach is Wood (1961).

23.2 A Research Report Checklist

With regard to the technical and substantive audiences, there are a number of elements that should be included in the report.[2] This is the information that is essential in order to *evaluate, compare,* and *replicate* the study. Some of this information can be given in the main body of the report, some in the tables or footnotes, and some in appendices. The location of the information, however, is not as important as its inclusion.

A checklist of such essential information is given below, as well as the numbers of the chapters and sections in this volume where such items are described and discussed.

Model

1. Indicate the *research question* (Chapter 8) so that the matching of question, design, and results can be evaluated.
2. Give the *factor model* (Chapter 5) underlying the analysis.

Data

3. Describe the *data slice* (Section 8.3).
4. Give the *criteria* for inclusion and exclusion of variables and cases (Section 9.1.2).
5. Describe the *measurement characteristics* of the data (Section 9.1.3).
6. Describe the *data collection methods* (Section 10.1).
7. Give your assessment of *random and systematic error* (Sections 9.1.3.4 and 10.1.3).
8. Describe the amount of *missing data* and mode of estimation, if such estimates are used (Section 10.3).

Preliminary Computation

9. List the *distributional transformations* and criteria for their selection (Chapter 11). In studies involving large numbers of variables it may not be possible to give the specific transformations of each variable, but at the very least it should be indicated whether such transformations have been made, and the criteria involved should be identified.
10. Give the *matrix transformation* (Chapter 12) and the rationale for its choice. If a correlation matrix is computed, mention the correlation coefficient involved. The correlation matrix is important research

---

2. As Harris (1963a, p. 149) points out, the "general need for clearer descriptions of how any particular set of factors was arrived at is evident in many of the reports of research."

information in its own right and should normally be included in a report. If this is not possible due to editorial constraints or an unusually large number of variables, a copy of the matrix might be filed with a documents archive[3] so that others will have reference to it.

11. Give the *communality estimate* (Chapter 13), if one is made. If unities are employed as an estimate of communalities, that should be indicated. The communality estimates may be placed in the principal diagonal of the correlation matrix that is included in the report. If the estimates are squared multiple correlation coefficients, they are important in themselves, since information as to the multiple correlation of one variable with the $(m - 1)$ others is a significant addition to our knowledge.

The Factor Computation

12. The *factor technique* (Chapter 14) should be indicated. For a small number of variables, computer programs appear to be practically identical in their results. For large variable matrices, however (over 60 variables, say), different computer programs may differ in the first decimal place for some of the loadings and even in the number of factors. Such differences are due to the computing algorithm used and to whether computations are in double or single precision. Accordingly, the computing program employed might be indicated for large data matrices.

13. Give the *number-of-factors criterion* (Chapter 15).

14. If *rotation* is done, it should be indicated. If a rotated solution is published, indicate whether it is orthogonal (Chapter 16) or oblique (Chapter 17).

15. If analytic rotation is done (Section 16.4.2), the *rotation technique* must be indicated. In the case of oblique analytic rotation, the number of *major cycles* and *iterations*, the *precision level* (if relevant) of the result, and the *computer program* employed are important information. Oblique results can differ for the same data between, say, 10 cycles and 60 cycles. This information is therefore important for comparison and replication.

16. If other than simple structure rotation is done, the *rotating criteria* (Section 16.2) should be indicated. If target rotation (Section 16.4.2.3) is used, the target matrix should be displayed.

Factor Matrices

17. The unrotated and final rotated solution should be given. For the unrotated solution, the *communalities*, h^2, and *per cent of variance* (or

3. The American Society for Information Science, 2000 P Street N.W., Washington, D.C. 20036, maintains such an archive.

eigenvalues) for each factor should be included with the table. The h^2 enables interpretation of the fit of each variable to the factor space (Section 5.1), and the factor variance (Section 6.2) measures the strength of the relationships between variables and factors. For the oblique solution, it is important to include both the *structure* and *pattern* matrices (Section 17.1) if possible. For the primary pattern or reference structure matrix, the sum of squared coefficients for a factor may also be included as a measure of factor importance.

18. Give the *factor correlation matrix* for the oblique factors (Section 17.1.3). If there are a small number of factors, these correlations may be included with the oblique factor tables.

19. The *transformation matrix* (Section 17.1.4) for the oblique factors should be included for studies with a large number of variables and many factors. This enables others to adjust the published factors to new positions without the expense of starting the rotation anew.

Factor Scores

20. The *mode of computing factor scores* should be indicated (Section 19.2). If highly loaded variables are summed to approximate factor scores on a factor (Section 19.2.3), then it is important to describe the variables entering into each sum, the weight of each variable (e.g., weighted by square of loading), and whether variables are standardized prior to summing.

21. Give the *multiple correlation coefficient* of regression factor score estimates of the original data (Section 19.3). This indicates the uniqueness of the factor scores for the data.

22. For some data, e.g., that on nations, the cases will be of intrinsic interest. Then the *factor score matrix* should be shown or be available. For other data, e.g., a random sample of college students, the factor scores will probably be of little interest outside the study. If factor scores are included, the table should indicate whether they are standardized scores or not.

Factor Comparison

23. The *factor comparison technique* used (Chapter 20) should be indicated.

24. A *description of the two sets of findings* in terms of cases and variable similarity is important for evaluating the comparison. For example, it should be pointed out whether the cases differ between the two studies. The variables and factors entering into the comparison must be described.

Distances

25. A *distance matrix* (Chapter 22) itself may be too large to include, but summary statistics or the mean distance and standard deviation for the matrix can be given, as well as selected distances, for the most interesting cases.

26. Whether distances are computed on *weighted or unweighted factors* and precisely *what factors* are used should be indicated (Section 22.1.2).

24. Applications

Examples of the applications of factor analysis to social data will be the subject of this final chapter. Various studies will be listed and, where possible, a description of the design of the study will be given. These studies should be of help to the researcher and student interested in substantive applications in his own domain or in applied examples of specific research designs, such as Q-factor analysis.

The references given probably cover most of the nonpsychological studies done in the social sciences prior to 1965, and a number since then as well. With regard to nations, the listing of applied studies prior to 1965 should be virtually complete. Several studies in the natural sciences have also been included to demonstrate the versatility of factor analysis.

Psychological studies have been excluded for two reasons. By now the number of such factor analyses must run into the hundreds and even to list them would create an unwarranted bibliographic task for the purpose of this chapter. Secondly, students of factor analysis have easy access to the literature of psychological applications through such books and monographs as Cattell (1952a, 1957, 1965d), Fruchter

(1954), Thurstone (1947), Harman (1967), and Ahmavaara (1957). Studies outside of psychology, however, are not as numerous or as well referenced. Therefore, a list of applications such as that presented here may serve the dual function of (1) exemplifying factor analyses of subject matter closer to that with which the sociologist, political scientist, economist, or anthropologist has to deal, and (2) serving as a bibliography of such studies—the first of its kind.[1]

The references are divided into four major sections. The first is methodological and is concerned with factor analysis texts, matrix algebra sources, and artificial experiments exemplifying the nature of factor analysis. The second section presents factor analysis applications, ordered by the *political unit* analyzed, whether nation, tribe, or culture, intermediate political unit, urban area, legislative body, or court. The third section is concerned with applications to *nonpolitical* units at the organization, group, and individual level. The applications are arranged according to whether the substantive focus is organizations, small groups, roles, class, status, mobility, social choice, communications, attitudes and concepts, interpersonal behavior, or interaction. The final section presents some applications of factor analysis outside of the social sciences.

Where possible, references to applications are described, according to the following scheme: *goal; data; data slice; model and technique; results.* These categories may be helpful to the reader in selecting references for further study. "Goal" and "data" categories need no explanation. "Data slice" refers to the kind of data matrix being analyzed (Section 8.3) and to whether R-, Q-, or P-factor analysis has been applied, for example. "Model and technique" defines the factor model involved, which will usually be component or common factor analysis (Sections 5.2 and 5.3), the factoring technique, and the type of rotation. If factor comparison is involved, that also may be indicated. "Results" will usually give the factors found rather than the conclusion of the study, since the factors may be most useful to readers working in other domains.

For many applications, only a reference or a partial description is given. In the case of references without any description, I have not read the study and have no relevant information from other sources. In the case of references with partial descriptions, either I have read the study and the author did not give sufficient information for a complete

1. I would like to express my gratitude to Phillip M. Gregg for making his bibliography of factor analysis studies available for this chapter. I am also indebted for access to bibliographies prepared by Peter Stewart and William Bicker, and for the suggestions of Brian Berry, John W. Harbaugh, and Forrest Pitts.

description or my knowledge of it stems from information contained in a secondary source.

Only the author, year, and title are given for each reference, except for papers and articles, in which case the name of the journal or collection is also cited. Additional bibliographic information on each reference will be found in the bibliography that follows this chapter.

Hopefully, others will be encouraged to extend and improve the list of applications given here. Eventually we may be able to tag all such studies by type of variables and cases, design decisions, and factors found, so that factor comparison between different units and levels of analysis may be pursued. A *size* factor, for example, appears in studies of nations, states, cities, and small groups. It would be helpful if there were an indexing system to make possible the retrieval of all studies finding such a factor or including variables related to such a factor in an analysis.

24.1 Methodological

24.1.1 FACTOR ANALYSIS BOOKS AND MONOGRAPHS

The references included here are primarily concerned with the *methodology* of factor analysis and not with substantive results. The selections comprise those works generally available and include those references usually footnoted in applied studies. Where several editions of a work have been published, only the latest edition is referenced.

Adcock, C. J. 1954. *Factorial Analysis for Non-Mathematicians.*
    Using nontechnical language and relying on diagrams and examples, Adcock lays out the conceptual meaning and computations for correlation coefficients, factor loadings, and rotation. He limits the book to the centroid and multiple-group methods. For the researcher who must compute his own correlations and factors, the book may be helpful. There is little discussion of methodology aside from computational procedures.

Ahmavaara, Y. 1954b. "Transformation Analysis of Factorial Data."
    Annales Academiae Scientiarum Fennicae.
    This presents the full mathematical development of transformation analysis as a technique for comparing the factor analysis results of different studies. The mathematical presentation is clear, and psychological examples are fully worked through to show the applications of the technique. These examples are especially important for gaining a conceptual understanding of transformation analysis.

Another technique, called residual spectra, is also presented. This technique enables latent common factors to be uncovered that might not otherwise be delineated.

Ahmavaara, Y., and T. Markkanen. 1958. *The Unified Factor Model.* Part I is written by Ahmavaara; Part II, by Markkanen, applies transformation analysis to sociological data. Part I discusses the approaches to measurement and model building and relates "Cartesian" and "Hilbertian"—classical physics and quantum theory—forms of analysis to the factor model. For the researcher interested in the scientific nature of factor analysis and its relationship to traditional and modern science, Part I is among the best references. The logic of transformation analysis is also discussed; it is related to a three-step factor analysis design: factoring, rotation, and transformation analysis.

Burt, C. L. 1941. *The Factors of the Mind: An Introduction to Factor-analysis in Psychology.* Although part of this book is devoted to the methods of factor analysis, Burt's major concern is the logical and philosophical status of factors. Various sections discuss issues bearing on the selection of factor analysis as a technique and the interpretation of results. Of special importance is Burt's emphasis on linking factor analysis to metaphysical issues, logic, and natural science methods (e.g., quantum theory). The reader not interested in technique so much as in the meaning of factors is referred to Cattell (1952a), below, which nicely complements Burt. Cattell focuses on the application of factor analysis, while Burt emphasizes logical concerns.

Cattell, R. B. 1952a. *Factor Analysis: An Introduction and Manual for the Psychologist and Social Scientist.* This includes a very useful discussion of the philosophic status and methodological aspects of factor analysis. Applied concerns with data requirements, alternative research designs, types of data matrices, and interpretation of results are fully discussed. The technical aspects of different factor techniques and rotations are not as well covered. Cattell concentrates on the centroid method and oblique graphical rotation. For those wishing to do visual rotation, Cattell's layout of the procedures and many charts will be very helpful.

Fruchter, B. 1954. *Introduction to Factor Analysis.* This book focuses on the computing procedures for the various factor techniques and rotations. General research design and other methodological concerns are little discussed. The mathematics of the techniques are not developed, as in Harman (1967), but the computational procedures are more clearly and concisely presented and may be helpful to those wishing to understand the computational differences between techniques. Frequent examples are helpful and a chapter on applications in psychology is useful.

Harman, H. H. 1967. *Modern Factor Analysis.*

This is an excellent technical overview of factor analysis and the best source on the algebraic and geometric aspects of the factor model, as well as on the alternative factor and rotation techniques. The many examples, tables, and figures are quite helpful. The book is largely technical, with little discussion about the philosophy of factor analysis or the methodological concerns of most interest to the researcher, such as data measurement and transformation, alternative data slices, or different correlation coefficients. A weakness of the book for the researcher is that it begins with the product moment correlation matrix and assumes an R-factor analysis throughout.

Henrysson, S. 1957. *Applicability of Factor Analysis in the Behavioral Sciences: A Methodological Study.*

The concern is less with the procedures and model of factor analysis than with the scientific nature of the method and its applicability. A chapter on possible applications may be useful to the researcher. Henrysson's distinction between descriptive and explanatory factor analysis forms the basis for much of his discussion of the role of factor analysis in science.

Holzinger, K. J., and H. H. Harman. 1941. *Factor Analysis.*

This has now largely been rewritten by Harman (1960, 1967).

Horst, P. 1965. *Factor Analysis of Data Matrices.*

This book is for the factor methodologist. It is a compendium of various techniques and alternative computing procedures, many of which are new and unapplied. The emphasis is on matrix algebra, with no geometric interpretation and little general scientific or philosophic discussion. Of great importance is the inclusion of a FORTRAN program listing for each technique considered.

Jöreskog, K. G. 1963. *Statistical Estimation in Factor Analysis.*

This gives the mathematical development of a new factor analysis model related to image factor analysis. It is scale-free, does not require communality estimates, and incorporates tests of significance of the number of factors. The results of the model are compared with the centroid, principal axes, and maximum-likelihood techniques, and the nature of the model is explored in its application to real and to randomly generated data.

Lawley, D. N., and A. E. Maxwell. 1963. *Factor Analysis as a Statistical Method.*
A condensed statistical development and discussion of maximum-likelihood, centroid, and principal axes techniques and rotation. The emphasis is on statistical estimation and tests of significance. There is little nontechnical interpretation or general methodological discussion.

Spearman, C. 1927. *The Abilities of Man.*
Spearman reports on and seeks to justify 20 years of research on his two-factor psychological theory. The philosophical and substantive context and findings underlying the theory are fully presented in a largely nontechnical style. This well-written book is highly recommended to those contemplating a two-factor approach or theory in their own domain.

Stephenson, W. 1953. *The Study of Behavior.*
Most factor analysis books deal mainly with R-factor analysis, relegating the discussion of Q-factor analysis to a single chapter or section. Stephenson's whole book is a theoretical and methodological justification of Q-factor analysis. Many examples are used, and research procedures are given for applying the methodology. He is concerned with the research design, from the forming of the data matrix to applying analysis of variance to the groups of cases identified in the factor analysis.

Thomson, G. 1951. *The Factorial Analysis of Human Ability.*
A clearly written overview of factor analysis problems and techniques. A chapter presenting the geometric picture of factor analysis is excellent for intuitively comprehending the factor model. The many geometric diagrams throughout are helpful. Computational procedures for many techniques are given and the book has a good general discussion of the early two-factor and bifactor approaches. Parts of the book are devoted to Q-technique, the influence of univariate and multivariate selection on factor results, and the sample assumptions of the factor model. Several design problems, such as metric and oblique rotations, are considered in a final chapter.

Thurstone, L. L. 1935. *The Vectors of Mind.*
This is Thurstone's first full presentation of his multiple factor analysis approach and techniques of oblique rotation. The work is now of historical interest, since it has been completely rewritten and updated (Thurstone, 1947).

Thurstone, L. L. 1947. *Multiple-Factor Analysis.*
In terms of technical development and presentation on the one hand

and concern for applied problems and the philosophy of factor analysis on the other, this book stands between Harman (1967) and Cattell (1952a). A discussion of the factor problem and the applications of factor analysis to artificial data constructed to display the nature of factor analysis should be helpful in understanding factor results. The chapter on second-order factors is excellent. Physical examples are used to interpret the meaning of the higher orders. Thurstone was the originator of the simple structure rotation criterion, and this is the best reference for its description and justification.

24.1.2 ARTIFICIAL EXPERIMENTS

An understanding of a mathematical model can be increased by application to simple well-known physical objects. The results better enable one to interpret findings on less well-known data and to have confidence in the results when moving into unanalyzed domains. A number of applications of factor analysis to well-known processes have been made. Since a study of artificial experiments may enable the researcher to better understand factor analysis, seven such applications are given here.

On boxes

Thurstone, L. L. 1947. *Multiple-Factor Analysis*, pp. 140–46, and *passim* (see his index).

On cylinders

Shepard, R. N. 1964. "Extracting Latent Structure from Behavioral Data." In *Proceedings of the 1964 Symposium of Digital Computing* (applications of dimensional analyses).

Thurstone, L. L. 1947. *Multiple-Factor Analysis*, pp. 117–24.

On trapezoids

Thurstone, L. L. 1947. *Multiple-Factor Analysis*, pp. 427–36.

On cups of coffee

Cattell, R. B., and W. Sullivan. 1962. "The Scientific Nature of Factors: A Demonstration by Cups of Coffee." *Behavioral Science*.

On the dynamics of balls

Cattell, R. B., and K. Dickman. 1962. "A Dynamic Model of Physical Influences Demonstrating the Necessity of Oblique Simple Structure." *Psychological Bulletin*.

On random numbers

Cattell, R. B., and R. L. Gorsuch. 1963. "The Uniqueness and Significance of Simple Structure Demonstrated by Contrasting Organic 'Natural Structure' and 'Random Structure' Data." *Psychometrika.*

On human body measurements

Harman, H. H. 1960. *Modern Factor Analysis* (see his index under "eight physical variables").

24.1.3 MATRIX (LINEAR) ALGEBRA TEXTS

Many factor analysis texts begin with a section on matrix algebra, among the better of which are Thurstone (1947) and Harman (1967). For a more complete treatment, however, this section will list some of the sources that may be particularly helpful in understanding the matrix manipulations and geometric interpretations employed in factor analysis. If the six texts listed were to be ordered in terms of simplicity, excellence of diagrams and examples, and relevance to understanding the factor model, the order would be: Owen (1961), Davis (1965), Paige and Swift (1961), Horst (1963), Hohn (1958), and Mostow *et al.* (1963).

Davis, P. J. 1965. *The Mathematics of Matrices.*
> Presented at a very simplified level with frequent diagrams, pictures, and empirical examples; the student new to matrices is gradually led into the algebra and geometry (vector spaces) involved.

Hohn, F. E. 1958. *Elementary Matrix Algebra.*
> Less elementary than Paige and Swift (1961) or Horst (1963), this book contains more information and theorems than either. It is nonetheless highly useful at the elementary level and nicely complements the material presented in Paige and Swift (1961).

Horst, P. 1963. *Matrix Algebra for Social Scientists.*
> Horst presents an especially clear introduction to the algebraic manipulation of matrices. The multiplication of matrices and meaning of matrix rank are well brought out. Matrix computation of eigenvalues-eigenvectors (basic structure), correlation matrices, and simple statistics are clearly shown. Unfortunately, the geometric relevance and meaning of the manipulations are not discussed, nor is some of the terminology well integrated with that in the mathematical or factor analysis literature.

Mostow, G. D., J. H. Sampson, and J. Meyer. 1963. *Fundamental Structures of Algebra.*
> An advanced book for those wishing a rigorous mathematical

development of matrix algebra, vector spaces, and linear transformations.

Owen, G. E. 1961. *Fundamentals of Scientific Mathematics.*
Written for high school seniors, this book is a must for those first
approaching matrices and factor analysis. The discussion is clear,
with frequent examples and diagrams. The section on the quadratic
form is among the best for understanding the geometric meaning
of principal axes, eigenvalues, and eigenvectors.

Paige, L. J., and J. D. Swift. 1961. *Elements of Linear Algebra.*
The subject of matrix algebra is geometrically presented from a
vector space perspective. The text is elementary at the beginning,
assuming nothing but elementary algebra on the part of the reader,
but works gradually into some advanced topics. The presentation
is very helpful for an understanding of the geometry of factor
analysis.

24.2 Political Units

24.2.1 NATIONS

Adelman, I., and C. T. Morris. 1965. "Factor Analysis of the Interrelationship Between Social and Political Variables and Per Capita
Gross National Product." *Quarterly Journal of Economics.*

Adelman, I., and C. T. Morris. 1966. "A Quantitative Study of Social
and Political Determinants of Fertility." *Economic Development
and Cultural Change.*

Alker, H., Jr. 1964. "Dimensions of Conflict in the General Assembly."
American Political Science Review.
Goal: To uncover principal dimensions of conflict underlying the
UN General Assembly votes and to determine the scores of
nations on these dimensions.
Data: Roll-call votes of the Sixteenth General Assembly (1961–62).
Data slice: R-factor analysis.
Model and technique: Component factor analysis and orthogonal
rotation.
Results: Delineated major dimensions of self-determination, UN
supranationalism, cold war membership, and Moslem voting.

Alker, H., Jr. 1965b. "Supranationalism in the United Nations,"
Peace Research Society: Papers, III.
Goal: To test for predispositions to use UN peacekeeping mechanisms as a regular component of UN General Assembly roll
calls.

Data: Roll-call votes in all special and emergency UN sessions.

Data slice: R-factor analysis.

Model and technique: Component factor analysis and orthogonal rotation.

Results: Found cold war, anti-intervention, supranationalism, and Palestine settlement components. A predisposition to regularly use UN peacekeeping mechanisms does appear.

Alker, H., Jr., and B. Russett. 1965. *World Politics in the General Assembly.*

Goal: To identify the distinctive issues in the UN, the alignments of states on these issues, and the elements influencing these alignments.

Data: Roll call votes in the 1947, 1952, 1957, and 1961 UN General Assembly sessions.

Data slice: R-factor analysis.

Model and technique: Component factor analysis and orthogonal rotation.

Results: Found cold war, self-determination, supranationalism, Palestine-related questions, and anti-interventionism (Africa) components.

Bacon, M., *et al.* 1965. "A Cross-Cultural Study of Drinking." *Quarterly Journal of Studies of Alcohol.*

Banks, A. S., and P. M. Gregg. 1965. "Grouping Political Systems: Q-factor Analysis of *A Cross-Polity Survey.*" *American Behavioral Scientist.*

Goal: To group nations on their political characteristics.

Data: Sixty-eight variables for 115 nations; 63 variables are from Banks and Textor (1963) on circa 1960 data.

Data slice: Q-factor analysis.

Model and technique: Component factor analysis and orthogonal rotation.

Results: Nations grouped into polyarchic, elitist, centrist, personalist, and traditional profiles.

Berry, B. J. L. 1960. "An Inductive Approach to the Regionalization of Economic Development." In *Essays on Geography and Economic Development,* ed. N. Ginsburg.

Goal: To identify and differentiate underdeveloped nations and test hypotheses concerning their characteristics.

Data: Forty-three variables for 95 nations on circa 1955 data.

Data slice: R-factor analysis; Q-factor analysis.

Model and technique: Component factor analysis model and direct factor analysis technique.

Results: Found countries differentiated on technological, demographic, size, and contrast in income and external relations factors.

Berry, B. J. L. 1961b. "Basic Patterns of Economic Development." In *Atlas of Economic Development*, ed. N. Ginsburg.

Goal: A summary of the factor analysis results reported in Berry (1960).

Berry, J. L. 1966. *Essays on Commodity Flows and Spatial Structure of the Indian Economy.*

Cattell, R. B. 1949a. "The Dimensions of Culture Patterns by Factorization of National Characters." *Journal of Abnormal and Social Psychology.*

Goal: To discover the major psychological dimensions defining national cultures.

Data: Seventy-two cross-national variables for 69 nations on 1837–1937 data.

Data slice: R-factor analysis.

Model and technique: Common factor analysis and oblique rotation.

Results: Found factors of: size and cultural pressure versus direct ergic expression; enlightened affluence versus narrow poverty; conservative patriarchal solidarity versus ferment of release; emancipated urban rationalism versus unsophisticated stability; thoughtful industriousness versus emotionality; vigorous, self-willed order versus unadapted perseveration; bourgeois philistinism versus reckless Bohemianism; residual or peaceful progressiveness; fastidiousness versus forcefulness; Buddhism-Mongolism; and poor cultural integration and morale versus good internal morality.

Cattell, R. B. 1950. "The Principal Culture Patterns Discoverable in the Syntal Dimensions of Existing Nations." *Journal of Social Psychology.*

Goal: To identify the major cultural grouping of nations on Cattell's factors (1949a).

Data: Factor score composites for 69 nations on 12 factors.

Data slice: Q-factor analysis.

Model and technique: Pattern-magnitude coefficient employed to intercorrelate nations on their factor score profiles; cluster search applied to correlation matrix.

Results: Profiles grouped into clusters of Catholic, Eastern European, older Catholic colonial, Mohammedan, East Baltic, Scandinavian, Oriental, infused Catholic colonial, and infused Hamitic patterns.

Cattell, R. B. 1953. "A Quantitative Analysis of the Changes in the

Culture Pattern of Great Britain, 1837–1937, by P-Technique."
Acta Psychologica.

Goal: To uncover the historical directions of change in the cultural patterns of Great Britain; comparison with cross-national results of Cattell (1949a) and Cattell and Adelson (1951).

Data: Forty-eight variables measured for each of the years, 1837–1937, for Great Britain.

Data slice: P-factor analysis.

Model and technique: Common factor analysis and oblique rotation.

Results: The interpretable factors found are: cultural pressure; war; stress versus ease of living; emancipation versus reign enlightenment; and slum morale versus cultural integration. Several of these factors have a similarity to those found in Cattell (1949a), and in a P-factor analysis of the U.S. in Cattell and Adelson (1951).

Cattell, R. B., and M. Adelson. 1951. "The Dimensions of Social Change in the U.S.A. as Determined by P-Technique." *Social Forces.*

Goal: To uncover the historical directions of change in the cultural patterns of the United States; comparison with cross-sectional results of Cattell (1949a).

Data: Forty-four variables measured for each of 98 years for the United States, beginning with 1845.

Data slice: P-factor analysis.

Model and technique: Common factor analysis and oblique rotation.

Results: Six factors, five of which are interpreted as: cultural pressure or complication; expansive ease of living versus restrictive hard times; emancipated urbanism versus rural stability; conformity versus individualism; and primitive, inexpensive self-sufficiency versus relaxed dependence on larger organization. Only one factor clearly identified with those of the Cattell (1949a) study.

Cattell, R. B., H. Breul, and H. P. Hartman. 1951. "An Attempt at More Refined Definitions of the Cultural Dimensions of Syntality in Modern Nations." *American Sociological Review.*

Goal: To redo Cattell (1949a) analysis, eliminating 29 nations with the most missing data.

Data: Seventy-two cross-national variables for 40 nations on 1837–1937 data.

Data slice: R-factor analysis.

Model and technique: Common factor analysis and oblique rotation.

Results: Same number of factors; five of the factors were the same as Cattell (1949a), five modified, and two different. The same factors were size, enlightened affluence, cultural pressure, vigorous order, and morale.

Cattell, R. B., and R. L. Gorsuch. 1965. "The Definition and Measurement of National Morale and Morality." *Journal of Social Psychology.*

> *Goal:* To replicate the morale factor appearing in Cattell (1949a) and Cattell *et al.* (1951).
>
> *Data:* Fifty-one cross-national variables (including 3 random number variables) for 52 nations on 1953–1958 data.
>
> *Data slice:* R-factor analysis.
>
> *Model and technique:* Common factor analysis and oblique rotation; factor comparison with salience index.
>
> *Results:* Found 14 factors, one of which is a morale factor similar to that of previous studies; majority of other factors are also replicated.

Denton, F. H. 1966. "Some Regularities in International Conflict, 1820–1949," *Background.*

> *Goal:* To detect and summarize regularities in war between social groups.
>
> *Data:* Organized conflicts between social groups resulting in 3,000 or more deaths between 1820 and 1949.
>
> *Data slice:* P-factor analysis.
>
> *Model and technique:* Target rotations.
>
> *Results:* Found factors of size of sovereign war, classical imperialism, sovereign-subservient conflict, and civil war.

Feierabend, I. K., and R. L. Feierabend. 1966. "Aggressive Behaviors Within Polities, 1948–1962: A Cross-National Study." *Journal of Conflict Resolution.*

> *Goal:* To determine dimensions of conflict behavior within nations.
>
> *Data:* Thirty measures of political stability for 1948–1962 data on 84 nations.
>
> *Data slice:* R-factor analysis.
>
> *Model and technique:* Component factor analysis and orthogonal rotation.
>
> *Results:* Found factors of turmoil, revolt, purge, riot, election, demonstrations, imprisonment, civil war, guerrilla warfare.

Gibb, C. A. 1956. "Changes in the Culture Pattern of Australia, 1906–1946, as Determined by *p*-Technique." *Journal of Social Psychology.*

> *Goal:* To replicate for Australia the Cattell and Adelson (1951) and Cattell (1953) studies on the U.S. and Great Britain.
>
> *Data:* Forty variables measured for each year, 1906–46, for Australia.

Data slice: P-factor analysis.

Model and technique: Orthogonal target rotation.

Results: Five factors found and interpreted as growth, depression, war stress, urban slum conditions, and expansive ease of living; findings resemble those of similar studies of U.S. and Great Britain.

Gregg, P. M., and A. S. Banks. 1965. "Dimensions of Political Systems: Factor Analysis of *A Cross-Polity Survey.*" *American Political Science Review.*

Goal: To define the basic dimensions of political systems and their relevance to conflict behavior.

Data: Sixty-eight cross-national variables, 57 of which are from Banks and Textor (1963), for about 100 nations on circa 1960 data.

Data slice: R-factor analysis.

Model and technique: Component factor analysis and orthogonal rotation.

Results: Found factors of access, differentiation, consensus, sectionalism, legitimation, interest, and leadership.

Hatt, P., N. L. Farr, and E. Weinstein. 1955. "Types of Population Balance." *American Sociological Review.*

Goal: To test the adequacy of the categorization of population growth into incipient decline, transitorial growth, and high growth potential.

Data: Six demographic related characteristics for 21 nations.

Data slice: Q-factor analysis.

Model and technique: Common factor analysis and oblique rotation.

Results: Concludes that the categorization tested obscures real and important differences.

Laulicht, J. 1965. "An Analysis of Canadian Foreign Policy Attitudes." *Peace Research Society: Papers, III.*

Goal: To search for similarities in structure of attitudes toward foreign policy by different groups.

Data: Interview data from a nationwide sample of 1,000 Canadians and from business, labor, and political groups.

Result: Religious ideology and, to a lesser extent, fear of socialism are associated with cold war attitudes; fear of economic consequences of disarmament not so associated.

Laulicht, J., and N. Z. Alcock. 1966. "The Support of Peace Research." *Journal of Conflict Resolution.*

McClelland, C. A., *et al.* 1965. *The Communist Chinese Performance in Crisis and Non-Crisis: Quantitative Studies of the Taiwan Straits Confrontation, 1950–1964.*

Megee, M. 1966. "Problems in Regionalizing and Measurement." *Peace Research Society: Papers, IV.*

Morris, C. 1956. *Varieties of Human Values.*
Goal: To determine the cross-cultural patterns of values.
Data: Value scores of foreign students from the U.S., India, Japan, China, and Norway.

Rhodes, E. C. 1937. "The Construction of an Index of Business Activity." *Royal Statistical Society Journal.*
Goal: To determine weights for combining various indicators of change into one series.
Data: Index numbers to the same base for 14 indicators of economic change in England for 48 months, July 1931–June 1935.
Data slice: P-factor analysis.
Results: One general factor indicating similar cyclical movement in almost all the indicators.

Rummel, R. J. 1963. "Dimensions of Conflict Behavior Within and Between Nations." *General Systems.*
Goal: To determine the major empirical concepts for describing conflict behavior and the relationship between foreign and domestic conflict.
Data: Nine domestic and thirteen foreign conflict behavior variables for 77 nations on 1955–57 data.
Data slice: R-factor analysis.
Model and technique: Component factor analysis model and orthogonal rotations.
Results: Turmoil, revolution, and subversion dimensions of domestic conflict; war, diplomatic and belligerent dimensions of foreign conflict; domestic and foreign conflict found to be independent.

Rummel, R. J. 1965a. "A Field Theory of Social Action with Application to Conflict Within Nations." *General Systems.*
Goal: To illustrate the operationalization of an aspect of a mathematical field theory and to replicate the findings on domestic conflict of Rummel (1963).
Data: Ten domestic conflict variables for 105 nations on 1962–63 and 1963–64 data.
Data slice: R-factor analysis.
Model and technique: Component factor and common factor analyses; orthogonal and oblique rotation; factor comparison between all factor studies on domestic conflict using transformation analysis (Ahmavaara, 1954b).
Results: Turmoil a distinct and highly replicable dimension;

revolution and subversion also appear as distinct, but not always separate, dimensions.

Rummel, R. J. 1965b. "A Social Field Theory of Foreign Conflict Behavior." *Peace Research Society: Papers, IV.*

Goal: To operationalize the behavioral and attributes vector spaces of nations to test a theory relating behavior of nations to their attribute distances.

Data: Foreign conflict data (1955–57) for 91 pairs of nations; factor scores on dimensions of voting in 1955 UN General Assembly sessions, on dimensions of political systems, and on dimensions of 236 cross-national variables.

Data slice: R-factor analysis.

Model and technique: Component factor analysis and orthogonal rotation applied to the factor scores of several studies; separate component factor analysis and orthogonal rotation of foreign conflict data; regression of conflict results into attribute dimensions.

Results: Confirmation of the predictions of the theory that conflict is a resultant of distances between nations of social rank, value, geographic, and power attribute dimensions.

Rummel, R. J. 1966b. "Dimensions of Conflict Behavior Within Nations: 1946–1959." *Journal of Conflict Resolution.*

Goal: To replicate Rummel (1963) findings on domestic conflict.

Data: Thirteen conflict behavior variables for 113 nations and colonies on 1946–59 data.

Data slice: R-factor analysis.

Model and technique: Component factor analysis and orthogonal and oblique rotation.

Results: Same three domestic conflict dimensions found.

Rummel, R. J. 1967b. "Some Dimensions in the Foreign Behavior of Nations." *Journal of Peace Research.*

Goal: To determine the major empirical concepts and basic indicators for describing international relations.

Data: Ninety-four variables for 82 nations on 1955 data.

Data slice: R-factor analysis.

Model and technique: Component factor analysis and orthogonal rotation.

Results: Major dimensions of international relations are participation, conflict, aid, ideology, international popularity, Latin America, and immigration. Trade and threats are among the basic indicators found.

Rummel, R. J. 1967c. "Dimensions of Dyadic War, 1820–1952." *Journal of Conflict Resolution.*

Goal: To determine the major concepts for describing the involvement of groups and nations in violent conflict.

Data: Twenty-one variables were formed from Lewis F. Richardson's (1960b) data for 779 pairs of belligerents (groups or nations) over the years 1820–1952.

Data slice: R-factor analysis.

Model and technique: Component factor analysis; orthogonal and oblique rotations applied separately to all data and to nations only.

Results: The violence between pairs of nations was found to vary along size of war, cultural distance, social distance, and time of occurrence dimensions.

Rummel, R. J. 1968a. "Dimensions of Domestic Conflict Behavior: Review of Findings." In *Theories of International Conflict*, ed. D. Pruitt and R. Snyder.

Goal: To summarize and relate to each other all factor analysis results involving two or more conflict variables.

Results: Domestic and foreign conflict are generally found to be independent; turmoil is found to be a major domestic conflict dimension; revolution and subversion are major domestic conflict dimensions, either separately or combined into one internal war dimension; foreign conflict occurs along diplomatic and belligerent dimensions.

Rummel, R. J. 1968b. "Dimensions of Error in Cross-National Data." In *A Handbook of Method in Cultural Anthropology*, R. Naroll and R. Cohen, eds.

Goal: To determine the major dimensions of error in cross-national data and relate them to the attributes of nations.

Data: Sixty-six error measures for 82 nations on 1955 data.

Data slice: R-factor analysis.

Model and technique: Four component factor analyses and orthogonal rotations for various levels of missing data among the error measures; inclusion of resulting factor scores on the dimensions in a 236-variable factor analysis of nations (Rummel *et al.*, 1968).

Results: Demographic and economic welfare data error dimensions found; these two clusters of error found related to economic development and the political dimensions respectively.

Rummel, R. J. 1969. *Dimensions of Nations.*

Goal: To determine the major dimensions of variation of nations.

Data: For 82 nations 236 variables on 1955 data.

Data slice: R-factor analysis.

Model and technique: Component factor analysis and orthogonal and oblique rotation; factor comparisons using Ahmavaara's (1954b) transformation analysis.

Russett, B. M. 1966. "Discovering Voting Groups in the United Nations." *American Political Science Review.*

Goal: To empirically delineate UN voting groups.

Data: Sixty-six roll-call votes for UN members in the 18th (1963) General Assembly session.

Data slice: Q-factor analysis.

Model and technique: Component factor analysis and orthogonal rotation.

Results: Found nations groupings were into Western Community, Brazzaville Africans, Afro-Asians, Communist bloc, conservative Arabs, and Iberia.

Russett, B. M. 1967a. "Delineating International Regions." In *Quantitative International Politics*, ed. J. D. Singer.

Goal: To determine the major dimensions and regional grouping of nations in terms of their economic, political, and cultural attributes.

Data: Fifty-four variables for 82 nations on circa 1960 data.

Data slice: R-factor analysis; Q-factor analysis on factor scores.

Model and technique: Component factor analysis; orthogonal and oblique rotation.

Results: Found factors of economic development, Communism, size, Catholic culture, and intensive agriculture; Q-factor analysis of nations yielded Asian, Latin American, Western European, and Eastern European groups.

Russett, B. M. 1967b. *International Regions and International Integration.*

Goal: A more extensive presentation and elaboration of the material presented in Russett (1967a).

Model and technique: Factor comparisons are done with similar studies, and distances between nations are analyzed.

Schnore, L. F. 1961. "The Statistical Measurement of Urbanization and Economic Development." *Land Economics.*

Goal: To determine the relationship of economic development and urbanization.

Data: Twelve economic and urbanization variables for 75 nations on circa 1950–55 data.

Data slice: R-factor analysis.

Results: Found a factor common to economic development and urbanization.

Schutz, R. E. 1956. "A Factor Analysis of Educational Development

in the United States." *Educational and Psychological Measurement.*
Tanter, R. 1965. "Dimensions of Conflict Behavior Within Nations, 1955–60: Turmoil and Internal War," *Peace Research Society: Papers, III.*

Goal: To replicate Rummel (1963) and Tanter (1966) results for domestic conflict behavior.

Data: Same variables as Rummel (1963) for 74 nations on 1955–60 data; 8 domestic conflict variables for 66 nations for 1948–62 data.

Data slice: R-factor analysis.

Model and technique: Component analysis and orthogonal rotation.

Results: Confirmed dimensions previously found; an internal war dimension combined revolution and subversion components as in Tanter (1966)

Tanter, R. 1966. "Dimensions of Conflict Behavior Within and Between Nations, 1958–60." *Journal of Conflict Resolution.*

Goal: To replicate Rummel (1963) results for domestic and foreign conflict behavior.

Data: Same variables as Rummel for 83 nations on 1958–60 data.

Data slice: R- factor analysis.

Model and technique: Component analysis and orthogonal rotation.

Results: Confirmed dimensions previously found, except that an internal war dimension combined revolution and subversion components.

24.2.2 TRIBES AND CULTURAL GROUPS

Driver, H. E., and K. F. Schuessler. 1957. "Factor Analysis of Ethnographic Data." *American Anthropologist.*

Goal: To determine an objective classification of tribes on the basis of their characteristics.

Data: Twenty-five hundred characteristics of 16 Indian tribes.

Data slice: Q-factor analysis.

Gouldner, A. W., and R. A. Peterson. 1962. *Notes on Technology and the Moral Order.*

Goal: To identify fundamental dimensions common to primitive societies.

Data: Fifty-nine variables for 71 primitive societies from the Human Relations Area Files.

Data slice: R-factor analysis.

Model and technique: Component factor analysis and orthogonal rotation.

Results: Found dimensions of lineality, sex dominance, technology level, and Apollonianism or norm-sending.

Hickman, J. M. 1962. "Dimensions of a Complex Concept: A Method Exemplified." *Human Organization.*

Goal: To empirically evaluate the complex concept of a "folk-urban continuum."

Data: Thirteen cultural characteristics on data from the Human Relations Area File.

Data slice: R-factor analysis.

Model and technique: Orthogonal rotation.

Results: Found factors of kinship organization, size-complexity, and relative isolation.

Howells, W. W. 1957. "The Cranial Vault: Factors of Size and Shape." *American Journal of Physical Anthropology.*

Kluckhohn, F. R., and F. L. Strodtbeck. 1961. *Variations in Value Orientations.*

Goal: To determine the value orientation of five culture communities in the American Southwest.

Data: Interview responses.

Technique: Component factor analysis; direct factor analysis.

LeVine, R. A., and J. Sawyer. 1966. "Cultural Dimensions: A Factor Analysis of the World Ethnographic Sample." *American Anthropologist.*

Goal: To determine the major cultural dimensions of Murdock's world ethnographic sample.

Data: Thirty characteristics for 565 cultural groups.

Data slice: R-factor analysis.

Model and technique: Component factor analysis and orthogonal rotation.

Results: Found basic dimensions of agriculture, animal husbandry, fishing, hunting and gathering, nuclear family households, patrilineality, matrilineality, cross-cousin marriage, and sociopolitical stratification.

Rettig, S. 1964. "Invariance of Factor Structure of Ethical Judgments by Indian and American College Students." *Sociometry.*

Model and technique: Ahmavaara's (1957) factor comparison technique.

Results: Found similarity in ethical judgments of Indian and American college students.

Rettig, S., and B. Pasamanick. 1962. "Invariance in Factor Structure of Moral Value Judgments from American and Korean College Students." *Sociometry.*

Goal: To determine structure similarity of value judgments in cultural heterogeneous groups.

Data: Data on 489 American and 513 Korean students.

Data slice: R-factor analysis.

Model and technique: Orthogonal rotation and factor comparison, using Ahmavaara's (1957) comparison technique.

Result: Agreement of moral judgment in both groups.

Schuessler, K. F., and H. Driver. 1956. "A Factor Analysis of Sixteen Primitive Societies." *American Sociological Review.*

Goal: A discussion and elaboration of the results also given in Driver and Schuessler (1957).

Wolfe, A. W. 1966. *Social Structural Bases of Art.*

Goal: To assess interrelations among characteristics of societies possibly associated with art.

Data: Twelve variables for 53 societies.

Data slice: R-factor analysis.

Model and technique: Component factor analysis and orthogonal rotation; Guttman scaling to develop factor scales.

24.2.3 INTERMEDIATE POLITICAL UNITS (STATES, PROVINCES, ETC.)

Allardt, E. 1964. "Institutionalized versus Diffuse Support for Radical Political Movements." *Transactions of the Fifth World Congress in Sociology.*

Goal: To determine the components of radicalism in Finland.

Data: Variables on the communes of five areas of Finland.

Data slice: R-factor analysis.

Model and technique: Analysis of each area separately and factor comparison of different results; orthogonal rotation.

Results: Political radicalism is stronger in more economically developed areas with pressure toward uniformity, or in economically backward areas with weaker pressure toward uniformity.

Allardt, E. 1966. "Implications of Within-Nation Variations and Regional Imbalances for Cross-National Research." In *Comparing Nations*, ed. Richard Merritt and Stein Rokkan.

Bell, W. H., and D. W. Stevenson. 1964. "An Index of Economic Health for Ontario Counties and Districts." *Ontario Economic Review.*

Berry, B. J. L. 1961a. "A Method for Deriving Multi-Factor Uniform Regions." *Polish Geographical Review.*

Goal: To describe a method for delineating regions.

Data: Six characteristics of the nine regional census divisions (e.g., New England) of the U.S.

Data slice: R-factor analysis; Q-factor analysis.

Model and technique: Component factor analysis and direct factor analysis; distances; grouping of distances.

Blalock, H. M., Jr. 1957. "Per Cent Non-White and Discrimination in the South." *American Sociological Review.*

Goal: To investigate the relationship between various indices of discrimination and rate of nonwhite increase.

Data: Data on 150 Southern American counties.

Data slice: R-factor analysis.

Results: Only a weak relationship found.

Buckatzsch, E. J. 1947. "The Influence of Social Conditions on Mortality Rates." *Population Studies.*

Goal: To determine the influence of social conditions on mortality rates; to construct an index of social conditions to employ in a regression analysis of mortality rates.

Data: Five variables for 81 county boroughs of England and Wales.

Data slice: R-factor analysis.

Model and technique: Common factor analysis.

Digman, J. M., and D. W. Tuttle. 1961. "An Interpretation of an Election by Means of Obverse Factor Analysis." *Journal of Social Psychology.*

Goal: To determine meaningful cognitive dimensions of voting.

Data: Precinct returns and a sample of ballots of the Hawaiian 1954 general elections.

Data slice: Q-factor analysis.

Model and technique: Target rotation.

Results: Party is a major dimension, with ethnic considerations playing a strong secondary role.

Eber, H. W. 1966a. *Multivariate Analysis of a Vocational Rehabilitation System.*

Data: Socioeconomic characteristics of American counties.

George, W. 1951. "Social Conditions and the Labour Vote in the County Boroughs of England and Wales." *British Journal of Sociology.*

Goal: To develop an index of social conditions by applying the factor weights derived from Buckatzsch (1947). This index is correlated with Labour Party votes for 1931, 1935, 1945, and 1950, and regression equations are computed. George concludes that there is a close association between per cent of Labour votes and social conditions.

Hagood, M. J. 1943. "Statistical Methods for Delineation of Regions Applied to Data on Agriculture and Population." *Social Forces.*

Goal: To exemplify the use of statistical methods in delineating regions.

Data: States of the U.S.

Data slice: R-factor analysis.

Model and technique: Component factor analysis.

Hagood, M. J., N. Danilevsky, and C. O. Beum. 1941. "An Examination of the Use of Factor Analysis in the Problem of Sub-regional Delineation." *Rural Sociology.*

Goal: To exemplify the use of factor analysis in delineating regions.

Data: Ohio counties.

Data slice: R-factor analysis.

Hofstaetter, P. R. 1951. "A Factorial Study of Culture Patterns in the U.S." *Journal of Psychology.*

Goal: To explore the dimensionality of American states.

Data: Sixteen variables on 48 American states for circa 1948 data.

Data slice: R-factor analysis.

Model and technique: Orthogonal rotation; calculates factor profiles of selected states.

Jonassen, C. T. 1961. "Functional Unities in Eighty-eight Community Systems." *American Sociological Review.*

Goal: A briefer presentation of the results given in Jonassen and Peres (1960).

Jonassen, C. T., and S. H. Peres. 1960. *Interrelationships of Dimensions of Community Systems.*

Goal: To develop quantitative measures of communities and to identify the essential factors.

Data: Eighty-two community variables for 88 countries on circa 1950 data.

Data slice: R-factor analysis.

Model and technique: Component factor analysis and orthogonal rotation.

Results: Seven factors were identified: urbanism, welfare, influx, poverty, magni-complexity, educational effort, and proletarianism.

Jones, B. G., and W. W. Goldsmith. 1965. *Studies in Regional Development: A Factor Analysis Approach to Sub-regional Definition in Chenago, Delaware, and Otsego Counties.*

MacRae, D., Jr., and J. A. Meldrum. 1960. "Critical Elections in Illinois: 1888–1958." *American Political Science Review.*

Model and technique: Component factor analysis model and direct factor analysis technique.

Pettigrew, T. F., and R. B. Spier. 1962. "The Ecological Structure of Negro Homicide." *American Journal of Sociology.*

Goal: To account for Negro homicide rates by differential state characteristics.

Data: Five state characteristics and one homicide measure.

Data slice: R-factor analysis.

Results: Suppose tradition of violence hypothesis of homicide.

Ray, D. M., and B. J. L. Berry. 1965. "Multivariate Socio-Economic Regionalization; A Pilot Study in Central Canada." In *Regional Statistical Studies*, T. Rymes and S. Ostrey, eds.

Model and technique: Distances; grouping on distances.

Soares, G. 1964. "Congruency and Incongruency Among Indicators of Economic Development." International Conference on Comparative Social Research in Developing Countries.

Goal: To define indicators on economic development.

Data: Forty-three variables for 20 Venezuelan states; similar data for Brazil.

Data slice: R-factor analysis.

Results: For Venezuela found factors of economic development, oil industry, and mining; for Brazil found factors of economic development and industrialization.

Soares, G. 1965. *Economic Development and Political Radicalism.*

Goal: To determine the factors of comparative national development.

Data: Data on 9 indicators of social development for regions in Venezuela, 7 indicators for Brazilian states, and 13 indicators for Japanese prefectures.

Data slice: R-factor analysis for each nation.

Model and technique: Orthogonal rotation.

Results: Found a social development factor accounting for 52.3 per cent of the total communality in Venezuela, and the same general factor accounting for 52.1 per cent of communality in Brazil, and 44.5 per cent of communality in Japan.

Stone, R. 1960. "A Comparison of the Economic Structure of Regions Based on the Concept of Distance." *Journal of Regional Science.*

Data: Eleven economic type variables on 12 civil defense regions of the United Kingdom.

Model and technique: Distances, groups on distances.

Thompson, J. H., S. C. Sufrin, P. R. Gould, and M. A. Buck. 1962. "Toward a Geography of Economic Health: The Case of New York." *Association of American Geographers, Annals.*

Goal: To determine the indicators and components of variation in economic health.

Data: Nine indicators of economic health for 58 New York counties on 1947–58 data.

Data slice: R-factor analysis.

Model and technique: Component factor analysis.

Results: Found factors of general economic health, rural-urban, and economic-demographic growth.

24.2.4 URBAN AREAS (CITIES, TOWNS, ETC.)

Anderson, T. R., and J. E. Egeland. 1961. "Spatial Aspects of Social Area Analysis," *American Sociological Review.*

Bell, W. 1955. "Economic, Family, and Ethnic Status: An Empirical Test." *American Sociological Review.*

Berry, B. J. L. 1961c. "City Size Distributions and Economic Development." *Economic Development and Cultural Change.*

Berry, B. J. L. 1964b. "Cities as Systems Within Systems of Cities." *Regional Science Association, Papers.*

Berry, B. J. L. 1965a. *Metropolitan Planning Guidelines Phase One: Background Documents.*

> *Goal:* To develop an understanding of the socioeconomic characteristics of northeastern Illinois.
>
> *Data:* Characteristics of 147 metropolitan municipalities in northeastern Illinois.
>
> *Data slice:* R-factor analysis.
>
> *Model and technique:* Component factor analysis and orthogonal rotation; factor scores of municipalities and groupings on them.
>
> *Results:* For one of the analyses seven dimensions were found: size, social status, family structure, new suburbs, housing vacancies, race, and distance density.

Berry, B. J. L. 1965b. "The Retail Component of the Urban Model." *Journal of American Institute of Planners.*

> *Goal:* To describe the interdependencies in the commercial structure of urban areas.
>
> *Data:* Sixteen variables describing the business centers of northeastern Illinois.
>
> *Data slice:* R-factor analysis.
>
> *Model and technique:* Separate factor analyses of planned and unplanned centers.
>
> *Results:* The largest factor in both cases is one of size.

Berry, B. J. L., and H. G. Barnum. 1962. "Aggregate Relations and Elemental Components of Central Place Systems." *Journal of Regional Science.*

Goal: To justify and present the direct factor loadings discussed in Berry *et al.* (1962).

Berry, B. J. L., H. G. Barnum, and R. J. Tennant. 1962. "Retail Location and Consumer Behavior." *Regional Science Association, Papers.*

Goal: To determine the interdependencies among the various aspects of central place systems.

Data: Eighty central place functions for 76 selected establishments in southwestern Iowa.

Data slice: R-factor analysis; Q-factor analysis.

Model and technique: Component factor analysis model and direct factor analysis technique.

Results: Found overall pattern of size relation and functions arranged in a hierarchy of hamlets, villages, towns, and cities.

Berry, B. J. L., K. B. Cooke, and D. M. Ray. 1965. "Identification of Declining Regions: An Empirical Study of the Dimensions of Rural Poverty." Conference on Areas of Economic Stress.

Goal: To identify the patterns of rural poverty in Ontario.

Data: Thirty-one variables on 555 municipalities.

Data slice: R-factor analysis.

Model and technique: Component factor analysis and orthogonal rotation; distances and groupings on distances.

Results: Found patterns of farm poverty, nonfarm poverty, density, and two patterns related to education.

Bordua, D. J. 1958–59. "Juvenile Delinquency and 'Anomie': An Attempt at Replication." *Social Problems.*

Goal: An attempt at replication on Detroit of Lander's (1954) results.

Borgatta, E. F., and J. K. Hadden. 1966. "A Profile of American Cities." *Trans-action.*

Goal: To present a profile of American cities in terms of their scores on the major dimensions of variations in their characteristics. The factor analysis results presented are from Hadden and Borgatta (1965).

Cartwright, D. S., and K. I. Howard. 1966. "Multivariate Analysis of Gang Delinquency: I. Ecologic Influences." *Multivariate Behavioral Research.*

Goal: To determine the conditions underlying gang delinquency.

Data: Sixteen delinquent gangs in Chicago, 1960.

Model and technique: Intercorrelated census tract and behavior factors for 16 gangs.

Results: Gang neighborhoods lower on socioeconomic status and stable family; higher on disorganization-deprivation.

Chilton, R. J. 1964. "Continuity in Delinquency Area Research: A Comparison of Studies for Baltimore, Detroit, and Indianapolis." *American Sociological Review.*

Goal: To reconcile contradictory findings in delinquency area research of Lander (1954) and Bordua (1958–59).

Data: Census tract characteristics and delinquency rates for Indianapolis, Detroit, and Baltimore.

Data slice: R-factor analysis.

Model and technique: Orthogonal rotation; factor comparison.

Results: Delinquency related to transiency, poor housing, and economic indices.

Gosnell, H. F. 1937. *Machine Politics: Chicago Model.*

Goal: To determine economic and social background of voting behavior.

Data: Voting and economic and social data for 174 areas of Chicago on the presidential and nonpresidential years 1932–1936.

Results: Three factors found: traditional Democratic machine vote, wet and extravagant tendencies of renters, and special influence favoring Democratic candidates.

Gosnell, H. F., and N. N. Gill. 1935. "A Factor Analysis of the 1932 Presidential Vote in Chicago." *American Political Science Review.*

Goal: To determine the relations between voting behavior and social economic conditions.

Data: Voting and economic and social characteristics for Chicago in the 1928 and 1932 presidential elections.

Results: Weak relationship between Roosevelt vote and economic status; voting habits change slowly in period of rapid economic change.

Gosnell, H. F., and M. J. Schmidt. 1936. "Factorial and Correlational Analysis of the 1934 Vote in Chicago." *American Statistical Association Journal.*

Data: Characteristics and voting data for the 1930 and 1934 congressional elections in Chicago.

Data slice: R-factor analysis.

Results: Party tradition the most important influence.

Green, N. E. 1956. "Scale Analysis of Urban Structures." *American Sociological Review.*

Hadden, J. K., and E. F. Borgatta. 1965. *American Cities: Their Social Characteristics.*

Goal: To determine the dimensions of variation in American cities at various levels of city size and for different definitions of "city."

Data: Census data on 65 characteristics of 644 cities with at least 25,000 population.

Data slice: R-factor analysis.

Model and technique: Common factor analysis; orthogonal rotation; factor scores; factor comparisons of different results.

Results: Factors found were size, density, socioeconomic status, nonwhite concentration, foreign-born concentration, age composition, residential mobility, and educational center.

Hofstaetter, P. R. 1952. "'Your City' Revisited: A Factorial Study of Cultural Patterns." *American Catholic Sociological Review.*

Holzinger, K. J., and H. H. Harman. 1941. *Factor Analysis.*[2]

Goal: To illustrate application of factor analysis.

Data: Three voting variables on 1934 presidential elections and five socioeconomic variables for Chicago, Illinois.

Data slice: R-factor analysis.

Model and technique: Common factor analysis; and orthogonal and oblique rotation.

Results: Found factors of traditional Democratic vote and home permanency.

Hsü, E. H. 1953. "Note on Factor Analysis of American Culture: A Criticism." *Journal of Social Psychology.*

James, R. W., and H. L. Miller. 1958–59. "Factors in Community Action Programs." *Social Problems.*

Goal: To determine the underlying dimensions in action programs.

Technique: Orthogonal rotation.

Lander, B. 1954. *Towards an Understanding of Juvenile Delinquency.*

Data: Juvenile delinquency in Baltimore (8,464 cases).

Data slice: R-factor analysis.

Results: Found delinquency related to anomie and not specifically to the socioeconomic conditions of an area.

Moser, C. A., and W. Scott. 1961. *British Towns.*

Goal: To determine the socioeconomic characteristics of British towns.

Data: Fifty-seven characteristics for 157 towns.

Data slice: R-factor analysis.

Model and technique: Component factor analysis.

Results: The major components found were social class, population change between 1951 and 1959, and overcrowding.

---

2. These results are also reported in Harman (1960, 1967; see "eight political variables" in index to Harman, 1960).

Ogburn, W. F. 1935. "Factors in the Variation of Crime Among Cities." *American Statistical Association Journal.*

Pitts, F. 1967. "Basic Dimensions of Variation in Korean Urban Structures." Pacific Coast Regional Conference of the Association for Asian Studies.

Goal: To measure the variations in Korean urban functions.

Data: Data on 258 characteristics of 257 Korean urban places.

Data slice: R-factor analysis.

Model and technique: Component factor analysis and orthogonal rotation; group urban places on their distances in factor space.

Results: Three major factors are: intellectual orientation and white color dominance; light manufacturing and wholesaling; and agricultural servicing.

Price, D. O. 1942. "Factor Analysis in the Study of Metropolitan Centers." *Social Forces.*

Goal: To determine occupational characteristics and their social and economic correlates.

Data: Fifteen socioeconomic variables for 93 American cities on 1930 census data.

Model and technique: Orthogonal and oblique rotation.

Results: Four major factors, two of which were size and occupational structure.

Schmid, C. F. 1960. "Urban Crime Areas: Part 1." *American Sociological Review.*

Goal: To analyze and describe spatial distribution of crime in Seattle.

Data: Twenty crime indices and 18 socioeconomic characteristics for census tracts of Seattle on 1949–51 data.

Model and technique: Orthogonal rotation; grouping on factor scores.

Results: Spatial variations described by factors of low social cohesion (low family status), low occupational status, low family and economic status, population mobility, a typical crime pattern, low mobility, and race.

Schuessler, K. F. 1962. "Components of Variation in City Crime Rates." *Social Problems.*

Goal: To determine whether variation in crime rate among cities could be explained by a small number of factors and to establish the sociological meaning of factors that do emerge.

Data: Seven criminal offense variables and 20 social characteristics variables for 105 cities on 1950 data.

Data slice: R-factor analysis.

Model and technique: Orthogonal rotation.

Results: Five factors emerged and three were interpreted as social frustration, institutional control, and industrialization.

Schuessler, K. F., and G. Slatin. 1964. "Sources of Variation in U.S. City Crime, 1950 and 1960." *Journal of Research in Crime and Delinquency.*

Goal: To replicate and extend Schuessler (1962).

Data: Seven offense variables and social characteristics for cities of over 100,000 population on 1950 and 1960 data.

Data slice: R-factor analysis.

Model and technique: Orthogonal rotation.

Results: Crimes against persons are related to a minority relations factor; crimes against property are related to an economic factor.

Schutz, R. E. 1960. "A Factor Analysis of Academic Achievement and Community Characteristics." *Educational and Psychological Measurement.*

Straits, B. C. 1965. "Factor Analysis of Demographic and Political Characteristics of American Cities."

Goal: To determine the dimensions of urban variation.

Results: Found factors of socioeconomic status, age, growth, and decline and size.

Van Arsdol, M. D., Jr., S. F. Camilleri, and C. F. Schmid. 1958. "The Generality of Urban Social Area Indexes." *American Sociological Review.*

Goal: To test the hypothesis that urban communities can be differentiated in terms of social rank, urbanization, and segregation.

Data: Six variables for 10 cities on 1950 data.

Data slice: R-factor analysis.

Model and technique: Target rotation.

Results· Hypothesis confirmed.

Wood, R. C. 1961. *1400 Governments.*

Goal: To determine the major community socioeconomic characteristics that might be correlated with their budgetary expenditures.

Data: Twenty characteristics for 64 middle-sized New Jersey municipalities on circa 1950 data.

Data slice: R-factor analysis.

Model and technique: Common factor analysis and orthogonal rotation.

Results: Found community factors of size, industrialization, housing density, age, low-income prevalence, residential affluence, and land reserve.

24.2.5 LEGISLATURES AND COURTS

Carlson, H. B., and W. Harrell. 1942. "Voting Groups Among Leading Congressmen Obtained by Means of the Inverted Factor Technique." *Journal of Social Psychology.*

Cureton, E. E. 1968. *Factor Analysis of Senate Votes.*
Goal: To identify four to six basic attitudes underlying record votes.
Data: Forty-two record vote variables on 92 senators in the 85th Congress.

Grumm, J. G. 1963. "A Factor Analysis of Legislative Behavior." *Midwest Journal of Political Science.*
Goal: To identify and assess the factors influencing legislators.
Data: Forty-one votes for members of the Kansas Senate for the 1957 and 1954 sessions.
Data slice: Q-factor analysis.
Model and technique: Oblique rotation.
Results: Finds Republican, growth and decline, and urban-rural factors in the Senate; finds same factors in the House except for the addition of a Democratic factor.

Harris, C. W. 1948. "A Factor Analysis of Selected Senate Roll-Calls, 80th Congress." *Educational and Psychological Measurement.*
Goal: To analyze the voting record of the Senate on nine issues.
Data: Nine roll calls and one party variable for 95 senators.
Data slice: R-factor analysis.
Model and technique: Common factor analysis, and orthogonal and oblique rotation.
Results: Two interpretable factors were party (or attitude toward big business) and isolationist-internationalist.

Lingoes, J. C. 1962. "A Multiple Scalogram Analysis of Selected Issues of the Eighty-third United States Senate." Annual Convention of the American Psychological Association.
Goal: To demonstrate statistical analysis of legislative voting.
Data: Votes of 88 senators on 112 issues in the U.S. Senate.
Data slice: R-factor analysis.
Model and technique: Common factor analysis of scales and of issues in the U.S. Senate.
Results: In factoring scales, found factors of tax and atomic energy issues, farm issues, and foreign aid.

Schubert, G. 1962. "The 1960 Term of the Supreme Court: A Psychological Analysis." *American Political Science Review.*
Goal: To describe a multidimensional model of the U.S. Supreme Court and to test the hypothesis that variations in Court voting are functions of a small number of issues.

Data: Data on 867 votes of Supreme Court Justices on cases heard before the Court during the 1960 term.

Data slice: Q-factor analysis.

Model and Technique: Target rotation to Guttman scales.

Schubert, G. 1965. *The Liberal Mind.*

> *Goal:* To factor analyze the voting positions of Supreme Court justices for a large number of U.S. Supreme Court sessions.

Thurstone, L. L., and J. W. Degan. 1951. "A Factorial Study of the Supreme Court." *Psychometric Laboratory Report.*

> *Goal:* A Q-factor analysis of the U.S. Supreme Court as reported in Fruchter (1954, pp. 176–79).

24.3 Social and Economic Groups, Processes, and Behavior

24.3.1 ORGANIZATIONS

Findikyan, N., and S. B. Sells, 1964a. *The Dimensional Structure of Campus Student Organizations.*

Findikyan, N., and S. B. Sells. 1964b. "Social Structure of Campus Student Organizations." Annual Convention of the Southwestern Psychological Association.

Godfrey, E. P., F. E. Fiedler, and D. M. Hall. 1958. *Boards, Management, and Company Success.*

> *Goal:* To determine the factors making for the effectiveness of complex organizations.
>
> *Data:* Eighty-one characteristics of 32 companies.
>
> *Data slice:* R-factor analysis.
>
> *Model and technique:* Component factor analysis and orthogonal rotation.
>
> *Results:* Determined components of county economic base, size, volume of feed sales, level of living, company efficiency and growth, and socioeconomic conditions.

Hemphill, J. K., D. E. Griffiths, and N. Frederiksen. 1962. *Administrative Performance and Personality.*

Sells, S. B., and N. Findikyan. 1965. *Dimensions of Organizational Structure.*

Somit, A., and J. Tanenhaus. 1964. *American Political Science.*

> *Goal:* To determine major differences of opinion within the political science profession.
>
> *Data:* Answers to 26 questionnaire items by over 400 American political scientists.

Data slice: R-factor analysis.

Model and technique: Component factor analysis; common factor analysis; orthogonal rotation.

Results: Seven major differences of opinion were found, among which were dimensions of behaviorism, state of the discipline, adequacy of political science, and existence of an establishment.

Stogdill, R. M. 1966. "Brief Report: Some Possible Uses of Factor Analysis in Multivariate Studies." *Multivariate Behavioral Research.*

Stogdill, R. M. 1967. "The Structure of Organization Behavior." *Multivariate Behavioral Research.*

Data: Thirty variables describing the productivity, morale, and cohesiveness of 30 foremen and a manager of a manufacturing plant.

Results: Found factors of employee satisfaction, supervising behavior and status, and group performance.

Stogdill, R. M., O. S. Goode, and D. R. Day. 1963. "The Leader Behavior of Corporation Presidents." *Personal Psychology.*

Stogdill, R. M., et al. 1965. *Managers, Employees, and Organizations.*

24.3.2 SMALL GROUPS

Blake, R. R., J. S. Mouton, and B. Fruchter. 1962. "A Factor Analysis of Training Group Behavior." *Journal of Social Psychology.*

Data: Eleven scale reactions on 20 eight-member training groups.

Data slice: R-factor analysis.

Results: Found dimensions of cohesion and group accomplishment and group development feedback.

Blau, P. M. 1962. "Patterns of Choice in Interpersonal Relations." *American Sociological Review.*

Goal: To determine the effect of individual attributes on interpersonal choices.

Data: Thirty-one specific attributes for members of work groups.

Borgatta, E. F., and L. S. Cottrell, Jr. 1955. "On the Classification of Groups." *Sociometry.*

Goal: To identify the basic variables for describing groups.

Data: Thirty-four variables on 166 three-person groups.

Data slice: R-factor analysis.

Results: Found factors of tension-neutral activity, involvement activity, group identification, leader structure, discussional involvement, task interest, and maturity.

Borgatta, E. G., L. S. Cottrell, Jr., and H. J. Meyer. 1956. "On the Dimensions of Group Behavior." *Sociometry.*

Goal: To review and criticize factor analysis studies of group characteristics.

Cattell, R. B., and E. D. Lawson. 1962. "Sex Differences in Small Group Performance." *Journal of Social Psychology.*

Cattell, R. B., R. Saunders, and G. F. Stice. 1953. "The Dimensions of Syntality in Small Groups." *Human Relations.*

Goal: To establish the chief functionally meaningful group dimensions.

Data: Ninety-three variables (including 32 personality indicators) for 80 newly formed groups of 6–12 men each.

Data slice: R-factor analysis.

Model and technique: Common factor analysis and oblique rotation.

Results: First factors largely determined by personality variables; found factors of purposefulness, democratic procedures, high motivation, and rigidity.

Cattell, R. B., and G. F. Stice. 1960. *The Dimensions of Groups and Their Relations to the Behavior of Members.*

Data: Over 100 variables defining the members of a group, their action, and the group itself.

Coombs, C. H., and G. A. Satter. 1949. "A Factorial Approach to Job Families." *Psychometrika.*

Friedlander, F. 1965. *Behavioral Dimensions of Traditional Work Groups.*

Hagstrom, W. O., and H. C. Selvin. 1965. "Two Dimensions of Cohesiveness in Small Groups." *Sociometry.*

Data: Nineteen possible indicators of cohesiveness in 20 college-living groups.

Results: Found dimensions of social satisfaction and sociometric cohesion.

Hamblin, R., and K. Miller. 1961. "Variation in Interaction Profiles and Group Size." *Sociological Quarterly.*

Goal: To determine dependencies of interaction profiles on group size.

Data: Twelve interaction categories and group size.

Model and technique: Oblique rotation.

Result: Group size found related to two interaction factors.

Levinger, G. 1964. "Task and Social Behavior in Marriage." *Sociometry.*

Data: Family groups.

Results: Found task specialization and socioemotional mutuality.

Lorr, M. 1966. "Dimensions of Interaction in Group Therapy." *Multivariate Behavioral Research.*

Mann, R. D. 1961. "Dimensions of Individual Performance in Small

Groups Under Task and Socio-Emotional Conditions." *Journal of Abnormal and Social Psychology.*
> *Goal:* To test the proposal that three major factors account for much of the variance in measures of performance in small groups.
> *Data:* Performance measures under two different experimental conditions for 20 five-men groups.
> *Results:* Found factors of task prominence, likability, and tension.

Rinn, J. L. 1961. "Q Methodology: An Application to Group Phenomena." *Educational and Psychological Measurement.*

Selvin, H. C., and W. O. Hagstrom. 1963. "The Empirical Classification of Formal Groups," *American Sociological Review.*
> *Goal:* To show through an example how to use factor analysis to develop a classification of groups.

Short, J. F., Jr., R. A. Tennyson, and K. I. Howard. 1963. "Behavior Dimensions of Group Delinquency." *American Sociological Review.*
> *Goal:* To determine the dimensions of variation in gang delinquency.
> *Data:* Thirty-seven activity variables for 578 delinquent gang members.
> *Data slice:* R-factor analysis.
> *Model and technique:* Common factor analysis and orthogonal rotation.
> *Results:* Dimensions found are conflict, stable corner activities, stable sex, realist, and authority protest.

Smith, B., J. Fawcett, R. Ezekiel, and S. Roth. 1963. "A Factorial Study of Morale Among Peace Corps Teachers in Ghana." *Journal of Social Issues.*
> *Goal:* To identify a common dimension of morale among Peace Corps teachers and its stability over time.
> *Data:* Forty-one Peace Corps teachers on rating of morale measured for three time periods.
> *Data slice:* R-factor analysis.
> *Model and technique:* Orthogonal and oblique rotation.
> *Results:* A stable factor of general morale emerged.

Weiss, R. F., and B. Pasamanick. 1962. "Individual and Group Goals: A Factor Analysis." *Journal of Social Psychology.*
> *Goal:* To determine the dimensions of individual and group goals.
> *Data:* Fifty questionnaire items dealing with individual and group goals.
> *Data slice:* R-factor analysis.
> *Results:* Found dimensions of judgment, drive, individual versus group goals, and cooperation-conflict.

24.3.3 ROLES

Cattell, R. B. 1962a. "Group Theory, Personality and Role: A Model for Experimental Researchers." In *NATO Symposium on Defense Psychology*, ed. F. A. Geldard.

Goal: To present a model of role behavior based on the mathematical structure of the factor model.

Gouldner, A. W. 1957b. "Cosmopolitans and Locals: Toward an Analysis of Latent Social Roles—II." *Administrative Science Quarterly.*

Goal: To define concepts of latent roles determined in Gouldner (1957a).

Data: Ninety-four questions of 125 faculty members of a small private liberal arts college.

Data slice: R-factor analysis.

Model and technique: Orthogonal rotation.

Results: Found factors of the dedicated, true bureaucrat, the home guard, the elders, the outsiders, and the empire builders.

Kahn, R. L., D. M. Wolfe, R. P. Quinn, and J. D. Snoek. 1964. *Organizational Stress: Studies in Role Conflict and Ambiguity.*

Goal: To determine the basic dimensions defining the normative expectations of role-senders in organizations.

Data: Responses of 381 role-senders as to their advocacy of compliance with behavior described by 36 norms.

Data slice: R-factor analysis.

Model and technique: Orthogonal rotation; analysis of factor scores.

Results: Found factors of rules orientation, nurturing of subordinates, closeness of supervision, universalism, and promotion-achievement orientation.

24.3.4 CLASS, STATUS, AND MOBILITY

Cattell, R. B. 1942. "The Concept of Social Status." *Journal of Social Psychology.*

Data: Five social status measures and 25 occupational variables.

Data slice: R-factor analysis.

Results: Found a general factor of social status.

Hatt, P. 1948. "Class and Ethnic Attitudes." *American Sociological Review.*

Goal: To demonstrate the relationship between class attitudes and ethnic attitudes.

Results: Finds consistent attitude patterns.

Kahl, J. A., and J. A. Davis. 1955. "A Comparison of Indexes of Socio-Economic Status." *American Sociological Review.*

Data: Nineteen stratification indices for 219 men.

Results: Factors of occupation and of status.

Klausner, S. 1953. "Social Class and Self-Concept." *Journal of Social Psychology.*

Data slice: R-factor analysis.

Data: Q-sort measures of self-concept and questionnaire recorded socioeconomic information.

Results: Factors of reactive aggression, adjusted inferiority, and socially isolated self-aggressors.

Sewell, W. H., and A. O. Haller. 1959. "Factors in the Relationship Between Social Status and the Personality Adjustment of the Child." *American Sociological Review.*

Data: Personality test items most highly associated with social status in a group of 1,462 elementary school children.

Data slice: R-factor analysis.

Results: Identified factors of concern over status, concern over achievement, rejection of family, and nervous symptoms; these factors were more associated with low status children than high.

Westof, C. F., M. Bressler, and P. Sagi. 1960. "The Concept of Social Mobility: An Empirical Inquiry." *American Sociological Review.*

Goal: To find the smallest number of mobility dimensions.

Data: Eleven objective and eleven subjective measures of mobility for married couples.

Result: Concludes that social mobility is a complex multidimensional concept.

24.3.5 SOCIAL CHOICE

Bock, D., and H. Suraya. 1952. "Factors of the Tale: A Preliminary Report." *Sociometry.*

Goal: To identify choice factors in sociometric data.

Data: Sixteen ninth grade science students.

Results: Two factors emerged: sex and science ability.

MacRae, D., Jr. 1960. "Direct Factor Analysis of Sociometric Data." *Sociometry.*

Goal: To illustrate the use of direct factor analysis on social choice matrices.

Data: Choices of friends among 67 prison inmates.

Data slice: R-factor analysis; Q-factor analysis.

Model and technique: Component factor analysis model and direct factor analysis technique.

Results: Eleven factors of choosers and eleven of chosen.

Peterson, R. J., S. S. Komorita, and H. C. Quay. 1964. "Determinants of Sociometric Choices." *Journal of Social Psychology.*

Wright, B., and M. S. Evitts. 1961. "Direct Factor Analysis in Sociometry." *Sociometry.*

Goal: To exemplify use of direct factor analysis and multiple regression.

Data: Q-sort to form sociometric choice matrices.

Data slice: R-factor analysis; Q-factor analysis.

Model and technique: Component factor analysis model and direct factor analysis technique.

Wright, B., and M. S. Evitts. 1963. "Multiple Regression in the Explanation of Social Structure." *Journal of Social Psychology.*

Data: Social choice matrix.

Data slice: R-factor analysis; Q-factor analysis.

Model and technique: Component factor analysis model and direct factor analysis technique.

24.3.6 COMMUNICATION

Carter, R. F. n.d. "The Perceived Appeals of TV Program Content." *University of Wisconsin, TV Research Laboratory, Research Bulletin.*

Deutschmann, P. J., and D. Kiel. 1960. *A Factor Analytic Study of Attitudes Toward the Mass Media.*

Data: Fifty respondents in each of nine cities and 100 respondents in New York City of 24 semantic-differential scales.

Donnahoe, A. S. 1960. "The Public Image of the Advertising Media." *Business and Government Review.*

Grossack, M. 1964. "Testing TV Commercials." In *Understanding Consumer Behavior,* ed. M. Grossack.

Data: TV commercials rated on eight semantic differential scales on different geographic regions.

Kirsch, A. D., and S. Banks. 1962. "Program Types Defined by Factor Analysis." *Journal of Advertising Research.*

Data: Program viewing of 62 TV programs by 596 sampling units.

Lyle, J. 1960. "Semantic Differential Scales for Newspaper Research." *Journalism Quarterly.*

Data: Thirty-two semantic-differential scales measuring readers' attitudes.

Result: Four interpretable factors emerged: newsworthiness, bias, accuracy, and general quality.

Maclean, M., Jr., and W. Hazard. 1953. "Women's Interest in Pictures: The Badger Village Study." *Journalism Quarterly.*

Goal: To determine the major appeals of pictures.

Data: Fifty-one pictures.

Data slice: R-factor analysis.

Results: The major appeal factors were found to be idolatry, social problems, picturesqueness, war, blood and violence, and spectator sports.

Nafziger, R. O., *et al.* 1951. "Useful Tools for Interpreting Newspaper Readership Data." *Journalism Quarterly.*

Data: Newspaper readers' interest in 21 parts of a newspaper—data on metropolitan and small city newspapers.

Ossorio, P. G. 1966. "Classification Space: A Multivariate Procedure for Automatic Document Indexing and Retrieval." *Multivariate Behavioral Research.*

Stempel, G., III. 1963. "An Empirical Exploration of the News," in *Paul J. Deutschmann Memorial Papers in Mass Communications Research*, ed. W. A. Danielson.

Goal: To determine factors influencing newspaper selection of AP and UPI news wire releases.

Data: Thirty-two stories for 25 newspapers.

Results: Factors are suspense, conflict, public affairs, human interest timeliness, positiveness, and political controversy.

Tannenbaum, P. H. 1963. "Public Images of Media Institutions." In *Paul J. Deutschmann Memorial Papers in Mass Communications Research*, ed. W. A. Danielson.

Tannenbaum, P. H., H. K. Jacobson, and E. L. Norris. 1964. "An Experimental Investigation of Typeface Connotations." *Journalism Quarterly.*

Twedt, D. W. 1952. "A Multiple Factor Analysis of Advertising Readership." *Journal of Applied Psychology.*

Goal: To determine the relationship of possible determinants of advertising readership to per cent readership.

Data: Thirty-four determinants.

Results: Major determinants are number of pictures of product, number of colors, number of words, and square inches of illustration.

Westley, B., and M. Lynch. 1962. "A Multiple Factor Analysis of Dichotomous Audience Data." *Journalism Quarterly.*

Data: Program viewing of 50 programs by 670 subjects was used to form 38 conditional probabilities.

Data slice: R-factor analysis.

Technique: Canonical factor analysis.

24.3.7 ATTITUDES AND CONCEPTS

Allen, E. E., and R. W. Hites. 1961. "Factors in Religious Attitudes of Older Adolescents." *Journal of Social Psychology.*

Result: Found religious aspects of our culture are multidimensional.

Boe, E. E., E. F. Gocka, and W. S. Kogan. 1966. "A Factor Analysis of Individual Social Desirability Scale Values." *Multivariate Behavioral Research.*

Data: Data on 112 college students on 100 MMPI (Minnesota Multiphasic Personal Inventory) items of individual judgments of social desirability.

Data slice: R-factor analysis; Q-factor analysis.

Results: Found a large general social desirability factor.

Borgatta, E. F., and J. Hulquist. 1956–57. "A Reanalysis of Some Data From Stouffer's *Communism, Conformity, and Civil Liberties.*" *Public Opinion Quarterly.*

Data: Thirty-three variables from Stouffer's original questionnaire.

Results: Found factors of tolerance for nonconformity, urban Catholicism, youth, threat, interest in issues, and socioeconomic responsibility.

Broen, W. E., Jr. 1957. "A Factor-Analytic Study of Religious Attitudes." *Journal of Abnormal and Social Psychology.*

Data: Twenty-four clergymen representing five major religious groupings.

Data slice: Q-factor analysis.

Camilleri, S. F. 1959. "A Factor Analysis of the F-Scale." *Social Forces.*

Goal: To determine whether the F-scale is consistent with the underlying theory.

Cattell, R. B., and J. Horn. 1963. "An Integrating Study of the Factor Structure of Adult Attitude-Interests." *Genetic Psychology Monographs.*

Goal: An overview of factor analysis research in this area.

Dennis, J. 1966. "Support for the Party System by the Mass Public." *American Political Science Review.*

Goal: To determine the distinguishable elements of support for the political party system.

Data: An area cluster of probability sample of the adult population of Wisconsin.

Data slice: R-factor analysis.

Model and technique: Component factor analysis and orthogonal rotation. Resulting factor scores were refactored with nine attribute variables.

Results: Found factors of diffuse support, responsible parties support, contributor support, and cleavage function support.

Deutschmann, P. J., *et al.* 1959. "The Semantic Differential: Its Use and Abuse." *Public Opinion Quarterly.*

Digman, J. M. 1962. "The Dimensionality of Social Attitudes." *Journal of Social Psychology.*

  Data: Thirty-nine statements of social opinion for 149 residents of Hawaii.

  Data slice: R-factor analysis.

  Model and technique: Common factor analysis and orthogonal rotation.

  Results: Major factors found were authoritarian beliefs and attitudes, equalitarianism, social liberalism, religionism, political liberalism, nationalism, tendermindedness, and sex permissiveness.

Eysenck, H. J. 1954. *The Psychology of Politics.*

  Data: Responses on attitudinal and political questionnaire items of several thousand British.

  Results: Generally found that political attitudes were accounted for by two factors: radicalism-conservatism and toughminded-ness-tendermindedness.

Eysenck, H. J., and S. Crown. 1948–49. "National Stereotypes: An Experimental and Methodological Study." *International Journal of Opinion and Attitude Research.*

  Goal: To determine the interrelationship between racial stereotypes and other traits.

  Data: Data on 165 urban middle class adults.

  Results: General favorableness toward national groupings appears related to toughmindedness-tendermindedness; pro-Semitic attitudes more strongly related to a radicalism-conservatism factor.

Ford, R. N., and D. Henderson. 1942. "A Multiple-Factor Analysis of Ford's White-Negro Experience Scales." *Social Forces.*

  Goal: To test for the unidimensional of two scales measuring the friendliness of whites towards Negroes.

  Data: Two samples of 100 students each from a northern and a southern university.

  Data slice: R-factor analysis.

  Model and technique: Oblique rotation.

  Results: Unidimensionality rejected.

Kassebaum, G. G., D. A. Ward, and D. M. Wilner. 1964. "Some Correlates of Staff Ideology in the Prison." *Journal of Research in Crime and Delinquency.*

  Data: Twenty-eight attitude items on prison staff members.

Model and technique: Factor scores correlated with background variables on respondent.

Results: Custodial staff found more traditional in outlook than treatment staff.

Knapp, R. H. 1962. "Attitudes Toward Time and Aesthetic Choice." *Journal of Social Psychology.*

Data: Questionnaire responses dealing with time, management, and responses.

Results: Factors of time-servant versus time-master, and time-obliviousness versus efficient time-management; the first factor related to aesthetic preference.

Kumata, M., and W. Schramm. 1956. "A Pilot Study of Cross-Cultural Meaning." *Public Opinion Quarterly.*

Lurie, W. A. 1937. "A Study of Spranger's Value-Types by the Method of Factor Analysis." *Journal of Social Psychology.*

Goal: To empirically find generalized value attitudes.

Data: Data on 144 items classed according to Spranger's value types administered to 203 college students.

Data slice: R-factor analysis.

Model and technique: Oblique rotation.

Results: Four basic attitudes by type are social, philistine, theoretical, and religious.

Messick, S. 1960. "Dimensions of Social Desirability." *Journal of Consulting Psychology.*

Goal: To determine the unidimensionality of social desirability.

Data: Forty-two items of the Edwards Personal Preference Schedule administered to 108 mental hospital patients.

Results: Nine resulting factors argue against hypothesis of unidimensionality.

Messick, S. 1961. "The Perceived Structure of Political Relationship." *Sociometry.*

Data: Ratings of 836 undergraduates on similarity to themselves of 20 well-known political figures.

Miller, C. R., and E. W. Butler. 1966. "Anomia and Eunomia: A Methodological Evaluation of Srole's Anomia Scale." *American Sociological Review.*

O'Neil, W. M., and D. J. Levinson. 1954. "A Factorial Exploration of Authoritarianism and Some of Its Ideological Concomitants." *Journal of Personality.*

Data: Responses of 200 students to 64 scale items.

Results: Extracted factors of religious conventionalism, authoritarian submission, and masculine strength facade; concludes that correlations among scales often used may be due to heterogeneity within the scales.

Osgood, C. E. 1952. "The Nature and Measurement of Meaning." *Psychological Bulletin.*

Osgood, C. E., and G. J. Suci. 1955. "Factor Analysis of Meaning." *Journal of Experimental Psychology.*

   Results: Authors find the same factors reported in Osgood *et al.* (1957).

Osgood, C. E., G. J. Suci, and P. H. Tannenbaum. 1957. *The Measurement of Meaning.*

   Goal: To determine the dimensions of semantic variation.

   Model and technique: Orthogonal rotation; analysis of distance.

   Results: Found evaluative, potency, and activity dimensions.

Rettig, S., and B. Pasamanick. 1959. "Changes in Moral Values Among College Students: A Factorial Study." *American Sociological Review.*

   Data: Ranking of morality (rightness) of 50 kinds of behavior by 89 college students.

Rettig, S., and B. Pasamanick. 1961. "Moral Value Structure and Social Class." *Sociometry.*

   Data: Mail questionnaire data on 1743 Ohio State University graduates and 499 blue-collar workers.

   Results: Found general morality, religious, family, puritanical, explorative-manipulative, and economic factors.

Smith, R. G. 1961. "A Semantic Differential for Theatre Concepts." *Speech Monographs.*

Solomon, L., and E. Klein. 1963. "The Relationship Between Agreeing Response Set and Social Desirability." *Journal of Abnormal and Social Psychology.*

Stein, K. B., H. G. Gough, and T. R. Sarbin. 1966. "The Dimensionality of the CPI Socialization Scale and an Empirically Derived Typology Among Delinquent and Nondelinquent Boys." *Multivariate Behavioral Research.*

Tanaka, Y., T. Oyama, and C. E. Osgood. 1963. "A Cross-Culture and Cross-Concept Study of the Generality of Semantic Spaces." *Journal of Verbal Learning and Verbal Behavior.*

Triandis, H. C. 1964. "Exploratory Factor Analyses of the Behavioral Component of Social Attitudes." *Journal of Abnormal and Social Psychology.*

Triandis, H. C., and C. E. Osgood. 1958. "A Comparative Factorial Analysis of Semantic Structure in Monolingual Greek and American College Students." *Journal of Abnormal and Social Psychology.*

Goal: To determine the cross-national invariance of the semantic-differential.

Data: Thirty semantic-differential items on 89 Greek and 43 American monolingual students.

Data slice: R-factor analysis.

Model and technique: Orthogonal rotation and factor comparison.

Results: Similar results for both cultures.

24.3.8 INTERPERSONAL BEHAVIOR AND INTERACTION

Ahmavaara, Y., and T. Markkanen. 1958. *The Unified Factor Model.*
  Goal: To determine social characteristics related to drinking.
  Model and technique: Oblique rotation factor comparison using Ahmavaara's technique.

Boocock, S. S. 1966. "An Experimental Study of the Learning Effects of Two Games with Simulated Environments." *American Behavioral Scientist.*

Borgatta, E. F. 1965. "The Analysis of Patterns of Social Interaction." *Social Forces.*

Farber, B. 1962. "Elements of Competence in Interpersonal Relations: A Factor Analysis." *Sociometry.*
  Data: Responses of 495 husbands to 104 items regarded as representing competence in interpersonal relations.
  Data slice: R-factor analysis.
  Model and technique: Orthogonal rotation.
  Results: Found 11 factors grouped by content into perceived empathy.

Gibb, C. A. 1947. "The Principles and Traits of Leadership." *Journal of Abnormal and Social Psychology.*

Hamblin, R. 1962. "The Dynamics of Racial Discrimination." *Social Problems.*
  Data: Quota sample of 100 St. Louis adults.

Hart, H. H., R. L. Jenkins, S. Axelrad, and P. I. Sperling. 1943. "Multiple Factor Analysis of Traits of Delinquent Boys." *Journal of Social Psychology.*
  Data: Twenty-five traits of 300 adolescent institutionalized boys.
  Results: Found factors of temper-assault, compensatory behavior, aggressiveness, leadership, street gang activity, and group stealing.

Inbar, M. 1966. "The Differential Impact of a Game Simulating a Community Disaster." *American Behavioral Scientist.*

Lorr, M., and D. M. McNair. 1963. "An Interpersonal Behavior Circle." *Journal of Abnormal and Social Psychology.*
  Model and technique: Guttman's circumplex factor structure.

Neal, A., and S. Rettig. 1963. "Dimensions of Alienation Among Manual and Non-Manual Workers." *American Sociological Review.*
> *Goal:* To test for three orthogonal dimensions of alienation: powerlessness, normlessness, anomie; to explore a general dimension underlying alienation.
> *Data:* Different samples of 301 and 302 manual and nonmanual workers.
> *Data slice:* R-factor analysis.
> *Model and technique:* Orthogonal Rotation.

Peterson, D. R., H. C. Quay, and G. R. Cameron. 1959. "Personality and Background Factors in Juvenile Delinquency as Inferred from Questionnaire Responses." *Journal of Consulting Psychology.*
> *Data:* Responses to two delinquency scales.
> *Data slice:* R-factor analysis.
> *Model and technique:* Oblique rotation.
> *Results:* Found personality factors of psychopathy, neuroticism, inadequacy, and background factors of family dissension and scholastic maladjustment.

Sears, R. R., E. E. Maccoby, and H. Levin. 1957. *Patterns of Child Rearing.*

Zimmer, H. 1956. "Motivational Factors in Dyadic Interaction." *Journal of Personality.*
> *Data:* Eight personality dimensions upon which 73 aircrew members were rank-ordered.
> *Data slice:* R-factor analysis.
> *Results:* Found factors of ascendance-submission, maturity-immaturity, and adjustment-maladjustment.

24.3.9 MISCELLANEOUS

Cureton, T. K. 1947. *Physical Fitness, Appraisal and Guidance.*

Gotterer, M., ed. 1965. *Proceedings of the Third Annual Computer Personnel Research Conference.*

Hammond, W. H. 1946. "Factor Analysis as Applied to Social and Economic Data." *British Journal of Educational Psychology.*

Ryans, D. G. 1960. *Characteristics of Teachers: Their Description, Comparison, and Appraisal.*

24.4 Natural Sciences

Higman, B. 1964. *Applied Group-Theoretic and Matrix Methods.*
> *Goal:* To demonstrate the use of factor analysis by application to a chemistry problem (Section 11.8).

Harbaugh, J. W., and F. Demirmen. 1964. "Application of Factor Analysis to Petrologic Variations of American Limestone (Lower Permian), Kansas and Oklahoma." *Kansas Geological Survey.*

Imbrie, J., and E. G. Purdy. 1962. "Classification of Modern Bahamian Carbonate Sediments." In *Classification of Carbonate Rocks*, W. E. Ham, ed.

Krumbein, W. C., and J. Imbrie. 1963. "Stratigraphic Factor Maps." *American Association of Petroleum Geologists, Bulletin.*

Merriam, D. F. 1965. "Geology and the Computer." *New Scientist.*

Sokal, R. R., and P. E. Hunter. 1955. "A Morphometric Analysis of DDT-Resistant and Non-Resistant House Fly Strains." *Entomological Society of America, Annals.*

Sokal, R. R., and P. H. A. Sneath. 1963. *Principles of Numerical Taxonomy.*

Results: Section 7.3.3 discusses the use of factor analysis on taxonomic analysis and also gives reference to such applications.

Spencer, D. W. 1966. *Factor Analysis.*

Toomey, D. F. 1966. "Application of Factor Analysis to a Facies Study of the Leavenworth Limestone (Pennsylvanian-Virgilian) of Kansas and Environs." *Kansas Geological Survey.*

Wallis, J. R. 1965. "Multivariate Statistical Methods in Hydrology— A Comparison Using Data of Known Functional Relationship." *Water Resources Research.*

Woodbury, M. A., R. C. Clelland, and R. J. Hickey. 1963. "Applications of a Factor-Analytic Model in the Prediction of Biological Data." *Behavioral Science.*

Bibliography

Abel, T. 1953. "The Operation Called *Verstehen*." In *Readings in the Philosophy of Science*, eds. H. Feigl and M. Brodbeck. New York: Appleton-Century-Crofts, pp. 677–87.

Adcock, C. J. 1954. *Factorial Analysis for Non-Mathematicians*. Victoria Australia: Melbourne University Press.

Adelman, I., and C. T. Morris. 1965. "A Factor Analysis of the Interrelationship Between Social and Political Variables and Per Capita Gross National Product." *Quarterly Journal of Economics* 79: 555–78.

———, and ———. 1966. "A Quantitative Study of Social and Political Determinants of Fertility." *Economic Development and Cultural Change* 14: 129–57.

Adelson, M. 1950. "A P-Technique Analysis of Social Change in the United States of America, 1845–1942." Master's Thesis, University of Illinois.

Ahmavaara, Y. 1954a. "The Mathematical Theory of Factorial Invariance Under Selection." *Psychometrika* 19: 27–38.

———. 1954b. "Transformation Analysis of Factorial Data." *Annales Academiae Scientiarum Fennicae* 88: 1–150.

———. 1957. "On the Unified Factor Theory of Mind." *Annales Academiae Scientiarum Fennicae* 106: 1–176.

————, and T. Markkanen. 1958. *The Unified Factor Model.* Helsinki: Finnish Foundation for Alcohol Studies.

Aitchison, J., and J. A. C. Brown. 1963. *The Lognormal Distribution.* Cambridge: Cambridge University Press.

Albert, A. A. 1944a. "The Matrices of Factor Analysis." *National Academy of Sciences, Proceedings* 30: 90–95.

————. 1944b. "The Minimum Rank of a Correlation Matrix." *National Academy of Sciences, Proceedings* 30: 144–46.

Aleamoni, L. M. 1966. "An Empirical Exploration of Three Possible Sources of Factorial Variation." Paper presented at Psychometric Society Meeting, New York University, September 2, 1966.

Alexander, C. 1964. *Notes on the Synthesis of Form.* Cambridge: Harvard University Press.

Alker, H., Jr. 1962. "An IBM 709 Program for the Gross Analysis of Transaction Flows." *Behavioral Science* 7: 498–99.

————. 1964. "Dimensions of Conflict in the General Assembly." *American Political Science Review* 58: 642–57.

————, 1965a. *Mathematics and Politics.* New York: Macmillan.

————. 1965b. "Supranationalism in the United Nations." *Peace Research Society: Papers, III.* Chicago Conference, 1964, pp. 197–212.

————, and B. Russett. 1964. "On Measuring Inequality." *Behavioral Science* 9: 207–18.

————, and ————. 1965. *World Politics in the General Assembly.* New Haven: Yale University Press.

Allardt, E. 1964. "Institutionalized versus Diffuse Support for Radical Political Movements." *Transactions of the Fifth World Congress in Sociology* 4: 369–80.

————. 1966. "Implications of Within-Nation Variations and Regional Imbalances for Cross-National Research." In *Comparing Nations*, eds. R. Merritt and S. Rokkan. New Haven: Yale University Press, pp. 337–48.

Allen, E. E., and R. W. Hites. 1961. "Factors in Religious Attitudes of Older Adolescents." *Journal of Social Psychology* 55: 265–73.

Anderson, T. R., and J. E. Egeland. 1961. "Spatial Aspects of Social Area Analysis." *American Sociological Review* 26: 392–98.

Anderson, T. W. 1957. "Maximum Likelihood Estimates for a Multivariate Normal Distribution When Some Observations Are Missing." *American Statistical Association Journal* 52: 200–203.

————. 1958. *An Introduction to Multivariate Statistical Analysis.* New York: Wiley.

————. 1963. "The Use of Factor Analysis in the Statistical Analysis of Multiple Time Series." *Psychometrika.* 28: 1–25.

————, and H. Rubin. 1956. "Statistical Inference in Factor Analysis." In *Third Berkeley Symposium on Mathematical Statistics and Probability*, ed., J. Neyman. Berkeley: University of California Press, pp. 111–50.

Anscombe, F. J. 1948. "The Transformation of Poisson, Binomial and Negative-Binomial Data." *Biometrika* 35: 246–54.

———. 1960. "Rejection of Outliers." *Technometrics* 2: 123–47.

Attneave, F. 1950. "Dimensions of Similarity." *American Journal of Psychology* 63: 516–56.

Bacon, M., *et al.* 1965. "A Cross-Cultural Study of Drinking." *Quarterly Journal of Studies of Alcohol*, Supplement No. 3.

Banks, A. S. 1964. "A Cross-Polity Survey: Preliminary Analysis." Paper presented at the annual convention of the American Political Association, September 9–12, 1964.

———. 1965. "Review of Russett, Bruce, *et al.*, *World Handbook of Political and Social Indicators.*" *American Political Science Review* 59: 144–46.

———, and P. M. Gregg. 1965. "Grouping Political Systems: Q-Factor Analysis of *A Cross-Polity Survey.*" *American Behavioral Scientist* 9: 3–6.

———, and R. B. Textor. 1963. *A Cross-Polity Survey.* Cambridge: M.I.T. Press.

Barlow, J. A., and C. L. Burt. 1954. "The Identification of Factors from Different Experiments." *British Journal of Statistical Psychology, Statistical Section* 7: 52–56.

Bartlett, M. S. 1950. "Tests of Significance in Factor Analysis." *British Journal of Psychology, Statistical Section* 3: 77–85.

———. 1951. "A Further Note on Tests of Significance in Factor Analysis." *British Journal of Psychology, Statistical Section* 4: 1–2.

Barzun, J., and H. Graff. 1957. *The Modern Researcher.* New York: Harcourt, Brace & World.

Bechtoldt, H. P. 1961. "An Empirical Study of the Factor Analysis Stability Hypothesis." *Psychometrika* 26: 405–32.

———. 1962. *Perceptual and Motor Skills.* 14: 319–42.

Bell, W. 1955. "Economic, Family, and Ethnic Status: An Empirical Test." *American Sociological Review* 20: 45–52.

Bell, W. H., and D. W. Stevenson. 1964. "An Index of Economic Health for Ontario Counties and Districts." *Ontario Economic Review* 2: 4–10.

Berelson, B. 1952. *Content Analysis in Communication Research.* Glencoe: Free Press.

Berliner, J. S. 1962. "The Feet of the Natives are Large: An Essay on Anthropology by an Economist." *Current Anthropology* 3: 47–77.

Berry, B. J. L. 1960. "An Inductive Approach to the Regionalization of Economic Development." In *Essays on Geography and Economic Development*, ed. N. Ginsburg. Chicago: University of Chicago, Department of Geography Research Paper No. 62.

———. 1961a. "A Method for Deriving Multi-Factor Uniform Regions." *Polish Geographical Review* 33: 263–82.

———. 1961b. "Basic Patterns of Economic Development." In *Atlas of*

Economic Development, ed. N. Ginsburg. Chicago: University of Chicago Press, pp. 110–19.

———. 1961c. "City Size Distributions and Economic Development." *Economic Development and Cultural Change* 9: 573–88.

———. 1964a. "Approaches to Regional Analysis: A Synthesis." *Association of American Geographers, Annals* 54: 2–11.

———. 1964b, "Cities as Systems Within Systems of Cities." *Regional Science Association, Papers* 13: 147–63.

———. 1965a. *Metropolitan Planning Guidelines Phase One: Background Documents*. Chicago: Northeastern Illinois Planning Commission.

———. 1965b. "The Retail Component of the Urban Model." *Journal of American Institute of Planners* 31: 150–55.

———. 1966. *Essays on Commodity Flows and Spatial Structure of the Indian Economy*. Chicago: University of Chicago, Department of Geography Research Paper No. 111.

———, and H. G. Barnum. 1962. "Aggregate Relations and Elemental Components of Central Place Systems." *Journal of Regional Science* 4: 35–68.

———, ———, and R. J. Tennant. 1962. "Retail Location and Consumer Behavior." *Regional Science Association, Papers* 9: 65–106.

———, K. B. Cooke, and D. M. Ray. 1965. "Identification of Declining Regions: An Empirical Study of the Dimensions of Rural Poverty." Paper presented at the Conference on Areas of Economic Stress, Queen's University, Kingston, Ontario, January 21–22, 1965.

Binder, A. 1959. "Considerations of the Place of Assumptions in Correlational Analysis." *American Psychologist* 14: 504–10.

Blake, R. R., J. S. Mouton, and B. Fruchter. 1962. "A Factor Analysis of Training Group Behavior." *Journal of Social Psychology* 58: 121–30.

Blalock, H. M., Jr. 1957. "Per Cent Non-White and Discrimination in the South." *American Sociological Review* 22: 677–82.

———. 1960. *Social Statistics*. New York: McGraw-Hill.

———. 1961. *Causal Inferences in Nonexperimental Research*. Chapel Hill: The University of North Carolina Press.

———. 1963. "Correlated Independent Variables: The Problems of Multicollinearity." *Social Forces* 42: 233–37.

Blau, P. M. 1962. "Patterns of Choice in Interpersonal Relations." *American Sociological Review* 27: 41–55.

Bloch, M. 1953. *The Historians Craft*. New York: Knopf.

Bock, D., and H. Suraya. 1952. "Factors of the Tale: A Preliminary Report." *Sociometry* 15: 206–19.

Boe, E. E., E. F. Gocka, and W. S. Kogan. 1966. "A Factor Analysis of Individual Social Desirability Scale Values." *Multivariate Behavioral Research* 1: 287–92.

Boocock, S. S. 1966. "An Experimental Study of the Learning Effects of Two Games with Simulated Environments." *American Behavioral Scientist* 10: 8–17.

Bordua, D. J. 1958–59. "Juvenile Delinquency and 'Anomie': An Attempt at Replication." *Social Problems* 6: 230–38.

Borgatta, E. F. 1965. "The Analysis of Patterns of Social Interaction." *Social Forces* 44: 27–34.

———, and L. S. Cottrell, Jr. 1955. "On the Classification of Groups." *Sociometry* 18: 665–78.

———, ———, and H. J. Meyer. 1956. "On the Dimensions of Group Behavior." *Sociometry* 19: 223–40.

———, and J. K. Hadden. 1966. "A Profile of American Cities." *Trans-Action* 3: 40–43.

———, and J. Hulquist. 1956–57. "A Reanalysis of Some Data from Stouffer's *Communism, Conformity, and Civil Liberties.*" *Public Opinion Quarterly* 20: 631–50.

Borko, H., ed. 1962. *Computer Applications in the Behavioral Sciences.* Englewood Cliffs, N.J.: Prentice-Hall.

Brams, S. J. 1966. *The Salience and Symmetry of Diplomatic Exchanges: Configurations and Correlates in the International System.* Ph.D. Dissertation, Northwestern University.

Brody, R. 1963. "Some Systemic Effects of the Spread of Nuclear Weapons Technology: A Study Through Simulation of a Multi-Nuclear Future." *Journal of Conflict Resolution* 7: 663–753.

Broen, W. E., Jr., 1957. "A Factor-Analytic Study of Religious Attitudes." *Journal of Abnormal and Social Psychology* 54: 176–79.

Broverman, D. M. 1961. "Effects of Score Transformations in Q and R Factor Analysis Techniques." *Psychological Review* 68: 68–80.

———. 1962. "Normative and Ipsative Measurement in Psychology." *Psychological Review.* 69: 295–305.

———. 1963. "Comments on the Note by MacAndrew and Forgy." *Psychological Review* 70: 119–20.

Buckatzsch, E. J. 1947. "The Influence of Social Conditions on Mortality Rates." *Population Studies* 1: 229–48.

Burket, G. R. 1964. "A Study of Reduced Rank Models for Multiple Prediction." *Psychometric Monographs*, No. 12.

Burt, C. L. 1937. "Correlations Between Persons." *British Journal of Psychology* 28: 56–96.

———. 1938. "The Unit Hierarchy and Its Properties." *Psychometrika* 3: 151–67.

———. 1941. *The Factors of the Mind: An Introduction to Factor-analysis in Psychology.* New York: Macmillan.

———. 1950. "The Factorial Analysis of Qualitative Data." *British Journal of Psychology, Statistical Section* 3: 166–85.

———. 1952. "Tests of Significance in Factor Analysis." *British Journal of Psychology, Statistical Section* 5: 109–33.

———. 1953. "Scale Analysis and Factor Analysis." *British Journal of Statistical Psychology* 6: 5–23.

————. 1966. "The Early History of Multivariate Techniques in Psychological Research." *Multivariate Behavioral Research* 1: 24–42.

Burtt, E. A. 1932. *The Metaphysical Foundations of Modern Science.* Rev. ed. Garden City, N.Y.: Doubleday.

Camilleri, S. F. 1959. "A Factor Analysis of the F-Scale." *Social Forces* 37: 316–23.

Carlson, H. B., and W. Harrell. 1942. "Voting Groups Among Leading Congressmen Obtained by Means of the Inverted Factor Technique." *Journal of Social Psychology* 16: 51–61.

Carroll, J. B. 1945. "The Effect of Difficulty and Chance Success on Correlations Between Items or Between Tests." *Psychometrika* 10: 1–19.

————. 1953. "An Analytical Solution for Approximating Simple Structure in Factor Analysis." *Psychometrika* 18: 23–38.

————. 1957. "Biquartimin Criterion for Rotation to Oblique Simple Structure in Factor Analysis." *Science* 126: 1114–15.

————. 1958. "Oblimin Rotation Solution in Factor Analysis." *Computing Program for the IBM 704.* Mimeographed.

————. 1961. "The Nature of the Data, or How to Choose a Correlation Coefficient." *Psychometrika* 26: 347–72.

Carter, R. F. n.d. "The Perceived Appeals of TV Program Content." Madison: University of Wisconsin TV Laboratory, *Research Bulletin* No. 8.

Cartwright, D. S. 1965. "A Misapplication of Factor Analysis." *American Sociological Review* 30: 249–51.

————, and K. I. Howard. 1966. "Multivariate Analysis of Gang Delinquency: I. Ecologic Influences." *Multivariate Behavioral Research* 1: 321–71.

Cattell, R. B. 1942. "The Concept of Social Status." *Journal of Social Psychology* 15: 293–08.

————. 1944. "Psychological Measurement: Normative, Ipsative, Interactive." *Psychological Review* 51: 293–303.

————. 1949a. "The Dimensions of Culture Patterns by Factorization of National Characters." *Journal of Abnormal and Social Psychology* 44: 443–69.

————. 1949b. "r_p and other Coefficients of Pattern Similarity." *Psychometrika* 14: 279–98.

————. 1950. "The Principal Culture Patterns Discoverable in the Syntal Dimensions of Existing Nations." *Journal of Social Psychology* 32: 215–53.

————. 1952a. *Factor Analysis: An Introduction and Manual for the Psychologist and Social Scientist.* New York: Harper and Row.

————. 1952b. "The Three Basic Factor-Analytic Research Designs—Their Intercorrelations and Derivatives." *Psychological Bulletin* 49: 499–520.

————. 1953. "A Quantitative Analysis of the Changes in the Culture

Pattern of Great Britain, 1837–1937, by P-Technique." *Acta Psychologica* 9: 99–121.

———. 1957. *Personality and Motivation Structure and Measurement.* Yonkers-on-Hudson: World Book.

———. 1958. "Extracting the Correct Number of Factors in Factor Analysis." *Educational and Psychological Measurement* 18: 791–837.

———. 1961. "The Theory of Situational, Instrument, Second Order, and Refraction Factors in Personality Structure Research." *Psychological Bulletin* 58: 160–74.

———. 1962a. "Group Theory, Personality and Role: A Model for Experimental Researches." In *NATO Symposium on Defense Psychology*, ed. F. A. Geldard. New York: Pergamon Press, pp. 209–59.

———. 1962b. "The Basis of Recognition and Interpretation of Factors." *Educational and Psychological Measurement* 22: 667–97.

———. 1962c. "The Relational Simplex Theory of Equal Interval and Absolute Scaling." *Acta Psychologica* 20: 139–58.

———. 1963. "The Structuring of Change by *P*-Technique and Incremental *R*-Technique." In *Problems in Measuring Change*, ed. C. W. Harris. Madison: University of Wisconsin Press, pp. 167–98.

———. 1965a. "Factor Analysis: An Introduction to Essentials." *Biometrics* 21: 190–215.

———. 1965b. "Higher Order Factor Structures and Reticular—vs—Hierarchical Formulae for their Interpretation." In *Studies in Psychology*, eds. C. Banks and P. L. Broadhurst. London: University of London Press, pp. 223–66.

———. 1965c. "The Configurative Method for Surer Identification of Personality Dimensions, Notably in Child Study." *Psychological Reports* 16: 269–70.

———. 1965d. *The Scientific Study of Personality.* Baltimore: Penguin Books.

———. 1966a. "Guest Editorial: Multivariate Behavioral Research and the Integrative Challenge." *Multivariate Behavioral Research* 1: 4–23.

———, ed. 1966b. *Handbook of Multivariate Experimental Psychology* Chicago: Rand McNally.

———. 1966c. "The Scree Test for the Number of Factors." *Multivariate Behavioral Research* 1: 245–76.

———, and M. Adelson. 1951. "The Dimensions of Social Change in the U.S.A. as Determined by P-Technique." *Social Forces* 30: 190–201.

———, and A. R. Baggaley. 1960. "The Salient Variable Similarity Index for Factor Matching." *British Journal of Statistical Psychology* 13: 33–46.

———, H. Breul, and H. P. Hartman. 1951. "An Attempt at More Refined Definitions of the Cultural Dimensions of Syntality in Modern Nations." *American Sociological Review* 17: 408–21.

———, and A. K. S. Cattell. 1955. "Factor Rotation for Proportional

Profiles: Analytical Solution and an Example." *British Journal of Statistical Psychology* 8: 83–92.

———, and K. Dickman. 1962. "A Dynamic Model of Physical Influences Demonstrating the Necessity of Oblique Simple Structure." *Psychological Bulletin* 59: 389–400.

———, and M. J. Foster. 1963. "The Rotoplot Program for Multiple Singleplane, Visually Guided Rotation." *Behavioral Science* 8: 156–65.

———, and R. L. Gorsuch. 1963. "The Uniqueness and Significance of Simple Structure Demonstrated by Contrasting Organic 'Natural Structure' and 'Random Structure' Data." *Psychometrika* 28: 55–67.

———, and ———. 1965. "The Definition and Measurement of National Morale and Morality." *Journal of Social Psychology* 67: 77–96.

———, and J. Horn. 1963. "An Integrating Study of the Factor Structure of Adult Attitude-Interests." *Genetic Psychology Monographs* 67: 89–149.

———, and E. D. Lawson. 1962. "Sex Differences in Small Group Performance." *Journal of Social Psychology* 58: 141–45.

———, and J. L. Muerle. 1960. "The 'Maxplane' Program for Factor Rotation to Oblique Simple Structure." *Educational and Psychological Measurement* 20: 269–90.

———, R. Saunders, and G. F. Stice. 1953. "The Dimensions of Syntality in Small Groups." *Human Relations* 6: 331–56.

———, and G. F. Stice. 1960. *The Dimensions of Groups and Their Relations to the Behavior of Members*. Rev. ed. Champaign, Ill.: Institute for Personality and Ability Testing.

———, and W. Sullivan. 1962. "The Scientific Nature of Factors: A Demonstration by Cups of Coffee." *Behavioral Science* 7: 184–93.

Chapin, F. S. 1947. *Experimental Designs in Sociological Research*. New York: Harper and Row.

Chilton, R. J. 1964. "Continuity in Delinquency Area Research: A Comparison of Studies for Baltimore, Detroit, and Indianapolis." *American Sociological Review* 29: 71–83.

Cohen, M. R., and E. Nagel. 1934. *An Introduction to Logic and Scientific Method*. New York: Harcourt, Brace & World.

Coleman, J. S. 1957. "Multidimensional Scale Analysis." *American Journal of Sociology* 63: 253–63.

———. 1964. *Introduction to Mathematical Sociology*. Glencoe: Free Press.

——— and D. MacRae, Jr. 1960. "Electron Processing of Sociometric Data for Groups Up to 1,000 in Size." *American Sociological Review* 25: 722–27.

Comrey, A. L., and E. Levonian. 1958. "A Comparison of Three Point Coefficients in Factor Analysis of MMPI Items." *Educational and Psychological Measurement* 18: 739–55.

Cooley, W. W., and P. R. Lohnes. 1962. *Multivariate Procedures for the Behavioral Sciences*. New York: Wiley.

Coombs, C. H. 1964. *A Theory of Data.* New York: Wiley.

———, and R. C. Kao. 1955. *Nonmetric Factor Analysis.* Ann Arbor: Engineering Research Institute, University of Michigan.

———, and ———. 1960. "On a Connection Between Factor Analysis and Multidimensional Unfolding." *Psychometrika* 25: 219–31.

———, and G. A. Satter. 1949. "A Factorial Approach to Job Families." *Psychometrika* 14: 33–42.

Cronbach, Lee J. 1951. "Coefficient Alpha and the Internal Structure of Tests." *Psychometrika* 16: 297–334.

———, N. Rajaratnam, and G. C. Gleser. 1963. "Theory of Generalizability: A Liberalization of Reliability Theory." *British Journal of Statistical Psychology* 16: 137–63.

Cureton, E. E. 1959. "Note on ϕ Max." *Psychometrika* 24: 89–91.

———. 1968. "Factor Analysis of Senate Votes." Unpublished paper.

Cureton, T. K. 1947. *Physical Fitness, Appraisal and Guidance.* St. Louis: Mosby.

Cutright, P. 1963. "National Political Development: Measurement and Analysis." *American Sociological Review* 28: 253–64.

———. 1965. "Political Structure, Economic Development, and National Social Security Programs." *American Journal of Sociology* 70: 537–50.

Davis, P. J. 1965. *The Mathematics of Matrices.* New York: Blaisdell.

Dear, R. E. 1959. *A Principal-Component Missing-Data Method for Multiple Regression Models.* Santa Monica: System Development Corporation.

Dennis, J. 1966. "Support for the Party System by the Mass Public." *American Political Science Review* 60: 600–15.

Denton, F. H. 1966. "Some Regularities in International Conflict, 1820–1949." *Background* 9: 283–96.

———, and R. D. Jones. 1966. "Testing Hypotheses Concerning the Causes of War." N.p.: mimeograph.

De Soto, C. B., and J. L. Kuethe. 1960. "On the Relations Between Two Variables." *Educational and Psychological Measurement* 20: 743–49.

Deutsch, K. W. 1960. "Toward an Inventory of Basic Trends and Patterns in Comparative and International Politics." *American Political Science Review* 54: 34–57.

Deutschmann, P. J., and D. Kiel. 1960. *A Factor Analytic Study of Attitudes Toward the Mass Media.* Cincinnati: Scripps-Howard Research.

——— et al. 1959. "The Semantic Differential: Its Use and Abuse." *Public Opinion Quarterly* 23: 435–38.

Digman, J. M. 1962. "The Dimensionality of Social Attitudes." *Journal of Social Psychology* 57: 433–44.

———. 1967. "The Procrustes Class of Factor-Analytic Transformations." *Multivariate Behavioral Research* 2: 89–94.

———, and D. W. Tuttle. 1961. "An Interpretation of an Election by Means of Obverse Factor Analysis." *Journal of Social Psychology* 53: 183–94.

Dingman, H. F., C. R. Miller, and R. K. Eyman. 1964. "A Comparison Between Two Analytic Rotational Solutions Where the Number of Factors Is Indeterminate." *Behavioral Science* 9: 76–80.

Dixon, W. J. 1953. "Processing Data for Outliers." *Biometrics* 9: 74–89.

———. 1960. "Simplified Estimation from Censored Normal Samples." *Annals of Mathematical Statistics* 31: 385–91.

———, and F. J. Massey, Jr. 1957. *Introduction to Statistical Analysis*, 2nd ed. New York: McGraw-Hill.

Donnahoe, A. S. 1960. "The Public Image of the Advertising Media." *Business and Government Review* 1: 29.

Dornbusch, S. M., and C. F. Schmid. 1955. *A Primer of Social Statistics*. New York: McGraw-Hill.

Driver, H. E. 1961. "Introduction to Statistics for Comparative Research." In *Readings in Cross-Cultural Anthropology*, ed. F. W. Moore. New Haven: Human Relations Area Files, pp. 310–38.

———, and K. F. Schuessler. 1957. "Factor Analysis of Ethnographic Data." *American Anthropologist* 59: 655–63.

DuBois, P. H. 1957. *Multivariate Correlational Analysis*. New York: Harper and Row.

Duncan, O. D., R. P. Cuzzort, and B. Duncan. 1961. *Statistical Geography*. Glencoe: Free Press.

Dwyer, P. S. 1940. "The Evaluation of Multiple and Partial Correlation Coefficients from the Factorial Matrix." *Psychometrika* 5: 211–32.

Eber, H. W. 1966a. *Multivariate Analysis of a Vocational Rehabilitation System. Multivariate Behavioral Research Monograph*, No. 66–1. Fort Worth: Society of Multivariate Experimental Psychology.

———. 1966b. "Toward Oblique Simple Structure: Maxplane." *Multivariate Behavioral Research* 1: 112–25.

Ekman, G. 1954. "Dimensions of Color Vision." *Journal of Psychology* 38: 467–74.

———. 1955. "Dimensions of Emotion." *Acta Psychologica* 11: 279–88.

Eysenck, H. J. 1953. *The Structure of Human Personality*. London: Methuen.

———. 1954. *The Psychology of Politics*. London: Routledge and Kegan Paul.

———, and S. Crown. 1948–49. "National Stereotypes: An Experimental and Methodological Study." *International Journal of Opinion and Attitude Research* 2: 26–39.

Ezekiel, M., and K. A. Fox. 1959. *Methods of Correlation and Regression Analysis*. New York: Wiley.

Farber, B. 1962. "Elements of Competence in Interpersonal Relations: A Factor Analysis." *Sociometry* 25: 30–47.

Fasteau, H. H., J. J. Ingram, and R. Mills. 1962. "Study of the Reliability of the Coding of Census Returns." *American Statistical Association, Proceedings, Social Statistics Section*, pp. 104–15.

———, ———, and G. Minton. 1964. "Control of Quality of Coding in the 1960 Censuses." *American Statistical Association Journal* 59: 120–32.

Feierabend, I. K., and R. L. Feierabend. 1966. "Aggressive Behaviors Within Polities, 1948–1962: A Cross-National Study." *Journal of Conflict Resolution* 10: 249–71.

Feigl, H., and M. Brodbeck, eds. 1953. *Readings in the Philosophy of Science.* New York: Appleton-Century-Crofts.

Feller, W. 1962. *An Introduction to Probability Theory and Its Applications,* 2nd ed. New York: Wiley, Vol. I.

Ferguson, G. A. 1941. "The Factorial Interpretation of Test Difficulty." *Psychometrika* 6: 323–29.

––––––. 1954. "The Concept of Parsimony in Factor Analysis." *Psychometrika* 19: 281–90.

Festinger, L., and D. Katz, eds. 1953. *Research Methods in the Behavioral Sciences.* New York: Dryden.

Findikyan, N., and S. B. Sells. 1964a. *The Dimensional Structure of Campus Student Organizations.* Technical Report No. 5. Ft. Worth: Institute of Behavioral Research.

––––––, and ––––––. 1964b. "Social Structure of Campus Student Organizations." Paper Presented at the Annual Convention of the Southwestern Psychological Association, April 10, 1964. Ft. Worth: Institute of Behavioral Research.

Finetti, B. de. 1961. "The Bayesian Approach to the Rejection of Outliers." In *Fourth Berkeley Symposium on Mathematical Statistics and Probability,* ed., J. Neyman. Berkeley: University of California Press, Vol. I, pp. 199–210.

Fisher, R. A. 1958. *Statistical Methods for Research Workers,* 13th ed. New York: Hafner.

––––––. 1960. *The Design of Experiments,* 7th ed. New York: Hafner.

Flinn, T. A. 1964. "Party Responsibility in the States: Some Causal Factors." *American Political Science Review* 58: 60–71.

Ford, R. N., and D. Henderson. 1942. "A Multiple-Factor Analysis of Ford's White-Negro Experience Scales." *Social Forces* 21: 28–34.

Frank, P. 1955. *Modern Science and Its Philosophy.* New York: Braziller.

Friedlander, F. 1965. *Behavioral Dimensions of Traditional Work Groups.* China Lake, Calif.: U.S. Naval Ordnance Test Station.

Friedmann, J., and W. Alonso, eds. 1964. *Regional Development and Planning,* Cambridge: M.I.T. Press.

Fruchter, B. 1954. *Introduction to Factor Analysis.* New York: Van Nostrand.

––––––, and E. Jennings. 1962. "Factor Analysis." In *Computer Applications in the Behavioral Sciences,* ed. H. Borko. Englewood Cliffs, N.J.: Prentice-Hall, pp. 238–65.

Fuller, E. L., Jr., and W. J. Hemmerle. 1966. "Robustness of the Maximum-Likelihood Estimation Procedure in Factor Analysis." *Psychometrika* 31: 255–66.

Gaier, E. L., and M. C. Lee. 1953. "Pattern Analysis: The Configural Approach to Predictive Measurement." *Psychological Bulletin* 50: 140–48.

George, W. 1951. "Social Conditions and the Labour Vote in the County Boroughs of England and Wales." *British Journal of Sociology* 2: 255–59.

Gibb, C. A. 1947. "The Principles and Traits of Leadership." *Journal of Abnormal and Social Psychology* 42: 267–84.

———. 1956. "Changes in the Culture Pattern of Australia, 1906–1946, as Determined by *p*-Technique." *Journal of Social Psychology* 43: 225–38.

Gibson, W. A. 1963. "On the Symmetric Treatment of an Asymmetric Approach to Factor Analysis." *Psychometrika* 28: 423–26.

Godfrey, E. P., F. E. Fiedler, and D. M. Hall. 1958. *Boards, Management, and Company Success.* Danville, Ill.: Interstate Printers and Publishers.

Gold, D. 1964. "Some Problems in Generalizing Aggregate Associations." *American Behavioral Scientist* 8: 16–18.

Goldfarb, N. 1960. *An Introduction to Longitudinal Statistical Analysis.* Glencoe: Free Press.

Goldfried, M. R., and J. Drasgow. 1964. "A Normal Distribution for What?" *Journal of General Psychology* 70: 21–28.

Goodman, L. 1963. "Statistical Methods for the Preliminary Analysis of Transaction Flows." *Econometrica* 31: 197–208.

Gorsuch, R. L. 1962. *National Morale, Morality and Cultural Integration.* Master's Thesis, University of Illinois.

Gosnell, H. F. 1937. *Machine Politics: Chicago Model.* Chicago: University of Chicago Press.

———, and N. N. Gill. 1935. "A Factor Analysis of the 1932 Presidential Vote in Chicago." *American Political Science Review* 29: 967–84.

———, and M. J. Schmidt. 1936. "Factorial and Correlational Analysis of the 1934 Vote in Chicago." *American Statistical Association Journal* 31: 507–18.

Gotterer, M., ed. 1965. *Proceedings of the Third Annual Computer Personnel Research Conference.* Silver Spring, Md.: Computer Personnel Research Group.

Gouldner, A. W. 1957a. "Cosmopolitans and Locals: Toward an Analysis of Latent Social Roles—I." *Administrative Science Quarterly* 2: 281–306.

———. 1957b. "Cosmopolitans and Locals: Toward an Analysis of Latent Social Roles—II." *Administrative Science Quarterly* 2: 444–80.

———, and R. A. Peterson. 1962. *Notes on Technology and the Moral Order.* Indianapolis: Bobbs-Merrill.

Green, B. F. 1954. "Attitude Measurement." In *Handbook of Social Psychology,* ed. G. Lindzey. Reading, Mass.: Addison-Wesley, Vol. I, pp. 335–69.

———. 1963. *Digital Computers in Research, An Introduction for Behavioral and Social Scientists.* New York: McGraw-Hill.

Green, N. E. 1956. "Scale Analysis of Urban Structures." *American Sociological Review* 21: 8–13.

Gregg, P. M., and A. S. Banks. 1965. "Dimensions of Political Systems: Factor Analysis of *A Cross-Polity Survey.*" *American Political Science Review* 59: 602–14.

Grossack, M. 1964. "Testing TV Commercials." In *Understanding Consumer Behavior*, ed. M. Grossack. Boston: Christopher Publishing House, pp. 221–29.

Grumm, J. G. 1963. "A Factor Analysis of Legislative Behavior." *Midwest Journal of Political Science* 7: 336–56.

Guetzkow, H., *et al.* 1963. *Simulation in International Relations: Developments for Research and Teaching.* Englewood Cliffs, N.J.: Prentice-Hall.

Guilford, J. P. 1954. *Psychometric Methods*, 2nd ed. New York: McGraw-Hill.

———. 1961. "Factorial Angles to Psychology." *Psychological Review* 68: 1–19.

———. 1963. "Preparation of Item Scores for the Correlations Between Persons in a Q Factor Analysis." *Educational and Psychological Measurement* 23: 13–22.

———. 1965. "The Minimal Phi Coefficient and the Maximal Phi." *Educational and Psychological Measurement* 25: 3–8.

———, and W. B. Michael. 1950. "Changes in Common-Factor Loadings as Tests Are Altered Homogeneously in Length." *Psychometrika* 15: 237–49.

———, and W. S. Zimmerman. 1963. "Some Variable-Sampling Problems in the Rotation of Axes in Factor Analysis." *Psychological Bulletin* 60: 289–301.

Guttman, L. 1940. "Multiple Rectilinear Prediction and the Resolution into Components." *Psychometrika* 5: 75–99.

———. 1953. "Image Theory for the Structure of Quantitative Variates." *Psychometrika* 18: 277–96.

———. 1954. "Some Necessary Conditions for Common-Factor Analysis." *Psychometrika* 19: 149–61.

———. 1955. "The Determinacy of Factor Score Matrices with Implications for Five Other Basic Problems of Common-Factor Theory." *British Journal of Statistical Psychology* 8: 65–81.

———. 1956. "'Best Possible' Systematic Estimates of Communalities." *Psychometrika* 21: 273–85.

———. 1957a. "A Necessary and Sufficient Formula for Matrix Factoring." *Psychometrika* 22: 79–81.

———. 1957b. "Simple Proofs of Relations Between the Communality Problem and Multiple Correlation." *Psychometrika* 22: 147–57.

———. 1958a. "To What Extent Can Communalities Reduce Rank?" *Psychometrika* 23: 297–308.

———. 1958b. "What Lies Ahead for Factor Analysis?" *Educational and Psychological Measurement* 18: 497–515.

————. 1959. "Metricizing Rank-ordered or Unordered Data for a Linear Factor Analysis." *Sankhya* 21: 257–68.

————. 1967. "A General Nonmetric Technique for Finding the Smallest Euclidean Space for a Configuration of Points." Unpublished paper.

————, and J. Cohen. 1943. "Multiple Rectilinear Prediction and the Resolution into Components: II." *Psychometrika* 8: 169–83.

Hadden, J. K. and E. F. Borgatta. 1965. *American Cities: Their Social Characteristics.* Chicago: Rand McNally.

Hadley, G. 1961. *Linear Algebra.* Reading, Mass.: Addison-Wesley.

Haggard, E. A., and H. C. Gupta. 1958. *Interclass Correlation with the Analysis of Variance.* New York: Dryden Press.

Hagood, M. J. 1943. "Statistical Methods for Delineation of Regions Applied to Data on Agriculture and Population." *Social Forces* 21: 287–97.

————, N. Danilevsky, and C. O. Beum. 1941. "An Examination of the Use of Factor Analysis in the Problem of Sub-regional Delineation." *Rural Sociology* 6: 216–34.

Hagstrom, W. O., and H. C. Selvin. 1965. "Two Dimensions of Cohesiveness in Small Groups." *Sociometry* 28: 30–43.

Hald, A. 1952. *Statistical Theory, With Engineering Applications.* New York: Wiley.

Hamblin, R. 1962. "The Dynamics of Racial Discrimination." *Social Problems* 10: 103–21.

————, and K. Miller. 1961. "Variation in Interaction Profiles and Group Size." *Sociological Quarterly* 2: 105–17.

Hammond, W. H. 1946. "Factor Analysis as Applied to Social and Economic Data." *British Journal of Educational Psychology* 16: 178.

Hansen, M. H., *et al.* 1953. *Sample Survey Methods and Theory.* New York: Wiley.

Hanson, N. R. 1958. *Patterns of Discovery.* Cambridge: Cambridge University Press.

————. 1959. "On the Symmetry Between Explanation and Prediction." *Philosophical Review* 68: 349–58.

Harbaugh, J. W., and F. Demirmen. 1964. "Application of Factor Analysis to Petrologic Variations of American Limestone (Lower Permian), Kansas and Oklahoma." *Kansas Geological Survey, Special Publication* No. 15.

Harman, H. H. 1960. *Modern Factor Analysis.* Chicago: University of Chicago Press.

————. 1967. *Modern Factor Analysis,* rev. ed. Chicago: University of Chicago Press.

————, and W. H. Jones. 1966. "Factor Analysis by Minimizing Residuals (Minres)." *Psychometrika* 31: 351–68.

Harris, C. W. 1948. "A Factor Analysis of Selected Senate Roll-Calls, 80th Congress." *Educational and Psychological Measurement* 8: 583–91.

———. 1955. "Separation of Data as a Principle in Factor Analysis." *Psychometrika* 20: 23–28.

———. 1956. "Relationships Between Two Systems of Factor Analysis." *Psychometrika* 21: 185–90.

———. 1962. "Some Rao-Guttman Relationships." *Psychometrika* 27: 247–63.

———. 1963a. "Canonical Factor Models for the Description of Change." In *Problems in Measuring Change*, ed. C. W. Harris. Madison: University of Wisconsin Press, pp. 138–55.

———, ed. 1963b. *Problems in Measuring Change.* Madison: University of Wisconsin Press.

———. 1964a. "Four Models for Factor Analysis." Paper presented at the American Psychological Association Convention, September 8, 1964.

———. 1964b. "Some Recent Developments in Factor Analysis." *Educational and Psychological Measurement* 24: 193–206.

———, and H. F. Kaiser. 1964. "Oblique Factor Analytic Solutions by Orthogonal Transformations." *Psychometrika* 29: 347–62.

Hart, H. H., R. L. Jenkins, S. Axelrad, and P. I. Sperling. 1943. "Multiple Factor Analysis of Traits of Delinquent Boys." *Journal of Social Psychology* 17: 191–201.

Hartley, H. O. 1958. "Maximum Likelihood Estimation from Incomplete Data." *Biometrics* 14: 174–94.

Hatt, P. 1948. "Class and Ethnic Attitudes." *American Sociological Review* 13: 36–43.

———, N. L. Farr, and E. Weinstein. 1955. "Types of Population Balance." *American Sociological Review* 20: 14–21.

Heath, H. A. 1961. "An Empirical Study of Correlation Involving a Half-Normal Distribution." *Psychological Reports* 9: 85–86.

Heerman, E. F. 1964. "The Geometry of Factorial Indeterminacy." *Psychometrika* 29: 371–81.

Hempel, C. G. 1952. "Fundamentals of Concept Formation in Empirical Science." *International Encyclopedia of Unified Science.* Chicago: University of Chicago Press, Vol. II, No. 7.

———. 1965. *Aspects of Scientific Explanation.* New York: Free Press.

Hemphill, J. K., D. E. Griffiths, and N. Frederiksen. 1962. *Administrative Performance and Personality.* New York: Teachers College, Columbia University.

Hendrickson, A. E., and P. O. White. 1964. "Promax: A Quick Method for Rotation to Oblique Simple Structure." *British Journal of Statistical Psychology* 17: 65–70.

Henrysson, S. 1950. "The Significance of Factor Loadings: Lawley's Test Examined by Artificial Samples." *British Journal of Psychology, Statistical Section* 3: 159–65.

———. 1957. *Applicability of Factor Analysis in the Behavioral Sciences: A Methodological Study.* Stockholm: Almqvist and Wiksell.

Hickman, J. M. 1962. "Dimensions of a Complex Concept: A Method Exemplified." *Human Organization* 21: 214–18.

Higman, B. 1964. *Applied Group-Theoretic and Matrix Methods.* New York: Dover.

Hofstaetter, P. R. 1951. "A Factorial Study of Culture Patterns in the U.S." *Journal of Psychology* 32: 99–113.

———. 1952. "'Your City' Revisited; A Factorial Study of Cultural Patterns." *American Catholic Sociological Review* 13: 159–68.

Hogben, L. 1957. *Statistical Theory: The Relationship of Probability, Credibility, and Error.* New York: Norton.

Hohn, F. E. 1958. *Elementary Matrix Algebra,* 2nd ed. New York: Macmillan.

Holzinger, K. J., and H. H. Harman. 1941. *Factor Analysis.* Chicago: University of Chicago Press.

Horn, J. L. 1965a. "An Empirical Comparison of Methods for Estimating Factor Scores." *Educational and Psychological Measurement* 25: 313–22.

———. 1965b. "A Rationale and Test for the Number of Factors in Factor Analysis." *Psychometrika* 30: 179–85.

———, and K. B. Little. 1966. "Isolating Change and Invariance in Patterns of Behavior." *Multivariate Behavioral Research* 1: 219–28.

Horst, P. 1963. *Matrix Algebra for Social Scientists.* New York: Holt, Rinehart and Winston.

———. 1965. *Factor Analysis of Data Matrices.* New York: Holt, Rinehart and Winston.

Hotelling, H. 1933. "Analysis of a Complex of Statistical Variables into Principal Components." *Journal of Educational Psychology* 24: 417–41, 498–520.

———. 1936. "Relations Between Two Sets of Variates." *Biometrika* 28: 321–77.

———. 1957. "The Relations of the Newer Multivariate Statistical Methods to Factor Analysis." *British Journal of Statistical Psychology* 10: 69–79.

Householder, A. S., and H. D. Landahl. 1945. *Mathematical Biophysics of the Central Nervous System.* Bloomington, Ind.: Principia.

Howard, K. I., and D. S. Cartwright. 1962. "An Empirical Note on the Communality Problem in Factor Analysis." *Psychological Reports* 10: 797–98.

———, and R. A. Gordon. 1963. "Empirical Note on the 'Number of Factors' Problem in Factor Analysis." *Psychological Reports* 12: 247–50.

Howells, W. W. 1952. "A Factorial Study of Constitutional Type." *American Journal of Physical Anthropology* 15: 91–118.

———. 1957. "The Cranial Vault: Factors of Size and Shape." *American Journal of Physical Anthropology* 15: 19–48.

Hsü, E. H. 1953. "Note on Factor Analysis of American Culture: A Criticism." *Journal of Social Psychology* 38: 137–40.

Hume, D. 1902. "An Enquiry Concerning Human Understanding." In

Enquiries, 2nd ed., ed. L. A. Selby-Bigge. Oxford: Clarendon Press, pp. 1–165.

Humphreys, L. G. 1964. "Number of Cases and Number of Factors: An Example Where N is Very Large." *Educational and Psychological Measurement* 24: 457–66.

Hunka, S. 1966. "Alpha Factor Analysis." *Behavioral Science* 11: 80.

Huntington, E. 1945. *Mainsprings of Civilization.* New York: Wiley.

Hurley, J. R., and R. B. Cattell. 1962. "The Procrustes Program: Producing Direct Rotation to Test a Hypothesized Factor Structure." *Behavioral Science* 7: 258–62.

Hyman, H., *et al.* 1954. *Interviewing in Social Research.* Chicago: University of Chicago Press.

———. 1955. *Survey Design and Analysis.* Glencoe: Free Press.

Imbrie, J., and E. G. Purdy. 1962. "Classification of Modern Bahamian Carbonate Sediments." In *Classification of Carbonate Rocks*, ed. W. E. Ham. Tulsa: American Association of Petroleum Geologists, pp. 253–72.

Inbar, M. 1966. "The Differential Impact of a Game Simulating a Community Disaster." *American Behavioral Scientist* 10: 18–27.

Ipsen, D. C. 1960. *Units, Dimensions, and Dimensionless Numbers.* New York: McGraw-Hill.

Jackson, D. 1924. "The Trigonometry of Correlation." *American Mathematical Monthly* 31: 275–80.

James, R. W., and H. L. Miller. 1958–59. "Factors in Community Action Programs." *Social Problems* 6: 51–59.

Janda, K. 1965. *Data Processing: Applications to Political Research.* Evanston: Northwestern University Press.

Jennrich, R. I., and P. F. Sampson. 1966. "Rotation for Simple Loadings." *Psychometrika* 31: 313–23.

Johnson, P. O. 1949. *Statistical Methods in Research.* Englewood Cliffs, N. J.: Prentice-Hall.

———, and R. Jackson. 1959. *Modern Statistical Methods.* Chicago: Rand McNally.

Johnston, J. 1963. *Econometric Methods.* New York: McGraw-Hill.

Jonassen, C. T. 1961. "Functional Unities in Eighty-eight Community Systems." *American Sociological Review* 26: 399–407.

———, and Sherwood H. Peres. 1960. *Interrelationships of Dimensions of Community Systems.* Columbus: Ohio State University Press.

Jones, B. G., and W. W. Goldsmith. 1965. *Studies in Regional Development: A Factor Analysis Approach to Sub-Regional Definition in Chenango, Delaware, and Otsego Counties.* Ithaca: Center for Housing and Environmental Studies, Cornell University.

Jones, M. B. 1961. *Practice as a Process of Simplification.* Pensacola: U.S. Naval Aviation Medical Center, *Research Report* No. 2.

Jöreskog, K. G. 1963. *Statistical Estimation in Factor Analysis.* Stockholm: Almqvist and Wiksell.

————. 1966. "Testing a Simple Structure Hypothesis in Factor Analysis." *Psychometrika* 31: 165–78.

Kahl, J. A., and J. A. Davis. 1955. "A Comparison of Indexes of Socio-Economic Status." *American Sociological Review* 20: 317–25.

Kahn, R. L., D. M. Wolfe, R. P. Quinn, and J. D. Snoek. 1964. *Organizational Stress: Studies in Role Conflict and Ambiguity.* New York: Wiley.

Kaiser, H. F. 1956. *The Varimax Method of Factor Analysis.* Ph.D. Dissertation, University of California.

————. 1958. "The Varimax Criterion for Analytic Rotation in Factor Analysis." *Psychometrika* 23: 187–200.

————. 1959. "Computer Program for Varimax Rotation in Factor Analysis." *Educational and Psychological Measurement* 19: 413–20.

————. 1960a. "Comments on Communalities and the Number of Factors." Paper presented at an Informal Conference on the Communality Problem in Factor Analysis, St. Louis: Washington University, May 14, 1960.

————. 1960b. "The Application of Electronic Computers to Factor Analysis." *Educational and Psychological Measurement* 20: 141–51.

————. 1961. "A Note on Guttman's Lower Bound for the Number of Common Factors." *British Journal of Statistical Psychology* 14: 1–2.

————. 1962. "Formulas for Component Scores." *Psychometrika* 27: 83–87.

————. 1963. "Image Analysis." In *Problems in Measuring Change,* ed. C. W. Harris. Madison: University of Wisconsin Press, pp. 156–66.

————. 1964. "Psychometric Approaches to Factor Analysis." Paper presented at the Invitational Conference on Testing Problems, Educational Testing Service, Princeton, N.J., October 31, 1964.

————, and J. Caffrey. 1965. "Alpha Factor Analysis." *Psychometrika* 30: 1–14.

————, and K. W. Dickman. 1959. "Analytic Determination of Common Factors." Paper presented at the Annual Convention of the American Psychological Association, September 3–9, 1959.

Kassebaum, G. G., D. A. Ward, and D. M. Wilner. 1964. "Some Correlates of Staff Ideology in the Prison." *Journal of Research in Crime and Delinquency* 1: 96–109.

Kaufmann, F. 1958. *Methodology of the Social Sciences.* New York: Humanities Press.

Kemeny, J. G. 1958. *A Philosopher Looks at Science.* New York: Van Nostrand.

————, H. Mirkil, J. L. Snell, and G. L. Thompson. 1959. *Finite Mathematical Structures.* Englewood Cliffs, N. J.: Prentice-Hall.

Kendall, M. 1957. *A Course in Multivariate Analysis.* London: Griffin.

————, and A. Stuart. 1958. *The Advanced Theory of Statistics.* New York: Hafner. Vol. I. *Distribution Theory.*

————, and ————. 1961. *The Advanced Theory of Statistics*. New York: Hafner. Vol. II. *Inference and Relationship*.

Kerlinger, F. N. 1964. *Foundations of Behavioral Research*. New York: Holt, Rinehart and Winston.

Kestelman, H. 1952. "The Fundamental Equation of Factor Analysis." *British Journal of Psychology, Statistical Section* 5: 1–6.

Kiel, D., and C. Wrigley. 1960. "Effects Upon the Factorial Structure of Rotating Varying Numbers of Factors." Paper presented at the Annual Convention of the American Psychological Association, September 1–7, 1960.

Kirsch, A. D., and S. Banks. 1962. "Program Types Defined by Factor Analysis." *Journal of Advertising Research* 2: 29–31.

Klausner, S. 1953. "Social Class and Self-Concept." *Journal of Social Psychology* 38: 201–5.

Klein, M. W. 1966. "Factors Related to Juvenile Gang Membership Patterns." *Sociology and Social Research* 51: 49–62.

Kluckhohn, F. R., and F. L. Strodtbeck. 1961. *Variations in Value Orientations*. Evanston: Row, Peterson.

Knapp, R. H. 1962. "Attitudes Toward Time and Aesthetic Choice." *Journal of Social Psychology* 56: 79–87.

Koons, P. B. 1962. "Canonical Analysis." In *Computer Applications in the Behavioral Sciences*, ed. H. Borko. Englewood Cliffs, N.J.: Prentice-Hall, pp. 267–79.

Krause, M. S. 1966. "Ordinal Scale Construction for Convergent Validity, Object Discrimination, and Resolving Power." *Multivariate Behavioral Research* 1: 379–85.

Krumbein, W. C., and J. Imbrie. 1963. "Stratigraphic Factor Maps." *American Association of Petroleum Geologists, Bulletin* 47: 698–701.

Kruskal, J. B. 1964a. "Multidimensional Scaling by Optimizing Goodness of Fit to a Nonmetric Hypothesis." *Psychometrika* 29: 1–28.

————. 1964b. "Nonmetric Multidimensional Scaling: A Numerical Method." *Psychometrika* 29: 115–29.

Kuder, G. F., and M. W. Richardson. 1937. "The Theory of the Estimation of Test Reliability." *Psychometrika* 2: 151–60.

Kumata, M., and W. Schramm. 1956. "A Pilot Study of Cross-Cultural Meaning." *Public Opinion Quarterly* 20: 229–38.

Ladinsky, J. 1963. "Careers of Lawyers, Law Practice, and Legal Institutions." *American Sociological Review* 28: 47–54.

LaForge, R. 1958. "Comment on the 'Needless Assumption of Normality in Pearson's r'." *American Psychologist* 13: 546.

Landahl, H. D. 1945. "Neural Mechanisms for the Concepts of Difference and Similarity." *Bulletin of Mathematical Biophysics* 7: 83–88.

Lander, B. 1954. *Towards an Understanding of Juvenile Delinquency: A Study of 8,464 Cases of Juvenile Delinquency in Baltimore*. New York: Columbia University Press.

Laulicht, J. 1965. "An Analysis of Canadian Foreign Policy Attitudes."

Peace Research Society: Papers, III, Chicago Conference, 1964, pp. 121–36.

————, and N. Z. Alcock. 1966. "The Support of Peace Research." *Journal of Conflict Resolution* 10: 198–208.

Lawley, D. N. 1940. "The Estimation of Factor Loadings by the Method of Maximum Likelihood." *Royal Society of Edinburgh, Proceedings* A40, pp. 64–82.

————. 1942. "Further Investigations in Factor Estimation." *Royal Society of Edinburgh, Proceedings* 61: 176–85.

————. 1943. "The Application of the Maximum Likelihood Method to Factor Analysis." *British Journal of Psychology* 33: 172–75.

————, and A. E. Maxwell. 1963. *Factor Analysis as a Statistical Method.* London: Butterworth.

————, and Z. Swanson. 1954. "Tests of Significance in a Factor Analysis of Artificial Data." *British Journal of Statistical Psychology* 7: 75–79.

Lazarsfeld, P. F. 1954. "A Conceptual Introduction to Latent Structure Analysis." In *Mathematical Thinking in the Social Sciences,* ed. P. F. Lazarsfeld. Glencoe: Free Press, pp. 347–87.

————, and A. H. Barton. 1951. "Qualitative Measurement in the Social Sciences: Classification, Typologies and Indices." In *The Policy Sciences,* ed. D. Lerner and H. D. Lasswell. Stanford: Stanford University Press, pp. 155–192.

————, and M. Rosenberg, eds. 1955. *The Language of Social Research.* Glencoe: Free Press.

Lerner, D. 1957. "Communication Systems and Social Systems: A Statistical Exploration in History and Policy." *Behavioral Science* 2: 266–75.

———— and H. D. Lasswell, eds. 1951. *The Policy Sciences.* Stanford: Stanford University Press.

Levin, J. 1963. *Three-Mode Factor Analysis.* Urbana: Department of Psychology, University of Illinois.

————. 1965. "Three-Mode Factor Analysis." *Psychological Bulletin* 64: 442–52.

————. 1966. "Simultaneous Factor Analysis of Several Gramian Matrices." *Psychometrika* 31: 413–19.

LeVine, R. A., and J. Sawyer. 1966. "Cultural Dimensions: A Factor Analysis of the World Ethnographic Sample." *American Anthropologist* 68: 708–31.

Levinger, G. 1964. "Task and Social Behavior in Marriage." *Sociometry* 27: 433–48.

Levonian, E., and A. L. Comrey. 1966. "Factorial Stability as a Function of the Number of Orthogonally-Rotated Factors." *Behavioral Science* 11: 400–4.

Lingoes, J. C. 1962. "A Multiple Scalogram Analysis of Selected Issues of the Eighty-third United States Senate." Paper presented at the Annual Convention of the American Psychological Association, August 30–September 5, 1962.

————. 1963. "Multiple Scalogram Analysis: A Set-theoretic Model for Analyzing Dichotomous Items." *Educational and Psychological Measurement* 23: 501–24.

————. 1966a. "An IBM-7090 Program for Guttman-Lingoes Smallest Space Analysis—IV." *Behavioral Science* 11: 407.

————. 1966b. "Recent Computational Advances in Nonmetric Methodology for the Behavioral Sciences." Mimeograph.

Lord, F. M. 1955. "Estimation of Parameters from Incomplete Data." *Journal of American Statistical Association* 50: 870–76.

————. 1963. "Elementary Models for Measuring Change." In *Problems in Measuring Change*, ed. C. W. Harris. Madison: University of Wisconsin Press, pp. 21–38.

Lorr, M. 1966. "Dimensions of Interaction in Group Therapy." *Multivariate Behavioral Research* 1: 67–73.

————, and D. M. McNair. 1963. "An Interpersonal Behavior Circle." *Journal of Abnormal and Social Psychology* 67: 68–75.

Luce, R. D., and J. W. Tukey. 1964. "Simultaneous Conjoint Measurement: A New Type of Fundamental Measurement." *Journal of Mathematical Psychology* 1: 1–27.

Lurie, W. A. 1937. "A Study of Spranger's Value-Types by the Method of Factor Analysis." *Journal of Social Psychology* 8: 17–27.

Lyle, J. 1960. "Semantic Differential Scales for Newspaper Research." *Journalism Quarterly* 37: 559–62, 646.

MacAndrew, C., and E. Forgy. 1963. "A Note on the Effects of Score Transformations in Q and R Factor Analysis Techniques." *Psychological Review* 70: 116–18.

McClelland, C. A. 1958. "Systems and History in International Relations: Some Perspectives for Empirical Research and Theory." *General Systems* 3: 221–47.

————, et al. 1965. *The Communist Chinese Performance in Crisis and Non-Crisis: Quantitative Studies of the Taiwan Straits Confrontation 1950–1964.* China Lake, Calif.: Naval Ordnance Test Station, Final Report to the Behavioral Sciences Group.

McClelland, D. C. 1961. *The Achieving Society.* New York: Van Nostrand.

McDonald, R. P. 1962. "A General Approach to Nonlinear Factor Analysis." *Psychometrika* 27: 397–415.

————. 1965. "Difficulty Factors and Non-Linear Factor Analysis." *British Journal of Mathematical and Statistical Psychology* 18: 11–23.

McGinnis, R. 1958. "Logical Status of the Concept of Association." *Midwest Sociologist* 20: 72–77.

Maclean, M., Jr., and W. Hazard. 1953. "Women's Interest in Pictures: The Badger Village Study." *Journalism Quarterly* 30: 139–62.

McMurray, C. 1964. "Some Problems in the Application of Factor Analytic Techniques to Roll Call Votes, Judicial Decisions, and Survey Responses." Paper presented at the Annual Meeting of the American Political Science Association, September 9–12, 1964.

McQuitty, L. 1957. "Elementary Linkage Analysis for Isolating Ortho-gonal and Oblique Types and Typal Relevancies." *Educational and Psychological Measurement* 17: 207–29.

———. 1964. "Some Hierarchical Methods of Classification for Isolating Single and Multiple Taxonomic Systems, Both Independent and Intersecting." Revised paper presented at the Conference on Micro-bial Classification, Quebec City, Canada, August 31–September 4, 1964.

———. 1965. "A Conjunction of Rank Order Typal Analysis and Item Selection." *Educational and Psychological Measurement* 25: 949–61.

———. 1966a. "Multiple Rank Order Typal Analysis for the Isolation of Independent Types." *Educational and Psychological Measurement* 26: 3–11.

———. 1966b. "Single and Multiple Hierarchical Classification by Re-ciprocal Pairs and Rank Order Types." *Educational and Psychological Measurement* 26: 253–65.

MacRae, D., Jr. 1959. *Direct Factor Analysis With the Turanski Routine.* Mimeograph.

———. 1960. "Direct Factor Analysis of Sociometric Data." *Sociometry* 23: 360–71.

———, and J. A. Meldrum. 1960. "Critical Elections in Illinois: 1888–1958." *American Political Science Review* 54: 669–83.

Madansky, A. 1959. "The Fitting of Straight Lines When Both Variables are Subject to Error." *Journal of American Statistical Association* 54: 173–205.

Mann, R. D. 1961. "Dimensions of Individual Performance in Small Groups Under Task and Social-Emotional Conditions." *Journal of Abnormal and Social Psychology* 62: 674–82.

Manson, V., and J. Imbrie. 1964. "Fortran Program for Factor and Vector Analysis of Geologic Data Using an IBM 7090 or 7904/1401 Com-puter System." *Kansas Geological Survey, Special Publication*, No. 13.

Margenau, H. 1950. *The Nature of Physical Reality.* New York: McGraw-Hill.

Matthai, A. 1951. "Estimation of Parameters from Incomplete Data with Application to Design of Sample Surveys. *Sankhya* 11: 145–52.

Maxwell, A. E. 1964. "Calculating Maximum-likelihood Factor Loadings." *Royal Statistical Society Journal* 127: 238–41.

Megee, M. 1966. "Problems in Regionalizing and Measurement." *Peace Research Society: Papers, IV,* Krakow Conference, 1965, pp. 7–35.

Meredith, W. 1964a. "Notes on Factorial Invariance." *Psychometrika* 29: 177–86.

———. 1964b. "Rotation to Achieve Factorial Invariance." *Psychometrika* 29: 187–206.

Merriam, D. F. 1965. "Geology and the Computer." *New Scientist* (May 20), pp. 513–16.

Messick, S. 1960. "Dimensions of Social Desirability." *Journal of Consulting Psychology* 24: 279–87.

———. 1961. "The Perceived Structure of Political Relationships." *Sociometry* 24: 270–78.

Michael, W. B., R. A. Jones, L. W. Gaddis, and H. F. Kaiser. 1962. "Abacs for Determination of a Correlation Coefficient Corrected for Restriction of Range." *Psychometrika* 27: 197–202.

Miller, C. R., and E. W. Butler. 1966. "Anomia and Eunomia: A Methodological Evaluation of Srole's Anomia Scale." *American Sociological Review* 31: 400–6.

Moore, F. W., ed. 1961. *Readings in Cross-Cultural Methodology.* New Haven: Human Relations Area Files Press.

Morgenstern, O. 1963. *On the Accuracy of Economic Observations,* 2nd ed. Princeton: Princeton University Press.

Morris, C. 1956. *Varieties of Human Values.* Chicago: University of Chicago Press.

Moser, C. A., and W. Scott. 1961. *British Towns.* London: Oliver and Boyd.

Mosier, C. I. 1939. "Influence of Chance Error on Simple Structure." *Psychometrika* 4: 33–44.

Mostow, G. D., J. H. Sampson, and J. Meyer. 1963. *Fundamental Structures of Algebra.* New York: McGraw-Hill.

Muldoon, J. F., and O. S. Ray. 1958. "A Comparison of Pattern Similarity as Measured by Six Statistical Techniques and Eleven Clinicians." *Educational and Psychological Measurement* 18: 775–81.

Nafziger, R. O. *et al.* 1951. "Useful Tools for Interpreting Newspaper Readership Data." *Journalism Quarterly* 28: 441–56.

Nagel, E. 1961. *The Structure of Science.* New York: Harcourt, Brace & World.

Naroll, R. 1962. *Data Quality Control—A New Research Technique.* Glencoe: Free Press.

Neal, A., and S. Rettig. 1963. "Dimensions of Alienation Among Manual and Non-Manual Workers." *American Sociological Review* 28: 599–608.

———, and ———. 1967. "On the Multidimensionality of Alienation." *American Sociological Review* 32: 54–64.

Nefzger, M. D., and J. Drasgow. 1957. "The Needless Assumption of Normality in Pearson's *r.*" *American Psychologist* 12: 623–25.

Neuhaus, J. O., and C. Wrigley. 1954. "The Quartimax Method: An Analytical Approach to Orthogonal Simple Structure." *British Journal of Statistical Psychology* 7: 81–91.

Newman, J. R., ed. 1956. *The World of Mathematics.* New York: Simon and Schuster.

Nicholson, G. E., Jr. 1957. "Estimation of Parameters from Incomplete Multivariate Samples." *Journal of American Statistical Association* 52: 523–26.

Norris, R. C., and H. F. Hjelm. 1961. "Nonnormality and Product

Moment Correlation." *Journal of Experimental Education* 29: 261–70.

North, R. C., *et al.* 1963. *Content Analysis.* Evanston: Northwestern University Press.

Ogburn, W. F. 1935. "Factors in the Variation of Crime Among Cities." *Journal of American Statistical Association* 30: 12–34.

O'Neil, W. M., and D. J. Levinson. 1954. "A Factorial Exploration of Authoritarianism and Some of Its Ideological Concomitants." *Journal of Personality* 22: 449–63.

Osgood, C. E. 1952. "The Nature and Measurement of Meaning." *Psychological Bulletin* 49: 197–237.

———, and G. J. Suci. 1955. "Factor Analysis of Meaning." *Journal of Experimental Psychology* 50: 325–38.

———, ———, and P. H. Tannenbaum. 1957. *The Measurement of Meaning.* Urbana: University of Illinois Press.

Ossorio, P. G. 1966. "Classification Space: A Multivariate Procedure for Automatic Document Indexing and Retrieval." *Multivariate Behavioral Research* 1: 479–524.

Overall, J. E. 1964. "Note on the Scientific Status of Factors." *Psychological Bulletin* 61: 270–76.

Owen, G. E. 1961. *Fundamentals of Scientific Mathematics.* New York: Harper & Row.

Paige, L. J., and J. D. Swift. 1961. *Elements of Linear Algebra.* New York: Ginn.

Peterson, R. J., S. S. Komorita, and H. C. Quay. 1964. "Determinants of Sociometric Choices." *Journal of Social Psychology* 62: 65–75.

Peterson, D. R., H. C. Quay, and G. R. Cameron. 1959. "Personality and Background Factors in Juvenile Delinquency as Inferred from Questionnaire Responses." *Journal of Consulting Psychology* 23: 395–99.

Pettigrew, T. F., and R. B. Spier. 1962. "The Ecological Structure of Negro Homicide." *American Journal of Sociology* 67: 621–29.

Pinzka, C., and D. R. Saunders. 1954. *Analytic Rotation to Simple Structure, II: Extension to an Oblique Solution.* Princeton, N.J.: Educational Testing Service Research Bulletin (RB-54-31).

Pitts, F. 1967. "Basic Dimensions of Variation in Korean Urban Structures." Paper presented at the Pacific Coast Regional Conference of the Association for Asian Studies, June 15–17, 1966.

Pool, I. de S., ed. 1959. *Trends in Content Analysis.* Urbana: University of Illinois Press.

Price, D. O. 1942. "Factor Analysis in the Study of Metropolitan Centers." *Social Forces* 20: 449–55.

Problems in the Collection and Comparability of International Statistics, 1949. Papers presented at the Round Table on International Statistics, Conference of the Milbank Memorial Fund, New York, November 17–18, 1948.

Rajaratnam, N., L. J. Cronbach, and G. C. Gleser. 1965. "Generalizability of Stratified-Parallel Tests." *Psychometrika* 30: 39–56.

Rao, C. R. 1955. "Estimation and Tests of Significance in Factor Analysis." *Psychometrica* 20: 93–111.

———. 1956. "Analysis of Dispersion with Incomplete Observations on One of the Characters." *Journal of Royal Statistical Society* 18: 259–64.

Ray, D. M., and B. J. L. Berry. 1965. "Multivariate Socio-Economic Regionalization: A Pilot Study in Central Canada." In *Regional Statistical Studies*, ed. T. Rymes and S. Ostrey. Toronto: University of Toronto Press.

Regan, M. C. 1965. "Development and Classification of Models for Multivariate Analysis." *Educational and Psychological Measurement* 25: 997–1010.

Reiselbach, L. N. 1960. "Quantitative Techniques for Studying Voting Behavior in the UN General Assembly." *International Organization* 14: 291–306.

Rettig, S. 1964. "Invariance of Factor Structure of Ethical Judgments by Indian and American College Students." *Sociometry* 27: 96–113.

———, and B. Pasamanick. 1959. "Changes in Moral Values Among College Students: A Factorial Study." *American Sociological Review* 24: 856–63.

———, and ———. 1961. "Moral Value Structure and Social Class." *Sociometry* 24: 21–35.

———, and ———. 1962. "Invariance in Factor Structure of Moral Value Judgments from American and Korean College Students." *Sociometry* 25: 73–84.

Rhodes, E. C. 1937. "The Construction of An Index of Business Activity." *Royal Statistical Society Journal* 100: 18–39.

Richardson, L. F. 1960a. *Arms and Insecurity*. Pittsburgh: Boxwood Press.

———. 1960b. *Statistics of Deadly Quarrels*. Pittsburgh: Boxwood Press.

Rinn, J. L. 1961. "Q Methodology: An Application to Group Phenomena." *Educational and Psychological Measurement* 21: 315–29.

Rokeach, M., et al. 1960. *The Open and Closed Mind*. New York: Basic Books.

Rosenblatt, M., ed. 1963. *Symposium on Time Series Analysis*. New York: Wiley.

Ross, J. 1963. "The Relation Between Test and Person Factors." *Psychological Review* 70: 432–43.

———, and N. Cliff. 1964. "A Generalization of the Interpoint Distance Model." *Psychometrika* 29: 167–76.

Royce, J. R. 1950. "A Synthesis of Experimental Designs in Program Research." *Journal of General Psychology* 43: 295–303.

———. 1958. "The Development of Factor Analysis." *Journal of General Psychology* 58: 139–64.

———. 1963. "Factors as Theoretical Constructs." *American Psychologist* 18: 522–28.

Rozeboom, W. W. 1965. "Linear Correlations Between Sets of Variables." *Psychometrika* 30: 57–71.

Rummel, R. J. 1963. "Dimensions of Conflict Behavior Within and Between Nations." *General Systems* 8: 1–50.

———. 1964. "Testing Some Predictors of Conflict Behavior Within and Between Nations." *Peace Research Society: Papers, I*, Chicago Conference, 1963, pp. 79–111.

———. 1965a. "A Field Theory of Social Action With Application to Conflict Within Nations." *General Systems* 10: 183–211.

———. 1965b. "A Social Field Theory of Foreign Conflict Behavior." *Peace Research Society: Papers, IV*, Krakow Conference, 1965, pp. 131–50.

———. 1966a. "A Foreign Conflict Code Sheet." *World Politics* 18: 283–96.

———. 1966b. "Dimensions of Conflict Behavior Within Nations: 1946–1959." *Journal of Conflict Resolution* 10: 65–73.

———. 1966c. "The Dimensionality of Nations Project." In *Comparing Nations*, eds. R. L. Merritt and S. Rokkan. New Haven: Yale University Press.

———. 1967a. "Some Attribute and Behavioral Patterns of Nations." *Journal of Peace Research*, No. 2, pp. 196–206.

———. 1967b. "Some Dimensions in the Foreign Behavior of Nations." *Journal of Peace Research*, No. 3, pp. 201–24.

———. 1967c. "Dimensions of Dyadic War, 1820–1952." *Journal of Conflict Resolution* 11: 176–83.

———. 1968a. "Dimensions of Domestic Conflict Behavior: Review of Findings." In *Theories of International Conflict*, eds. D. Pruitt and R. Snyder (forthcoming).

———. 1968b. "Dimensions of Error in Cross-National Data." In *A Handbook of Method in Cultural Anthropology*, eds. R. Naroll and R. Cohen (forthcoming).

———. 1969. *Dimensions of Nations* (forthcoming).

Russett, B. M. 1963. *Community and Contention*. Cambridge: M.I.T. Press.

———. 1965. "A Note on the Evaluation of Error and Transformation in Data Analysis." *American Political Science Review* 59: 444–46.

———. 1966. "Discovering Voting Groups in the United Nations." *American Political Science Review* 60: 327–39.

———. 1967a. "Delineating International Regions." In *Quantitative International Politics*, ed. J. D. Singer. New York: Free Press, 1968.

———. 1967b. *International Regions and International Integration*. Chicago: Rand McNally.

———, H. Alker, Jr., K. W. Deutsch, and H. Lasswell. 1964. *World Handbook of Political and Social Indicators*. New Haven: Yale University Press.

Ryans, D. G. 1960. *Characteristics of Teachers: Their Description, Com-*

parison and Appraisal. Washington: American Council of Education.

Rydberg, S. 1962. "Methods of Correcting Correlations for Indirect Restriction of Range with Non-Interval Data." *Psychometrika* 27: 49–58.

Saunders, D. R. 1948. "Factor Analysis I: Some Effects of Chance Error." *Psychometrika* 13: 251–57.

———. 1950. *Practical Methods in the Direct Factor Analysis of Psychological Score Matrices.* Ph.D. Dissertation, University of Illinois.

———. 1960. "A Computer Program to Find the Best-Fitting Orthogonal Factors for a Given Hypothesis." *Psychometrika* 25: 199–205.

Savage, I. R., and K. W. Deutsch. 1960. "A Statistical Model of the Gross Analysis of Transaction Flows." *Econometrica* 28: 551–72.

Schilpp, P. A., ed. 1949. *Albert Einstein: Philosopher-Scientist.* Evanston: Library of Living Philosophers.

Schmid, C. F. 1960. "Urban Crime Areas: Part I." *American Sociological Review* 25: 527–42.

Schmid, J., and J. M. Leiman. 1957. "The Development of Hierarchical Factor Solutions." *Psychometrika* 22: 53–61.

Schnore, L. F. 1961. "The Statistical Measurement of Urbanization and Economic Development." *Land Economics* 37: 229–45.

Schönemann, P. H. 1966. "Varisim: A New Machine Method for Orthogonal Rotation." *Psychometrika* 31: 235–48.

Schubert, G. 1962. "The 1960 Term of the Supreme Court: A Psychological Analysis." *American Political Science Review* 56: 90–107.

———. 1965. *The Liberal Mind.* Evanston: Northwestern University Press.

———, and C. Press. 1964. "Measuring Malapportionment." *American Political Science Review* 58: 302–27.

Schuessler, K. 1962. "Components of Variation in City Crime Rates." *Social Problems* 9: 314–23.

———, and H. Driver. 1956. "A Factor Analysis of Sixteen Primitive Societies." *American Sociological Review* 21: 493–99.

———, and G. Slatin. 1964. "Sources of Variation in U.S. City Crime, 1950 and 1960." *Journal of Research in Crime and Delinquency* 1: 127–48.

Schutz, R. E. 1956. "A Factor Analysis of Educational Development in the United States." *Educational and Psychological Measurement* 16: 324–32.

———. 1960. "A Factor Analysis of Academic Achievement and Community Characteristics." *Educational and Psychological Measurement* 20: 513–18.

Sears, R. R., E. E. Maccoby, and H. Levin. 1957. *Patterns of Child Rearing.* Evanston: Row, Peterson.

Sells, S. B., and N. Findikyan. 1965. *Dimensions of Organizational Structure.* Fort Worth: Institute of Behavioral Research, Technical Report No. 7.

Selltiz, C., M. Jahoda, M. Deutsch, and S. W. Cook. 1959. *Research Methods in Social Relations.* New York: Holt, Rinehart and Winston.

Selvin, H. C., and W. O. Hagstrom. 1963. "The Empirical Classification of Formal Groups." *American Sociological Review* 28: 399–411.

Senders, V. L. 1958. *Measurement and Statistics*. New York: Oxford University Press.

Sewell, W. H., and A. O. Haller. 1959. "Factors in the Relationship Between Social Status and the Personality Adjustment of the Child." *American Sociological Review* 24: 511–20.

Shepard, R. N. 1957. "Stimulus and Response Generalization: A Stochastic Model Relating Generalization to Distance in Psychological Space." *Psychometrika* 22: 325–45.

―――. 1958a. "Stimulus and Response Generalization: Deduction of the Generalization Gradient from a Trace Model." *Psychological Review* 65: 242–56.

―――. 1958b. "Stimulus and Response Generalization: Tests of a Model Relating Generalization to Distance in Psychological Space." *Journal of Experimental Psychology* 55: 509–23.

―――. 1962. "The Analysis of Proximities: Multidimensional Scaling with an Unknown Distance Function." *Psychometrika* 27: 125–40, 219–46.

―――. 1963. "Analysis of Proximities as a Technique for the Study of Information Processing in Man." *Human Factors* 5: 33–48.

―――. 1964. "Extracting Latent Structure from Behavioral Data." In *Proceedings of the 1964 Symposium of Digital Computing*. Murray Hill, N.J.: Bell Telephone Laboratories.

―――. 1965. *Metric Structures in Nonmetric Data*. Murray Hill, N.J.: Bell Telephone Laboratories.

―――, and J. D. Carroll. 1965. "Parametric Representation of Nonlinear Data Structures." Paper presented at the International Symposium on Multivariate Analysis, Dayton, Ohio, June 14–19, 1965.

Short, J. F., Jr., R. A. Tennyson, and K. I. Howard. 1963. "Behavior Dimensions of Gang Delinquency." *American Sociological Review* 28: 411–28.

Sidman, M. 1960. *Tactics of Scientific Research*. New York: Basic Books.

Siegel, S. 1956. *Nonparametric Statistics for the Behavioral Sciences*. New York: McGraw-Hill.

Smith, B., J. Fawcett, R. Ezekiel, and S. Roth. 1963. "A Factorial Study of Morale Among Peace Corps Teachers in Ghana." *Journal of Social Issues* 19: 10–32.

Smith, R. G. 1961. "A Semantic Differential for Theatre Concepts." *Speech Monographs* 28: 1–8.

Snedecor, G. W. 1956. *Statistical Methods*. 5th ed. Ames, Iowa: Iowa State University Press.

Soares, G. 1964. "Congruency and Incongruency Among Indicators of Economic Development." Paper presented at the International Conference on Comparative Social Research in Developing Countries, UNESCO, Buenos Aires, September 7–16.

————. 1965. *Economic Development and Political Radicalism.* Ph.D. Dissertation, Washington University, St. Louis.

Sokal, R. R. 1959. "A Comparison of Five Tests for Completeness of Factor Extraction." *Kansas Academy of Science, Transactions,* 62: 141–52.

————, and P. E. Hunter. 1955." A Morphometric Analysis of DDT-Resistant and Non-Resistant House Fly Strains." *Entomological Society of America, Annals* 48: 499–507.

————, and P. H. A. Sneath. 1963. *Principles of Numerical Taxonomy.* San Francisco: Freeman.

Solomon, H. 1960. "A Survey of Mathematical Models in Factor Analysis." In *Mathematical Thinking in the Measurement of Behavior,* ed. H. Solomon. Glencoe: Free Press, pp. 269–314.

Solomon, L., and E. Klein. 1963. "The Relationship Between Agreeing Responses Set and Social Desirability." *Journal of Abnormal and Social Psychology* 66: 176–79.

Somit, A., and J. Tanenhaus. 1963. "Trends in American Political Science: Some Analytical Notes." *American Political Science Review* 57: 933–47.

————, and ————. 1964. *American Political Science.* New York: Atherton Press.

Spearman, C. 1927. *The Abilities of Man.* New York: Macmillan.

Spencer, D. W. 1966. *Factor Analysis.* Woods Hole, Mass.: Oceanographic Institution, No. 66–39.

Spreen, O. 1963. "The Position of Time Estimation in a Factor Analysis and its Relation to Some Personality Variables." *Psychological Record* 13: 455–64.

Stein, K. B., H. G. Gough, and T. R. Sarbin. 1966. "The Dimensionality of the CPI Socialization Scale and an Empirically Derived Typology Among Delinquent and Nondeliquent Boys." *Multivariate Behavioral Research* 1: 197–208.

Stempel, G., III. 1963. "An Empirical Exploration of the News." In *Paul J. Deutschmann Memorial Papers in Mass Communication Research,* ed. W. A. Danielson. Cincinnati: Scripps-Howard Research, pp. 19–23.

Stephenson, W. 1953. *The Study of Behavior.* Chicago: University of Chicago Press.

Stevens, S. S. 1946. "On the Theory of Scales of Measurement." *Science* 103: pp. 677–80.

————. 1951. "Mathematics, Measurement, and Psychophysics." In *Handbook of Experimental Psychology,* ed. S. S. Stevens. New York: Wiley, pp. 1–49.

Stogdill, R. M. 1966. "Brief Report: Some Possible Uses of Factor Analysis in Multivariate Studies." *Multivariate Behavioral Research* 1: 387–95.

————. 1967. "The Structure of Organization Behavior." *Multivariate Behavioral Research* 2: 47–61.

————, O. S. Goode, and D. R. Day. 1963. "The Leader Behavior of Corporation Presidents " *Personnel Psychology* 16: 127–32.

————, et al. 1965. *Managers, Employees, Organizations.* Columbus: Ohio State University, Bureau of Business Research Monograph No. 125.

Stone, R. 1960. "A Comparison of the Economic Structure of Regions Based on the Concept of Distance." *Journal of Regional Science* 2: 1–20.

Stouffer, S., *et al.* 1950. *Studies in Social Psychology in World War II.* Princeton: Princeton University Press, Vol. IV.

Straits, B. C. 1965. "Factor Analysis of Demographic and Political Characteristics of American Cities." Chicago: Department of Sociology, University of Chicago.

Suits, D. B. 1957. "Use of Dummy Variables in Regression Equations." *Journal of American Statistical Association* 52: 548–51.

Suppes, P., and J. L. Zinnes. 1963. "Basic Measurement Theory." In *Handbook of Mathematical Psychology,* eds. R. D. Luce, R. R. Bush, and E. Galanter. New York: Wiley, Vol. I, pp. 1–76.

Tanaka, Y., T. Oyama, and C. E. Osgood. 1963. "A Cross-Culture and Cross-Concept Study of the Generality of Semantic Spaces." *Journal of Verbal Learning and Verbal Behavior* 2: 392–405.

Tannenbaum, P. H. 1963. "Public Images of Media Institutions." In *Paul J. Deutschmann Memorial Papers in Mass Communication Research,* ed. W. A. Davidson. Cincinnati: Scripps-Howard Research.

————, H. K. Jacobson, and E. L. Norris. 1964. "An Experimental Investigation of Typeface Connotations." *Journalism Quarterly* 41: 65–73.

Tanter, R. 1964. *Dimensions of Conflict Behavior Within and Between Nations, 1958–1960.* Ph.D. Dissertation, Indiana University.

————. 1965. "Dimensions of Conflict Behavior Within Nations, 1955–60: Turmoil and Internal War." *Peace Research Society: Papers, III,* Chicago Conference, 1964, pp. 159–83.

————. 1966. "Dimensions of Conflict Behavior Within and Between Nations, 1958–60." *Journal of Conflict Resolution* 10: 41–64.

Thompson, J. H., S. C. Sufrin, P. R. Gould, and M. A. Buck. 1962. "Toward a Geography of Economic Health: The Case of New York." *Association of American Geographers, Annals* 52: 1–20.

Thomson, G. 1951. *The Factorial Analysis of Human Ability,* 5th ed. Boston: Houghton Mifflin.

————, and W. Ledermann. 1939. "The Influence of Multivariate Selection on the Factorial Analysis of Ability." *British Journal of Psychology* 29: 288–306.

Thurstone, L. L. 1935. *The Vectors of Mind.* Chicago: University of Chicago Press.

————. 1947. *Multiple-Factor Analysis.* Chicago: University of Chicago Press.

————, and J. W. Degan. 1951. "A Factorial Study of the Supreme Court." *Psychometric Laboratory Report,* No. 64. Chicago: University of Chicago.

Toomey, D. F. 1966. "Application of Factor Analysis to a Facies Study of the Leavenworth Limestone (Pennsylvanian-Virgilian) of Kansas and Environs." *Kansas Geological Survey, Special Publication* No. 27.

Torgerson, W. S. 1958. *Theory and Methods of Scaling.* New York: Wiley.

————. 1965. "Multidimensional Scaling of Similarity." *Psychometrika* 30: 379–93.

Trawinski, I. M., and R. E. Bargmann. 1964. "Maximum Likelihood Estimation with Incomplete Multivariate Data." *Annals of Mathematical Statistics* 35: 647–57.

Triandis, H. C. 1964. "Exploratory Factor Analyses of the Behavioral Component of Social Attitudes." *Journal of Abnormal and Social Psychology* 68: 420–30.

————, and C. E. Osgood. 1958. "A Comparative Factorial Analysis of Semantic Structure in Monolingual Greek and American College Students." *Journal of Abnormal and Social Psychology* 57: 187–96.

Tryon, R. C. 1958. "General Dimensions of Individual Differences: Cluster Analysis vs. Multiple Factor Analysis." *Educational and Psychological Measurement* 18: 477–95.

————. 1959. "Domain Sampling Formulation of Cluster and Factor Analysis." *Psychometrika* 24: 113–35.

————. 1961. "Salient Dimensionality vs. the Fallacy of 'Minimal Rank' in Factor Analysis." *American Psychologist* 16: 467.

Tucker, L. R. 1963. "Implications of Factor Analysis of Three-Way Matrices for Measurement of Change." In *Problems in Measuring Change,* ed. C. W. Harris. Madison: University of Wisconsin Press, pp. 122–37.

————. 1966. "Some Mathematical Notes on Three-Mode Factor Analysis." *Psychometrika* 31: 279–311.

Twedt, D. W. 1952. "A Multiple Factor Analysis of Advertising Readership." *Journal of Applied Psychology* 36: 207–15.

Tyler, F., and W. B. Michael. 1958. "An Empirical Study of the Comparability of Factor Structure When Unities and Communality Estimates Are Used." *Educational and Psychological Measurement* 18: 347–54.

United Nations. 1954. *Report on International Definition and Measurement of Standards and Levels of Living.* New York: United Nations.

Van Arsdol, M. D., Jr., S. F. Camilleri, and C. F. Schmid. 1958. "The Generality of Urban Social Area Indexes." *American Sociological Review* 23: 277–84.

Van Dyke, V. 1960. *Political Science: A Philosophical Analysis.* Stanford: Stanford University Press.

Wald, A. 1940. "The Fitting of Straight Lines if Both Variables Are Subject to Error." *Annals of Mathematical Statistics* 11: 284–300.

Wallis, J. R. 1965. "Multivariate Statistical Methods in Hydrology—A Comparison Using Data of Known Functional Relationship." *Water Resources Research* 1: 447–61.

Walsh, J. E. 1959. *Computer-Feasible General Method for Fitting and Using Regression Function When Data Incomplete*. Santa Monica: System Development Corporation.

Warburton, F. W. 1963. "Analytic Methods of Factor Rotation." *British Journal of Statistical Psychology* 16: 165–74.

Webster, H. A. 1952. "A Note on Profile Similarity." *Psychological Bulletin* 49: 538–39.

Weiss, R. F., and B. Pasamanick. 1962. "Individual and Group Goals: A Factor Analysis." *Journal of Social Psychology* 58: 131–39.

Westley, B., and M. Lynch. 1962. "Multiple Factor Analysis of Dichotomous Audience Data." *Journalism Quarterly* 39: 369–72.

Westof, C. F., M. Bressler, and P. Sagi. 1960. "The Concept of Social Mobility: An Empirical Inquiry." *American Sociological Review* 25: 375–85.

Wherry, R. J., and R. H. Gaylord. 1944. "Factor Pattern of Test Items and Tests as a Function of the Correlation Coefficient: Content, Difficulty, and Constant Error Factors." *Psychometrika* 9: 237–44.

White, O. 1966. "Some Properties of Three Factor Contribution Matrices." *Multivariate Behavioral Research* 1: 373–78.

Wilkinson, G. N. 1958. "Estimation of Missing Values for the Analysis of Incomplete Data." *Biometrics* 14: 257–86.

Wilks, S. S. 1932. "Moments and Distributions of Estimates of Population Parameters from Fragmentary Samples." *Annals of Mathematical Statistics* 3: 163–95.

Williams, E. J. 1959. *Regression Analysis*. New York: Wiley.

Wilson, E. B. 1952. *An Introduction to Scientific Research*. New York: McGraw-Hill.

Wolfe, A. W. 1966. *Social Structural Bases of Art*. Final Report to the National Institute of Mental Health. St. Louis: Washington University.

Wolfe, D. 1940. *Factor Analysis to 1940*. Psychometric Monograph, No. 3. Chicago: University of Chicago Press.

Wood, R. C. 1961. *1400 Governments*. Cambridge: Harvard University Press.

Woodbury, M. A., R. C. Clelland, and R. J. Hickey. 1963. "Applications of a Factor-Analytic Model in the Prediction of Biological Data." *Behavioral Science* 8: 347–54.

———, and W. Siles. 1966. "Factor Analysis with Missing Data." *New York Academy of Sciences, Annals* 128: 746–54.

Wright, B., and M. S. Evitts. 1961. "Direct Factor Analysis in Sociometry." *Sociometry* 24: 82–98.

———, and ———. 1963. "Multiple Regression in the Explanation of Social Structure." *Journal of Social Psychology* 61: 87–98.

Wright, Q. 1955. *The Study of International Relations*. New York: Appleton-Century-Crofts.

Yates, F. 1933. "The Analysis of Replicated Experiments When the Field

Results are Incomplete." *Empire Journal of Experimental Agriculture* 1: 129–42.

Young, G., and A. S. Householder. 1938. "Discussion of a Set of Points in Terms of Their Mutual Distances." *Psychometrika* 3: 19–22.

Zimmer, H. 1956. "Motivational Factors in Dyadic Interaction." *Journal of Personality* 24: 251–61.

Name Index

Subject Index

Additivity, 25 n.32, 213–14; and factor analysis, 17–18
Aggregate data, 214
Alpha factor analysis, 129–30; communality in, 131, 312–13; number of factors, 131, 355–56. *See also* Communality; Component (factor) analysis
Analysis of variance, 188
Anti-image analysis. *See* Image factor analysis
Association, 187
Attenuation, 227 n.36
Autocorrelation, 244 n

Basic variable. *See* Factor scores
Basis: defined, 67–68; and eigenvectors, 97; and vector space, 369–72, 411
Bifactor approach, 330, 348
Binormamin. *See* Oblique rotation
Biquartimin. *See* Oblique rotation
Bivariate. *See* Distribution; Research question

Black box, 19–20

Calculus, 507, 513
Canonical analysis, 121, 187–88, 467
Canonical factor analysis, 121–26; and common factor analysis, 122; communality in, 125, 312–13; and component analysis, 122; number of factors, 355–56, 366; scale-free, 122–23; and statistical tests, 122, 124–25, 129
Cases. *See* Number of cases
Cause, 20, 24–26; analysis of, 384–85, 471. *See also* Factor interpretation
Centroid technique, 335–37, 348, 373, 375. *See also* Factor technique
Change measurement, 234–39; deviational, 239; and error, 236–37; incremental, 235–37; positional, 239; relative, 237–38; and zero boundary, 237–38. *See also* Regression effect
Characteristic equation, 96–97